D1270931

Psychology: A Study of a Science

STUDY I. CONCEPTUAL AND SYSTEMATIC

Volume 1. Sensory, Perceptual, and Physiological Formulations

PSYCHOLOGY: A STUDY OF A SCIENCE

The Series

STUDY I. CONCEPTUAL AND SYSTEMATIC

Volume 1. Sensory, Perceptual, and Physiological Formulations

CONTRIBUTORS: *Albert A. Blank, James J. Gibson, C. H. Graham, D. O. Hebb, Harry Helson, J. C. R. Licklider, Clifford T. Morgan, Kenneth N. Ogle, M. H. Pirenne and F. H. C. Marriott, Leo Postman and Edward C. Tolman, W. C. H. Prentice*

Volume 2. General Systematic Formulations, Learning, and Special Processes

CONTRIBUTORS: *Dorwin Cartwright, Douglas G. Ellson, W. K. Estes, F. C. Frick, Edwin R. Guthrie, Harry F. Harlow, R. A. Hinde, Arthur L. Irion, Frank A. Logan, Neal E. Miller, B. F. Skinner, Edward C. Tolman*

Volume 3. Formulations of the Person and the Social Context

CONTRIBUTORS: *Solomon E. Asch, Raymond B. Cattell, Franz J. Kallmann, Daniel Katz and Ezra Stotland, Paul F. Lazarsfeld, Henry A. Murray, Theodore M. Newcomb, Talcott Parsons, David Rapaport, Carl R. Rogers, Herbert A. Thelen*

STUDY II. EMPIRICAL SUBSTRUCTURE AND RELATIONS WITH OTHER SCIENCES

(These titles in preparation)

Volume 4. Biologically Oriented Fields: Their Place in Psychology and in Biological Science

Volume 5. The Process Areas, the Person, and Some Applied Fields: Their Place in Psychology and in Science

Volume 6. Investigations of Man as Socius: Their Place in Psychology and the Social Sciences

POSTSCRIPT TO THE STUDY

Volume 7. Psychology and the Human Agent: A View of Problems in the Enaction of a Science (*by Sigmund Koch*)

Psychology: A Study of a Science

STUDY I. CONCEPTUAL AND SYSTEMATIC

Volume 1. Sensory, Perceptual, and Physiological Formulations

Edited by Sigmund Koch
DUKE UNIVERSITY

McGRAW-HILL BOOK COMPANY, INC.
New York Toronto London
1959

PSYCHOLOGY: A STUDY OF A SCIENCE was made possible by funds granted by the National Science Foundation to the American Psychological Association, and carried out under the sponsorship of the latter organization. Neither agency, however, is to be construed as endorsing any of the published findings or conclusions of the Study.

 Library of Congress Catalog Card Number 57-14691

II

35270

THE MAPLE PRESS COMPANY, YORK, PA.

PREFACE

When one looks back over the history of science, the successes are likely to be stressed and the failures forgotten. Thus one tends to see science as starting with a sure sense of direction and progressing neatly to its present form. Or so it is for the older and well established branches of science; but not for psychology. Psychology has not one sure sense of direction but several quite unsure directions. Growth is erratic and there is much casting about for the most crucial problems and the most powerful methods. These apparent differences between psychology and the older branches of science may result from the difficulty of developing a science of man; it is perhaps significant that many of the problems of psychology were not attacked by the methods of science until so late a date in history. Or the differences may be an illusion resulting from the much closer view we have of the beginning struggles to develop a science of psychology than we now have of the beginning efforts in the older sciences.

Certainly psychology has its problems, and they are not easy. Nevertheless, knowledge has grown rapidly in the short history of man's efforts to develop a science of behavior, and the time seems appropriate for a major effort to examine the progress that has been made in attempting to find a way, or ways, to the attainment of the explanatory power that we like to think of as characteristic of science. A growing body of empirical information, a serious concern over methodological issues, and a variety of efforts to bring a selected body of fact into the organizing framework of theory all emphasize the need for that line of questioning—always going on in science—which explores the shape of knowledge, the range and inner connections of the ideas through which it has been developed and organized, the changing substructures of empirical data, and their emerging relations to each other and to the findings of other sciences. The seven volumes of *Psychology: A Study of a Science* are a response to this need.

The first three volumes, which bear the collective title *Study I. Conceptual and Systematic*, are concerned with many of the systematic formulations of recent and current influence which psychologists have developed to account for the phenomena in which they are interested.

Each systematic position is analyzed by its originator, or a person connected with its development, in a way which gives attention to the problems it seeks to solve, the empirical basis on which it rests, its degree of success, and its relations to other formulations.

A second set of three volumes, collectively called *Study II. Empirical Substructure and Relations with Other Sciences*, inquires, again through the efforts of creatively active investigators, into the organization of various fields of empirical knowledge, the relations of one to another, and to work going forward in other sciences. It also examines such problems in reverse through the participation of social and biological scientists who consider the relations of their own special fields to various parts of psychology. The three volumes of Study II, now in preparation, will be published at a later date.

Volume 7—*Psychology and the Human Agent*—will present the Study Director's view of certain problems of psychological inquiry in the light of the findings of the project.

Primary credit for the initiation of these studies goes to the Association's Policy and Planning Board, which decided in 1952 that the time had come for a thorough and critical examination of the status and development of psychology. The National Science Foundation agreed upon the desirability of such an undertaking and has generously supported the effort. When funds from the National Science Foundation were found to be insufficient for all of the expenses of the studies, the American Psychological Association provided the supplementary funds necessary to complete the work.

From the beginning, the study was divided into two parts. One part dealt with the education of psychologists and the factors conducive to research productivity in psychology. That part was directed by Professor Kenneth Clark of the University of Minnesota, who has reported the findings in *America's Psychologists: A Survey of a Growing Profession*, published by the American Psychological Association in 1957.

The other part, the part with which the present series of volumes is concerned, has dealt with the substance of psychological thought and data. Professor Sigmund Koch of Duke University has been responsible for this part of the study. Working closely with him has been a panel of consultants consisting of Lyle H. Lanier, Howard H. Kendler, Conrad G. Mueller, and Karl E. Zener. These men, but chiefly Dr. Koch, have planned, organized, interpreted and edited the work, and successfully enlisted the cooperation of the approximately 80 authors whose original papers will constitute the basic material of the series.

In the background, at a safe distance from the labors that have sometimes engulfed Dr. Koch, his panel of consultants, and the primary authors, has been a steering committee on which I had the pleasure of serving as chairman, and having as colleagues Clarence H. Graham, Lyle H. Lanier, Robert B. MacLeod, Eliot H. Rodnick, M. Brewster Smith, and Robert L. Thorndike. The steering committee helped to make administrative arrangements and helped to decide on the scope of the studies, but takes no credit for their successful completion.

In the preface to *America's Psychologists* we have already acknowledged our gratitude to Kenneth Clark and his collaborators who helped to produce that volume. It is our final pleasant duty to express our thanks to Duke University for making Dr. Koch's time available; to the National Science Foundation for its necessary and generous financial support and for the counsel and support of John T. Wilson, Assistant Director for the Biological Sciences; to Lyle H. Lanier, Howard H. Kendler, Conrad G. Mueller, and Karl E. Zener for their critical and devoted help; to all of the authors whose names appear on the title pages for their original contributions; and—most of all—to Sigmund Koch for directing and driving through to completion what we hope will be an oft-consulted aid to the scholars and research workers who are striving to increase the rigor and further the development of scientific psychology.

Dael Wolfle, CHAIRMAN
STEERING COMMITTEE
POLICY AND PLANNING BOARD

CONTENTS

GENERAL INTRODUCTION TO THE SERIES

THE SPIRIT OF THE STUDY

Psychology: A Study of a Science is a report of investigations into the nature and tendency of a roughly definable cluster of human knowledge-seeking activities known as psychological science. It is a long report of far-ranging endeavors. Seven volumes, in fact, will be required for the full story. The present portion—*Study I Conceptual and Systematic*—comprises the initial three volumes of the series.

Though the story is long, there are certain defenses against tedium. Perhaps the one offering most security to the reader is that the story will be rendered in the tongues, each with its individual accent, of some eighty contributors. Nor is there any question of these tongues blending into a single narrative, or some unitary theme. Our authors' tongues are attached to diverse human sensibilities which, in turn, will be reflecting markedly different backgrounds, values, styles. And each of these sensibilities will be functioning in that special area of concern which has at once formed and been molded by it. Yet different groups of our authors will be addressing roughly similar questions to their individual topics, so that private sensibilities may publicly converse and plurally illuminate the status of our science.

It is tempting to search for a portentous metaphor to characterize the spirit of this Study after the years of hard work by many individuals. One can reach towards the faithful clichés of the building trades and define the Study as concerned with the "foundations" of psychology, or some other architectonic attribute. One can borrow the usual tidy images from the anatomist, geographer, or cartographer. One can look wistfully toward the logician and talk about the "logic" of psychology; its propositional or "postulational" structure. One can requisition from the philosopher the "analysis" of psychology, or petition the axiologist for the right to its "assessment." In more cozy vein, one can don the apron of the greengrocer and "take stock." Though in some sense applicable, we must reject all such metaphors. It is not merely that they are trite; they imply too orderly a subject matter and too orderly a result. In fact, they convey an attitude toward the study of a science which—

to the extent that it "succeeds"—could well render science less worth while.

Any metaphor which might characterize the incidence of a meaningful inquiry into science, however modest, must be a hopelessly mixed one. For a study of a science must hold science and *its* science in view, and the resources of metaphor break down before what even a superficial view discloses.

A science is *not* a body of sentences, a hierarchically ordered tissue of theory, or a collection of such "bodies" and "tissues." It is *not* an explanatory web, a predictive network, a descriptive grammar, an experiential map, a technological abacus, a practical almanac, or a moral calculus. It is *not* a reservoir of generalizations, principles, or laws. It is *not* an arsenal of methods—logical, mathematical, or instrumentative.

A science is *not* a summation of restless human curiosities about the world, nor the resulting processes of search and observation; it is *not* that occasional gift of the world to cognitive desire known, in its private form, as understanding and, in public guise, as knowledge. A science is *not* a cumulative progression of attitudes toward knowledge-getting, of methodological strategies, cognitive and predictive ends in view, leading ideas, hypotheses, unifying insights, or the testing and codification of these. It is *not* a collectivity of persons, animated by relatively similar objectives, working on more or less common problems, as regulated by roughly uniform traditions of craft and largely shared rules for efficient inquiry. It is *not* a specifiable number of individuals inviting creativity in solipsistic privacy. It is *not* a group of problem-confronting organisms mediating the survival and enrichment of their species by a self-conscious, if fumbling, attack on the vicissitudes of nature. It is *not* an association of gourmets with an exquisite hunger for order, permanence, essence, necessity, truth, beauty, comprehension. It is *not* a band of individuals seeking livelihood, personal significance, respect, and other answers to the human condition.

Science is *not* a congeries of laboratories, university departments, professional organizations, foundations, and other institutional entities. It is *not* an assortment of educational philosophies, traditions, programs, or devices, nor the administrative apparatus through which the educative process is shaped. It is *not* a lattice of institutional roles, expectations, suppressions, conceptual cant, culturally defined routes, constraints, and rewards. It is *not* a discontinuous progression of fads and fashions, or of such security and prestige symbols as favored patterns among the practices of other sciences, legitimate modes of observation, honorific conceptual categories, modes of instrumentation, research problems, and styles.

Science is *not* a *tabula rasa* for the grandiloquent scribbling of the

Zeitgeist, nor is it a screen which catches the projections of a civilization, culture, or society. It is *not* a segment of the wave front of history.

A science is *all of these things and much else.* Any study, then, which comes to terms with a science requires a spirit, a style, which can be captured in no metaphor, however complexly mixed. Nothing less than a rhetoric will do, a rhetoric which must echo throughout inquiry, varying in volume with the given object of study, but always distinctly there, always honestly dissonant.

The limits of communication will demand that given parts of the rich and disorderly matrix of a science be considered independently, or relatively so. The conditions of understanding will demand selection, abstraction, "causal" weighting of those components which are to become the object of study. Selection will, as always, be based on mixed criteria—some having rational warrant but many enforced by calculations of historical relevance, of probabilities of expeditious progress, of priorities with respect to estimated requirements of the field, related sciences, and even (one hopes) the culture at large. Having selected a given part of the matrix for analysis, it is necessary to look closely, and the terrifying problem of scale about a thing like science is that what one sees will even then be immense. The sustained squint all too easily loosens into a "perspective," and a perspective is but a step away from total vision.

It is the fate, then, of fragments which get segregated for study to displace the wholes from which they derive. Set that down as a condition of human inquiry into entities having the scale, the ramified complexity of a science. In recent decades much of the study of special sciences, or of science, has shown this tendency for expert, specialized squinting to burgeon into total vision. Thus, in some quarters, the sentential end products of science have usurped science, or science has been displaced variously by its codifiable methods, its historico-cultural molds, its sociological texture, its technological fruits (and threats), or indeed any of its other aspects of the sort catalogued above. For this tendency in the study of science, there can be only one corrective. It must be the determination to keep our pluralistic rhetoric echoing around the margins of inquiry at all times—to see, aggressively and constantly, the aspect of science under investigation in relation to the matrix, while remembering that the matrix *is* disorderly.

This may prove more easily accomplished than one might think. Whatever the matrix of science might contain, man, its agent, is at its center. It is an incorrigible—though often strangely understressed—fact that science is by, of, and for human beings, that it is an activity of human agents continuous with other functionings of those agents. And when man is on the scene in proper force, the echoes of complexity cannot fail to be heard.

It is of the nature of "spirits" that they can be defined only allusively. In the conduct of *Psychology: A Study of a Science,* we have tried to view psychology and science, and within these immensities our delimited objects of investigation, in a way inspirited by such considerations as have been broached. Such considerations were weighty in selecting our objects of inquiry and in defining the context and incidence of inquiry with respect to each. They were influential in the choice and in the widely ranging diversification of our contributors. They were paramount in the invention and use of those editorial arrangements intended to make it possible for the present reader, the future analyst, to bring the differential sensibilities of our authors to bear on certain common themes. They governed the tone and content of the editorial suggestions made to the authors.

Our Study is thus "biased." It is biased in the infinitude of directions coherent with the spirit we have tried to convey. It is biased for contentual and methodological pluralism in psychology and in science—for the emergence of multiple criteria of *significance* for the practice of our science, criteria which themselves could be insignificant yet take the preservation of significance as their object. It is biased in favor of a scientific community of communicating deviants. The bias would be for a general recognition that behind an idea, method, or experiment there lurks a man—one corollary of which is that the cultivation of a scientist must implicate the cultivation of a man. The bias is stoutly for the restoration, perhaps emergence, of man to a fitting dimension within our *conception* of science. Indeed, the bias is even for the restoration of man as an object of serious, direct, and unembarrassed inquiry within certain segments of psychological science.

It is man's great good fortune to be a "double agent": he is a first-order actor and a second-order reflector, reappraiser, reviser of the course and consequences of action. Wherever there is an end in view—be it reasonable, effective, appropriate, or virtuous action—man's second agency must be as strongly committed as his first. He luckily has no choice. That intensely self-critical form of inquiring action known as scientific action might almost be defined as a crafty surrender of man's first agency to the discipline of his second. Thus in science man's two agencies are everywhere in taut collusion; the second-order questioning often being so fused with first-order assertion as to make man an undivided agent, after all.

To raise questions—broad or narrow—concerning the ends, strategies, instrumentalities; problems, observations, experiments; concepts, hypotheses, theories; meanings, judgments, prejudgments; history, status, tendency of any part of a science, or of a science, is to practice science.

To practice science is, at least in part, incessantly to raise such questions. This is not to suggest that such second-order questioning preempt first-order action (as has sometimes been known to happen in our field); it is merely to say science is suspended when man's second agency is idle.

So much for the spirit of this Study, and now, the letter.

THE PLAN OF STUDY

Historical: In the fall of 1952, this Study was given the rather generous mandate of carrying out an analysis of the "methodological, theoretical, and empirical status of psychological science." If the sponsoring groups had not delivered this mandate in open-ended form, the immensity of the challenge would, one fears, have disqualified action. Since the results of action are continuous with its history, a few paragraphs on the origins of the Study may be in order.

Some time before the inception of the Study, the idea of a series of investigations into psychological knowledge, and the institutional and occupational arrangements which have evolved in its pursuit, had recommended itself to the members of the Policy and Planning Board of the American Psychological Association. The National Science Foundation proved interested in supporting such a venture, and made a grant to the American Psychological Association as official steward for the enterprise.

From the beginning, it had been apparent that the aims of the Policy and Planning Board required for their realization two relatively independent lines of work: one taking the status of psychological knowledge as its object, and the other to be concerned with "occupational, educational, and institutional problems." Two corresponding projects, bearing the cryptic but not illogical designations "A" and "B," were thus constituted. Professor Kenneth Clark of the University of Minnesota served as Director of Project B (and has already reported its results in his book, *America's Psychologists*[1]). The present editor served as Director of Project A. How Project A evolved into *Psychology: A Study of a Science* will now be briefly told.

Shortly after the Directors were appointed, an Advisory Committee to the two enterprises, under Dael Wolfle's chairmanship, was established. Dr. Wolfle has described the relations of this group to the projects in his preface; what he did not mention was its remarkable spirit of helpfulness in the problems of the Directors, and the sensitive wisdom of his own leadership. Early in the planning phase, each Director nominated to the Advisory Committee a number of individuals to serve as a specialized panel of consultants in connection with his task. Project

[1] K. E. Clark, *America's Psychologists: A Survey of a Growing Profession*, Washington, D.C., American Psychological Association, 1957.

A was fortunate in finding Professors Howard H. Kendler, Lyle H. Lanier, Conrad G. Mueller, and Karl E. Zener willing to become members of its panel.

It is difficult not to sound dramatic in conveying the tone of the problem faced in planning Project A. The conception of a massive, collaborative appraisal of the "status" of a broad field of science—too youthful to have attained stability in any of its rapidly proliferating areas—was a bold one. It was also a frightening one. The status of a science *is* a science, whereas the exposition of a "status" must be a myth. It was frightening because *edifying* myths are ones which form slowly over history and are always judgments of the past. More literally, the task was challenging in the sense that sheer dimension entails unique responsibilities. There was not even the reassurance of precedent. Such a study had never been attempted in our science, nor in any other.

Our immediate response to the challenge was a natural, perhaps inevitable one. If inevitable, it can still be said to have been the most rational decision in the history of the project. It was the decision to proceed slowly until a plan—sober, limited in objective, but offering some hope of winning knowledge that might not otherwise be gained—could be evolved. It was thus decided that no design would be translated into formal inquiry until it proved capable of stirring a reasonable community of imaginations, and until there were at least some grounds for confidence in its practicability. Some of the landmarks in the route towards such ends of planning were these:

In the academic year 1952–1953, the Project Director, while a Fulbright Lecturer in England, devoted part of his time to developing a design for a series of investigations. A memorandum recommending three major studies, and subspecified into thirteen possible lines of inquiry, was the result. These suggestions were discussed at a meeting of the Advisory Committee in January, 1953. During the rest of the year in England, further thought was given toward an operating plan for each of the possible studies, and copies of the initial memorandum were sent for evaluation to a large number of psychologists in the United States.

In the late summer of 1953, the members of the panel generously made themselves available for a six-day "seminar" on the plans as they had evolved until that point. An outgrowth of this meeting was the preparation of an expanded and realigned set of suggestions which was submitted early that fall to the Advisory Committee. From among those proposals, the design for the investigation that was to become *Study I Conceptual and Systematic,* of *Psychology: A Study of a Science* was given first priority.

Only after such preparation did we feel ready to commit inquiry to the sea of action. At this point, however, we were still in transition towards the full-scale plunge. Further planning concerning *Study II Empirical Substructure and Relations with Other Sciences* and, to some extent, the more slender venture of the Director's book, *Psychology and the Human Agent,* continued—with frequent help from the panel members, and occasional review by the Committee—through October, 1954. The second group study was launched at that time.

Rationale of the planning. Certain of the desirable directions of planning were implicit in the very difficulties occasioned by the generality of our initial mandate. There is a way of perceiving difficulty which can render "obstacles" advantages. How so perceive?

Some lines of perception were obvious. Thus, for instance, it was clear that the project must eventuate in a selection of delimited investigations, perhaps more intensive than similar inquiry in the ordinary course, but of still modest scope and pretension. It was clear, further, that any set of inquiries to be chosen had best converge on some *part* of the tissue of psychological action; and it seemed reasonable, as an initial narrowing of the area of choice, to concentrate on problems of so-called "fundamental" psychology. It seemed clear also that a "status" of a science is not a present but a time-slice, and there seemed good grounds to decide that the time-reference of any investigation should fall roughly within the interval, 1930 to the present. Moreover, it was apparent that the tissue of psychological action had long before become so complex that only dim illumination of any sizable segment could come from any one individual. It seemed obvious that a multiplicity of expert sensibilities, each generating light from its own position in the tissue of action, was required.

But does not *group* investigation involve a danger: that of some dehumanized consensus, of some lowest common denominator of its worst insights—or just as bad, its best? Not if a group is a plurality of *individuals* of diverse human character, scientific temperament, and scholarly proprietorship. Not if such individuals pursue in privacy their independent tasks via their individual bents.

But a plurality of individuals is a summation of solipsisms. As history has so often demonstrated, the juxtaposing in one place of such plural private visions must be a collage and not a colligation. To this one might answer that science, too, is more collage than colligation. One might go further, though, and add that when plural solipsisms address a *common theme*—only then may definitions of the "real" emerge which are not entirely fictive.

A common theme? But does this not mean a strait-jacketing of sensibility—the undoing of everything that might be gained by *not* conceiving of group inquiry as involving a collection of cooperating agreers?

Quite clearly not more so than in any adaptive action in science, or in life itself. There is certainly a sense in which no epistemologist has a right to complain if we *define* science (and much of life) as a multiple viewing of common objects, common themes, by different sensibilities.

But what is to be the fate of these plural views of common themes? Are they to be averaged out, superimposed into some official "myth," some glibly ordered schema of disorder? Nothing could be more catastrophic. Every participant must have a vision of his science—a vision in which personal action may be located, environed with significance. But that vision must be *his own*. An official vision has always meant the end of science. Even limited diversity of personal visions means the impoverishment of science. The fate, then, of our multiple, expert views of common themes must be to remain *multiple,* and each to meet the gaze of other men in full quiddity.

Each actor in a science acts from and in his own image of that science. The happy paradox of science is that the vision, image, must be his *own,* yet partly formed and tested by the visions of others. A vision of a science must be unique, private; yet that view will not be *in* science unless fed by other viewers, present or past. The assemblage, then, of multiple expert views of common themes and their publication can enlarge, sharpen, or confirm the private vision of any individual viewers of these views. The reader—student, investigator, analyst, or civil man—may confront these assembled views and see a total pattern, or a selective one of any conformation.

Call the above considerations "criteria" of planning, if you like, or call them the beginning of the plan. Each further step may now fit into a geography.

The *direction* of the next step is clear, though its taking is not easy. If multiple minds are to converge on common themes, questions, segments in the tissue of scientific action, what specifically should these *objects* of investigation be? Much of the early planning had to do with the attempt to discriminate those themes, the engagement of which might promise most for the future of our science. Though there is a sense in which the body of a science wears certain of its general problems, its scars of anguish, conspicuously, these are still too numerous for any single study. Moreover, some of these lesions are superficial; some go deeper into invisible layers (where strange entanglements are possible). Any given problem itself presents a multiplicity of facets of differing accessibility, and each of different promise for advance.

One consideration which dominated the proposals ultimately made is worthy of emphasis, though difficult to convey briefly. Something like this:

To see science as the work of man is to see scientific action as everywhere conditioned by human decision, human hypothesis, human creative option. Though it is customary to represent each link in the long chain of decisions which present action presupposes as governed by "rational" criteria, every actor who has tasted inquiry knows that this is not the case. Man *commits* himself to action. Certain links in that chain may be arbitrary relative to forseeable consequences; others may be largely forged by temperament, taste, convenience, or wish in varied compounds; still others are preformed by precedent, fashion, the interests of the day, and drop into their places ready made. The *ends* of science may justly be described in a language of the "rational," but it is up to action to approximate these ends, and action is extrarational. Action is action; it is neither "rational" nor "irrational": these denote flexible yardsticks —extrinsic to action—for its measure. But a language of the ends, and hoped-for end products of science, too easily becomes the language of the actional processes of science.

For each actor in science, the chain of decisions which fathers action dangles vastly off into indeterminacy. The remote reaches of this chain disappear in distant history—but it is well that present science not be too continuous with its past. Among the more recent—and decisive—links, however, there are often many that are observable but not observed, recapturable but not captured. There are many forces in science, and its men, which all too easily cut present action off from its optative "presuppositions." Such forces require careful study by men of science, but at some level of knowing, their *existence* is known to all. Certainly, the search for order which is science carries with it its own public and private *idiom* of order which, like all idiom, too easily becomes the mold of truth. In recent years, this hopeful language of order has perhaps become more dominant in science, especially in its young and more baffled branches, than ever before.

Thus in our consideration of problems for inquiry, it was felt that the greatest values could emerge by selections that might invite from creative actors at the frontiers of our science a reconstruction—perhaps reassessment—of important links in the "presuppositional chains" of their current actions. Moreover, when a possible topic made the business of the analyst the actions of *others,* it was felt that attempts to infer critical links in those others' presuppositional chains might perhaps be more studiously made than is usual. It was felt that if themes could be found and phrased in a way which did in fact invite such efforts, progress in some degree would be inevitable. Many of an actor's commitments—orienting attitudes, evaluations of ends and guesses towards means, inherited judgments and self-formed tastes—are *there* for the looking. In a youthful science, when testing the actional consequences of varied commitments is most critical, why not look? Can in fact a youthful science—whose *immediate* aim cannot be much grander than the forming of commitments with rich promise for the parentage of future action—*afford* the deceptions of a premature language of order?

It was within such a climate that we considered the many possible themes and problems. As our suggestions multiplied, it became evident that they formed four extensive classes of inquiry, as follows:

COMPARATIVE ANALYSIS OF SYSTEMATIC FORMULATIONS. Here the emphasis of inquiry was to be on the presuppositional basis, conceptual content and structure, empirical grounds and consequences, explanatory promise, potential for future inquiry, of *specific* organizations of psychological knowledge enacted by individuals (singly or in collaboration).

Such organizations of knowledge are the products of the actor's optative efforts to perceive order in that flux of phenomena selected as the context of his inquiry; these products are recorded and made public in the actor's "systematic formulations." "Systematic," in this connection, does not mean "theoretical" in any of the recently standardized senses of the term; it in fact has an extension as well as an intension, and denotes any set of conceptual tools, no matter how unpretentious, for ordering empirical knowledge with regard to some specifiable domain of events, or furthering the discovery of such knowledge.

It was believed that an important forward step in this type of analysis—particularly as regards increasing insight into the detailed relations between orienting commitment and creative conceptual action—could be made by inviting the originators of systematic formulations to inquire into their *own* work, rather than to sponsor inquiries of the more conventional sort by independent analysts (however valuable such work may be). It was also believed important to study a wider *range* of the richly varied conceptual and systematic sallies in recent psychology than had previously received sustained analytic attention. In this connection, it was felt especially desirable to surmount that ideocentric predicament resulting from the tendency to conceive of most strategic and procedural problems of psychology in the terms posed by learning and "behavior" theories.

THE "PRESYSTEMATIC" COMMITMENTS OF PSYCHOLOGICAL SCIENCE. This theme of inquiry stressed the analysis of those links in the presupposition chains of actors, or groups of them, which genetically precede or causally condition attempts toward the systematic organization of phenomena within a given field of inquiry.

The questions conceived as relevant to this theme are those relatively general problems in presystematic strategy which crosscut the presupposition chains of diverse actors in a science in their creative movement towards the discovery and ordering of knowledge. In some form, many of the problems that recent fashion has called "methodological" would fall into this area: for instance, problems having to do with a fruitful, meaningful, and appropriate "observation base" for psychological science; problems concerning the initial definition and meaning-metabolism of empirical concepts ("empirical definition"); the many questions having to do with aims and strategies of "prediction" and "explanation," of descriptive, representational, and heuristic devices for the ordering of knowledge (e.g., role and limits of various mensurational and mathematical approaches, and of specifiable types of "models").

It was felt that many such questions could be profitably discussed—but only if considered in connection with *specified segments* of the tissue of psychological action, if dissociated from the prescriptionistic tone of much recent analysis, *and* if approached as problems in the genesis of creative knowledge-seeking action, rather than as extrinsically presolved issues in the "logic" of science. Many of the specific recommendations indeed urged a reappraisal of the abstract schema of "theoretical" practice which, during the preceding decades, psychology had tended increasingly to import (and further schematize) from the philosophy of science and other extrinsic sources. The pattern of study recommended was consonant with the "multiple expert individual" conception already conveyed. Since advance seemed contingent on that liberalization of attitude which must result from fuller understanding of the *diversity* of knowledge-seeking procedures in other sciences, it was recommended that a number of creative men from special fields of biological and natural science, from the history of science, philosophy, and logic participate in addition to psychologists.

INTERNAL RELATIONS AND "EXTRINSIC ASSOCIATIONS" OF PSYCHOLOGICAL SCIENCE. The actor in science is necessarily engrossed in his own sphere of action, yet his very effort causes the tissue of action of his science ever to differentiate. No actor can arrive at a precise "fix" on his place in this labile medium, but each perforce must guide, judge, and deploy his actions in terms of his best view of the environing topography. Often that view is determined by hidden links in the presuppositional chain of his action—or by rusted links, or links formed by fashion and rarely rescrutinized. At best, the actor's view of the ever-changing tissue of action must be obsolescent in some degree. Despite such limits, much of man's inquiring effort in science must be somehow to achieve whatever fidelity of larger vision may be possible.

Thus, our plan recommended a series of investigations, again by specialized, creative men, into the relations among various of the emerging subfields of psychological science, and into the growing interpenetrations between the tissue of psychological action and that of *other* sciences concerned with overlapping *objects* of inquiry. In the language of one of our memorandums:

The present part of the project, therefore, proposes to sponsor a series of analyses in which interrelationship issues will be considered as they affect, not specific and fragmentary theories, but more broadly conceived bodies of knowledge. These subject-matter areas would correspond, in some contexts, to major subdivisions of psychological science and, in others, to psychology as a whole in relation to other disciplines. In these analyses the emphasis would be placed upon interrelations among empirical variables distinguished within specified subject-matter areas; upon cross-area functional dependencies and formal relationships; upon interrelations concerning types of problems dealt with, investigative methods, techniques for the systematization of knowledge, general aims, etc.

Again, the suggested pattern of investigation called for the participation of many individuals, each of whom, in *this* case, would bring his research experience in a given area of psychological, social, or biological science to bear on a survey of the interrelations between his field and other specified parts of psychology and/or related sciences. It was felt desirable that the participants be men who had committed some substantial part of their careers to research which, in fact, "bridged" given disciplines or areas, and that each make this personal context of activity central in his analysis.

Empirical inner structure of special fields of inquiry. Each actor perceives his inquiry as falling into an area inhabited by others whose objects of inquiry are judged to be similar or closely related. The need for mutual orientation among coinquiring agents over time will give that "area" conventionalized boundaries and a name. The topography of a science is a fluid, changing distribution of such stipulatively bounded areas. The line of study proposed under *Internal relations of psychological science* emphasized established or emerging interconnections as among such areas. The theme here proposed stresses inquiry into the inner structure of those areas.

Whatever their *systematic* options, investigators in psychology locate their efforts in one of a limited number of grossly defined, and, by now, rather rigidly institutionalized "research areas" (e.g., perception, learning, motivation, personality, social psychology, etc.). Investigators are apprised that these "areas" reflect early-made stipulations, and that the rapid increase in volume and diversity of research has made each such area highly heterogeneous, but in unknown ways. They have doubts about the coherence of these areas, about the clusterings of knowledge within them, and even about the relative distribution of dependably "sharable" and significant knowledge, as against "knowledge-forms" which—either because of the conditions of their "discovery" or the manner of formulation—may be expendable. The difficulties in making such discriminations are compounded by certain common links in the presupposition chains of many actors who conduct inquiry into the structure of knowledge. For instance, the understandable desire of the agents in a young science to achieve predictively rich empirical relationships of some *generality* has often led to the grouping together of quite *disparate* variables—manipulated and recorded under widely different conditions of actual inquiry—under a *common designation.* Again (and leading in practice to the same result), inquirers have often unwittingly expressed the results of empirical research conducted under "local" circumstances in the relatively general language of their own systematic predilections. Moreover, this blurring of the outlines of warranted empirical knowledge can be augmented by the failure of investigators to identify with precision the empirical variables actually manipulated or recorded in specific inquiries.

With such considerations in the background, our plan proposed a somewhat novel *genre* in the assay of empirical knowledge. The suggested mode of analysis involved starting with a selection of the *conventionally discriminated* variables believed to be important in a given area (e.g., lists roughly as distinguished in handbooks and similar sources) and testing the functional coherence of such "variables" by tracking down their empirical realizations in the relevant research literature of the preceding thirty or forty years. In this way one might hope to test more or less standardized beliefs about the structure of empirical knowledge (increasingly objects of doubt even to their holders) against careful estimates of the variables actually manipulated and recorded in concrete research contexts. An elaborate pattern of analysis was suggested toward such ends, and its application to two or three representative subject-matter areas recommended. As always, the planning contemplated convergence of multiple, specialized sensibilities on analysis of each area.

Each of these four classes of inquiry seemed important; each, when approached with responsibility to the germane issues as posed by recent psychological science, became immense. The problem in the later stages of planning was clearly that of some kind of selection as among the four classes of inquiry, yet a selection which would not unduly compromise the objectives of any given one. The solution ultimately adopted was to place primary emphasis on *two* of the recommended lines of inquiry, yet translate them into action in a way which to the fullest extent possible might realize certain aims of the other two. Fortunately, these four of the possible ways of analytically viewing the body of a science are themselves interlaced in a way which permits such a solution.

With these requirements in mind, the clear choice was to select the first and third classes of inquiry (*Comparative analysis of systematic formulations,* and *Internal relations and "extrinsic associations" of psy-*

chological science) as the core emphases of the Study. Even in the terms of their initial conception, adequate pursuit of these would guarantee a certain yield of insight into the problems of *The "presystematic" commitments of psychological science,* and *Empirical inner structure of special fields of inquiry.* Moreover, the chosen lines of inquiry offered excellent opportunities for adaptation in a way which might include certain of the *specific* problems of the two latter.

Thus emerged the contours of the two group studies which form the bulk of *Psychology: A Study of a Science.* A final, slender part of the plan seeks to appose to these a single view of problems suggested by the recent history of psychology—not excluding that of the present project. Individual views, as diffused over the problems of a science, have their limits—limits which are underscored in the plan for the first six volumes of this Study. Yet molar views by individuals have their place, too: science must have its case histories. The final volume, then, will be a book by the Director, which will (*a*) record those dispositions toward *a* science and science which necessarily color in some degree the spirit of the Study, (*b*) construct trends from the massive findings of the two group studies, and (*c*) consider in the light of the Study's premises and apparent trends certain of the problems of psychological inquiry suggested by the practice of the past few decades. This book is offered on individual responsibility as a kind of personal postscript to the Study.

So much for the *rationale* of our planning. It should be emphasized that a rationale is not a history. Yet this rationale is close enough to history to convey something of its flavor.

Synopsis of the final plan. The spirit and governing criteria of planning shade inseparably into the plan, and the reader will by now have formed a general impression of the final structure and methods of the project. As is evident, the three lines of effort upon which planning slowly converged became the *plan;* the plan eventuated in the manifold labors ultimately reported in the three divisions of *Psychology: A Study of a Science.*

STUDY I CONCEPTUAL AND SYSTEMATIC. This is the final, implemented form of the lines of inquiry into the "systematic formulations" of psychological science and related issues, proposed in the first and, to some extent, the second theme of the earlier planning (as described in the above "rationale"). In brief, the study involved the intensive analysis of 34 "systematic formulations"—of widely varying type and subject-matter reference—all of substantial influence in recent and current psychology. Each such "systematic formulation" is the end product of a dedicated human effort to see and state order in a given domain of the events studied by our science. Each analysis was therefore made either by the *originator*(*s*) of the formulation in question, or (in a few cases) by individuals actively and creatively associated with the *development* of formulations of which they were not the primary authors. Each analyst, moreover, undertook reflective inquiry into his position with the intention of bearing in mind certain common *themes of analysis*.

These themes, by and large, were designed to invite a convergence of creative insight on those problems of systematization which had emerged from the history of inquiry in the preceding two or three decades. Some of these problems had been figural in the systematic and "metasystematic" discussion of the preceding years, but required in our opinion exposure to a wider range of systematically schooled sensibilities than had previously been the case. Others seemed critically posed by recent systematic thought, yet had been given little or no explicit attention.

The results of Study I are contained, of course, in the three initial volumes of the series, namely: *Sensory, Perceptual, and Physiological Formulations; General Systematic Formulations, Learning, and Special Processes; Formulations of the Person and the Social Context.*

The operating procedures and methods of the study are described in the *Introduction to Study I* (pp. 19–40).

STUDY II EMPIRICAL SUBSTRUCTURE AND RELATIONS WITH OTHER SCIENCES. This is the translation into action of that combination of the third and fourth inquiry-areas already mentioned in the discussion of "rationale." The emphasis of Study II is on the exploration of interrelations among the parts of psychological science, and on the place of psychology within the matrix of scientific activity. But clarification of such relationships is conceived as contingent on prior efforts to chart knowledge *within* the fields whose cross-connections are under analysis, and thus the study offers quite general possibilities for sharpening vision into the emerging topography of psychological and related knowledge. Unlike Study I, which stresses conceptual and systematic issues, this study concentrates on the relations among "systematically neutral" bodies of knowledge (to whatever extent such discriminations are possible).

It is not suggested that consideration of "interrelationship issues" has been bypassed in recent decades. On the contrary, much scientific work and many administrative and pedagogical arrangements have been premised on judgments concerning such issues. The strategic weight of these judgments, however, has not always been matched by the weight of analysis on which they are based, nor has their impact on inquiry received the continuing assessment that is desirable. For example, many systematists—championing either a "purely behavioral" or a "physiological" frame of reference for their concepts—have proceeded to the construction of ambitious systematic formulations *before* essaying detailed analysis of actual and possible relations between physiology and psychology. Again, much effort has gone toward "interdisciplinary" integration of psychological and social science, with little prior exploration of the nature and degree of integration of the relevant sciences taken separately. Conventionally discriminated areas of psychological science are variously held to be supplementary, independent, reducible one to the other, related according to one or another set of "bridging laws," or improperly subdivided, but such positions are not always based on intensive content-analyses of the areas in question. A variety of dogmas exists with regard to the training and professional roles of clinical and other applied psychologists, but there has been little sustained consideration of relations—present and prospective—between specific fields of "fundamental" psychology and given bodies of applicational knowledge.

The units of subject matter available to Study II for the initiation of its inquiries can, of course, be no more "rationally" bounded than the "fields" distinguished by current convention. Morover, the intentions of Study II could clearly go no further than interesting a number of individuals with established research commitments to cross-field or cross-discipline problems, in a creative facing of the issues: the intentions were certainly not comprehensive, nor is it possible to say what "comprehensiveness" could mean in such a connection. Within this framework, the "fields" ultimately arrived at for consideration in their relationships were (*a*) from within *psychology*—sensory psychology, perception, physiological psychology, learning, personality, social psychology, psycholinguistics, clinical psychology, and human engineering, (*b*) from within *biological science*—aspects of physiology, neuroanatomy, and genetics, (*c*) from within *social science*—aspects of sociology, anthropology, linguistics, economics, and political science.

The design of Study II called for individuals whose primary affiliation was in some one of the "fields" indicated above to consider its relations to some specified one or combination of the others. In the terminology of the study, the field which the analyst represents, by virtue of professional affiliation, is the "field of primary reference"; the "field of secondary reference" is the domain whose relationship to his "own" field the analyst proposes to explore. The specific bounding, for purposes of the analysis, of *both* fields of reference is, of course, the option of the analyst, an option always influenced in some degree by his particular cross-field research history. Though contributors were invited to stress in their discussions the specific problems on which they had done "bridging" research they were by no means discouraged from considering broader questions of structure and relationship.

A *plurality* of individuals of differing background and specialized cross-area interest was invited to "represent" *each* field of primary reference. The hope was that—depending on the breadth and density of a given field—it might be represented by between two and five individuals. For most of the fields of primary reference designated above, this hope was realized. Forty-two explorations of such substructural and interrelationship topics, all carried out by individuals with distinguished, relevant research backgrounds, are going forward. It is hoped that precisely that number will comprise Study II, when completed.

As in the case of Study I, an attempt to invite a convergence of vision on certain crosscutting issues, and to facilitate collation of findings, was made in the form of proposed *themes of analysis*. The themes for Study II constitute a rather differentiated breakdown of the senses in which questions of "mapping" subject-matter structure and exploring field interrelations might be entertained. In both group studies, the proposed discussion plans were offered as frameworks to be used *only* to the extent that contributors found them congenial to personal inclination and to the demands of their topics. It was felt that—no matter how freely and selectively they might be used—a minimum result would be the creation of an atmosphere which might encourage concrete viewing.

This brief description of Study II is given so that the reader may locate each part of *Psychology: A Study of a Science* within the whole. An adequate account of the aims and working methods of Study II must await publication of its results. These will be reported in the fourth through sixth volumes of the present series, as follows: *Biologically Oriented Fields: Their Place in Psychology and in Biological Science; The Process Areas, the Person, and Some Applied Fields: Their Place in Psychology and in Science; Investigations of Man as Socius: Their Place in Psychology and the Social Sciences.*

VOLUME 7, PSYCHOLOGY AND THE HUMAN AGENT. This is not properly a subdivision of the Study but rather a postscript to it representing certain views of the Director which crystallized during the years of work on Project A, nor is this book primarily a *summary* of the major studies, even though an estimate of trends is included.

The intention, as already suggested, is to record a set of attitudes towards psychology, and the forces which have influenced its recent history. The consequences of this viewpoint will—in the light of the Study's findings—be traced out for a variety of special issues concerning the values, ends, presuppositional bases, creative sources, and strategic options of psychological inquiry. The issues selected represent the author's estimate of critical problems suggested by the systematic efforts of investigators as these have been defined over the past twenty-five years, more or less. Though many of the issues raised relate in some sense to problems which have been discussed in terms variously of the "methodology," "metatheory," or "logic" of psychology, they are approached in a way which seeks to keep the *processes* of science, rather than its rationalized products, at the center of analysis. In this sense, the approach may be considered as stressing what is coming to be called "sociology of science" or its "psychology"—but it is an implication of the view developed that such terms are deceptive in that the critical function in science cannot confidently wait upon the object of its concern somehow to equip its armamentarium.

It would hardly be appropriate to the nature of a "postscript" to give any further indication of the content of Volume 7 at this place.

INTRODUCTION TO STUDY I CONCEPTUAL AND SYSTEMATIC

Study I seeks to promote a sharpening of vision into recent searches for order within those refractory domains that psychological scientists have had the courage to study.

The search for order in science is mediated by the predispositions which human actors bring to the domains of their interest, and by the creative reformations of such predispositions during those interactions between delimited curiosities and natural events known as *inquiry.* The specialized predispositions brought by the actor to inquiry may be called "concepts"; their patterning into interpretive, expectational, and action-regulating schemas relative to an object of inquiry may be called "conceptual systems." Each conceptual unit is a transient terminal link in a causal-genetic presupposition chain of vast but indeterminate length and heterogeneous composition—or more accurately the terminal convergence point of some intertangled plurality of such chains. Given links may be self-formed or formed by others; they may have been formed in course of inquiry into similar or quite different domains, or they may be creative options of present inquiry. They may be set in place during technical inquiry or in the ordinary course of human problematic action; they may find their place either by calculation or fortune, direction or indirection. They may be compounded from any areas—namable or unnamable—of sensibility, experience, or imagination that comprise the content of man.

If such a mode of talk about the search for order is granted any legitimacy, then a number of things should be obvious. A "sharpening of vision" into any broadly bounded segment of the search for order, if nonillusory, can be effected only in small uneven increments. Vision can only focus at given levels of the search for order, but even then vision must be cautious: the "level" at which vision resolves is one *chosen* by vision. Vision has *no choice but* to see at levels; yet it is up to vision to adjust its view by frequent shifts of focus.

"Conceptual systems," as brought by actors to inquiry and formed, reformed, and transformed in process of inquiry, are systems of events within the inquirer. They do not comprise *inquiry;* they comprise what the inquirer brings to the *object* of inquiry. They govern what he does toward and to the *object* of inquiry, and they reflect what the object of inquiry permits the inquirer to take away. At all stages of inquiry, "conceptual systems" are in some sense registered within the functioning of the inquirer by a system of representational or sign-events of private or public significance. Such systems of representational events may be called "systematic formulations." When expressed within the resources of a publicly standardized language, they are among the most decisive artifacts of a science, for it is through them that individual inquiry may become plural and convergent relative to given objects. It is through these artifacts that inquiry may in some degree be cumulative and progressive over time, and its sharable results applied to the manifold requirements of man.

Study I directs vision toward the publicly specified "systematic formulations" of recent psychological science. Such registrations of the search for order were broadly defined in the ground plan of Study I as "any set of sentences formulated as a tool for ordering empirical knowledge with respect to some specifiable domain of events, or furthering the discovery of such knowledge." As the original definition of the domain of study further pointed out:

> A "systematic formulation" may vary from one or a few orienting ideas toward the conduct of research, or toward the organization of extant knowledge within a given empirical domain (of any scope), to an explicit, elegant, and quantified systematization. Such highly diverse expressions as "viewpoint," "research philosophy," "*Weltanschauung*," "exploratory hypothesis" or set of such, "frame of reference," "dimensional system," "systematic (or theoretical) framework," "explanatory (or descriptive) system," "hypothetico-deductive system," "theory," "explanatory mechanism" (or set of such), "model," etc., may all be subsumed under "systematic formulation," as we wish to use this phrase.

"Systematic formulations" are significant artifacts of a science, but not the exclusive ones. Moreover, they *are artifacts,* products. It is a premise of Study I that the meaning and potentialities of these artifacts cannot be adequately appreciated when divorced from the processes of which they are products. Such processes may within limits be inferred from study of the artifacts in which they have eventuated; inferences of this sort, however remote, are (and must be) ubiquitously made in science. Study I seeks in its analyses some slight narrowing of the inferential distance between process and artifacts, by inviting relevant inferences from inquirers who can in some sense be said to "own" *both* process and artifact.

Even within the restrictions already suggested, Study I is perforce selective in many other ways. Its study of "systematic formulations" can certainly not pretend to be encyclopedic. Nor does it claim "representativeness" in any formal sense—there is no sampling theory for the distribution of systematic actions in a science. Nor would Study I lay claim to secret a priori knowledge even of where to draw the bounds of current psychological inquiry. It can hope only to include enough of its illimitable subject within its limited purview to permit individuals to test—perhaps enrich—their divers views.

The pattern of Study I has been conveyed in the General Introduction to the Series. Its detailed working methods must now be described.

COMPOSITION OF THE DOMAIN OF STUDY

The "domain" of Study I consists of 34 "systematic formulations." How did this domain emerge?

It emerged on the basis of mixed criteria, mingled and applied by the best efforts of many minds. These minds asked themselves some such question as "what does my view of the distribution of systematic effort in psychology tell me about the requirements for clarifying and perhaps extending that view?" Over and above this, it emerged from such pellucidly rational considerations as the number of pages it might be decent to publish. Its emergence was certainly shaped also by the availability of systematists willing or free to inquire into their own inquiry.

A few of the criteria which were felt to have a rational basis and which, in retrospect, indeed seem to have strongly shaped the final domain may now be given. They can assuredly be assigned no relative weights.

1. It was felt that the principle of multiple specialized viewing—central to the conception of the role of project participants—should also be applied to the selection of systematic domains for inquiry, and thus by the terms of Study I, to the participants themselves. As a point of departure, a working list of some sixty nodes of systematic effort was evolved by the members of the Project A panel over several months of individual thought and group exchange. During this initial phase, individual panel members sought widespread advice from others whom they deemed more discriminating than themselves. Once formed, the list did not remain static. It was, over several additional months, expanded, contracted, and realigned in connection with constant efforts to share the knowledge of still other expert viewers. The list at no point was made public—advice was solicited from consultants only by requesting their suggestions for the significant representation of their own fields. It may be added that at no time before completion of the study did even the contributors have full knowledge of the final domain.

2. Any principle of "statistical representativeness" was, of course, seen as meaningless from the start. In lieu of this, a dominating criterion was maximum diversification with respect to (*a*) problematic or subject-matter fields to which the systematic formulations were addressed, and (*b*) within given fields, the conceptual content, presuppositional basis, and other characteristics in which formulations may vary. With regard to fields in which recent history has provided a plurality of formulations having similar or overlapping explanatory objectives but different conceptual, predictive, or programmatic import, efforts were made to insure a balanced representation of major lines of work.

3. A limiting framework for diversification was presented from the beginning by three arbitrary, if pragmatically imposed, decisions:

a. The domain was to be bounded, by and large, by the intellectual climate of American psychology. Such thoroughly regrettable chauvinism was enforced by the unavailability, for any close collaboration, of competent appraisers of the European and world scene, and of course by the technical difficulties of administering a study of the present type on an international basis. This decision, it should be noted, did not prevent the crossing of national boundaries in connection with systematic efforts which, though of figural interest on the American scene, were best represented by European inquirers.

b. Formulations relevant primarily to the concerns of "fundamental" or "pure" psychology were to be included. The line separating such formulations from those having primarily applicational objectives is of course drawn differently by different viewers, but some such line was drawn by all.

c. An approximate limitation in the number of "systematic formulations" that could practicably be included had, of course, to be set. Most people perceived that number as in the range of thirty to forty.

4. All persons whose views determined the domain were of course guided by their individual criteria of the *significant*. All, being human, were aware that any criterion of significance must in some degree be confounded by the *influence* of given systematic positions on the distribution and volume of inquiry in given fields—thus on the ideas of inquirers, not excluding the viewer himself. Viewers were making judgments of significance, and these judgments were reflecting objective social facts of influence; an inevitable confounding, but not entirely unfortunate relative to a study with the present aims. If vision is to be refreshed and sharpened with respect to the ends, means, and prospects of

a science, it is well that it be directed toward lines of effort which proliferate widely in its present tissue of action. Still, there is a sense in which any self-determining individual's criterion of the significant is at once a criterion of fruitful deviance. And it is fair to hope that this ineluctable quality is not unrepresented in the final domain.

These, then, were our criteria of selection. Clearly, the kind of "problem" to which they are addressed does not permit a unique solution. The group of formulations chosen for inclusion could well have been different without significant compromise of the selective criteria. Yet a glance at the Tables of Contents will make it evident that the group could not have been totally different, and most readers will further agree that—within the numerical and other arbitrary restrictions on choice—the representation could not have been radically different.

Further understanding of the grounds for the composition of the present domain—and perhaps some feeling for the realities of a study of the present sort—may be given by mention of a few additional circumstances (of quite varied type) which conditioned the outcome of planning.

1. Most individuals in touch with the early planning looked upon the core conception of Study I as a bold one, holding a unique potential for clarification of systematic issues. But most—not excluding the Director—agreed that the intrinsic promise of the conception was matched by an excellent chance that it would not prove workable. Now that the study is a published fact, it may be difficult for the reader to appreciate the mood of those responsible for its conduct in the early days. The study was inviting sustained analytico-creative effort from precisely those persons in psychological science who could be expected to be most heavily preoccupied with other endeavors. It was asking for a lengthy interruption of other commitments and could offer in return little more than the Cartesian pains of analytic self-doubt, the hope of contributing in some measure to an illumination of problems in the enaction of our science, and the chance that reflective scrutiny of past thinking might lead to the subtle gratifications of its creative restructuring. It requires little imagination to see that there were other hazards. The question of *current* significance, however, is, to what extent did these reality conditions determine the final domain?

The answer is surprising—very little. Rarely has a science seen a demonstration of altruism by so many of the very individuals whose commitments must make this *beau geste* most costly. Very few of the individuals invited failed to accept. Very few of those who accepted failed to complete their contributions. It would, of course, unfairly represent the continuities between science and life to suggest that this result was immediate and automatic. That it was *possible* is itself sufficient token of the spirit of those who are extending the frontiers of psychological science.

Still, there *were* people who could not participate, and there were defections. If matters had gone exactly as planned, how would the representation have differed?

a. There would have been a fuller representation of recent systematic developments relative to *physiological psychology*. Of all areas within the province of the study, this is the most thinly sampled. To some extent, this imbalance is redressed in Study II, which contains more contributions in the physiological area than in most others, but the present limitation—particularly in light of the rapid recent advances in psycho-physiology—is a real one.

b. There would have been a more diversified representation of effort in *social psychology* (particularly in respect to systematic formulations of attitudes and of varied "small-group" phenomena) and in *personality*. With regard to the latter area, there would have been fuller coverage of systematic treatments of the *development* of personality, and of the formulations which link basic psychological theory with problems of psychopathology. There would also have appeared an analysis of one of the major and more sophisticated approaches to constitutional typology, and the consideration of psychoanalytic theory would have been pluralized. Nevertheless, it might be said that so richly varied are the current investigations of the person and the social context that more comprehensive inclusions would have thrown our third volume badly out of balance with the other two, thus jeopardizing a critical condition of harmony.

c. There would have been slightly better-balanced coverage of other major areas. Sensory psychology would have been represented by two additional topics, formulations of learning by one. There would have been fuller representation of information theory, especially in its substantively oriented psychological applications.

d. Two types of formulation not directly treated in the present collection—the cybernetic point of view and general systems theory—would have been represented. The projected analysis of cybernetics would, incidentally, have stressed its bearing on recent neurophysiological thought, thus widening coverage of the physiological area.

2. In most areas, psychology is still in a phase such that the "natural" basis for bounding its systematic idea-clusters is that of primary authorship, either by individuals or small and tightly organized groups. Major

systematic ideas in the public domain are still "imaged" (and, at this point in our science, rightly so) as the ideas of the people who put them there. This fact is inevitably reflected in the design of the study.

Still, there are areas of psychology, and islands here and there, where the continuity of ideas, and the multiplicity of their authorship, already renders surnames inappropriate to major systematic clusterings. By and large, systematists working in areas of this sort are not creating "their" theory; they are developing widely shared bodies of systematic knowledge, long in the public domain. The extent to which such a condition obtains in an area, or the precise date of its arrival, are subtle questions whose answers must admit graded transition. But few would disagree that this condition exists in much of *sensory psychology,* certain areas of *perception* and *physiological psychology,* and even such "classical" fields as verbal and rote learning. The reader will note that these considerations were active at various places in determining the domain of the present study. It is also well to note that authors dealing with such areas were faced with problems of a somewhat different order than those confronting analysts of formulations more "uniquely" their own, and that corresponding differences in the mode of analysis were enforced.

Such a difference of incidence is of course most evident in the sensory area in which Graham, Licklider, and to an appreciable extent Pirenne and Marriott, were perforce dealing with broad ranges of systematico-experimental knowledge which have evolved in the long-range investigation of important visual and auditory problems. While on this topic, it might be added that in considering the representation of so densely developed a field as sensory psychology, it was never the intention to "sample" every modality, or include analysis of "every" type of problem. Here, as elsewhere, the aim was to secure outstanding analysis in depth of *characteristic* topics, yet in sufficient diversity to give a sense of the range of creative problems that systematists face.

3. The critical artifacts of a science toward which systematic activity is keyed are, of course, formulations having *substantive* import—which make objectively contingent assertions about those *phenomena* which the actors of a science strive to order. In all science, however, the long and circuitous route toward cognitively rich substantive formulations is necessarily punctuated by systematic formulations having themselves no reference to the empirical domain of study, but providing relational analyses applicable to a *class* of possible substantive formulations, and having the power to facilitate the elaboration or refinement of the latter. In their most general guises, such systems take the form of systems of pure mathematics and logic; these in turn are often subspecified or developed in order to meet special demands of substantive systematization, or indeed, new relational inventions of specialized types may be

made for a similar purpose. In this latter category fall the special techniques evolved for the processing of certain classes of data, restricted or specialized statistical methods, systematic mensurational and "scaling" devices, formulations of the sort currently called "models," etc. If as a class we refer to such systematic formulations as "methodic" rather than substantive, it is clear that the *general* definition of the domain of Study I (see p. 20) does not exclude formulations of the methodic variety.

Few will quibble with the observation that the status of a science is first and foremost the status of knowledge about its subject matter, and thus with our feeling that the primary emphasis of Study I be on adequate treatment of *substantive* systematic ideas. But in a science which—because of historic predicament and unique subject-matter challenges—must devote much of its energy to the invention of *means* for the pursuit of knowledge, methodic formulations can comprise a large part of the systematic fabric. Indeed, when it is appreciated that many formulations with substantive intent are (perforce) largely procedural prolegomena to future substantive action, the line between the "substantive" and the "methodic" becomes difficult to draw. We may at least note in passing that such a line is more tortuous than that drawn by the logic of science between "empirical" and "formal" systems.

Our response to this complex of considerations was, we think, well adjusted to the nature of the realities which suggested them. It was to forget about the "substantive-methodic" distinction as a principle of *selection*—to constitute our domain in terms of such criteria of multiply judged diversification, significance, and influence as have already been described. Short of a set to the effect that our business was not to compile a survey of specialized statistical techniques, or mathematical meta-models, our attitude toward the distribution of the substantive vs. the methodic was mainly curiosity over the result.

It might be of interest to anticipate that result:

Two formulations of unequivocally methodic intent turned up on the final lists. One of these was Lazarsfeld's suggestive development of "latent structure analysis"—a methodic formulation of particular importance because of the generality throughout psychological and social science of the problems to which it is a response. The other—also a formulation relevant to the theory of measurement but with special applicability to the analysis of decision processes—must remain nameless in that its protagonist ultimately found it necessary to withdraw.

In doing any kind of justice to the current distribution of systematic action it was, of course, inevitable that information theory and linear frequency theory be represented. Though these formulation-classes, as is well known, have been bent toward substantive ends within psychology, it will be quite clear from the capable analyses of Frick and Ellson that both formulations must be considered, in the first and only unambiguous instance, "methodic" (in the present terms).

All other formulations in the present volumes may be considered as substantive in *intent,* albeit varying hugely in the presence, prominence, or pervasiveness of ancillary methodic components.

4. Finally, we must sadly note the deaths during the course of the study of two distinguished men who would have been among our contributors—Egon Brunswik and William J. Crozier. Crozier had planned to conduct an analysis of his theory of brightness vision, and Brunswik was to have contributed on his probabilistic theory of perception. To the good fortune of readers of this series, Professors Postman and Tolman were willing to carry out a "surrogate" analysis of Brunswik's position, as a memorial to their brilliant colleague.

THE THEMES OF ANALYSIS

The problems faced in devising the suggested themes of analysis were various and subtle.

Basically, we wished a breakdown of topics which would invite analysis both in depth and extent, and which, in particular, might stimulate authors to develop materials that could illumine the relations between process and product, creative source and systematic outcome. In the terms of the distinction made at the beginning of this Introduction, we sought insight into connections between "conceptual systems" as systems of events within the inquirer, and "systematic formulations"; moreover, we hoped analysis might be sufficiently stratified to lay bare certain of the causal-genetic factors, the presupposition chains, which converged on the inquirer's conceptual system. We were inclined to feel—and strongly hoped—that the type of sustained reappraisal of a man's position that might be prompted by such analytic aims would not only clarify it, but would have a creative impact on its development. It is too often forgotten that analysis, even when merely evaluative or judicial, can have creative consequences. The type of analysis which we wished to invite, however, was as much geared to creative as to explicative objectives—a neglected *genre* in the analytic literature of psychology, but one uniquely within reach in this study where creative agent of a formulation and analyst are one.

There were other desiderata:

We wished a breakdown sufficiently flexible to permit analytic discussion of the widest possible range of "systematic formulations"—irrespective of objective, content, underlying rationale, method, and mode of formulation. We wished such flexibility and at the same time enough specificity to stimulate concrete and differentiated discussion of all formulations independently of type.

We wished a set of themes that might invite enough commonality among the questions entertained by different authors to give readers and future analysts a purchase for the detection of similarities, differences, and trends. Though opportunity for significant collation of the various analyses was an important aim, it was felt equally important that this not be pursued in a way which might impose commensurable analtyic molds on incommensurable materials.

Finally, we wished a set of themes which, while reflecting all the above objectives, would invite from our diverse systematists a convergence of experience and judgment on certain key issues of systematic inquiry. In this way, it was hoped that the study would result in materials that might not only deepen and extend knowledge of the tissue of systematic action, but also appraise recent doctrine and belief about the ends and instrumentalities of systematic work.

In short, the hope was to capture in the proposed discussion topics, and in all editorial materials, the spectrum of values and special emphases comprising the spirit of the study. Reductions of spirit to letter constitute no easy task—least of all when letter must diffuse spirit over a most various range of sensibility. Whatever the shortcomings of the discussion themes, it can assuredly be said that no single document addressed to the ends in view could have achieved more than qualified success. It should be noted that the Suggested Discussion Topics carried only part of the burden in this substantialization of spirit. There were other descriptive materials concerning Study I and its place in the project and perhaps most important in realizing the "atmosphere" of the study was the editorial correspondence with individual contributors over the years.

Perhaps the most trying problem faced in the formulation of the discussion themes was a special (and many-faceted) case of the tradition-innovation antinomy. We wished to invite essays which might promote a recentering of the conception of analysis in psychology in the ways already indicated. To effect such an invitation, we required a language in which we might talk about the details of systematic work with reasonable intelligibility and precision to individuals of diverse background. Short of some set of boldly new, thus arbitrary counters—of uncertain aptness and open to idiosyncratic construal—there is only one solution to such problems: the use, *as a point of departure,* of a language which already exists. Joycean solutions have their limitations, even in literature. Fortunately, the "meaning-horizons" and combinatorial possibilities of words are such that new meanings are not preempted by established terms.

Accordingly, it was inevitable in the formulation of discussion themes that we speak a language deriving in part from those contexts of inquiry in which systematic activity in science had been given explicit attention. It was inevitable that we borrow certain idioms from the philosophy and methodology of science, and more directly from the rough-and-ready counters and distinctions which had evolved in the course of analytic and "metasystematic" discussion in psychology. Such terms and distinctions, however, were used eclectically, and with doctrinal neutrality, as descriptive tools for isolating the many questions which comprehensive and stratified analysis of a systematic formulation would seem to demand. Reliance was rarely placed on the semantic "backlog" of these terms, elucidation being given for most. An attempt was made to sharpen, or subspecify, certain of the distinctions used, and in some cases to suggest new ones (e.g., "systematic" vs. "empirical" variables, "*immediate* data language") designed to draw interest toward important but analytically neglected aspects of systematic work. In devising the discussion topics, however, no great value was set upon providing some ultimate and impeccable analytic vocabulary (too many of them are already available); the objective was merely sufficiently clear descriptive resources for the purpose at hand.

There were other considerations which argued against too great a break with the idiom and, to some extent, the concerns of recent psychological methodology. As already indicated, one of the special opportunities of the study was the pooling of an unprecedented range of experience with regard to problems of systematic inquiry that had been suggested by the work of the past decades. These problems are defined, in the first and most meaningful instance, by the intimate interaction between individual inquirers and the specificities of their objects of inquiry—by the arduous counterpoint of problematic aim, objective barrier and constraint, conceptual posit, procedural option, empirical verdict. In any coherent time-slice of a science, however, the interchanges among systematic actors, together with secondary analyses of systematic practice, result in the discrimination (correct or otherwise) of certain cross-cutting aims, barriers, conceptual modes, methodic strategems, etc., believed to be common to going systematic pursuits, or specialized classes thereof. It is not long before such generalizations congeal into conventionalized schemata of the ends and instrumentalities of systematic work. These images necessarily define part of the context for further systematic work; inevitably they acquire heuristic, if not stipulative, overtones. Sooner or later inquirers, wittingly or unwittingly, take many of their cues from such schemata—sometimes long after the point at which their grounds have been obscured in history. Ultimately, deviation from the prevailing image of systematic action involves a counterstress against orthodoxy occasioned only by the impact of the most insistent subject-matter demands on sensibilities of unusual moral strength.

It is a healthy thing, then, unflinchingly to scrutinize the prevailing image of systematic action in a science, and thus of the science, from time to time. At this juncture in psychology the need for such scrutiny is great. For, during the past three decades or thereabouts, systematic action has been strongly influenced by a value-inducing and procedural image of unusual stability.

A science must always image its path partly in terms of indigenous considerations and partly through its conception of the ends and systematic polity of science *in general.* In a young science, or a baffled one, or one beset by *sui generis* difficulties of untoward intricacy, the dependence on reigning general conceptions of science can become very great, even to the point of undue subordination of local polity to some authoritative general schema of correct scientific conduct. Ever since psychology inherited its appalling problematic challenges, it has been ready to embrace general conceptions of science which seem to offer a clear sense of direction. There is a sense in which the history of psychology has been a succession of passionate identifications with such views of science. When, in the early thirties, the world was becoming aware of an orderly, positive, and in many ways illuminating theory of science which had been inconspicuously evolving since the late nineteenth century within philosophy of science, logic, and related disciplines, it was natural for psychologists to show great interest. When it became apparent that this view was based on a reconstruction of the criterion achievements of natural science, that it seemed to carry with it a recipe for systematic progress, and that it was finding broad acceptance in the world of ideas, psychology found it irresistible. Reigning theories of science remain remarkably stable over time—or at least seem so to individuals at a distance from their intimate technical fluxions. To the extent that psychology's image of its own path of systematic action has been ancillary to its theory of recent theories of science, that image has been correspondingly stable.

It is the fate of words rarely to capture required shades of gray with ultimate nicety. Though systematic action in psychology has been strongly conditioned by an imported theory of science, often moralistically espoused, there have been (and increasingly of late) frequent adaptations, even violations, of canon law. Though there is a level at which one can talk about psychology's dominant image of systematic ends and means, there have been minority imaginations, and no two majority imaginations have been identical. Moreover, the pressure of the indigenous can force even votaries of a reigning image into disloyalty, sometimes unconsciously, during the course of systematic action. There is in fact a strong presumption that a gap already exists between conventional verbalizations of systematic polity for psychology, and the actual tissue of systematic action. There is an equally strong possibility that the authority of the reigning "image" has acted, and continues to act, as a constraint on contextual imagination and has perhaps narrowed the range of problematic interests and creative options that are likely to be asserted in inquiry.

For the above reasons, it was considered of the greatest importance to *test* the code of systematic polity which, at least as an explicit ideology, has so strongly colored the recent past, against the concrete inquiring actions generated by our systematists in their far-flung searches for order. It is hard to conceive of a more fitting context for such an assessment. Inquirers whose investigative histories had formed a prominent part of the tissue of systematic action were to appose these histories to an image of systematic practice which (at least by presumption) had at once conditioned and generalized them. The resulting possibilities for an assessment of the guiding values and procedural ideas of an epoch, for a much-needed collation and possible readjustment of image to practice, for a determination of where we stand systematically in contradistinction to "methodological" stereotypes thereof, are self-evident. Many of the detailed questions among the discussion themes were designed to invite precisely such an evaluation. A rather amusing measure of the hold on psychology of exactly that "code" of systematic action which the study was calling into constructive question was the extreme difficulty experienced in convincing certain contributors that certain of the items were *not* included as inquisitorial devices to expose sinful deviations from respectability.

Range of the discussion themes. The set of discussion topics sent to contributors and an introductory statement of rationale that was part of the original document are given in the Appendix. A careful reading will show that, in one way or another, an attempt was made to translate into suggested themes of inquiry the spectrum of special interests already conveyed. The demands of such a translation necessarily resulted in a densely specified document.

The guiding conception of inviting a mode of analysis at once stratified and comprehensive—a mode which might liberate analysis from its conventional preoccupation with the sentential snow on the top of the iceberg—was reflected in the representation among the items of five broadly defined categories of concern, as follows:

ATTITUDINAL, VALUATIONAL, AND OTHER PREDISPOSITIONAL FACTORS (brought by the inquirer to the search for systematic order, and conditioning its conduct). This concern is prominently introduced by theme {1} on "Background factors and orienting attitudes." What may initially be less evident to the reader, however, is that the concern with the creative sources of systematic work, both in human option and cultural influence, is made to echo in various ways throughout the other items. Thus, in one or another of the subtopics under each major rubric, questions are introduced which call for the reconstruction of optative grounds and origins with regard to specified contentual, procedural, or programmatic components of the formulation, or for evaluations strongly diagnostic of such matters.

Examples of subitems which seek information concerning such "deeper propulsions" are these: {3}*b* (why were initial evidential grounds considered strategic); {4}*b* and *d* (rationale of, and grounds for confidence in mode of inferring functional relations; grounds for favoring use or nonuse of intervening variables); {5}*c* and *d* (e.g., *d*, views re limitations, in principle, on "level" of measurement and quantifiability of "own" system and systematic efforts in psychology generally); {6}*b* and *c* (e.g., *c*, views re degree of formal explicitness for which it is desirable to aim); {7}*b* (intended, ultimate scope and *grounds* for delimitation; plans and programmatic devices for extension). It would be wasteful to reproduce the some one-half to two-thirds of the discussion outline given to the realization of such "echos"; for other examples the reader may consult items {2}*d*, {7}*c*, {8}*b*, {9}*b*, *c*, and *d*, and all of {10} {11} and {12}.

CONCEPTUAL CONTENT AND EVIDENTIAL BASIS OF THE SYSTEM. Themes {2}, "Structure of the system as thus far developed," and {3}, "Initial evidential grounds for assumptions," call for a resumé of conceptual content, together with a consideration of the problematic interests, foundation-data options, and specialized empirical findings which guided or "in any way suggest[ed]" the major assumptions of the system. Most presentations of a conventional sort dwell primarily on considerations relevant to these themes.

The subitems for these themes project modes of analysis which could render disparate formulations (though certainly not all) structurally, and thus contentually commensurable, but it will be noted in the "explanations" that these analytic modes are suggested as subject to the contributor's estimate of their applicability or utility. It will also be appreciated that the suggested lines of analysis provide a purchase for the evaluation against practice of a vast backlog of "metasystematic" doctrine concerning the status of major conceptual components of psychological formulations—the doctrine of "variables": intervening, independent, dependent, and the various elaborations of these in meaning and nomenclature. Finally, it should be noted that themes {2} and {3} direct attention not merely toward a statement of formal product, but toward the *interplay* between conceptual content and evidential basis, as registered within the sensibility of the systematist and objectified in his definitional and other methods. Indeed, whatever the sense in which the analyst feels it appropriate to interpret these items, their "atmosphere" is such as to focus concern on questions having to do with the *linkage* between empirical datum and concept, empirical "locus of discovery," and creative context of construction.

STRATEGIC-METHODOLOGICAL. Themes {4}, "Construction of function forms," {5}, "Mensurational and quantificational procedures," and {6}, "Formal organization of the system," supplement and further specify the lines of concern introduced more inclusively in items {2} and {3}, in this case directing the thin end of the wedge of analytic interest toward strategic and procedural issues of the type conspicuous in the "methodological" discussion of recent decades. Though the trend in recent "imaging" of systematic action has often been to settle these issue-clusters by prejudgment, they point to important questions of strategy and method relative to the systematic aims and properties of the subject-matter domain—questions to which, in some form, all systematists must creatively respond. Thus, themes {4}, {5}, and {6} can elicit information about significant dimensions of systematic action, *and* at the same time can pose the terms for an assessment of certain of the most congealed areas of belief and dogma in recent imaging of systematic action.

Theme {4}, which asks essentially, from where do the systematic concepts and their assumed relations come, raises from another perspective concerns already implicit in items {2} and {3}. It calls into question issues on which major systematists of the past decades—particularly those who have sought "theoretical" constructions of high generality—have taken figural positions. The prominence within the "methodology" of the recent past of considerations pertaining to the role of measurement and mathematics, theme {5}, and desirable modes of formal specification, theme {6}, need hardly be pointed up. It should be noted that the lines of approach suggested by the subitems are such as to invite probing reference to the particularities of inquiring experience, rather than treatment in terms of stereotype. It is also worth noting that for each of these themes (as indeed for most others) directions of discussion are suggested which relate technical proposal to judgmental and evaluative substrate, past experience to future prospect, present feasibilities to estimated *principled* limits.

EVIDENTIAL STATUS. Themes {7}, "Scope or range of application," {8}, "History of system to date in mediating research," and {9} "Evidence for the system," invite full and frank consideration of the relations between the systematic aims and their current realization with respect to increased ordering of the empirical world. The concern here, of course, overlaps with theme {3}, "Initial evidential grounds," but the emphasis of theme {3} is on "evidence" in the context of primary concept and hypothesis formation, whereas the present interest is "evidence" in the context of more detailed elaboration and confirmation.

It should be underlined that the present group of themes does not conceive of "evidential status" in the restricted sense of the logical theory of evidence. Though, in calling for an assessment of the research "instigated" by the system, item {8} *a* does not rule out cases in which a study represents a test of a logical consequence of the system, it *definitely rules in* studies or observations stemming from "suggestive or heuristic guidance." Moreover, item {8}*b* directs attention to an often overlooked problem in the relation of system to "evidence"; i.e., precisely *what* among the many factors constitutive of a formulation at a given stage of development (e.g., orienting attitudes, explanatory imagery, methods, partly filled knowledge-forms, specific lawful or "lawlike" assumptions) stands in an implicative or suggestive-heuristic relation to given units of "evidence." May it further be noted that the subitems of theme {7} define a context which encourages the discussion of "evidence" and research impact relative to governing knowledge-seeking aims; whereas the subitems of {9} invite a canvass of contrary as well as positive evidence, a specification of designs which the systematist may deem especially telling for further evaluation, and *comparative* consideration, as against alternate formulations, of effectiveness in dealing with given classes of data.

Prospective considerations. Themes {10}, "Specific methods, concepts or principles . . . believed valuable outside the context of the system," {11}, "Degree of 'programmaticity,' " and {12}, "Intermediate and long-range strategy for the development of the system," taken together, form an important dimension of concern—one often underplayed in conventional analyses. A systematic formulation, as publicly specified at a given time, expresses a cross-section of a movement of creative inquiry over time. In the present phase of psychology, the gap between systematic intention and realization must necessarily be great; this makes peculiarly important the inquirer's plans for future development, his estimates of research priorities and barriers. Again, the youth of our science—with the consequent expectation that historic continuities will be general and irregular—makes of unusual interest the inquirer's judgments concerning relational trends vis à vis other systematic programs, and his beliefs concerning contentual and methodic components which may prove valuable independently of the detailed systemic context.

It may be noted that all themes in the final group are heavily diagnostic of the attitudinal and valuational factors brought by the inquirer to his systematic work. We thus arrive full circle with the emphases of the first category. It is felt that over the perimeter of that circle are arrayed, in one form or another, most of the kinds of questions it is possible at present to ask about a systematic formulation. Often the same kind of consideration is repeated in different themes or subitems, but from differing incidences or levels, the hope being that either by letter or spirit stratified analysis will be encouraged.

A perspective on the discussion themes. The discussion themes were an important part of the framework of Study I; it was therefore important that the reader be apprised of the aims and grounds of their composition. Yet they were only *part* of that framework, and the reader can have little feeling for the tone of the study without some appreciation of the broader setting within which the thematic suggestions were offered.

Nothing would have more blighted the values on which this study is founded than any assumption that *all* systematic formulations, irrespective of the ends in view and the character of the problems faced, could be (or worse, should be) set in rigid correspondence with the discussion topics. Authors were invited to use the themes selectively, to rearrange, supplement, or reinterpret them to whatever extent they felt desirable. In general it was urged that wherever the requirements of exposition or analysis came in conflict with the discussion topics, it was the topics which must give way. It was constantly made clear to contributors that themes reflecting issues on which recent "methodological" thought had been strongly stipulative were included primarily for evaluation in the light of diversified systematic practice, rather than as canons of practice.

The reader will find that all the above emphases were made in the introduction to the Suggested Discussion Topics sent to contributors (cf. Appendix). They were reinforced in the letters of invitation, and in a supplementary memorandum. Similar emphases were extended over time and individuated relative to the concrete problems of contributors in the often voluminous editorial correspondence during the course of each author's work. In all such correspondence, the principle governing editorial advice concerning the role of the themes was that of *contextualism*—sometimes to the point of suggesting their total disregard. In at least one case, the editor found himself in the position of urging a contributor that a paper originally prepared in close correspondence with the themes be rewritten without their "aid." Both agreed that the resulting revision was a distinct improvement.

Essentially, we strove to convey this attitude toward the use of discussion themes: for those reasons which we have already given, we felt it well to invite serious consideration of the topics. The values of even rough or partial commensurability of treatment are evident, as are the values of a convergence of judgments on common systematic problems, a multiple assessment of recent strategic-methodological dicta, etc. The value of a mode of analysis which deploys interest in depth and extent is evident. Yet the superordinate value was fidelity on the part of each man to his own creative inquiry and its outcome.

So much for the rationale and range of the themes and the environment of meanings which we hoped might govern their use. Such considerations are all at the level of editorial *intention*. Perspective on the import of the themes within the study will not be complete unless a word is added about the actual *expectations*, at the beginning of the study.

We felt that the themes would, at the minimum, be conducive of a mood of high seriousness—would encourage sustained and concrete analysis, even if the analytic dimensions were sliced in a markedly different way. Moreover, we expected that certain of the more general values and curiosities imbedded in the themes would almost inevitably be reflected in the author's field of concern: a point of departure will condition the course of a journey even when interpreted as a point *for* departure. Of these matters we felt confident. We expected, further, that the set toward differentiated questioning encouraged by the themes would lead—whatever the author's mode of treatment—to *some* overlap with the explicit issues raised. The universe of askable questions about a systematic formulation is, after all, limited, particularly when it is appreciated that that universe has a historic and sociological dimension as well as a logical one. Past this point our expectations were less sure, but our awareness of the variability of man's problems in science, together with the independent variability of man's temperament, inclined us to expect little *explicit* conformity with the themes. We were satisfied that the themes would significantly advantage the study, even if their effects were restricted to the less direct ones just mentioned.

SOME ANTICIPATIONS

A statement of certain trends of Study I, based on the essays in all three volumes, is offered as an epilogue in Volume 3.[2] Since it is central to the conception of the study that it provide "multiple views" for *individual* viewing and analysis by readers, the statement is brief and is restricted to those lines of convergence and difference which seem so conspicuous as to be almost self-defining.[3] Moreover, the judicious reader will not consult even this statement until he is in a position to

[2] The section of Volume 3 given to general comment on the study contains also a special supplement by Conrad Mueller on the significance of the essays in sensory psychology for certain methodological problems. Dr. Mueller generously served in a capacity much like that of sub-editor in the sensory area.

[3] Further discussion of the import of Study I (and Study II) is given in the final volume of the series, *Psychology and the Human Agent.*

check the broad generalities there presented against his own knowledge of a good range of the essays. At this place, however, the reader, who has followed the story of our plans and special hopes, will have a natural curiosity concerning the relations between these and the *results* of the study.

Though we do not wish to overstress the importance of the discussion themes—many of the study's values could have been realized without this editorial device—a word is in order concerning their effects on the essays. In general, we think it possible to say two things. The anticipated "indirect" effect of prompting sustained and concrete analysis—of a mode sufficiently differentiated in its concerns to provide a basis for that convergence of judgment on key systematic issues that the study had contemplated—is certainly manifest. More surprisingly, the "direct" effects in terms of the authors' *explicit* use of the themes, either as providing a total pattern for the organization of papers or as a source of questions to be selectively but directly addressed, proved remarkably greater than expected. The variations among authors in their use of the themes is still, we hasten to add, great enough to make it quite clear that neither individual bent nor contextual sensitivity was ever sacrificed to some compulsion toward correspondence.

If one can talk of something like a continuum of "degree of explicit use" of the discussion themes by the different authors, five major intervals of it might be distinguished:

1. Point-for-point correspondence (or almost so) with the themes. In the case of these essays, the themes are used with relatively little modification or rearrangement as the explicit plan of discussion. Examples would be the papers of Licklider (Volume 1), Cartwright (Volume 2), and Rapaport (Volume 3). For those interested in statistics, some nine papers fall into this group. Moreover, those interested in the sociology of knowledge may wish to know that of these papers four fall into Volume 1, two in Volume 2, and three in Volume 3.

2. Close but selective correspondence with the themes. The essays of this group explicitly address most, or even all, of the questions raised in the themes, but the plan of presentation, though overlapping with the thematic rubrics, departs from the list as given, in one or another degree. This difference may in one case be reflected primarily by the omission of certain of the formal items (e.g., Ogle, Volume 1), in another by the supplementation of the themes dealt with (e.g., Miller, Volume 2), in still another by the rearrangement of themes (e.g., Logan, Volume 2), or perhaps by some combination of the preceding types of alteration (e.g., Parsons, Volume 3). Some eleven papers are of this character.

3. Discursive presentation with concluding section which explicitly aligns the preceding discussion with the themes. In these papers, the

authors found that "natural" and contextually apt development of their formulation required an organization which, though giving attention to most or all of the thematic issues, did not always do so in a figural or explicit way. In each case, however, the bearing of the presentation on the relevant themes was explicitly pointed up in a concluding section. Examples of such papers are those of Postman and Tolman (Volume 1), Ellson (Volume 2), and Cattell (Volume 3). By our count, six of the papers fall clearly in this category. [It might be here noted that Tolman's paper (Volume 2) and Parsons' (Volume 3) also contain final sections in which a series of the thematic rubrics are discussed, but the general organization of their papers is such as to call for classification in group 2 above.]

4. Little or no explicit correspondence with the themes, but easily collatable with them in key contexts. In most of these cases, the expository requirements of the given formulation dictated a *sui generis* mode of organization throughout. In a few instances, notably Skinner (Volume 2) and Murray (Volume 3), the authors felt it fruitful to concentrate on selected aspects of their positions, choosing a mode of exposition which, by and large, makes their entire contribution relevant to the initial theme, "Background factors and orienting attitudes." In all papers of this group, however, the coverage is such that the reader may with little effort extract the author's position on, or attitude toward, most of the principal issues raised by the themes. There are six papers of this type.

5. No explicit use of themes, and only partially collatable with them. We would classify two papers in this way: Harlow's (Volume 2) and Kallmann's (Volume 3). These deal with immediate, relatively presystematic implications of specialized fields of research (learning sets and psychogenetic twin studies, respectively), both fields in which the status of systematic development is necessarily such as to make many of the thematic issues either premature or irrelevant.

In summary, then, it seems fair to say that what initially seemed the distant objective of fostering ready comparability of the different analyses—and thus the opportunity to derive a more or less integrated picture of the systematic status and problems of our science—has been largely realized. The fact, however, that it has been realized in a way which always places fidelity to the indigenous above what might otherwise be a procrustean uniformity must make (as it should) the reader an active participant in the construction of the differentiated view of current systematic psychology that the results of the study afford. "Comparability" is a property of materials rendered effective only by acts of comparison. As an aid to those readers interested in the detection of key convergences and divergences, index numbers corresponding to the principal thematic rubrics have been inserted, where relevant, in the individual tables of contents appearing before each paper. (This device is explained in the Appendix.)

Although the plan of Study I has resulted in invaluable materials for synthesis and secondary analysis by the general reader, student, or specialized scholar interested in crosscutting issues of systematic content and method, it is to be emphasized that each essay is a self-contained piece. The reader may approach each either with analytic collation in mind, or on the assumption that "a rose is a rose is a rose." The volumes may thus be used for reference or for extending a reader's base of knowledge in any direction he may choose. In our desire that the study pose a counterforce to the less happy consequences of the growing specialism in psychology, the constant editorial emphasis was that authors write at a level which, though avoiding the usual compromises of popularization, does not presuppose advanced technical competence in the areas covered. Since, in the great majority of cases, authors have achieved this difficult feat, individuals of quite varied backgrounds—not excluding the layman with a taste for close reasoning—may all find edification in the present volumes.

Of far greater importance than the formal organization of the essays are questions concerning their intrinsic content and value, and their collective significance for an assessment of the recent past and for the forward illumination of our systematic future. If it is difficult to make a few generalizations on this score without overtones of enthusiasm, it is only the dedicated and brilliant work of the contributing authors that has brought this about. May we thus summarily anticipate a few of the special qualities defined by the present collection of papers.

The central hope that the milieu of the study would lead to *creative* consequences has certainly been justified. It is fair to say that of the authors (the majority of the group) who were subjecting previously formulated results of systematic inquiry to reflective analysis, none failed to emerge from his Cartesian experience without a *changed* formulation, often in fundamental ways. Conspicuous examples of this quite general rule are the essays of Tolman, Guthrie, and Miller in Volume 2. In many cases authors were prompted to fuller and more comprehensive statement of the systematic implications of past effort than ever before: though examples must again be arbitrary, mention might be made of the papers of Licklider, Gibson, and Helson, Volume 1; Estes and Miller, Volume 2; Rogers, and Katz and Stotland, Volume 3. In not a few instances, areas in which little explicit systematization had previously been attempted were advanced toward preliminary conceptual organization, or toward a more explicit view of the problems confronting systematic effort (e.g., the papers of Harlow, Hinde, and Irion, Volume 2; Thelen,

Newcomb, Volume 3). In at least one impressive case, a field which long has been the arena of massive but scattered systematic efforts—often phrased in a rather closed idiom—has been assayed for its emerging systematic structure (Rapaport's essay on psychoanalytic theory, Volume 3). In two cases, the work of men who have been outlived by their systematic influence has been at once examined for its contemporary significance and creatively developed (the papers by Postman and Tolman on Brunswik, Volume 1; and Cartwright on Lewin, Volume 2).

In general, the results of the study should go far toward dispelling the connotation of negativism and aridity that sometimes attaches to the word "analysis." While providing for us a collective analytic perspective on near-history, our authors are at the same time creatively extending that history.

If our authors have succeeded in enriching current conceptions of analysis by throwing its creative dimension into relief, they have also recentered the conception of analysis in another way deemed important by the study. By and large, the hope that analysis might be liberated from the tendency of recent decades to concentrate on the rationalized end products of science—almost to the exclusion of the stratified events of human inquiry of which such products are a thin and contingent expression—has been impressively realized. Analysis, as defined in practice by the essays in these volumes, is no longer a routine exercise in the "logic" of science; it is an enterprise which uncovers the significance, potentialities, and limits of its objects by keeping carefully in view the relations between orienting commitment and scientific action, creative process and sentential product, methodic gamble and cognitive outcome.

Working in terms of some such conception of analysis, our authors have achieved results which, taken together, provide a truly remarkable clarification of the systematic problems and prospects of our science. They have been fluent in recognizing limits and difficulties, in bringing to the fore doubts, in making judgments—some of which might have remained below the threshold of public expression—about important elements of the past. They have been equally fluent in the generation of new gropings, orienting ideas, salients of conceptual action towards the future. They have withal been generous, modest, and responsible in a way which makes that future seem even more attractive.

THREE AUDITORY THEORIES

J. C. R. LICKLIDER
Bolt Beranek and Newman Inc.

* The bracketed numbers, when they occur in the tables of contents of the essays in this volume, indicate items in the Suggested Discussion Topics relevant to the headings which they follow. See Note on the Use of Discussion Topic Index Numbers in Appendix.

INTRODUCTION

There is no systematic, over-all theory of hearing. No one since Helmholtz has tried to handle anything like all the known problems within a single framework. Each of the several theories of hearing that are extant deals with a restricted set of questions.

Nevertheless, at least several of my colleagues in the field of psychoacoustics carry around in their heads rather broad conceptions of the auditory process. These conceptions have been pieced together out of several outstanding part theories and modified under the force of various experiments and experiences. They support predictions of various kinds. If the question lies within the domain of one of the part theories, the prediction may be quite quantitative and the predictor may be quite confident. If the question lies in an area between part theories, the prediction is likely to be a bit vague and the predictor a bit uncertain. Doubtless it would be a good thing if some of these covert conceptions of the over-all auditory process were written down and to some extent formalized. I wish this were an opportunity for trying to pull together my own.

Perhaps the situation in hearing—the existence of several parts but no systematically formulated over-all theory—is not so much different from the situations in other fields of psychology. Most of the theories discussed in this series are rather limited in domain. Yet, in hearing, there is a tantalizing possibility of drawing up a model that will account for a truly wide variety of accumulated facts. Contrasted with that possibility, systematic discussion of a part theory seems unexciting.

We start out, then, with the notion that comprehensive theories of hearing exist, if at all, only at a level below verbal formulation in a few brains, yet we feel that it would not be entirely satisfactory to focus attention here solely on one part theory. Of the unformulated, we cannot say much by way of systematic formulation. Let us, therefore, examine three of the part theories. Let us do this with the hope that discussing them under a common rubric will, to some extent, prepare the way for putting them together into something larger—or, if not that, reveal incompatibilities that stand in the way of synthesis. In order to increase the chance of consonance, we shall choose three part theories with overlapping domains: (1) a theory of signal detection, (2) a theory of speech intelligibility, and (3) a theory of pitch perception. These overlap in that all involve frequency analysis, which for a hundred years has been the central focus of auditory theory. Yet they are different enough to bring out basic difficulties, such as the status of subjective attributes (e.g., pitch) in a "psychology of the other one."

In each instance—theory of signal detection, theory of speech intelligibility, and theory of pitch perception—the word *theory* as I shall use it may refer either collectively to the several formulations that have been offered over the years or particularly to one formulation with which I, myself, am more or less ego-involved. In the case of signal detection, it is less; my connection with theory in that area is mainly a connection (friendship, colleagueship) with theorists, though on the experimental side I have been somewhat active. In the case of pitch perception, it is more; the particular theory to which I refer contains parts borrowed from others, but the pattern is my own. And, in the case of speech intelligibility, it is somewhere in between; my aim is to discuss the (other people's) theory that is implicit in the widely used computational procedures for predicting speech intelligibility, then to suggest, at the end of the chapter, a tentative modification of my own.

Selecting these three specific formulations to serve as foci does not imply that they are more important than other theories that we shall not discuss. In the case of the theory of pitch perception, in fact, it will be obvious that important parts, contributed, for example, by Helmholtz [36], Fletcher [16–23], Wever [92–94], and Schouten [66–70], are combined with precarious speculations to yield a sum surely less viable than the hardier of its components.

BACKGROUND FACTORS AND ORIENTING ATTITUDES

Two major background influences. It seems fair to single out one theory and one series of experiments as dominant influences upon our trio. They are Helmholtz's and Békésy's, respectively. Helmholtz's [36] resonance-place theory of auditory frequency analysis and pitch perception was for years the main force in the field of hearing. The fact that both main parts of it were largely wrong did not lessen its influence. Békésy's [6] direct observations of the inner ear in action altered the whole structure of the field. Almost overnight, the problem that everyone had been theorizing about was empirically solved, and theorists had either (1) to rush to bring their theories into line with the data or (2) to move out of the cochlea into a new domain for speculation.

Helmholtz's theory[1] said two things: (1) The first important operation in the process of hearing is separation of the compound stimulus wave into elementary sinusoidal[2] oscillations and allocation of each, according to its frequency, to its proper position along the length of the *basilar membrane*, which is the part of the inner ear on which the auditory receptor cells are arrayed. (2) Allocation determines the subjective pitch, the pitch being in one-to-one correspondence—pre-

[1] Most of the ideas can be traced back beyond him [5], but Helmholtz's contributions of synthesis and exposition fully warrant calling the theory his.

[2] Sinusoidal is the generic term for waves of simple harmonic motion. Sinusoids are physically pure tones. Cosine waves ($|\Theta| \cos 2\pi ft$) and sine waves [$|\Theta| \sin 2\pi ft = |\Theta| \cos (2\pi ft - \pi/2)$] are sinusoids. So is any other wave of the same shape [$|\Theta| \cos (2\pi ft + \phi)$]. The maximum amplitude of the oscillation is $|\Theta|$. The cyclic frequency is f. The argument $(2\pi ft + \phi)$ is the phase angle, of which, ordinarily, $2\pi ft$ is the varying and ϕ is the fixed part. The maximum amplitude (usually shortened simply to amplitude), the frequency, and the fixed part of the phase angle (often referred to simply as "the phase") are the three real numbers that specify the three "dimensions" of a sinusoid.

sumably as a result of projection of the pattern to higher auditory centers—with the allocated *place*. We shall examine these ideas in more detail later. Right now, we should note that Helmholtz's formulation suggests a system in which a single compound signal is broken up into elementary parts, and in which the elementary parts are transmitted in their own, separate channels, spatially distinct from one another. That conception appears again and again in auditory theory.

Békésy's observations showed that the mechanical (or hydrodynamic) action of the cochlea does indeed distribute different frequencies of oscillation to different locations along the basilar membrane. They also showed, however, that the analysis thus effected is not very sharp. A sinusoidal oscillation of any given frequency sets a large part of the basilar membrane into vibration. The distribution of vibration amplitude along the length of the membrane has a maximum, of course, but instead of fitting Helmholtz's picture—one single, highly resonant, transverse string vibrating, its neighbors quiescent—the distribution is impressively broad. Alternatively, we can focus on one point along the length of the basilar membrane and ask what it takes to make it vibrate. For producing vibrations at one place, there is one frequency of acoustic stimulation that is best, but others as far removed as half an octave may be half as good. This dullness of the mechanical frequency analysis—the equivalent of severe blurring in vision—changes our conception of the auditory system. Instead of discrete, distinct, spatially separated channels, we have a continuum of channels that are, at the level of the mechanical analysis, broad and overlapping. Each has in a restricted sense its own, proper frequency, but it responds also to other frequencies quite a way up and (especially) down the scale from it.

Background in mathematics, physics, and engineering. The cochlear analysis we have been discussing is essentially hydrodynamic, and its experimental investigation involves a combination of engineering, anatomy, physiology, acoustics, optics, and electronics. The topic, and the theorist and the experimenter, highlight the interdisciplinary character of the study of hearing. We shall here take note briefly of other parts of the background in mathematics, physics, and engineering.

Signal detection is a part of psychophysics to which physicists contributed importantly from Fechner on. Throughout most of its history, the psychophysics of signal detection was a matter of determining thresholds. Now, however, the threshold has competition for its place as a basic concept. The ideas of statistical decision theory were taken from mathematical statistics into engineering when it became necessary to have theories of the detection of targets by radar systems and of radars by countermeasures systems. In connection with those problems, several kinds of ideal observer were defined (none had a "threshold"), and the false-alarm probability and the payoff matrix became fundamental concepts. From engineering these things were brought into psychology by psychologists who were working with engineers: e.g., Smith and Wilson [74] at the M.I.T. Lincoln Laboratory; Tanner and Swets [87, 88] at the University of Michigan Engineering Research Institute, and Marill [54] at the M.I.T. Research Laboratory of Electronics. Combining the general theory of signal detection with Fletcher's [17, 18, 20, 22, 23] critical-band theory of auditory masking—to yield a theory of auditory signal detection—was so natural that it happened at once without any formality.

The background of theory of speech intelligibility is even more strongly physical and technological. To guide development of the telephone, objective measurements of intelligibility and understanding of the dependence of intelligibility upon the parameters of the telephone system were required. The pioneer work was done largely at the Bell Telephone Laboratories in a program initiated and inspired by the acoustician Harvey Fletcher. This work led to a computational procedure for predicting intelligibility from physical parameters. The procedure amounts—if we accept a very limited sense of the term—to a theory of intelligibility. In addition, many of the ideas about the process of speech perception have sprung from work aimed at eventual construction of automatic stenographers and devices for translating oral speech into readily transmissible code.

In the theory of pitch perception, frequency analysis is fundamental. Probably the most important conceptual operations—analysis of waves into elementary sinusoidal components, which we have already encountered, and synthesis of waves from those components—are derived from the physicist-mathematician Fourier [24]. Fourier's ideas got into the field of hearing in time to influence Helmholtz. They have been, and are, basic and essential for handling the mechanical part of the auditory process. But I think they have been applied beyond their realm of applicability. It seems to me that the power of the Fourier transformations and the tractability of the assumption of linearity (not applicable to the later stages of the process) trapped auditory research into a long and unfortunate preoccupation with pure tones as auditory stimuli. Another pair of possibly fundamental operations, cross- and autocorrelational analysis, is part of the background, partly in mathematics and partly in engineering. Moreover, the basic observations that appear now to have placed theory on the defensive were made by a physicist [66–70] and an engineer [39].

Background in anatomy and physiology. Other sciences, also, have influenced one or more of our three theories. Musicology has had an important bearing on theory of pitch perception, linguistics and phonetics on theory of speech intelligibility. The effects of anatomy and physiology have been especially marked.

Probably because frequency analysis is so fundamental and because the cochlea—the organ in which the analysis is begun—is in animals so accessible, the initial phase of the process of hearing has been investigated almost to exhaustion. The mechanical action of the cochlea is, most of us now believe, reasonably well understood or, at least, accurately described. Even before it was so understood or described, it could be discussed in concrete mechanical or physical terms. This success of reductionism in handling the first step has influenced most of the work on the other steps. Many auditory theorists tend to refer to the cochlea, the cortex, neurons, etc., to attribute operator-like characteristics to those structures, and thereby to create as an agent or medium of process a conceptual nervous system blended of anatomy, physiology, electronics, and mathematics.

If the tendency just described confuses the metatheoretical picture, it also commits auditory theory to a pleasant degree of specificity. On the one hand, the data of electrophysiology are made directly relevant, even crucial. On the other, the ready convertibility between electronic and mathematico-logical models permits formalization whenever formalization is desired.

Orienting attitudes concerning psychological prediction and level of analysis. It is dangerous to try to speak for others about the presystematic judgments, values, and beliefs that have influenced their theoretical contributions. I am not sure it is less dangerous to try to speak for oneself. Evidently, however, all the auditory theorists who have had positivistic or behavioristic inclinations have been troubled by the circumstance that they were working on a *sensory* system. On one end, a sensory system connects directly with physically specifiable stimulation. On the other end, it connects directly with "conscious experience" but very indirectly with overt behavior.

Gradually I have ceased to verbalize my worry about the dichotomy of subjective and objective, of the experiential and the physical, that seemed so fundamental when as an undergraduate I encountered the mind-body problem. I have grown up in a subculture in which that problem is important, and in which behavioristic solutions to it have been dominant. It has become clear to me, as to most of my colleagues, that although one can learn more about hearing by listening ten minutes oneself than by conducting an hourlong formal measurement on 10 other subjects, the functions and relations on which a science is to be based should come from hourlong formal measurements on 10 other subjects.

The fact that I have a close-up, direct view of my own auditory experience does not let me give it to you. All it can do is help me formulate hypotheses relating stimulus variables to experiential variables. These may be obviously correct to me. By setting up crucial stimulus configurations for you to hear, I may even lead you to agree that they are obviously correct, and I may gain positive reinforcement from that accomplishment if I believe that your verbal mechanism is connected to your experiences the same way mine is to mine. But, in order to get the results down on paper, I must set up a procedure that will let me get behavior out of you and my other subjects and then let me work backward from your behavior to something that pertains to your hearing and not merely to your verbal response. That is very easy to do if the characteristic of your hearing that is under study is a lower bound on discriminatory capability, as it sometimes is in the areas of signal detection and speech intelligibility. No one will object to my reasoning that, if your motor system can respond in a discriminating manner to specified classes of acoustic stimulation, your auditory system can, also. But the problem is less simple when the question is the functional relation between a subjective attribute such as loudness or pitch and parameters of the stimulation.

In order to handle the latter problem, many have assumed, perhaps tacitly, that the experiential variables or dimensions called subjective attributes are reported upon in a direct and unambiguous manner by the verbal mechanism or by the finger that pushes the response button. If the connection is direct and unambiguous enough, it is not an important question whether the attributes are attributes of sensation or of perception or of response. Approximately, that condition appears to be met in current work [76, 78] on loudness. The subject responds to an acoustic stimulus by writing down a number. The number is accepted by the experimenter as being proportional (except for certain neutralizable biases) to the loudness, and the results of the measurements turn out to be fairly orderly. In such an instance, the value of the subjective attribute may indeed be said to be inferred from the overt behavior of the subject, but the inference is so direct that the variable that intervenes between stimulation and response lies only a little way ahead of the response.

At the other extreme is the postulation by Fletcher [16, 20] that loudness is proportional to the number of neurons in the auditory nerve that are excited by the stimulation. If such an assumption should be borne out by correlation between psychoacoustic and neurophysiological tests, it would be, I think, sheer coincidence, for there is nothing in Fletcher's theory that makes it more appropriate to say "auditory nerve" than to say, for example, "medial ectosylvian gyrus." Fletcher's operations are stimulus-response correlations; the names of his dependent variables are the names of subjective attributes; the anatomical locations assigned to them appear to a psychophysiologist to be inappropriate, to a metatheorist irrelevant.

It seems to me that an intermediate kind of formulation is preferable to either of those just mentioned. It is intended to be consistent with the anatomical and physiological pictures and to assimilate them to the extent that they are relevant and assimilable. It is intended, also, to support identifications of the subjective attributes. However, the elements of the model are not anatomical structures, and they are not subjective attributes. They are purely conceptual variables and operations with which physiological or experiential variables or operations may be connected by relations of identification. The identifying relations may be direct and unvarying, as in the instance of the hydrodynamic analyzer of the cochlea, or they may be dependent upon verbal training, as in the instance of pitch judgment. It is in the latter respect that the formulation diverges most markedly from others.

The emphasis of variability of identifications between variables of the model and, in particular, the subjective attributes is of course essentially an admission that the model is incomplete. I like the idea, however, that pitch *is* the way people have learned to use the word, pitch. Training in the use of that word varies greatly from verbal community to verbal community. I think that the link between the listener's verbal output and his sensory, auditory process is inherently more variable, from person to person or even from time to time for the same person, than is the distinctly sensory part of the auditory process.[3] It seems more prudent, therefore, to be satisfied with an incomplete theory than to undertake, at present, a complete theory involving verbal learning. In the case of loudness, it may be reasonable to get around the difficulty created by varied verbal training by averaging over, or taking the median judgment of, many listeners. There is practical justification for doing that, and Stevens [77] has done it with good effect. In the case of pitch, however, it would badly obscure the picture.

Utility, role, and comprehensiveness of models. In the field of hearing, as doubtless elsewhere, there are so many experimental facts that systematic organization of them without the aid of models amounts to cataloguing. Cataloguing is unsatisfactory in relation to

[3] The sensory part is, itself, quite variable, changing with the state of wakefulness, attention, etc.

the urge to understand what is going on in the auditory process. What is needed are models of the process to which many and varied experimental facts can be related. I use the plural, models, because competition among alternative formulations appears to stimulate productive activity. I think it should be considered perfectly fair for one theorist to be ego-involved in two incompatible theories. In fact, to have only one is dangerous, for it leads him to overprotect something he should have constructed mainly to attack.

Because my basic interest is to understand hearing and not to compare eight ways of determining the jnd, I want comprehensive models and theories. But I do not hope to find them very soon. At present, it seems best to be satisfied with limited models, related to several different, fundamental auditory problems, but to argue for setting up these models in a common language. Two influences facilitate use of a common language. One is the firm rooting in the physics of the stimulus, which makes the mathematical-acoustical language almost compulsory for description of stimulus variables. The other is our knowledge of the cochlear process, which we may note again as an influence toward thinking in terms of mechanical and physiological operations, or their mathematical counterparts.

Whereas the degree of quantitative specificity is great on the stimulus end, it is by no means necessarily so in other parts of auditory theory. Doubtless we should try at every opportunity to sharpen the precision of these other parts, but I do not think we should demand 0.1-db accuracy in the intervening variables while the problem is still to find some that promise to fit together in a reasonable way. In the stimulus realm we have both precision of control and infinite variety of pattern. The problem for theory is first to find out how the auditory process encodes the stimulus patterns—to ascertain the dimensions and the operations. After the process is blocked out, there will be time for improving precision.

Formality of organization. In so far as the purpose of a theory is to facilitate thought or to process data for effective presentation, the choice of degree of formality of organization is related to the habits of thought of the users of the theory. My own experience in thinking about auditory problems leads me to doubt that a highly formal axiomatic approach would be very helpful to me at the present stage. On the other hand, informal exposition (of the present kind) fills up a great amount of space if the problem is complex, and ideas that are widely separated in space or in time are hard to focus upon together. As a compromise, it may be convenient to think of the auditory process as a system of operations upon variables in approximately the way that analogue computer experts visualize their computational problems. This has the advantage of being (1) amenable to axiomatization so long as the input variables are (as they are) well defined, (2) describable in informal exposition with the aid of familiar analogies, and (3) concrete in the sense that, given enough time and parts, one could build a machine that would behave, operation for operation and variable for variable, in an entirely analogous way.

Between the axiomatic and the analogue levels, there is, I believe, complete translatability. The axiomatic level is better for examining theories *as theories*. Is a formulation internally consistent? Can it be stated more economically? The analogue level is better matched to most people's ordinary modes of thought and is, therefore, likely to facilitate interactions between theory and experiment. What would happen to the probability of detection if we made the passbands of the model's "cochlear" filters twice as wide? That kind of question unfortunately tends to get itself cluttered with jargon, but it makes immediate contact with experimental measurement.

In expressing a mild preference for the intermediate or analogue level of formulation over the axiomatic, I am suggesting only that auditory theory is in a formative stage and will probably not soon mature. There is more need to line the theories up with the facts than there is to state them in esthetically pleasing form. Even in mathematical logic, it appears, the road to understanding involves processes of thought quite different from those that are reflected in the final efficient, consistent, step-by-step deduction from postulates.

By analogue level, I emphatically do not mean "reasoning by analogy" in the popular sense. The structure of a model is an analogue of the actual situation or process that the structure represents. The identifications of the model relate specific quantities (parameters, variables, functions, operations) of the structure to corresponding quantities of the actual process. If the model is a good one, the actual dynamics or kinematics or entropics is paralleled by the dynamics or kinematics or entropics of the structure. Therefore, if the initial and boundary conditions of the structure are correct translations of those of the actual process, the behavior of the structure (the courses of its systematic dependent or output variables) will parallel the behavior of the actual process. Finally, the intervening variables of the structure will be important if variables can be found in the actual situation that may be identified with them, or if the interrelations of the intervening variables, one with another, constitute a much simpler system (e.g., one composed of orthogonal components) than do the systematic independent or the systematic dependent variables.

PLAN OF THIS CHAPTER

The main aim of this chapter is to examine the natures of the three theories as theories. We shall consider them one at a time, then try to draw things together. In order to know what we are talking about, we shall in each instance first look directly at the specific limited formulation that is the focus of the study. That will serve as a substantive anchor for the more derivative discussion that follows.

In each of the three cases, we shall try to follow the plan of discussion that is more or less common to the chapters of this series. Fundamental to that plan are the distinctions between the systematic variables and the empirical variables. The systematic variables are those of the theoretical structure, of the structure of the model. The empirical variables are those of the actual situation, the real world, information about which the theory or model is intended to organize. We shall use *model* in the sense of structure (e.g., a well-developed system of mathematical concepts) plus *identifications* (linkages between parts of the structure and parts of the actual situation modeled).

Following our résumé of each part theory, we shall examine (1) its variables and the interrelations among its constructs, (2) the initial evidence for its assumptions, (3) the way the forms of the functional relations within the structure were selected, (4) the procedures of measurement it presumes or specifies, (5) its level of formality of organization, (6) its scope and range of applicability, (7) its history of interaction with research, and (8) its future. Then we shall see whether or not the three part theories promise to fit together despite the differences in scope and form that will then be very evident.

THEORY OF SIGNAL DETECTION

The specific part theory of signal detection upon which we shall focus is the one presented by Tanner, Swets, and Green [89]. Let us call it TSG. It is a formulation in terms of statistical-decision theory, and it is presented as a preferred alternative to the conventional theory based upon fixed thresholds.

Summary of the theory. TSG is formulated in such a way as to be applicable[4] to detection trials in each of which (1) a signal, of specifications known more or less completely by the listener, is either pre-

[4] TSG is applicable also to experiments in which the signal is located in one of several intervals of space or time and the subject's task is to specify which one. (Stevens calls these forced-location experiments instead of forced-choice experiments because the subject is forced to make a choice also in experiments using other procedures.) TSG can be extended to most clearly defined detection situations. We shall limit the discussion here for the sake of brevity.

sented [s, with probability $P(s)$] or not presented [$\bar{s}$, with probability $P(\bar{s})$], and (2) a listener makes a response [S or $\bar{S}$] signifying whether or not, according to his judgment, the signal was presented.

The listener is assumed to know the a priori probabilities $P(s)$ and $P(\bar{s})$ governing signal presentation and to make his decision in relation to them and to a payoff matrix, or risk function, as well as to his sensory data. The payoff matrix M defines the values to the listener of the four possible pairings of stimulus and response events in Table 1.

TABLE 1. THE PAYOFF MATRIX*

Response	Stimulus	
	s	$\bar{s}$
S	V_{sS}	$V_{\bar{s}S}$
$\bar{S}$	$V_{s\bar{S}}$	$V_{\bar{s}\bar{S}}$

* V_{sS} is the value of a correct positive report ("hit"); $V_{s\bar{S}}$ of an incorrect negative report ("miss"), $V_{\bar{s}S}$ of an incorrect positive report ("false alarm"), and $V_{\bar{s}\bar{S}}$ of a correct negative report. Usually V_{sS} and $V_{\bar{s}\bar{S}}$ are positive values, $V_{s\bar{S}}$ and $V_{\bar{s}S}$ negative values or positive costs.

When it is presented, the signal is superposed upon noise. Some of the noise may be introduced by the experimenter or the external situation. But part of it is inherent in the sensory process; it is added to the signal clues that are delivered from the receptors to the decision process. The auditory channel between the receptors and the decision process has, in TSG, a "narrow-band property." At any moment, only a single, narrow frequency band of the external signal and noise, and of the internal noise, is delivered to the decision process. Although TSG is not entirely explicit about how the center frequency and the width of the band are selected or controlled—the theory specifies a narrow-band scanning filter, the center frequency of which can remain fixed or sweep along the frequency scale—we may assume, in the case of a long-duration sinusoidal signal, that the narrow band centers itself on the signal frequency and has the smallest width the auditory system can provide at that frequency.

The listener's decision is governed, according to TSG, by a decision process that uses in an optimal manner the a priori probabilities, the payoff matrix, and the sensory data. The decision process is extremely simple, but it is necessary to go through a rather complicated argument to show why such a simple process is admissible. In due course, we shall represent the listener's sensory datum by a single number $\mathcal{L}$ and his criterion by another single number $\mathcal{L}_c$, and we shall have him say S, "signal presented," if $\mathcal{L} \geq \mathcal{L}_c$, and $\bar{S}$, "signal not presented," if $\mathcal{L} < \mathcal{L}_c$. It will be that simple. But we shall have to make a detour through signal space and the maximum likelihood criterion before we reach that point.

It may clarify matters to point out here, as Marill has suggested, that what Tanner, Swets, and Green, and their colleagues, have done in TSG is to discover and call attention to the applicability of an existing mathematical structure to a body of empirical observations. The mathematical structure itself has inherently nothing to do with signals, with detection, or with psychophysics. It has to do with statistical hypothesis testing, with deciding between alternative hypotheses. At the simplest level, the problem with which it deals is the following: given a sample and two hypotheses, each of which determines a sampling distribution, make the best choice between the hypotheses. What is meant by "best?" The answer given by Neyman and Pearson is that, in any single instance, it has no definite meaning, but that one may follow a rule of behavior which, if followed consistently, will lead in the long run to maximization of certain expected values. If he adopts a definite payoff matrix, then he can find a rule that will maximize the expected payoff. The rule is: calculate the likelihood of the sample on each of the two hypotheses, take the ratio, and accept the first hypothesis if the ratio exceeds a given constant. We shall consider a little later the determination of the constant. Here let us note that the result is general and profound, that nothing is said about normality, homogeneity of variance, signals, or noise, and that the number of alternative hypotheses is exactly two.

The main obstacle standing in the way of connecting the mathematical structure of statistical hypothesis testing to the substantive observations of signal detection and psychophysics is that, in the latter, the "samples" of signals and noises are seen at first as continuous functions of time and not as discrete numbers or categorizable events. A way around that obstacle is provided by a theorem widely used in electrical engineering, the "sampling theorem" or the "2 WT theorem." In the following paragraphs, we shall first employ that theorem to give ourselves quantities to which statistical decision theory can readily be applied, and then we shall consider its application.

Signal space is a space of n dimensions in which a particular signal is represented by n coordinates. It is a standard mathematical-engineering concept, a part of the general theory of signal detection and of other theories, also. In order to have it make sense, it is necessary to see why any time function whose spectrum is limited to a

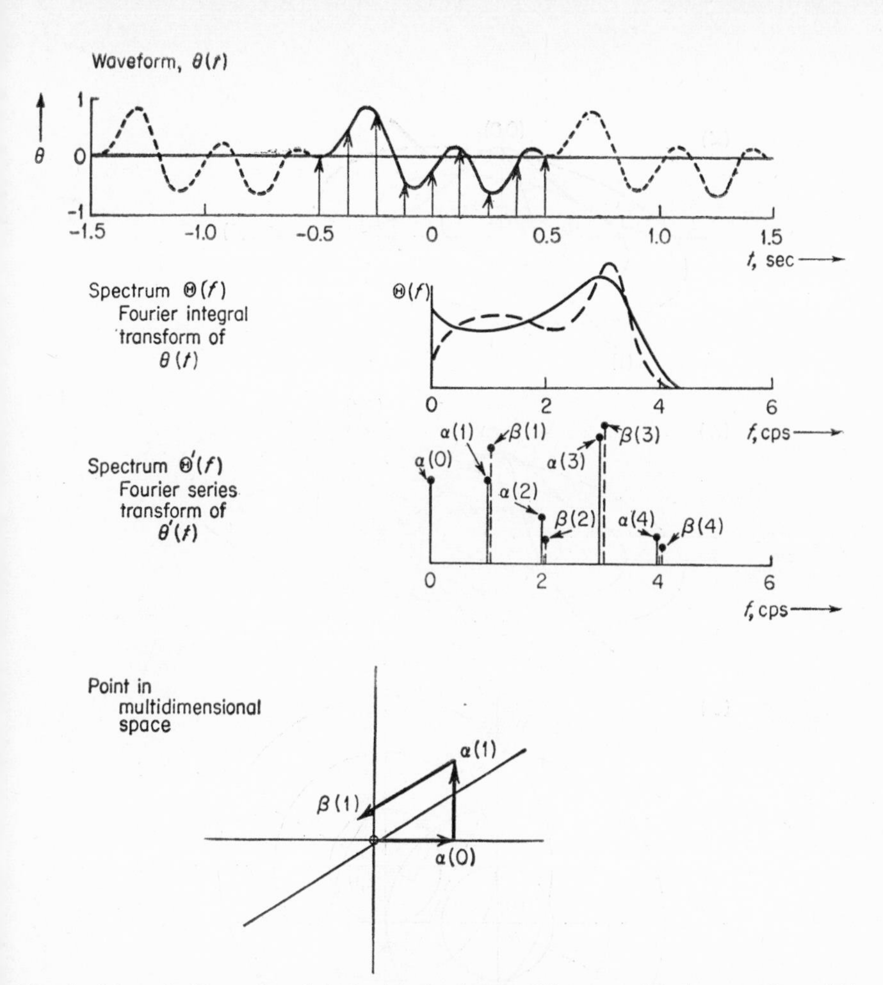

FIG. 1. *Schematic illustration of the* $2 \cdot \Delta f \cdot \Delta t$ *theorem*. We start with the waveform $\theta(t)$ shown as a solid curve at the top. It has nonzero values only within an interval 1 sec long. Its spectrum is $\Theta(f)$, a complex function of frequency, represented below the waveform. The solid line is the real part, the dashed line the imaginary part, of the spectrum. The spectrum is limited approximately to the band 0 to 4.5 cycles per second. In order to obtain a representation of $\theta(t)$ and $\Theta(f)$ in terms of a finite number of coefficients, we replicate the waveform over and over throughout all time, as suggested by the dashed extensions of $\theta(t)$. The spectrum of the resulting periodic waveform $\theta'(t)$ is $\Theta'(f)$, a function with real (or cosine) coefficients only at zero cycles per second and integral multiples of the fundamental frequency and with imaginary (or sine) coefficients only at integral multiples. The coefficients at frequencies above 4 cycles per second are insignificant because of the band limitation of $\Theta(f)$. There are, therefore, $9 = 2 \cdot \Delta f \cdot \Delta t$ coefficients. The lowermost graph shows three of them represented by a point in three-dimensional space and suggests how the original signal, $\theta(t)$, can be represented as a point in *nine*-dimensional space. Shannon's [71] sampling theorem shows that the $2 \cdot \Delta f \cdot \Delta t$ sample values of $\theta(t)$ indicated by the equally spaced arrows in the uppermost graph provide an equivalent representation of the wave. They may be used as the coordinates in an alternative n-dimensional space.

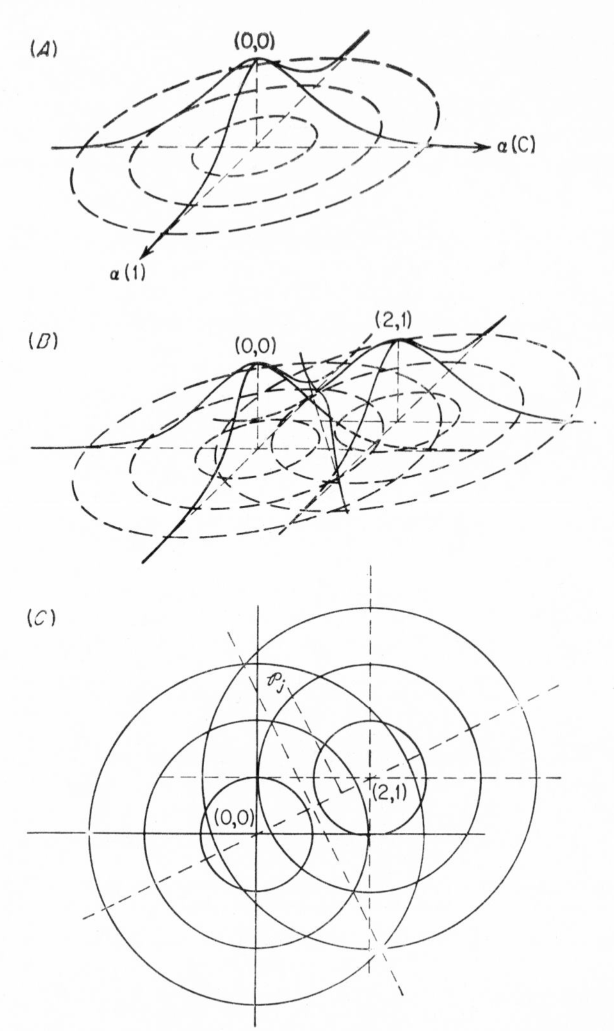

FIG. 2. *Representation in signal space.* For the sake of simplicity, only two of the dimensions of Fig. 1 are carried over into this figure. *A* shows the probability density function, in those two dimensions, of the noise alone. $\alpha(0)$ and $\alpha(1)$ are plotted in an oblique plane, and probability density is represented on the vertical scale. The figure is a normal zero-correlation surface centered upon the origin (0,0). The dotted rings are one standard-deviation unit apart. *B* shows simultaneously the probability density function that obtains on the condition that noise alone was presented and the probability density function that obtains on the condition that signal plus noise was presented. The signal point is (2,1). The effect of the noise in the signal-plus-noise case is to spread the probability in the way specified by the right-hand normal surface. On the left-hand side of the separating curve, the ordinates of the noise function are greater than those of the signal-plus-noise function, and on the right-hand side of the separating curve the ordinates of the signal-plus-noise function are the greater. On any given trial, the observation yields a point in the space [on the plane of $\alpha(0)$,

definite interval Δf of frequency and whose duration is Δt can be specified by $2 \cdot \Delta f \cdot \Delta t$ coefficients.[5]

If the signal lasts Δt seconds, we can repeat it over and over, $1/\Delta t$ times per second (see Fig. 1). The waveform thus produced is periodic and its spectrum[6] is, therefore, made up entirely of harmonics (integral multiples) of $1/\Delta t$. Because of the restriction of the spectrum to the interval Δf, only those harmonics in the interval Δf have coefficients that need to be specified. There are, therefore, $\Delta f/(1/\Delta t) = \Delta f \cdot \Delta t$ such harmonics, with coefficients $\Theta_j = \alpha_j + i\beta_j$. The αs and the βs are independently specifiable numbers. Consequently, there are $n = 2 \cdot \Delta f \cdot \Delta t$ numbers to specify in order to determine the periodic wave uniquely. Determining it uniquely is, of course, equivalent to specifying the original Δt-sec segment uniquely.

The signal space for signals Δt long and Δf wide is then a space of $n = 2 \cdot \Delta f \cdot \Delta t$ dimensions, and any specified signal of the class is represented by a point in the space. The "signal" could of course be a segment of tone. Equally well, it could be a segment of noise. Or it could be a segment of tone added to a segment of noise.

If we specify only certain parameters of a distribution from which a sample signal is drawn—not the precise waveform nor the spectrum of the particular sample—we do not say what point in the space corresponds to the sample. But we provide the information from which a person can pick out various points in the space and calculate from the specified parameters that it is this point with this probability (or probability density), that point with that probability, and so on. We thus specify a probability function throughout the space. For the

[5] Actually, the restrictions to Δf and Δt are incompatible, but it is rigorously true that a signal restricted to a frequency interval Δf cycles per second wide can be specified by $2 \cdot \Delta f$ numbers per second, and the "$2 \cdot \Delta f \cdot \Delta t$ rule" is usually approximately correct.

[6] The spectrum $\Theta(f)$ that corresponds to a waveform $\theta(t)$ is a complex function that specifies either the cosine and sine amplitudes or the resultant amplitude and phase of each of the sinusoids (see n. 2) that add together to produce the waveform. The concept of paired waveforms and spectra is based on Fourier series and integrals, which are discussed in standard textbooks of mathematics.

$\alpha(1)$, in this reduced representation], and the information it offers the ideal observer as a basis for his report is the ratio of the two ordinates. This ratio of the probability densities is the likelihood ratio. In *C*, the $\alpha(0)$, $\alpha(1)$ plane is the plane of the paper, and only the rings are shown to represent the probability density functions. The observation is represented by the point $\mathcal{P}_j$, which is about 2.3 standard-deviation units from the mean of the signal-plus-noise distribution and about 2.7 standard-deviation units from the origin or mean of the noise distribution. The ratio of the probability densities is 3.5, which is, in fact, the ratio of the probability densities anywhere along the projection from $\mathcal{P}_j$ to the line through (0,0) and (2,1). The problem is now to imagine all this in a space of n dimensions, instead of only two.

important class of noises called gaussian-process noises,[7] the distribution in the space is an n-dimensional, normal (gaussian) density sphere, centered on the origin. (If $n = 2$, it is the familiar, normal, zero-correlation surface, illustrated in Fig. 2. If $n = 3$, it can be visualized as a sunlike sphere, centered upon a particular point in the space and having its greatest density at that point, but extending indefinitely outward from the center with density decreasing according to a negative-exponential function.) Adding a precisely known signal to the noise moves the n-dimensional sphere to a new center, the point (which we shall call $\mathcal{S}$) corresponding to the precisely known signal.

Suppose that, on a particular trial of an experiment, a particular waveform is presented to the listener. In the model, the corresponding thing is a particular point $\mathcal{P}_j$ in the space. The experimenter knows whether he made the waveform by ($\bar{s}$) selecting a sample of noise alone or by (s) adding to a sample of noise a sample of tone. Let us suppose, for the time being, that the listener's sensory channels lose none of the information. Then the listener knows that he has made the observation $\mathcal{P}_j$, that the probabilities governing the experimenter's action were $P(s)$ for tone plus noise and $P(\bar{s})$ for noise alone, and that he is operating under the payoff matrix M. His task is to decide whether to report S or $\bar{S}$. The listener can do no more than figure out how likely it is that $\mathcal{P}_j$ came from s and how likely it is that $\mathcal{P}_j$ came from $\bar{s}$. He therefore examines the two probability density spheres mentioned earlier—the one centered at $\mathcal{S}$ and the one centered at the origin—and reads off the two values of probability density that pertain to his point $\mathcal{P}_j$. The ratio of the two values, which is the likelihood ratio, is the measure that he compares with the criterion in making his decision.

The likelihood ratio $\mathfrak{l}$ is the ratio of the likelihood (or probability density) $p_s(\mathcal{P}_j)$ that $\mathcal{P}_j$ would stem from s to the likelihood $p_{\bar{s}}(\mathcal{P}_j)$ that $\mathcal{P}_j$ would stem from $\bar{s}$. It depends only upon the relative locations of $\mathcal{P}_j$, $\mathcal{S}$, and the origin in signal space, and upon the size or spread of the noise density sphere. For various points $\mathcal{P}$, there are various values of $\mathfrak{l}$, though some different values of $\mathcal{P}$ have the same $\mathfrak{l}$. The important thing is, it is only the value of $\mathfrak{l}$, and nothing else about $\mathcal{P}$ or $\mathcal{S}$ or the noise sphere or the signal space, that, in making his judgment, the model listener uses as a measure of the stimulation. And $\mathfrak{l}$ is simply a number. The dimension on which it varies is called the

[7] The random or "white" noise familiar in psychoacoustic laboratories is approximately a gaussian-process noise. A gaussian process is defined as a process that generates signals for which the joint probability density distribution of any m coefficients is an m-dimensional normal distribution.

decision axis. The only question is whether $\mathfrak{l}$ is greater than or less than the criterion number $\mathfrak{l}_c$.

How is $\mathfrak{l}_c$ determined? Clearly, if the a priori probabilities $P(s)$ and $P(\bar{s})$ are equal and if the payoff matrix is homogeneous $V_{sS} = V_{\bar{s}\bar{S}} = -V_{s\bar{S}} = -V_{\bar{s}S}$ then the decision should be S if $p_s(\mathcal{P}_j) > p_{\bar{s}}(\mathcal{P}_j)$ and $\bar{S}$ if $p_{\bar{s}}(\mathcal{P}_j) > p_s(\mathcal{P}_j)$. The critical value of $\mathfrak{l}$ is therefore $\mathfrak{l}_c = 1$. But if the a priori probabilities $P(s)$ and $P(\bar{s})$ are unequal, or if the payoff matrix is not homogeneous, then it is necessary to determine the value of $\mathfrak{l}_c$ that maximizes the *expected* payoff, the average of the values in the payoff matrix weighted by their probabilities of being applied. Peterson, Birdsall, and Fox [59, 60]

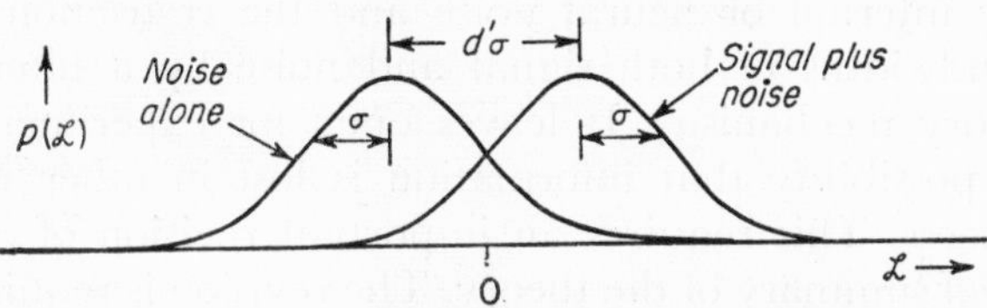

FIG. 3. *Probability density functions of $\mathcal{L}$, the logarithm of the likelihood ratio, on the decision axis.* The likelihood ratio is the ratio of the two probability density ordinates at $\mathcal{P}_j$ in Fig. 2. As $\mathcal{P}$ takes on various values from trial to trial, we have two probability density functions for the ratio, and therefore, two for its logarithm $\mathcal{L}$. One is for the trials on which noise alone is presented, the other for trials on which signal plus noise is presented. If the noise is gaussian-process noise, the two probability density functions for $\mathcal{L}$ are normal, as indicated, and their means are separated by the interval $d'\sigma = d'N^{1/2}$. N is the power density of the noise, and d' turns out, in the case of the ideal observer who knows exactly the specifications of the signal and the statistical parameters of the noise, to be $(2E/N)^{1/2}$, where E is the signal energy. Thus $d'\sigma$ is proportional to the rms sound pressure of the signal, σ is proportional to the rms sound pressure of the noise, and d', a dimensionless parameter, is $\sqrt{2}$ times the rms signal-noise ratio.

showed how a priori probabilities and the payoff function combine in the maximization. The cutoff point $\mathfrak{l}_c$ must be chosen to maximize $P_s(S) - \gamma P_{\bar{s}}(S)$ where $P_s(S)$ is the conditional probability that, if the signal actually was presented, the listener reports (correctly) that it was presented, $P_{\bar{s}}(S)$ is the conditional probability that, if the signal actually was not presented, the listener reports (incorrectly) that it was presented, and

$$\gamma = \frac{P(\bar{s})}{P(s)} \frac{V_{\bar{s}\bar{S}} - V_{\bar{s}S}}{V_{sS} - V_{s\bar{S}}}$$

The cutoff value that effects the maximization is $\mathfrak{l}_c = \gamma$.

TSG assumes that the distribution of the values of the logarithm $\mathcal{L}$ of $\mathfrak{l}$ for the no-signal trials is normal with variance σ^2—and that the distribution of $\mathcal{L}$ for the signal trials is also normal with variance σ^2, as illustrated in Fig. 3. (It is not essential that the distributions of the *logarithm* of $\mathcal{I}$ be normal. It is essential only that the distributions of some monotonic function of $\mathcal{I}$ be normal. We are making the assumption for the logarithm of $\mathcal{I}$ for the sake of specificity.)

The distance between the means of the two density functions in Fig. 3 divided by the standard deviation σ is called d' in TSG. It is the fundamental measure of effective signal strength. To each value of d' corresponds (for an optimal decision process, which the listener is assumed to have) a single-valued function relating $P_s(S)$ and $P_{\bar{s}}(S)$. Under fixed experimental conditions, therefore, the value of d' can be estimated from the relative frequencies of hits and false alarms.

As we noted earlier, TSG assumes the degrading of the sensory message by internal or neural noise and the restriction of the frequency bandwidths of both signal and noise by a filterlike action of the sensory mechanism. It leaves open for experimental investigation the possibility that information is lost in other ways in the sensory process. This requires an important revision of our thus far too simplified summary of the theory. The revision is required because there are two signal spaces, one in which the acoustic stimulus is located and another in which is located the message that, via the listener's sensory channels, reaches his (assumedly ideal) decision process.[8]

The dimensionality of the stimulus signal space is determined by the experimenter or the external environment that presents the signals. The dimensionality of the listener's internal signal space, on the other hand, is determined by characteristics of the auditory sensory and perceptual system. Both the auditory Δf and the auditory Δt *may* be adjusted by the listener to match the stimulus Δf and the stimulus Δt. The values of the auditory Δf and Δt are not assumed; they are left open to experimental investigation.

The points in the auditory signal space corresponding to $\mathcal{S}$ and $\mathcal{P}_j$ in stimulus signal space we may call $\mathcal{S}'$ and $\mathcal{P}_j'$. $\mathcal{S}'$ is the hypothetical point that would arise if the signal were presented alone, without external noise, and if the neural noise were turned off without affecting the auditory bandwidth or examination interval. $\mathcal{P}_j'$ is the point that represents the message actually received at the perceptual display region on trial j. The theory TSG is then essentially a restatement of the story given earlier, but with prime marks inserted to indicate that the listener's decision process operates on likelihood ratios derived from auditory signal space.

The value of d' for an ideal detector is readily derived for the case of a signal known exactly and presented in a uniform spectrum

[8] This distinction between the two signal spaces is not made explicitly in TSG. I am emphasizing it here because not seeing it at first caused me considerable difficulty.

gaussian-process noise.[9] If E is the energy of the signal and N is the power density (power per unit bandwidth)[10] of the noise, $d' = (2E/N)^{1/2}$. With the aid of that formula, TSG permits ready comparison between the performance of a human detector and the performance, under the same stimulus conditions, of an ideal detector. One simply estimates d' for the human detector from the relative frequencies of hits and false alarms and calculates d' for the ideal detector from $d' = (2E/N)^{1/2}$. The ratio of the two values of d' is an index of the human listener's efficiency, which in TSG is called η.

This summary of TSG has indicated how d' may be inferred from data of experiments based on a particular paradigm, has shown how d', the a priori probabilities $P(s)$ and $P(\bar{s})$, and the payoff matrix M govern the behavior of an optimal detector, and has given an idea of the nature of the decision process assumed to be used by listeners. Supporters of the theory trust that, in interaction with experiment, those parts of the theory concerned with parameters of the auditory system will take fuller shape and become quantitative. Some progress has been made in that direction and in the direction of relating the fundamental ideas of statistical-decision theory to other experimental paradigms, particularly the multilocation forced-choice paradigm.

The variables of the theory of signal detection. In the theory just outlined, most of the following variables were defined explicitly:

1. *Systematic independent variables*

$\mathfrak{s}$	A binary variable with the values s (signal presented) and $\bar{s}$ (signal not presented).
$P(s)$	The probability of s. $P(\bar{s}) = 1 - P(s)$.
$\mathcal{S}$	A variable of n dimensions, a particular value[11] of which is selected by the experimenter as the signal (which he may or may not present on any given trial).
E	The energy of the signal.
f	Frequency.
Δf	The frequency bandwidth within which the signal lies (also, the bandwidth of the noise).
t	Time.
Δt	The duration of the signal (also, the duration of the noise).

[9] It has been derived, also, for several other sets of conditions [25, 59, 60].

[10] Power density is analogous to probability density. It is the limit, as the bandwidth approaches zero, of the ratio of power in the band to width of the band. The unit of power is an erg per second. The unit of bandwidth is a cycle per second or, since the cycle itself is dimensionless, simply "per second." The unit of power density is therefore an erg; the seconds cancel. This makes $2E/N$ dimensionless.

[11] In a more advanced version of the theory, the signal may be drawn from a distribution of values of $\mathcal{S}$.

n	$n = 2 \cdot \Delta f \cdot \Delta t$.
$\mathcal{N}$	A variable of the n dimensions, a particular value $\mathcal{N}_j$ of which is selected at random from a given distribution to constitute the noise on a particular trial j.
j	The trial index.
N	The power density of the noise. N is a function $N(f)$ of f.
$\mathcal{P}$	A variable of the n dimensions, a particular value $\mathcal{P}_j$ of which is the quantity actually presented on trial j. $\mathcal{P}_j = \mathcal{S} + \mathcal{N}_j$ if s; $\mathcal{P}_j = \mathcal{N}_j$ if $\bar{s}$.
$p_s(\mathcal{P})$	The conditional probability density of $\mathcal{P}$ on the condition s; the likelihood that $\mathcal{P}$ will result if s.
$p_{\bar{s}}(\mathcal{P})$	The conditional probability density of $\mathcal{P}$ on the condition $\bar{s}$; the likelihood that $\mathcal{P}$ will result if $\bar{s}$.
M	A payoff matrix of values V.
$V_{\mathfrak{s}\mathfrak{r}}$	The value to the listener of making response $\mathfrak{r}$ if $\mathfrak{s}$ ($\mathfrak{s}$ is either s or $\bar{s}$).

2. *Systematic intervening variables*

$\mathcal{S}'$	A variable of n' dimensions derived from $\mathcal{S}$ by restricting the experimenter's signal to the $\Delta f'$ and $\Delta t'$ characteristic of the auditory system. To an approximation, $\Delta t' = \Delta t$ and $\Delta f'$ is the bandwidth of an "auditory filter." If we call the transfer operation of the filter $\mathcal{F}$, then $\mathcal{S}' = \mathcal{F}\mathcal{S}$.
$\mathcal{N}''$	"Neural" noise, a variable of the n' dimensions.
$\mathcal{P}'$	A variable of the n' dimensions, $\mathcal{P}' = \mathcal{F}\mathcal{P} + \mathcal{N}''$.
$\mathfrak{l}(\mathcal{P}')$	The likelihood ratio of $\mathcal{P}' : \mathfrak{l}(\mathcal{P}') = p_s(\mathcal{P}')/p_{\bar{s}}(\mathcal{P}')$.
$\mathcal{L}(\mathcal{P}')$	The logarithm of the likelihood ratio of $\mathcal{P}' : \mathcal{L}(\mathcal{P}') = \ln \mathfrak{l}(\mathcal{P}')$.
$p_s(\mathcal{L})$	The conditional probability density of $\mathcal{L}(\mathcal{P}')$ on the condition s; the likelihood that $\mathcal{L}(\mathcal{P}')$ will be the value of $\mathcal{L}$ on a given trial if the signal is presented on that trial.
$p_{\bar{s}}(\mathcal{L})$	The conditional probability density of $\mathcal{L}(\mathcal{P}')$ on the condition $\bar{s}$; the likelihood that $\mathcal{L}(\mathcal{P}')$ will be the value of $\mathcal{L}$ on a given trial if no signal is presented on that trial.
$\mathcal{L}_c$	The cutoff or critical value of $\mathcal{L}$ on the basis of which the listener makes his decision.

3. *Systematic dependent variables*

$\mathfrak{r}$	A binary variable with the values S (response signifying listener judges signal was presented) and $\bar{S}$ (response signifying listener judges signal was not presented): $\mathfrak{r} = S$ if $\mathcal{L} \geq \mathcal{L}_c$, $\mathfrak{r} = \bar{S}$ if $\mathcal{L} < \mathcal{L}_c$.
$P_s(S)$	The conditional probability of the response S on the condition s.

$P_{\bar{s}}(S)$ The conditional probability of the response S on the condition $\bar{s}$.

Mode of definition. As we see from inspection of the list, the primary definitions of the independent variables give only their mathematical characteristics. The references to experimenter, the nervous system ("neural"), etc., I have introduced only as mnemonic aids. Calling j the "trial index," for example, is a shorthand way of stating that it is a variable that takes on successive integral values from 1 to some number that is characteristic of an experiment. In effect, the *systematic* or *structural* independent variables have only mathematical properties.

It may be helpful, at this point, to examine somewhat more closely the concept of spectrum that plays such a basic role in the specification of the stimulus. We have used it as little as possible thus far, but it was essential to the discussion of the dimensionality of signal space and of the filtering operation performed upon the signal. It will enter even more fundamentally into our descriptions of the other two theories.

Any monaural acoustic stimulus can be specified, we said, by its waveform [time function $\theta(t)$] or, entirely equivalently, by its spectrum [frequency function $\Theta(f)$]. Since it represents an acoustical wave, the time function $\theta(t)$ is assumed to be real and single-valued. The spectrum $\Theta(f)$, the Fourier transform of $\theta(t)$, is in general complex. Its real part $\alpha(f)$ and its imaginary part $i\beta(f)$ are both functions of frequency. The real and imaginary coefficients, combined in two different ways, give first the amplitudes and second the phases of the sinusoids into which any stimulus may be analyzed, and thus specify the stimulus in terms that make immediate sense in relation to frequency analysis, which, as we have said, is the central auditory problem.

The spectrum specifies the amplitudes and phases of the sinusoidal components in this way: $\alpha(f)$ is the maximum amplitude (or simply amplitude) of a cosine wave $\alpha(f) \cos 2\pi ft$ of frequency f. $\beta(f)$ is the maximum amplitude of a sine wave $\beta(f) \sin 2\pi ft$ of frequency f. The single sinusoidal component of frequency f is the sum of the cosine wave and the sine wave, $\alpha(f) \cos 2\pi ft + \beta(f) \sin 2\pi ft$. This sum is $|\Theta(f)| \cos [2\pi ft + \phi(f)]$. The maximum amplitude of the sum is $|\Theta(f)| = [\alpha^2(f) + \beta^2(f)]^{1/2}$ and the phase angle of the sum is $\phi(f) = \tan^{-1} [\beta(f)/\alpha(f)]$. The stimulus waveform $\theta(t)$ is thought of as the result of adding together (superposing) a number of these elementary components of the form $|\Theta(f)| \cos [2\pi ft + \phi(f)]$, one for each frequency f. In a (conceptual) pure tone, there is only one such component, specified by its amplitude $|\Theta|$, its frequency f, and its phase $2\pi ft + \phi$ at an arbitrary time. In a compound tone, there are several elementary components, each with its three parameters. In a sample of speech or of "random noise," there is an infinite number of components, and in principle it is necessary—if one is to specify the sample uniquely—to give the amplitude $|\Theta|(f)$ and the phase angle $\phi(f)$ as functions of frequency. However, as we saw in our discussion of speech, the phase curve is often too complicated to handle. In a true random noise, all the phase angles are random, anyway, and only the amplitude curve is specified. Usually it is given in squared form, $N(f) = |\Theta(f)|^2 = [\alpha(f) + i\beta(f)][\alpha(f) - i\beta(f)]$.

A bothersome problem arises when we try to handle with a simple, constant notation the spectra of sounds that differ in certain ways. We may think of a sound either as having a finite duration or as existing throughout infinite time. A sound of the latter kind can be truly periodic (the waveform consisting of identical segments coming one after another in endless succession), but it need not be. In a rigorous discussion, the three different classes of sounds—finite duration, aperiodic; infinite duration, aperiodic; infinite duration, periodic—must be handled with techniques particularly suitable for them. But the distinctions are not wholly essential for our discussion, and we shall, therefore, not go much further than to observe that all the sounds with which we actually deal can in principle be synthesized from very (i.e., infinitely) many sinusoids of very small but appropriately selected amplitudes and appropriately selected phase angles. Since the actual sound is of finite duration and has finite energy, each of the elementary sinusoids has only infinitesimal energy. If we conceive of an aperiodic sound of infinite duration, we have to attribute to each elementary sound infinitesimal energy per unit time, or infinitesimal power. Only if the conceptual sound is periodic can we think of the elementary sinusoids (harmonics) as having finite power.

The foregoing excursion into the spectral sphere leaves us with the notion that, if we choose to make them so, the sinusoidal components can be our stimulus elements. As we saw, any monaural acoustic stimulus can be represented by a set of these elements, or simply by their amplitudes and phases given as functions of their frequencies. The only trouble with this way of looking at things is that the elements are timeless—or, more precisely, they extend over all time—and we often want to speak of changing the acoustic stimulus. There are elegant ways out of the difficulty, and some of them are very important for auditory theory. In the interest of getting on with the story, however, we shall try to get along without the elegance. Let us take comfort from the thought that, although each sinusoidal component runs from $t = -\infty$ to $t = \infty$, by adding together an infinitude of them we can make, for example, a wave that begins at $t = 0$ and stops at $t = 1$.

To be general, one must specify two spectra (or two waveforms) in order to define a binaural stimulus. Often, however, the main difference between the waves at the two ears is a difference in time of arrival. If the leading wave $\theta_r(t)$ reaches the right ear and the following wave $\theta_l(t) = \theta_r(t - \tau)$ reaches the left ear τ seconds later, the corresponding spectra are $\Theta_r(f) = |\Theta_r(f)| \cos [2\pi ft + \phi_r(f)]$ and $\Theta_l(f) = |\Theta_r(f)| \cos [2\pi ft + \phi_r(f) - 2\pi f\tau]$. This transforms the time difference into a phase difference, a shift (proportional to frequency) of the phases $\phi_r(f)$.

With an infinitude of stimulus elements and no constraints on how many of them we add together to make a stimulus, we can see at once that we can easily swamp ourselves with stimulus patterns. The preoccupation with pure tones, referred to earlier, was in part an effort to avoid the swamping. The current popularity of "white" noise as a stimulus is in part an overreaction: if we are going to have complexity, let us go all the way and have all possible components (up to some cutoff frequency f_c) in equal strength and random phase.

The systematic intervening variables are defined as functions of the systematic independent variables or of other (preceding) intervening variables. The operator $\mathfrak{F}$ I have introduced to provide a bridge between stimulus signal space and intervening signal space. TSG does not stress that distinction, as I said. But TSG clearly assumes that a sweepable auditory bandpass filter intervenes between the stimulus and the signal space. The numerous primes (except for the one in d') are my intrusions, also.

The single systematic dependent variable is defined as a go-no-go function of the intervening variables $\mathfrak{L}$ and $\mathfrak{L}_c$. That completes the structure in purely mathematical, functional form.

The only structural linkages that are not completely specified are $\mathfrak{F}$ and $\mathfrak{N}''$. They are the main objects of experimental investigation. Everything else is determined when the experimenter substitutes specific values for the variables under his control. Note, however, that the determination is that of a rigid formula (except for the randomness of $\mathfrak{N}''$) operating upon a random input. Perhaps one should not stress the word "rigid": the properties of $\mathfrak{F}$ may turn out to vary with time or with systematic independent variables.

Initial evidential grounds for assumptions. The main initial grounds for the assumptions were not evidential, but there was some evidence. Most of it was evidence *against* the rival formulation based on thresholds. It seems to me that most of this evidence can properly be directed against only a very limited concept of threshold that I think most of my contemporary colleagues have not held, but it is nevertheless true that the evidence had something to do with the adoption of the model based on statistical decision theory.

The main evidence against "the threshold" was that thresholds vary. It was suspected, but only later shown clearly, that a listener[12] could tell something more about the signals he reported absent ($\bar{S}$) than that he had decided to report them absent. He could, for example, say how confident he was that they were absent, and it turned out that he was more confident of the correctness of his $\bar{S}$ on $\bar{s}$-trials than on s-trials.

It has seemed to me, as I implied, that the evidence just mentioned is not critical against a modern version of the threshold concept. To set up an example of the latter, let us assume that we want to detect a segment of tone in fluctuating random noise. We do not know what absolute phase or level to expect, but we know the frequency and the duration that will characterize the signal if it comes. We construct a detector in which the input wave is passed through an amplifier with automatic gain control to stabilize its level against fluctuations of the noise and then into two narrow-band filters, identical except that one is centered upon the frequency of the expected signal and the other is set off to one side. (We chose filters with bandwidths equal approximately to the reciprocal of the expected signal duration.) The output of each filter we pass to an envelope-detecting circuit, and we subtract the envelope of the second filter channel from that of the first. Finally, now, we apply the difference time-function to a threshold circuit. It is a nonlinear device that yields output 1 if its input time-function is greater than some value γ', output 0 if its input is less than γ'. Does γ' have to be constant? No, we can arrange to make γ' adjustable by turning a knob, so that we can encourage the device to report 1 if it is very important not to miss the signal, or discourage it from reporting 1 if false alarms are very costly. My engineering friends build devices similar to the one just described, and they refer to the nonlinear circuit as a threshold circuit and speak of adjusting its threshold. The evidence against "the threshold concept" does not react against the idea that a human listener may process his input signal in a way analogous to the detector with a threshold circuit. In fact, one might say that the operation in the TSG model that makes $\mathfrak{r} = S$ if $\mathfrak{L} \geq \mathfrak{L}_c$ and $\mathfrak{r} = \bar{S}$ if $\mathfrak{L} < \mathfrak{L}_c$ is precisely that of a threshold operator.

In recent discussions with Tanner, Swets, and Green, I have

[12] I am using the word "listener" to maintain connection with auditory theory, but actually the theory was applied first [83, 87, 88] in vision.

discovered that they distinguish between "sensory" and "response" thresholds and oppose only the former. The distinction seems valuable. The threshold mechanism described in the last paragraph is a "response" mechanism. As a result of the discussions, moreover, I have been forced to recognize that the too limited concept is not just a straw man. The evidence that the listener knows something—which he can later report—about the signal he judges "not presented" indicates that the nonlinear circuit is located at a point following a path of access to his memory. It thus reveals very clearly the flaw in "correction for chance guessing." The fact that that correction has been widely used convinces me that the rigid concept of threshold has in fact been widely held.

In order to talk about evidence for or against a theory, we must know to what empirical independent and dependent variables the systematic dependent and independent variables are related, and by what linkages or identifications. In the present instance, the correspondences are probably so obvious as to require no discussion—or so technical as to inhibit discussion. Let us, therefore, pass over most of the possible treatment of this area and dwell only upon two points that may be unclear.

The empirical signal that corresponds to $\mathcal{S}$ is typically the result of transducing with an earphone the gated[13] output of a signal generator (usually an oscillator, a generator of sinusoidal signals of controlled frequency and amplitude). The oscillation may be turned on as it crosses the zero-voltage axis and then, at the end of an integral number of half-periods, off again as it again crosses zero. The bandwidth of such a signal is ideally infinite, but of course not practically infinite, since most of its energy is in the neighborhood of the nominal frequency, the frequency of the original, ungated oscillation. In fact, most of its energy lies in the frequency band within $1/\Delta t$ cycles per second of the nominal frequency.

That may raise a question concerning the dimensionality of the signal. We assumed that $\mathcal{S}$ had n dimensions, where $n = 2 \cdot \Delta f \cdot \Delta t$, and we did not limit Δf or Δt. The fact is that, since the waveform of the signal is fixed by its mode of generation, it has no dimensions of free variability. It is completely specified, and it is in principle no harder to specify it in the space in which the noise is specified than it is in the space of fewer dimensions to which it appears to be confined by the fact that $2 \cdot \Delta f \cdot \Delta t = 4$ when $\Delta f = 2/\Delta t$.

The empirical signal that corresponds to $\mathcal{N}$ is the filtered output, transduced into sound by an earphone, of a random noise generator. The source of the voltage fluctuations is the thermal motion of elec-

[13] Switched on for a specified interval Δt, then off.

trons in a resistor or the almost equally haphazard motion of ions in a gas tube. Those fluctuations are as nearly purely random as anything is likely to be in a real world. The bandwidth of the noise is ordinarily limited to some value such as 6,000 cycles per second by an electrical filter before the noise is delivered to the earphone. That is mainly to facilitate determining the noise power density, however, because the earphone itself acts as a low-pass filter with a cutoff (typically) of 7,000 cycles per second.

Usually no attempt is made to specify the empirical item corresponding to $\mathcal{N}_j$, the particular noise wave on any given trial. The only things that require specification are the probability density functions corresponding to $p_s(\mathcal{P})$ and $p_{\bar{s}}(\mathcal{P})$. The usual procedure is (1) to measure the over-all noise power in a band perhaps 1,000 cycles per second wide, centered on the signal frequency, (2) to check the uniformity of the power density spectrum $N(f)$ with the aid of a narrow-band scanning filter, (3) to determine the power density by dividing the over-all power by the 1,000-cycle-per-second bandwidth, and (4) to check that the distribution of instantaneous noise voltages is approximately normal. The power density is then known rather accurately. The n-dimensional normality corresponding to $p_s(\mathcal{P})$ and $p_{\bar{s}}(\mathcal{P})$ is never checked, I think, but the experimenter is usually nonetheless confident because of faith in the linearity of his equipment and in the power of the central limit theorem.

On the side of the dependent variable, the empirical situation is an experimenter's delight. There is either a double-throw switch or two buttons. The empirical correlates of S and $\bar{S}$ flow from them into relay scoring circuits or into an IBM card puncher.

Construction of function forms. The functions that relate succeeding variables to preceding variables are of two kinds. First, there are the operator $\mathcal{F}$ and the operation of superposing $\mathcal{F}\mathcal{P}$ upon the neural noise $\mathcal{N}''$. These "functions" are prescribed in rough outline by TSG, but their details are left for experimental study. In contrast are the operations performed upon the variables of the internal signal space. Those operations are wholly specified by the theory.

Actually, all TSG says about $\mathcal{F}$ is that it involves, as one step, the passage of the external signal through a sweepable bandpass filter of width $\Delta f'$. Implicit, however, is the idea that $\mathcal{F}$ involves other operations in addition to the filtering. One of them involves loss of some of the information about the phase pattern of $\mathcal{P}$ or, alternatively, of $\mathcal{S}$.

The over-all level and spectral distribution of the neural noise $\mathcal{N}''$ are left open for experimental investigation, but a feature of the probability density function of $\mathcal{N}''$ is prescribed indirectly by the assumption that the logarithms $\mathcal{L}_{\bar{s}}(\mathcal{P})$ and $\mathcal{L}_s(\mathcal{P})$—or at least some monotonic functions of the likelihood ratios of $\mathcal{F}\mathcal{N} + \mathcal{N}''$ and $\mathcal{F}(\mathcal{S} + \mathcal{N}) + \mathcal{N}''$—are normally distributed with equal variances.

The forms of the other functions in TSG are specified in full by the assumption that the human decision process is optimal. The decision process derives from the observation point $\mathcal{P}$ and the probability density functions $p_s(\mathcal{P})$ and $p_{\bar{s}}(\mathcal{P})$ the value of $\mathcal{L}$, and it derives from $P(s)$ and M the value of $\mathcal{L}_c$, in each instance following without any error or deviation at all the functions we have examined for those operations. It then compares $\mathcal{L}$ with $\mathcal{L}_c$ and triggers off the response S or the response $\bar{S}$. Probably an appropriate reaction to these assumptions is that they are too stringent to be realistic for a model of human judgment. It hardly seems reasonable to suppose that while the sensory system loses information the decision process is ideal. Actually, however, Tanner, Swets, and Green are entirely willing to qualify the assumption of idealness as soon as the experimental work progresses far enough to permit discrimination between sensory losses of information and losses due to uncertainties in the decision process. They point out, however, that the latter cannot be far from ideal in some situations, for the over-all performance of the human detector is sometimes only a little less good than that of an optimal device.

Measurement of independent and dependent variables. The procedures specified by TSG for the measurement of the independent and dependent variables are wholly quantitative and consistent with the requirements of the functions of the theory in every point except the payoff matrix M. The quantitative specification of the stimulus and response variables presents no problems, as we have noted, other than purely technical ones that are handled effectively with the aid of modern electroacoustic instrumentation. It is not yet possible, however, to measure or control with full authority the value system of the listener. That fact has led to an emphasis, in experimental work related to TSG, of the method of forced choice among alternative positions or intervals.

In the multilocation forced-choice method, almost all the assumptions about the values in the payoff matrix are neutralized or canceled. The one very plausible assumption that is not thus eliminated is that the values $V_{\mathcal{S}r}$ remain constant throughout the duration of a trial. In general, there are in a forced-choice trial m alternative stimulus intervals or positions. The listener's task is to report in which one of them the signal $\mathcal{S}$ appeared. According to the theory, as developed to apply to this situation, the listener derives m values of $\mathcal{L}$, corresponding to the m intervals, and reports the number of the interval for which $\mathcal{L}$ is greatest. If m were large, this would place a burden upon his memory, but m is usually 2, and rarely greater than 4. TSG includes a procedure for calculating d' from the percentage of correct responses in m location forced-choice tests, and thereby permits comparison between forced-choice results and yes-no results.

Within the context of the multilocation forced-choice method, we may say that TSG has essentially no serious measurement difficulties. It is quantitatively specific to as high a degree as most theories in physical science.

Formal organization of the system. In a sense, TSG is organized on a high level of axiomatization, for the published account presents eleven formal postulates. The question is, what kinds of deduction or derivation do the postulates support?

There are three answers to that question, depending upon the extent to which we read into the theory substantive properties of $\mathfrak{F}$ and $\mathfrak{N}''$. Without definite assumptions about these two functions, the postulates specify the *form* into which stimulus information is converted for digestion by the decision process, but not the *quantity*. With only the definite statements made in the postulates (that $\mathfrak{F}$ involves a sweepable bandpass filter characteristic, that $\mathfrak{N}'' > 0$), only very nonspecific, nonquantitative deductions can be made. With statements about $\mathfrak{F}$ and $\mathfrak{N}''$ of the type that are beginning to emerge from the experimental work, it should eventually be possible to build a quantitative auditory theory.

The situation just outlined suggests this characterization of TSG: It is a formal, axiomatized recipe for studying the auditory process. It is the bare beginning of a substantive theory. The main exceptions to that generalization are points upon which the formal theory makes statements about substantive properties of hearing; for example, that the auditory system involves a sweepable filter (instead of a manifold of filters with fixed center frequencies), and that the decision process is ideal. These points the theory might better have left for empirical study, for they will be so studied, in any case.

Inasmuch as it is unusual to find postulates in auditory theories, we might ask what led to the formality of the treatment. Almost surely, it was the unusual circumstance of finding, ready-made, a structure that appeared to have relevance to sensory processes. The initial task of the theorists was to discover how the structure of statistical decision theory could be lined up with the procedure of sensory experiments. That led to deliberate manipulation of the several pieces of the puzzle. When a promising alignment was achieved, it was quite natural to make a series of statements relating the corresponding parts. That was done first for vision. The auditory theory followed the same pattern. The formality of the auditory theory thus appears to be related to the fact that statistical-decision theory had already evolved and achieved formality in another field. If it is true that axiomatization is more valuable as a way of compressing an established theory for storage than as a way of bringing theory into contact with experiment, then we may see TSG lose some of its formality for a time.

Scope of the system. *Present and intended scopes.* The theory we have been calling TSG is actually the auditory part of what the group at Michigan views as a general sensory theory. There has been no need to say how general, but certainly the possible scope includes all the senses and other functions than detection per se.

A natural extension of the theory that we have examined involves relaxation of the assumption that the same signal, $\mathcal{S}$, is the signal for each trial. The mathematics has been worked out [59, 60] for detection in situations in which the signal (exclusive of the noise) is selected at random from a set of orthogonal signals. This is close to the basic paradigm for communication. The function of identifying the received signal as a particular one of the transmitted signals is usually called recognition or identification or classification. It differs from detection in that the crucial question is which signal was sent, not simply was a signal sent. When there are only two signals in the ensemble, however, the difference disappears. Tanner [84] has described the extension of TSG to recognition in a two-alternative situation. Moreover, he has pointed out the applicability of some of Birdsall's results on the case of m orthogonal alternatives to the recognition of speech sounds.

Detection is usually thought of as confined to the realm of weak signals, or of signals comparable in level to the noise. However, the extension of the theory to include recognition, identification, or classification automatically brings large signals into the picture. If alternative signals $\mathcal{S}_1$ and $\mathcal{S}_2$ are close enough together in signal space, it may take a high signal-noise ratio to permit high-probability identification of $\mathcal{S}_1$. Experimental work on problems suggested by this extension is now under way in the Engineering Research Institute at Michigan.

Interrelations with other formulations. TSG is very closely related, as mentioned earlier, to the less formal application of ideas of statistical-decision theory by Smith and Wilson [74] and to the more tutorial exposition of the ideas by Marill [54]. The three developments are so similar that they may be lumped together under the heading, "statistical-decision theories of auditory detection."

Also very closely related are models of the auditory process, or parts of it, that do not assume an ideal decision process, but which are nonetheless statistical. These have followed approximately the pattern described earlier as an example of a threshold mechanism not subject to the criticisms directed against the limited conception of threshold. Simple models of that kind have been described, for example, by Schafer et al. [65] and by Sherwin et al. [72]. These models are in one sense supplementary to TSG, for they are specific in detail about the parts of the process $\mathfrak{F}$ and $\mathfrak{N}''$ that TSG leaves open. On the other hand, they do not assume maximum likelihood decision, and in that respect differ fundamentally.

Considerably further away is the quantum hypothesis of sensory discrimination [75]. The quantum hypothesis assumes internal fluctuations of the sort that might be referred to as neural noise, and it holds that those fluctuations are continually taking the measure of signal strength up and down the scale past the critical, or quantal, levels at which it is marked. Passing a single quantal level is, therefore, not significant of a change in stimulation, but passing two quantal levels almost simultaneously is significant, for the fluctuations practically never move the measure very far in a short interval. The quantum theory does not go into detail about the spectrum of the fluctuations or about other intervening processes. Like TSG, it provides a recipe for, or a guide to, experimental investigation of important parameters. However, the important parameters of the two theories are quite different. That serves to insulate the theories from each other. Further insulation is imposed by the fact that the experimental procedures specified or suggested by the theorists are in some respects essentially incompatible. The sensory quantum theorists have argued for and have used a procedure in which the listener knows when the signal was presented and reports whether or not he heard it. This is completely contrary to the spirit of the statistical-decision theorists who, if they were serving as subjects, would say "I hear it" each time the signal was due. For them, the subject's obligation is not to give an accurate account of his sensory state but to maximize his payoff. It is unfortunate that the two theories are not in closer contact with each other. Perhaps they may be brought into contact despite the insulation.

Finally, there is the rigid sensory threshold theory that supports "correction for chance guessing." The statistical-decision theories collide vigorously with it. Happily, the collision is on a point susceptible to empirical test.

History of interaction with research. *Experiments related to the theory*. The experiments of Smith and Wilson [74] showed clearly that listeners can adjust their "thresholds" in response to the experimenter's verbal instructions concerning the relative costs of misses and false alarms. Tanner and Swets [87, 88], in a visual experiment, actually used a monetary payoff matrix, changes in which markedly affected the experimental estimates of $P_s(S)$ and $P_{\bar{s}}(S)$. They showed that application of corrections for chance led to "thresholds" that depended upon the false-alarm rate, thereby revealing the inconsistency in the rigid threshold concept. Then Tanner, Swets, and Green [89] demonstrated that the same applies to hearing.

The equality of the values of d' determined in yes-no and in multilocation forced-choice trials was demonstrated in vision [87, 88] and then in hearing [86, 89]. This must be regarded as a real accomplishment for the theory and a break in the trend that has been developing—to regard the results of a psychophysical test as meaningless except in relation to the procedure of the test.

The experimental results to date indicate that the curve of the function relating $P_s(S)$ to $P_{\bar{s}}(S)$ for constant stimulus conditions and varying payoff matrix is indeed approximately a curve of constant d'. That is the same as saying that the curve is approximately linear when the probabilities are plotted on normal probability paper. The finding is itself one with important practical application.

The extension to the study of recognition of one or the other of two tones differing in frequency involved the assumption that the recognition axis (the decision axis on which the cut is made between "higher" and "lower") is the axis of the resultant of two vectors. One vector is a value of $\mathcal{L}$ on the detection decision axis for the higher tone and the other is a value of $\mathcal{L}$ on the detection decision axis for the lower tone. From his data, Tanner [84] estimated the angle between the two detection decision axes. Zero corresponded to identity of the two axes; 90° corresponded to complete independence of the two component decisions. Tanner estimated the angle for various intervals of separation in frequency between the two tones, and it turned out that the separation required for effective independence, i.e., about 70°, was about the same as the critical bandwidth determined by Fletcher [17, 18] and by Schafer et al. [65]. That amounts to a demonstration that the theory can handle an important substantive problem. In the isolated instance, it offers no clear advantage over other formulations (Fletcher and Schafer et al. determined "thresholds"), but it holds out the promise of handling other problems within the same framework. Providing a common framework for the study of a variety of auditory problems would constitute an important contribution.

Apparently in an effort to develop such a role for the theory, the Michigan group has focused its attention during the last year on a series of substantive auditory problems. Until the results of these and still further studies are available, we cannot see how successful the theory is in its "framework" role. In one instance, however, there is a preliminary report [33], and also a simultaneous and independent study for comparison, a study made outside the specific framework of TSG but within the framework of statistical-decision theory [54].

Using the forced-choice procedure, Green [33] and Marill [54] studied the problem of "summation." If two segments of sinusoid $\mathcal{S}_1$ and $\mathcal{S}_2$ are equally detectable—have the same probability of correct response in forced-choice trials—how detectable is their sum $\mathcal{S}_3 = \mathcal{S}_1 + \mathcal{S}_2$? Both Green and Marill asked that question for pairs of frequencies within the interval of a critical bandwidth and also for pairs of frequencies more widely separated. Green used binaural (diotic) presentation, applying the same waveform to both ears of his listeners, whereas Marill used monaural presentation. When the two frequencies were within the critical bandwidth, there was summation in both experiments: $\mathcal{S}_3$ was detected more often than $\mathcal{S}_1$ or $\mathcal{S}_2$. But with widely spaced frequencies, Green found summation and Marill did not. That called for a careful investigation of all possibilities, which Green is now making with Marill's apparatus, and with both monaural and binaural (diotic) presentation. Thus far, Green's data are supporting the conclusion that there is more two-frequency summation with two ears than with one. Tanner [85] is therefore doing an experiment with three frequencies.

On the basis of the summary of research just given, it is obvious that it is too early to judge the theory on the basis of evidence *pro* and *con*. Thus far, there is no strong contrary evidence, but neither is there evidence capable of destroying all the alternatives. Actually, because of the nature of the theory, it is unlikely that it will be proved or disproved. Certainly parts of it will change, and new parts will be added. Despite its surface formality, the theory is flexible enough to adapt.

The most vulnerable point appears to me to be the "sweepable filter." It is a formulation, in the terms used by electronic and communication engineers, of a conception that is perhaps as accurately described in the very different terms of the searchlight analogy of attention. The searchlight sweeps back and forth across the data display surface, but it cannot illuminate the entire surface at once. A critical test of this notion in the auditory context would have to be made with signals that constitute better gestalten than do the compounds of sinusoids used in the experiments. The problem is to determine whether or not two widely separated components of the external signal can contribute simultaneously to the signal in internal signal space, and thereby to the measure on the decision axis. It might be possible to design a critical test by momentarily eliminating one narrow frequency band and then another of a random noise. The eliminations could be made of such short duration that a sweeping filter of the postulated bandwidth and sweep speed would miss some of them. The question would then be, of course, whether or not a listener would fail to notice some of them, too. My guess is that he would be embarrassingly sensitive to such changes in the noise spectrum. On the other hand, the theory may protect itself even here through its flexibility. The theory is not committed to any assumption of fixed bandwidth. Perhaps the filter would just broaden itself instead of sweeping.

The future of the theory. Early experiments mentioned in the preceding section were set up to test either the statistical-decision theory or a rival formulation. The later experiments were part of a program to bring within the framework of the theory various substantive parts of the field of hearing. We shall doubtless have more of both kinds. We shall also have experiments less directly, but nonetheless clearly, influenced by statistical-decision theory. They will employ payoff matrixes or the forced-choice procedure, but they will probably not assume maximum likelihood estimation.

The part of the program aimed at testing the theory will probably focus on the question of internal consistency: Do various procedures yield the same value of d'? It may prove possible to discriminate experimentally between TSG and formulations involving fluctuating thresholds. If so, there is sure to be activity along that line.

The part of the program aimed at unifying a considerable area of psychoacoustics within the statistical-decision framework will continue, if present plans are followed, with experiments on the detection of signals not specified exactly to the listener, on the recognition of signals selected from various numbers of alternatives, and on the progressive increase in detection probability with repeated presentation of the same signal. These experiments will get at such questions as the extent to which phase information is used by the auditory system, the precision with which frequency information is transmitted, the usefulness of the detection theory concepts in the realm of strong signals, and the properties of the neural noise.

Finally, the broader influence of statistical-decision theory, extending beyond the specific formulation we have discussed, will almost surely encompass most of psychoacoustics. More and more, workers in the field are growing dissatisfied with the classical psychophysical techniques, particularly with the method of "adjustment" or "production" that lets the listener attend to the stimulus for an unspecified length of time before deciding that he can "just hear it" and with the methods of "limits" and "constants" (in their usual forms) that ask the listener to report "present" or "absent" when he already knows "present." It is widely felt that the "thresholds" yielded by these procedures are on such an insecure semantic basis that they cannot serve as good building blocks for a quantitative science. That means that practically the whole of classical auditory psychophysics needs to be redone with payoff matrixes or forced choices among alternative locations. With the old areas to be resurveyed and with new horizons opening up it may be a busy time.

THEORY OF SPEECH INTELLIGIBILITY

As our focal theory of speech intelligibility, we shall take the theory implicit in a procedure for computing intelligibility from physical parameters. The particular formulation is a simplification by Beranek [7] of the procedure described by French and Steinberg [26]. It is very closely related to another version, described by Fletcher and Galt [21], of the Bell Telephone Laboratories formula.

Summary of the theory. This theory of speech intelligibility, which we shall examine in the following paragraphs, defines an intervening variable $\mathcal{A}$ as a particular function of stimulus variables, and then relates various measures A of intelligibility to the intervening variable $\mathcal{A}$. The latter step involves pairing values of A estimated from empirical tests with values of $\mathcal{A}$ calculated from the stimulus variables. The resulting relations are either appropriated to the theory or regarded as empirical extensions of it.

The fundamental characteristic of $\mathcal{A}$ is that it is the algebraic sum of contributions $\Delta\mathcal{A}$ associated with separate bands Δf of frequency. The theory of intelligibility is thus based upon an assumed frequency analysis of the stimulus. As we shall see, the "articulation index" $\mathcal{A}$ is the integral, over a distorted frequency scale, of the logarithm of a ratio R. With certain qualifications, R is the ratio of the power density of the speech to the power density of the background noise in the listener's ears.

For the purposes of the computational procedure, "speech" is defined (1) by a list or vocabulary of sentences or words or syllables or phons and (2) by a long-time average power density spectrum. All we need to know about the speech material is that, when the items are read by a talker over a distortionless, noisefree channel to a colingual listener, and recorded by the listener, the talker's list and the listener's list agree almost perfectly. The speech power density spectrum is the function that describes the distribution in frequency of the acoustic power of the speech at the listener's ears. (The speech waves at the two ears are assumed to be the same.) In the symbols that we shall use throughout the chapter, we may think of $\theta(t)$ as being the waveform of a very long (duration T approaching infinity) and representative sample of speech. As mentioned earlier, there is no good way of actually finding the corresponding spectrum $\Theta(f) = \alpha(f) + i\beta(f)$, though in principle it certainly exists, for the phase pattern [$\phi(f)$, where $\phi = \tan^{-1} \beta/\alpha$] is so complicated. The power density spectrum drops the phase information and tells us only the square of the amplitude $|\Theta|$ as a function of frequency:

$$\begin{aligned}\Phi(f) &= \lim_{T\to\infty} \frac{\Theta(f)\Theta^*(f)}{T} \\ &= \lim_{T\to\infty} \frac{(\alpha + i\beta)(\alpha - i\beta)}{T} \\ &= \lim_{T\to\infty} \frac{\alpha^2 + \beta^2}{T} \\ &= \lim_{T\to\infty} \frac{|\Theta(f)|^2}{T}\end{aligned}$$

Since α and β are both real, $\Phi(f)$ is real. $\Phi(f)$ can be approximated closely by physical measurement.

The power density spectrum $\Phi(f)$ gives us a picture of speech that is too completely anchored in the frequency domain to be wholly appropriate for our purpose. It is based on sinusoidal building blocks that do not vary in amplitude, and we have just thrown away the phase information that, in principle, would let us reconstruct the pattern of the variations in time of the over-all speech wave or of bands of its components. We must reintroduce to some extent the temporal factor. We do this by supposing, not altogether correctly, that the weak speech sounds collectively have a power density spectrum of the same shape as the power density spectrum of the strong speech sounds, that there is in fact a continuum of levels, the weakest being about 18 db[14] below the average and the strongest about 12 db above. We suppose (largely on the basis of empirical evidence) that some intelligibility will be lost when the weakest ones fall below the level of interfering noise, and that there will be no intelligibility at all if the strongest ones fall below the level of the noise. For later convenience, we define a "strongest speech sound" power density spectrum $\Phi'(f) = 16\Phi(f)$, that is, 12 db above the average.

[14] Decibels (db) are logarithmic units. One value, w_1, of power is x db greater than another, w_2, if $x = 10 \log_{10} (w_1/w_2)$. The same rule holds for other "quadratic quantities," quantities related (as power is) to the square of the voltage or the sound pressure of the signal.

The reason for bringing noise into the picture is that speech is usually heard against a background of undesired or adventitious acoustic disturbance. Often, the noise is the main factor governing intelligibility. We therefore assign a symbol to the ratio of the power density of the strongest speech sounds to the average power density of the noise, $R'(f) = \Phi'(f)/N(f)$. We shall use $\mathcal{R}'$ to represent ten times the logarithm (to base 10) of R', and we shall call $\mathcal{R}'$ the maximum speech-noise ratio in decibels.

If the speech is very weak, it may be in part or entirely inaudible even in a quiet place. The theory of intelligibility was formulated before the time when the influence of statistical-decision theory made one think twice before using the word "threshold," and it refers to a threshold of audibility, below which signals cannot be heard. However, the actual treatment does not involve the threshold concept directly. Instead, it postulates a "neural" noise $N''(f)$ which acts in precisely the same way as random-process noise of external origin and, in fact, adds to the external noise, just as in the theory of signal detection. We may therefore restate the definition of R' as the ratio of (strongest) speech power density to total noise power density, $R'(f) = \Phi'(f)/N'(f)$, where $N'(f) = N(f) + N''(f)$, N'' referring to the internal and N to the external noise. $\mathcal{R}'$ is of course now ten times the logarithm of this new R'. The difference is negligible except when the speech is exceedingly weak.

If, on the other hand, the speech is amplified too much, it may overload the listener's auditory mechanism. The theory handles that fact by setting an upper limit for speech power density. Beyond that limit there is no contribution to intelligibility. For the sake of simplicity, we may assume that our speech does not exceed that limit.

Having defined the main variables, we now focus on a narrow band[15] of frequencies and ask how does the contribution $\Delta\mathcal{A}$ of this band to over-all intelligibility vary with $\mathcal{R}'$, the maximum speech-noise ratio in decibels? There are data, and the theory essentially appropriates the empirical function, considerably idealized. The theory says that there is no contribution when the strongest speech power in the band is less than the noise power in the band, i.e., $\Delta\mathcal{A} = 0$ if $R'(f_b) < 1$ and $\mathcal{R}'(f_b) < 0$. If the strongest speech power is greater than the noise power but the weakest speech power is less than the noise power, the contribution is proportional to the maximum speech-noise ratio in decibels. $\Delta\mathcal{A} = K\mathcal{R}'(f_b)$ if $1 < R'(f_b) <$

[15] We shall assume that the width Δf of the frequency band is small enough that $R(f)$ is approximately constant over the band. Therefore, the ratio of speech power in the band to noise power in the band is approximately the same as the ratio $R(f_b)$ of the power densities anywhere in the band. We shall use $R(f_b)$ for either ratio.

1000 and $0 < \mathcal{R}'(f_b) < 30$. Finally, if the weakest speech power exceeds the noise power, the excess makes no contribution to intelligibility: $\Delta\mathcal{A} = 30K$ if $\mathcal{R}'(f_b) > 30$.

If we could assume, also, that $\Delta\mathcal{A}$ is proportional to Δf for constant $\mathcal{R}'(f_b)$, we would be nearly finished, but $\Delta\mathcal{A}$ is not proportional to Δf. Bands of speech in the range 200 to 1,500 cycles per second contribute more to intelligibility than do bands of equal width in cycles per second that are higher or lower on the frequency scale. The next step, therefore, is to find a new scale of frequency on which bands of equal width will contribute equally. Again there are data. The theory appropriates the empirical function $Y(f)$ that specifies the importance to intelligibility of a narrow band, of fixed width in cycles per second, centered upon f. On the new scale, the frequency variable $g = g(f)$ is expanded where $Y(f)$ is great and compressed where $Y(f)$ is small:[16]

$$g(f) = \int_0^f Y(\nu)d\nu$$

Note that g is a scale of finite extent, the upper limit being given by

$$g(\infty) = \int_0^\infty Y(f)df = 1$$

We select our bands, then, in such a way that they have equal widths on the g scale. If we let them grow narrower and narrower, summation of the contributions of the many bands approximates integration of $\mathcal{R}'$ over g, and we come to the approximate expression

$$\mathcal{A} = (1/30) \int_0^1 \mathcal{R}'(g)\, dg$$

That expression contains the essence of the theory, which is summarized in Fig. 4. All that remain are minor qualifications and a function relating the articulation index $\mathcal{A}$ to the articulation measure (e.g., per cent word articulation) A.

One of the qualifications is that, in the computational procedures, for the sake of convenience in calculation, the frequency scale is broken up into bands as we have just suggested, but into relatively few bands. In the procedures outlined by French and Steinberg [26] and Beranek [7], the number n of frequency bands is 20. Dividing the frequency scale into such a number of intervals simplifies calculation but somewhat complicates the conceptual picture. First we must go back to the separate speech and noise powers in each band by integrating $\Phi'(f)$ and then $N'(f)$ over each band. Then we find for each band the ratio of the two powers thus determined. Then we

[16] In the integral, we substitute ν for f in order to free f for use as the upper limit of integration. $\int_0^w Y(\nu)d\nu$ is of course equal to $\int_0^w Y(f)df$.

convert the ratios to decibels, restricting each result to the range 0 to 30 db. And finally, we add together the logarithmic quantities and divide by $30n$.

The importance function $Y(f)$ gets into the picture, in the n-band

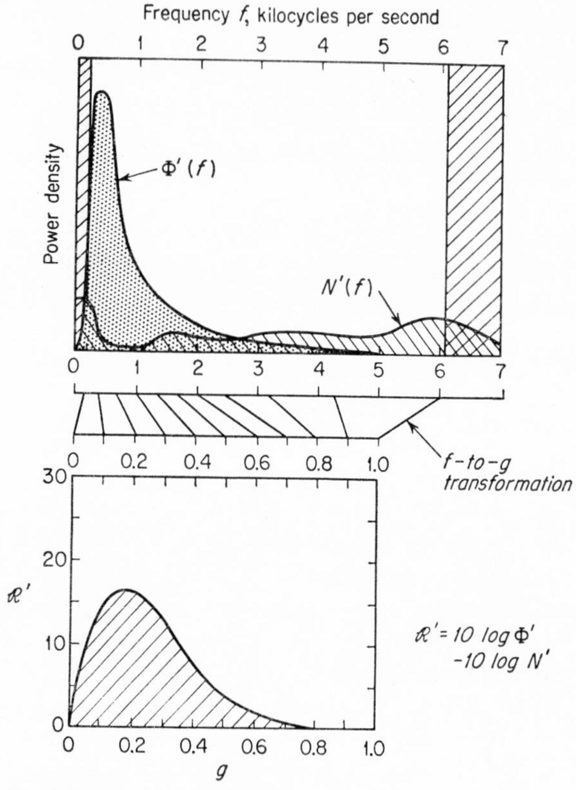

FIG. 4. *Illustration of formula for the articulation index.* The upper graph shows the power density spectra of the strongest speech sounds $\Phi'(f)$ and of the total noise $N'(f)$ at the listener's ear. The lower graph is derived from the upper by two transformations. First, $\mathcal{R}'$ is derived from Φ' and N' by the relation

$$\mathcal{R}' = 10 \log_{10} (\Phi'/N') = 10 \log_{10} \Phi' - 10 \log_{10} N'$$

After $\mathcal{R}'$ is determined as a function of frequency, the plot is distorted by the transformation of the frequency scale. The transformation from ordinary frequency f to the scale g is indicated by the transition lines between the two graphs. The gridded area under the curve of $\mathcal{R}'$ against g is then determined and divided by 30, the area of the entire lower plot, to yield the articulation index $\mathcal{A}$. In this example, it is 0.20.

procedure, through the selection of the limits of the n frequency bands. These limits are chosen to make the bands contribute equally to intelligibility. The jth cutoff frequency is then $f(j/n)$, where $f(g)$ is the inverse of $g(f)$. That is, $f[g(f_r)] = f_r$.

The main reason for setting up the computational procedure in terms of bands of frequencies is that noise measurements are usually made with bandpass filters. A bandpass filter inherently integrates power density over the frequency interval corresponding to its passband. However, the filters rarely if ever have the particular cutoff frequencies that are required by the 20-band procedure. One must therefore estimate the power density spectrum from the filter band measurements, then estimate from the power density spectrum the powers in the bands specified by the theory. That is devious. It seems better to draw the speech and noise power density curves on a graph with logarithmic ordinate scale and $g(f)$ abscissa scale and to measure the area between the two curves with the aid of a planimeter or by counting squares. That very nearly parallels the theory as we described it before discussing the band procedure. Measuring the area between the speech and noise power density curves on the distorted scale is equivalent to finding the integral $\mathcal{A} = (1/30) \int_0^1 \mathcal{R}'(g)\, dg$ because[17] $\mathcal{R}'(g) = \log \bar{\Phi}'(g) - \log \bar{N}'(g) = \log \Phi'(g) - \log N'(g)$ and therefore

$$1/30 \int_0^1 \mathcal{R}'(g)\, dg = 1/30 \int_0^1 [\log \Phi'(g) - \log N'(g)]\, dg$$

Before leaving the band procedure, however, we must note one other qualification that is a matter of theoretical importance rather than of practical convenience. It relates to the critical-band concept and also to the question of how to handle the infinite power densities of discrete-spectrum interference.

According to the critical-band hypothesis, all the noise in a band Δf_c cycles per second wide and centered upon a given frequency contributes to the masking of a signal component at that frequency. If the 20 bands of the computational procedure were critical bands, they would provide approximately the effect required by the critical-band hypothesis. Actually, the relative widths of the 20 bands are about right, but all the bands are too wide.[18] Moreover, in order to

[17] Let $\bar{\Phi}'(g)$ be the power density spectrum after substitution of the variable g for the variable f, and let $\bar{N}'(g)$ be the corresponding noise power density spectrum. Note that even though $\bar{\Phi}'(g) \neq \Phi'(g)$ and $\bar{N}(g) \neq N'(g)$, $\bar{\Phi}'(g)/\bar{N}'(g) = \Phi'(g)/N'(g)$.

[18] They are wider than Fletcher's critical bands, the widths of which were approximately confirmed by Schafer et al. However, recent measurements by Feldtkeller and Zwicker [14] and by Zwicker, Flottorp, and Stevens [96] yield wider bands—only very slightly narrower than those of the 20-band procedure. In part, the different estimates of bandwidth may be reconciled if it is supposed that the auditory channels have transmission-against-frequency characteristics similar to those of wave filters. These characteristics are never ideally rectangular. They have sloping skirts. The width 25 db down on the skirts is often considerably greater than the width 3 db below the peak.

provide more exactly the effect required, we should have to have an infinitude of overlapping bands, not just 20 contiguous ones.

A way to handle the matter conceptually is offered by the convolution integral. Working with the noise power density spectrum on the g scale, we convolve it with the function that we assume to approximate the characteristic of a "critical-band filter" at any point on that scale. The convolution is

$$\hat{N}'(g) = \int_{-1}^{1} \bar{N}'(g - \nu)h(\nu)\,d\nu$$

where $h(\nu)$ is the power transmission characteristic of a hypothetical critical-band filter centered at zero on a scale with the g-metric. (This scale extends in the negative direction as well as in the positive direction from zero, even though g is ordinarily limited to positive values.) $\bar{N}'(g - \nu)$ is the power density spectrum of the noise shifted by the amount ν on the g scale, and $\hat{N}'(g)$ is the smoothed power density spectrum of the noise. This treatment encounters some difficulty from end effects because of g's restriction to the interval from zero to unity, but they are not very serious because the filter bandwidth is only a small fraction of the interval.

The final step of the theory is the one relating the articulation index $\mathcal{A}$ to an articulation measure A. That step simply appropriates and smoothes or idealizes the empirical functions that have been obtained for nonsense syllables, words, sentences, etc. We may call the general function, which has different forms for different measures and even for different sets of listeners, $X(\mathcal{A})$, so that the central tendency of the measure A is $\bar{A} = X(\mathcal{A})$.

The articulation measure A is the score of a listener on an articulation test. There are n test words, drawn at random (except for a few constraints) from a master set Ω. The words on the talker's list are $w_1, w_2, \ldots w_j, \ldots w_n$. The listener hears them more or less clearly, depending upon the test conditions, and writes down $W_1, W_2, \ldots W_j, \ldots W_n$. The score is the fraction of the latter that are correct, that is, $w_j \equiv W_j$. Usually the scores of several tests with several talkers and listeners are averaged to provide a stable empirical measure of intelligibility.

The variables of the theory of intelligibility. In the theory of intelligibility, we have met the following variables:

1. *Systematic independent variables*

f	Frequency.
$\Phi(f)$	Power density spectrum of speech at the listener's ear.
$N(f)$	Power density spectrum of noise at the listener's ear.
j	An index.

n	The number of items (e.g., words) on an articulation (intelligibility) test, or the number of bands into which the frequency scale is subdivided.
Ω	A set of categories, from the members of which are drawn the items of an articulation test.
w_j	The jth item on an articulation test.

2. *Systematic intervening variables*

$Y(f)$	The "importance function," which measures the contribution to intelligibility made by the speech components in a narrow band centered at f. (By analogy with probability density and power density, the intelligibility density function.)
$g(f)$	$g(f) = \int_0^f Y(\nu)\, d\nu.$
$N''(f)$	Equivalent power density spectrum of the noise inherent in the data-processing system.
$N'(f)$	$N'(f) = N(f) + N''(f).$
$\bar{\Phi}(g)$	$\int_0^{g(x_1)} \bar{\Phi}(g)dg = \int_0^{x_1} \Phi(f)\, df$; $\bar{\Phi}(g)$ is the speech power density spectrum after the change of variable from f to g.
$\bar{N}'(g)$	$\int_0^{g(x_1)} \bar{N}'(g)\, dg = \int_0^{x_1} N'(f)\, df$; $\bar{N}'(g)$ is the total noise power density spectrum after the change of variable from f to g.
$\bar{\Phi}'(g)$	$\bar{\Phi}'(g) = 16\bar{\Phi}(g).$
$R'(g)$	$R'(g) = \bar{\Phi}'(g)/\bar{N}'(g).$
$\mathcal{R}'(g)$	$\mathcal{R}'(g) = 10 \log_{10} R'(g).$
$\mathcal{A}$	$\mathcal{A} = (1/30) \int_0^1 \mathcal{R}'(g)dg.$
$X(\mathcal{A})$	The function that transforms $\mathcal{A}$ to the scale of a measure of articulation.

3. *Systematic dependent variables*

$\bar{A}$	The predicted measure of articulation, $\bar{A} = X(\mathcal{A})$.
W_j	The listener's recorded response to the jth item of the articulation test. W_j is ordinarily constrained to be a member of Ω.
Z_j	$Z_j = 1$ if $w_j \equiv W_j$; $Z_j = 0$ if $w_j \not\equiv W_j$.
A	$A = \frac{1}{n} \sum_{j=1}^{n} Z_j.$

Mode of definition. The variables of the theory of intelligibility are of two different types. The aim of the theory is to bring them together in a formula.

Among the independent variables, f, Φ, and N are stimulus variables of the kind we met in the theory of signal detection. The others, j, n, Ω, and w, on the other hand, refer to a different level of description. If the first three are variables of the microscopic level, the last four are variables of the macroscopic level. The word "turn," for example, is a single category ("type") on the macroscopic level, whereas on the microscopic level it has a different waveform and a different spectrum each time it is uttered ("token"). Note, however, that the theory of intelligibility does not go into much detail, even on the microscopic level; it deals only with longtime-average power spectra.

As in the theory of signal detection, the definitions of the variables should be thought of as assigning only formal or mathematical properties to them. In the listing just given, notes describing the identifications between systematic and empirical variables are interspersed with, and in fact preponderate over, the mathematical definitions. However, the notes are definitional only in so far as (as in the cases of the power density spectra) they serve indirectly to specify the dimensions or units of the variables.

The intervening variables are defined either in terms of operations upon independent variables or as functions that contribute to such operations. The function $X(\mathcal{A})$ serves as the main bridge of the theory, transforming $\mathcal{A}$, derived wholly from the microscopic level, to $\bar{A}$, which is supposed, if the theory works properly, to coincide with the mean of a sufficient number of As derived wholly from the macroscopic level.

Handling the two different levels of variables together may appear to be confusing empirical with systematic variables, but I think it is not. Both the microscopic and the macroscopic systems are part of the structure of the theory; both have identifications that relate them to parts of the empirical situation.

Initial evidential grounds for assumptions. The fundamental assumption of the system, of course, is that the level of intelligibility is wholly determined by those statistical properties of speech and interference that are expressed by the power density spectra. That assumption cannot be pressed very far, for it is well known that in certain extreme cases the phase pattern of the speech and the interference markedly affect intelligibility, and the phase information is not expressed in the power density spectra. Examples are (1) playing recorded speech backward, which leaves the power density spectrum unchanged but alters both the phase pattern and the intelligibility, and (2) substituting a train of infrequent, randomly spaced impulses (e.g., "sparse" static) for continuous random noise. The latter substitution may be made in such a way as to leave the power density spectrum of the interference unchanged, but—unlike the random noise—the impulsive interference has regularities in its phase pattern. They account for the temporal gaps between impulses and thus for the fact that intelligibility is greater when speech is presented against a background of irregularly spaced pulses than it is when the background is random noise of equal strength.

Another limitation of the domain of the theory is imposed by what is called remote masking. In so far as interference components in one part of the spectrum mask speech in another, widely separated part, the theory (which assumes that the interference process is confined to local intervals on the frequency scale) is bound to fall short of perfect prediction.

We must begin the discussion of the theory, therefore, with a restriction of its domain to situations in which the phase pattern of the speech is not markedly distorted, in which the phase pattern of the interference is not significantly nonrandom, and in which the power density spectrum of the noise does not slope so steeply as to make remote masking a factor.

Another qualification concerns the power density spectrum of the speech, specified at the listener's ear. It must not be so greatly distorted that the inherent intelligibility of the speech is impaired.

Within the restrictions just mentioned, we must examine the initial evidential grounds for supposing that the system would predict intelligibility. That evidence stems in part from the experimental background that prescribed the restrictions.

First, the assumed primary importance of the speech-noise ratio in a local, narrow band of frequencies is simply an application of Fletcher's [18] critical-band theory. It was based upon experiments with tonal signals. The initial application to speech was a tentative extension made with the knowledge that it would be tested experimentally.

Second, the neglect of the phase patterns, except in so far as they are covered by the restrictions we have mentioned, stems from the long history of Helmholtz's phase rule. The auditory mechanism is widely regarded as "phase deaf," and Helmholtz is usually cited as the authority. However, Helmholtz was careful to qualify his statements about auditory phase sensitivity, though not very quantitative about the qualifications. During the course of the development of the telephone system (especially the long-distance lines, which used to introduce marked phase distortion), it was noticed that, although there were audible phase effects, intelligibility was remarkably insensitive to alterations of the phase pattern of speech. In short, relative indifference to phase distortion has been demonstrated over and over in studies of speech communication, and, although even yet we have no fully quantitative treatment of the matter, neglect of phase effects is a deeply rooted habit among workers in the field of speech communication.

The remaining "initial" evidential grounds were not precisely initial. The system was developed in interaction with a program of research on speech intelligibility at the Bell Telephone Laboratories. There was undoubtedly a considerable amount of variation and selection. The system evolved. The experimental antecedents of each step were in a sense initial grounds, but the essence of the development of the theory was interaction with experiment.

The experimental programs at the Bell Telephone Laboratories and, later, at the Harvard Psycho-Acoustic and Electro-Acoustic Laboratories, were organized on the two levels of the theory, macroscopic and microscopic.

On the macroscopic level, there were many articulation tests, tests with sentences, words of various numbers of syllables, "nonsense" syllables, and syllables that differed only in respect of a single phoneme. These tests were made under a great variety of experimental conditions, with communication systems having various amplitude against frequency characteristics and various noise spectra. Particularly important was a series of tests with high-pass and with low-pass filters. The importance function (intelligibility density function) was derived from the results of these tests. The linkages between systematic and empirical variables in this area are almost totally direct. We should note, however, that the linkages are direct only between the structure of the theory and the empirical situation of an articulation test. The extension of the linkages beyond the articulation test to a practical communication situation is another matter, one we must neglect in order to keep the discussion from exceeding all bounds on length. Looking back, we may see that a similar situation exists in the theory of signal detection, which would be difficult (though not impossible) to extend beyond empirical situations involving trials. The only fundamental problem is to identify a particular word recorded by a listener (a token) as a member of a particular category (a type) of the set Ω. This is in principle a very difficult procedure to handle, but in practice it is trivial, for rarely is there disagreement among scorers. In fact, the whole operation was conquered by automation in at least one instance [20].

On the microscopic level, determination of the longtime-average speech spectrum was particularly important. The empirical techniques employed in the spectrum measurements were part of the technological repertoire we mentioned in connection with linkages between systematic and empirical variables of the theory of signal detection. The linkages are quite direct and exact. Essentially the same techniques may be used in determining the noise power density spectrum. The noise, however, is usually measured in each instance of application, whereas the practice has been to use a standard speech power density function based on the several laboratory determinations.

Construction of function forms. The theory of intelligibility is, as we have seen, a particularly simple system of functions:

$$g = g(f)$$
$$\mathcal{R}'(g) = 10 \log_{10} [\bar{\Phi}'(g)/\bar{N}'(g)]$$
$$\mathcal{A} = \int_0^1 \mathcal{R}'(g)\, dg$$

and

$$\bar{A} = X(\mathcal{A})$$

The form of g was derived from several related sets of articulation data, but the significance of the form is broader than that. The function $g(f)$ is closely similar to $\int_0^f \kappa(\nu)d\nu$, the integral of Fletcher's [20] critical-band function that specifies the frequency bandwidths of the auditory channels. And $g(f)$ is also closely similar to the mel scale of subjective pitch [80, 81]. Evidently, $g(f)$ is determined largely by characteristics of the auditory system, but they are weighted by characteristics of speech. Speech appears to be anchored somewhat more to the low frequencies than is hearing, and $g(f)$ has somewhat steeper slope in the low-frequency region than do the other two functions.

The logarithmic unit, the decibel, has for years had an entrenched position in the field of communication, and quite evidently that entrenchment influenced the choice of the logarithmic function $\mathcal{R} = 10 \log_{10} R$. It is true, nevertheless, that empirical curves relating estimated articulation index[19] to speech-noise ratio in decibels may be approximated through their middle ranges by straight lines. If it were not true that curves of $\mathcal{A}$ against other functions of R are equally well approximated by straight lines, that would be good empirical basis for the selection.

The kingpin of the theory of intelligibility, however, is the assump-

[19] The articulation index $\mathcal{A}$ is estimated by entering $\bar{A} = X\mathcal{A}$ with the mean articulation score $\bar{A}$ and reading out the argument $\mathcal{A}$. $\mathcal{A}$ is here estimated by the actual scores on tests with bands of speech.

tion of additivity over frequency represented by the integral over g. This assumption appears to have considerable engineering validity even though it will almost surely not stand up under rigorous tests. The question is, does the contribution to intelligibility made by one band of speech depend upon the presence or absence of contributions from other bands? There is suggestive evidence that it does—that there is interaction among the bands that cannot be handled precisely by a theory based upon linear summation [62]. Nevertheless, it is remarkable that a simple linear formulation provides as close an approximation as it does, and it will take conclusive evidence plus a workable alternative formulation to displace the assumption of additivity of the articulation index.

Measurement of independent and dependent variables. As in the theory of signal detection, essentially no difficulties of measurement—other than difficulties inherent in the employment of complex instrumentation—beset the theory of intelligibility in the limited context of the articulation test. Power density spectra again are the basic stimulus functions to be measured. Again we shall have to accept on faith the assertion that the techniques of measuring power density spectra are under control.

We should pause, however, to question the legitimacy of using a standard power density curve as representative of "speech in general." The usual practice, mentioned earlier, is to use a standard curve for the power density of speech at a point 1 m in front of the talker's mouth in a free field (no reflectors). Engineering corrections are applied to that curve to yield the power density spectrum at the listener's ears. But this procedure fails to take into account the variations in spectrum from speaker to speaker, which are considerable, and also the variations that are caused by differences among the conditions encountered by a given speaker using a variety of communication systems or talking against various kinds of noise. Experiments have shown that the speech spectrum changes markedly as the talker raises or lowers his voice, and that the voice level depends upon the noise level and the gain of the channel through which the talker hears his own voice. In principle, therefore, it appears that the speech spectrum, as well as the noise spectrum, should be measured in the particular communication situation or situations under study.

On the microscopic level, it does not make much difference whether the setting is a practical communication situation or an articulation test. It is a little harder to isolate key test items and determine a spectrum characteristic of them than it is to take samples of the speech actually transmitted over a practical channel and analyze them. On the other hand, the noise is likely to be more homogeneous, and hence easier to measure, in the laboratory then in the practical setting. On the macroscopic level, however, extension of the theory to handle the practical situation would be difficult. The reason, of course, is that speech is usually highly redundant, its meaning spreading through several or many phonetic units. There are no convenient, discrete items to score. And the talker talks faster than the listener can write.

The practical solution to this problem has been to develop several empirical measures of intelligibility, ranging from sentences on down to "fundamental speech sounds," and to estimate the intelligibility of communication in a practical situation by substituting for the practical speech material the items of one of the kinds of articulation test. In so far as possible, the other conditions of communication are held constant.

The difficulty just mentioned has, in fact, not received much attention. It appears nevertheless to constitute an important problem, for there is little practical justification for perfecting the theory if there is to be a badly loose connection between the measure it predicts and the situation toward which attention is directed.

Formal organization of the system. The system under discussion is an engineering formula. In the interest of analysis, we have distinguished independent, intervening, and dependent variables, but in so far as actual use of the formula is concerned, it is just a guide to a series of steps of computation.

An engineering formula, supported as it is by an established body of technology, amounts essentially to a formal system. Usually, however, the presentation of the formula does not go back to truly primitive concepts. It plunges in at a fairly advanced level. As suggested in the two places where we avoided looking deep into the technical picture, it would be quite an undertaking to start with truly primitive notions and work up to the level at which the theory starts. The fact that a large amount of ground is skipped, however, does not make the system less fully quantitative. It may make the system less formal, but not in principle less fully formalizable.

Scope of the system. The system we are discussing was intended for use in connection with the design and development of speech communication equipment. Simplified (3- and 4-band) versions of it appear capable of handling some engineering problems in the control of sound in business offices, etc. On the other hand, more refined elaborations would be required to guide, for example, the selection of particularly intelligible words or of particularly interfering noises.

The present scope of the system is probably also the ultimate scope because, to take into account the additional factors that would be brought into the picture by a widening of scope, it would be necessary to supplement the power density spectra that constitute the basic microscopic descriptions of the stimulus. That would involve a fundamental change of the system.

History of interaction with research. The system was developed in interaction with research, as we have noted, and it has continued to interact with research, or at least to be challenged by empirical tests.

The predictions of articulation measures described by French and Steinberg [26] were extremely good. Predictions were made for a large assortment of telephone systems, including not only the three main series of tests of the program in connection with which the theory was developed but other, statistically independent tests as well. Examination of the graphs, said to be representative samples, indicates that the root-mean-square error of prediction was not more than 2 percentage points on the syllable articulation scale. That is only a little short of the limit on precision set by the sampling fluctuations of the articulation measures.

The measurements of speech intelligibility made at Harvard by Egan and Wiener [12, 13] during World War II afforded a second test of the system. That test led to a modification of the system—already incorporated in our description—that seems minor from one point of view and major from another. In the original formulation of French and Steinberg [26], the level of the strongest speech sounds had to be 6 db above the longtime-average noise power in order for there to be any intelligibility. Beranek's [7] analysis of the Harvard data led him to reduce the critical value to 0 db. In so far as the theoretical structure, itself, is concerned, that is not a very great change because, squeezed in one place, the structure can give in another. Except for instances in which the speech-noise ratio is right at the critical point, the 6-db shift in $\mathcal{R}'$ can be compensated for by a change in the function X relating articulation score A to articulation index $\mathcal{A}$.

The fact is, however, that the structure did not give in the other place. The curves relating word and syllable articulation to articulation index for the Bell Telephone Laboratories crews are not much different from corresponding curves for the Harvard crews. And it is almost too much to expect one group to accept a handicap of 6 db in speech-noise ratio and then to match another's performance. The fact that the Harvard tests showed fairly good agreement between the predictions of the modified theory and the experimental measurements (root-mean-square discrepancy approximately 3.5 units on the per cent articulation scale) is therefore rather overpowered by the discrepancy of 6 db between the Bell Telephone Laboratories and the Beranek formulations. Moreover, even within the Harvard tests there was a systematic deviation from predicted values. When comparisons were made between two speech communication systems with equal articulation indexes, one having high speech-noise ratio and low bandwidth and the other low speech-noise ratio and high bandwidth, the wide-band system usually turned in the better performance. The difference was not great, and it did not destroy the engineering usefulness of the theory, but it did provide food for thought. Evidence that, for a given crew and test procedure, A is not a fixed function of $\mathcal{A}$ strikes at a basic assumption of the system.

The next test of the system came from measurements by Pollack [62, 63]. He determined functions relating word articulation to the cutoff frequencies of high-pass and low-pass filters. Curves of that kind figured in the original determination of the importance function. They afford a critical test of the theory because the values of articulation index for complementary high-pass and low-pass filters (same cutoff frequency) must add to unity. One need not know the function X relating articulation score A to articulation index $\mathcal{A}$ to see whether or not a necessary consequence of the theory is checked by the data. If the score for the high-pass filter with cutoff frequency f_j is equal to the score for the low-pass filter with cutoff frequency f_k, then the score for low-pass f_j must equal the score for high-pass f_k. The only assumptions involved in that conclusion are (1) linear additivity of increments to the articulation index contributed by different frequency bands and (2) single-valuedness of the function $A = X(\mathcal{A})$. The test provided by Pollack's data did not turn out at all well for the system. In the tests in which masking and filtering were combined, the high-pass and low-pass functions did not show the kind of symmetry just described. The discrepancy was marked.

Next, Hirsh, Reynolds, and Joseph [37] made measurements that further shook the foundations of the system. They measured the intelligibilities of several kinds of speech material under masking and under filtering with high-pass and with low-pass filters. They confirmed Beranek's observation that the articulation score depends to some extent upon the shape of the region in the $\mathcal{R}$ against g plot and not upon its area alone. Perhaps even more disturbing, they found that the relations among the measured intelligibilities of the various categories of speech material were not invariant under changes of the physical treatment applied to the speech. They included in their tests nonsense syllables, monosyllabic words, dissyllables of iambic, trochaic, and spondaic stress, and words of three or more syllables.

We have been assuming that the articulation score for each category of speech material had its own fixed relation to articulation index $\mathcal{A}$. If that is a valid assumption, each of the word articulation measures should of course be a fixed function of the nonsense syllable articulation measure. But when Hirsh, Reynolds, and Joseph plotted their word scores against their nonsense syllable scores, they found that they had to draw separate curves not only for the various categories (numbers of syllables) but also, within each category, for filtering and masking. In the neighborhood of 50 per cent word articulation, the word articulation scores of the masking tests were 10 to 20 percentage points lower than the word articulation scores of filter tests that yielded the same values of nonsense syllable articulation. This may be interpreted as indicating that masking destroys contextual cues more than filtering does. On the other hand, it seems possible that the results for masking might be brought into line with those for filtering if an intensive search were made for a favorable way of averaging the speech power over time. In order to plot word articulation scores against corresponding syllable articulation scores, it is necessary—in the case of masking but not in the case of filtering—to be able to say when a single syllable is equal in intensity to a multisyllabic word. That judgment obviously depends upon how the measurements are made (rule of time averaging, etc.). We might argue that one cannot conclude that the masking and filtering results do not agree until one has demonstrated that they are not brought into agreement by any reasonable rule for specifying the speech intensities.

Putting together the findings of Pollack and of Hirsh, Reynolds, and Joseph may provide some consolation for supporters of the theory. The data that led to the conclusion that short fat regions in the plane of $\mathcal{R}'$ against g yield higher scores than tall thin regions of equal area came from nonsense syllable tests. We have seen that, for constant nonsense syllable score, filtering (which yields tall thin regions) leads to higher word articulation scores than does masking (which yields short fat regions). Evidently, if we are more interested in speech material in context than we are in nonsense syllables, we may not find the theory in such bad trouble after all. Unfortunately, since their main point concerned the lack of invariance in the relations among various measures of intelligibility, Hirsh, Reynolds, and Joseph gave only a qualitative description of their work with the articulation index. We cannot tell how evenly the opposing factors balance.

Whether or not we consider the theory to have withstood the tests described thus far, we are likely to conclude that it is in trouble as a result of measurements made by Pickett and Kryter [44, 45, 46, 61]. They determined the intelligibility of monosyllabic words at various speech-noise ratios in the presence of four different noises. The power density spectra of the noises had markedly different shapes, rising, constant, falling, and steeply falling with increasing frequency. Pickett and Kryter calculated the articulation index for each of the test conditions, using both French and Steinberg's formula and Beranek's formula. Then they plotted the articulation scores against the articulation indexes. If everything were as predicted by the theory, all the points in a plot would fall along one curve, $A = X(\mathcal{A})$, except for sampling fluctuations. Instead of that, there were clearly four curves, one for each of the noises. There was the expected difference between the plots based on French and Steinberg's formula and the plots based on Beranek's formula, but in both, the datum points fell along four separate curves, as described. The extreme discrepancy was 40 or 50 percentage points, which is a very considerable amount. Kryter is being very cautious, however, in interpreting the discrepancy. He has undertaken a new and more exhaustive series of tests, using nonsense syllables, and he is hesitant to conclude that the formulas have been shown to be inaccurate.

In the next and final test [52] of the theory, an effort was made to get maximum leverage on the question, whether or not equal areas in the plane of $\mathcal{R}'$ against g correspond to equal articulation scores. The tests used monosyllabic words. The speech was masked by interference consisting of various numbers of superposed sinusoids, i.e., various numbers of pure tones added together and then added to the speech wave at various ratios of over-all speech power to over-all interference power. The frequencies of the n sinusoids were chosen in such a way that, for each value of n, there was a sinusoid in the center of each of n bands of equal contribution to intelligibility. The tones were spaced at equal intervals on the g-scale. The over-all speech-interference ratio required to yield 50 per cent articulation was determined as a function of n. For values of n between 4 and 32, the required speech-interference ratio rose at a rate of 3 db per doubling of n. Beyond $n = 64$, the curve leveled out. Evidently, therefore, the critical bandwidth of the auditory system for speech reception is in the neighborhood of $1/32$ to $1/64$ on the g scale. When the interfering tones are spaced at intervals wider than one critical bandwidth, it is evident that changing their number n and then making compensating adjustments of the over-all speech-interference ratio is a direct way of determining the metric of the intensive scale that the theory assumes to be logarithmic. The test results suggest that the metric is not logarithmic—that it is linear in $(\Phi/N)^{1/2}$, which is the ratio of the root-mean-square speech and interference sound pressures.[20] This applies only to values of $(\Phi/N)^{1/2}$ for which the word articulation scores are about 50 per cent; the metric was not determined accurately in other regions.

On the basis of the evidence offered by the several tests, we must conclude that the system has troubles. If the aspiration level is not allowed to run too high, these troubles are not overpowering. They only restrict the scope of the system and/or increase the tolerances that must be allowed for the predictions. The system is, nevertheless, useful as a guide to preliminary design of speech communication equipment. In the development of the present intercommunication system for military aircraft, and in other similar programs, the computational procedure was used extensively and with good effect by the Radio Corporation of America [34]. On the other hand, it appears that the difficulties may be quite fundamental and that what constitutes a fair engineering approximation may not constitute a fair model for those whose interest is to understand the process of hearing.

The future of the system. Probably the future of the system will depend upon a reexamination of its basic assumptions. The early tests served mainly to measure the precision of predictions, not to diagnose difficulties. If the recent trend is followed, however, we shall have tests aimed directly at the appropriateness of the frequency transformation $g(f)$, or of the logarithmic metric of the scale of speech-noise ratio, or of the linear additivity of increments of the articulation index.

At the same time, we shall probably see efforts to extend the scope of the system, or of a competitive system, to include not entirely random interferences such as impulsive noise. In any event, there will have to be a sharpening of the boundaries of the zone of applicability of the system.

THEORY OF PITCH PERCEPTION

The specific theory of pitch perception that we shall examine is a recent "triplex" [51] extension of the "duplex" theory [48] I de-

[20] The reasoning is as follows: For constant articulation, and, therefore, constant articulation index, the ratio of over-all speech power to over-all interference power increases linearly with n. The over-all interference power required therefore *decreases* linearly with n, and the power per sinusoid decreases as n^2. Thus if we use twice as many components, we can reduce each to one-quarter its former power, or to one-half its former root-mean-square pressure. We trade width on an equal basis for height (constant area yields constant articulation) if the width metric is that of the g scale and the height metric is that of $(\Phi/N)^{1/2}$.

scribed a few years ago. It is called "triplex" because it tries to account for three different ways in which subjective pitch can arise from acoustic stimulation. Part of it, the part concerning the mechanical action of the cochlea, is hardly theory, for it is a direct appropriation of the empirical description provided by Békésy [6]. The remainder makes up for this anchoring in fact by being perhaps overly speculative.

Summary of the theory. The triplex theory assumes that the acoustic patterns delivered to the two ears are subjected to mechanical

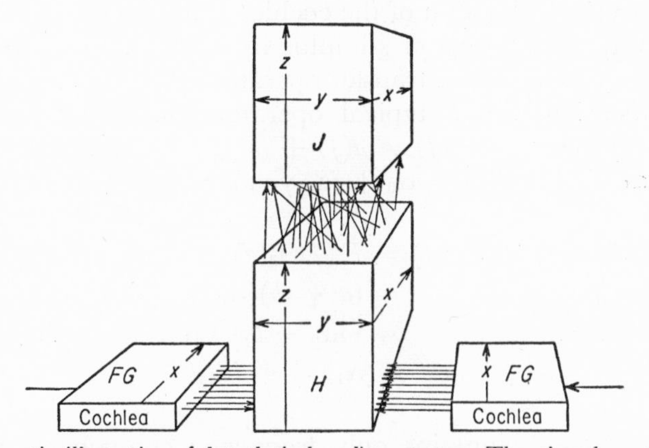

FIG. 5. *Schematic illustration of hypothetical auditory system.* The signals enter the two cochleas. The cochlear frequency analysis (F transformation) maps stimulus frequency into the spatial dimension x, and the ordinal relations along x are preserved in the excitation of the neurons of the auditory nerve (operation G). The time-domain analyzer H preserves the order in x but adds an analysis in the y dimension, based mainly on interaural time differences, and an analysis in the z dimension, based on periodicities in the wave envelope received from FG. In the projection from H to J, the x analysis is largely preserved, but each point in any frontal plane of H is, initially, connected to every point in the corresponding frontal plane of J. The H-J transformation organizes itself, according to rules imposed by the dynamics of the neuronal network, under the influence of acoustic stimulation. The patterns in J thereby acquire the properties that are reflected in pitch perception.

frequency analysis in the cochleas and that the products of that analysis are then subjected to a twofold coincidence or correlation analysis in unspecified centers of the nervous system. The first coincidence analysis in a sense correlates the signals from the two ears and mediates sound localization in phenomenal space. The second coincidence analysis, through a process called autocorrelation, exposes periodicities that may have appeared only in the envelope,[21] and not

[21] The envelope $\vartheta(t)$ is defined for narrow-band signals of the form $\vartheta(t)$ cos $[2\pi ft + \phi(t)]$. $\vartheta(t)$ is real and single-valued, a smooth function of time that bounds the oscillations.

necessarily in the waveform per se, of the acoustic stimuli. The theory includes a third step, not entirely essential but perhaps helpful in bringing the "neural" picture into a greater degree of isomorphism with subjective experience. The basic operation of this third step is ascribed to a selforganizing neuronal network.

The triplex theory can be outlined in terms of operations upon functions of stimulus variables. A block diagram is shown in Fig. 5. Let us start with the waveforms presented to the two ears. We may call them[22] $\theta_{0r}(t)$ and $\theta_{0l}(t)$.

The mechanical action of the cochlea is assumed to be linear over a reasonably wide range of stimulus intensities and to be governed by a system F of complex transfer operators, one for each point along the x dimension. Let a typical operator, characteristic of point j along x, be $F(\mathrm{x},f) = F_j(f) = a(f) + ib(f) = a + ib$. Applying it to $\Theta_0(f) = \alpha_0(f) + i\beta_0(f) = \alpha_0 + i\beta_0$ yields[23]

$$\begin{aligned} \Theta_1(\mathrm{x}, f) = \Theta_{1j}(f) &= F_j(f)\Theta_0(f) \\ &= (a + ib)(\alpha_0 + i\beta_0) \\ &= (a\alpha_0 - b\beta_0) + i(a\beta_0 + b\alpha_0) \\ &= \alpha_{1j}(f) + i\beta_{1j}(f) \end{aligned}$$

Evidently, $\Theta_1(\mathrm{x},f)$ contains only frequency components present in $\Theta_0(f)$. The amplitudes of those components have been affected selectively, and the components outside the particular frequency band that is appropriate to j are greatly reduced in amplitude. Also, the phases of the components have been shifted.

The relative amplitude coefficients and phase shifts for several points in the actual cochlea are shown in Fig. 6. The triplex theory simply accepts Békésy's [6] data as defining the set of transformations F. We may think of F as the operation of passing $\theta_0(t)$ through a large set of bandpass filters, one for each point of x, specified by curves such as Békésy's. To make the filter analogy appropriate, we should

[22] The numerical subscript will designate the level of the auditory system to which the signal belongs. The 0-level is external to the auditory system—the stimulus level. Letter subscripts will refer to positions along the spatial dimensions of the hypothetical mechanism. The letter subscripts j, k, and l will be paired with the spatial dimensions x, y, and z, respectively. As an alternative to using subscripts, we shall in some places use a notation in which italic x, y, z, and t are variables and roman x, y, z, and t have fixed values. Thus, $\mathrm{x} = x_j$, $\mathrm{y} = y_k$, $\mathrm{z} = z_l$. The roman subscripts r and l designate "right" and "left."

[23] $\Theta_0(f)$ is the spectrum, the Fourier transform mentioned earlier, of $\theta_0(t)$. For the moment we shall drop the subscripts r and l, since we shall be considering only one cochlea.

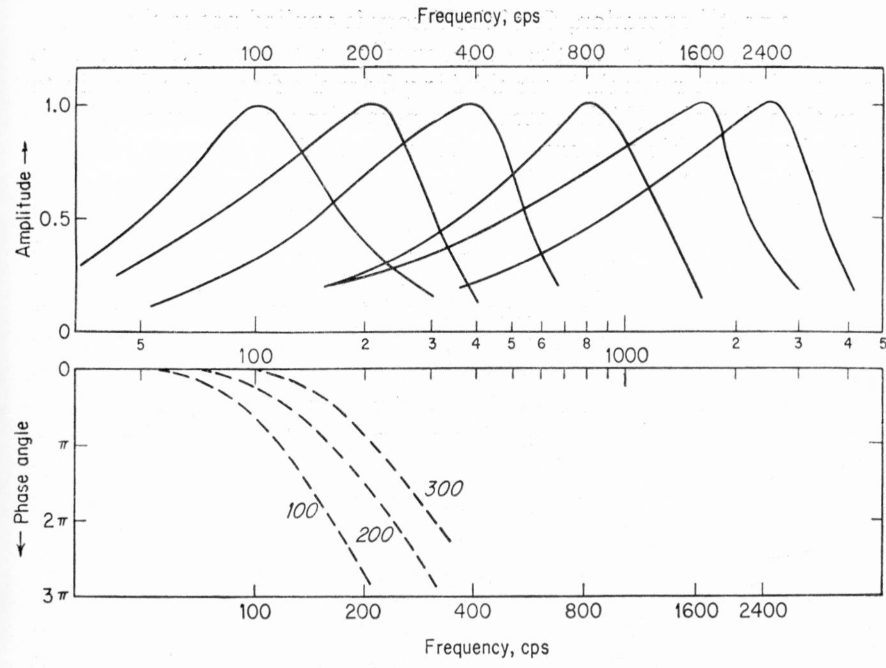

FIG. 6. *Curves defining the filtering operation F.* The amplitude against frequency and phase against frequency curves describe the mechanical (hydrodynamic) frequency analysis performed by the cochlea. They were determined by Békésy. Each upper curve shows the relative amplitude of vibration of a point on the cochlear partition as the stapes (input member) of the cochlea is driven sinusoidally at various frequencies with constant rms displacement. The six curves are for points "tuned" to 100, 200, 400, 800, 1,600, and 2,400 cycles per second. Unfortunately, no phase angle curves were obtained for that series of points, but Békésy did measure (relative to the phase angle at the stapes) the phase angle of the oscillation at 50, 100, 200, and 300 cycles per second as a function of distance from the stapes. The lower curves are a replot of the latter measurements. The amplitude curves with which the phase curves were paired were approximately equal in bandwidth to the corresponding amplitude curves shown here. To obtain roughly approximate phase curves for the other locations on the cochlear partition, one may assume that the phase shift is π radians at the resonance frequency and that the curves are shifted horizontally along the logarithmic frequency scale.

think of the many filters as connected one after another in cascade to form a transmission line with an input at one end and output taps distributed along its length. The transfer operator $F(\mathrm{x},f) = F_j(f)$ then operates upon the input $\Theta_0(f)$ to produce the output $\Theta_1(\mathrm{x},f) = \Theta_{1j}(f)$ at the jth output tap, which is x units of distance down the line from the input. Other transfer operators act in similar ways to produce outputs at other taps. We can symbolize the over-all transformation as $\Theta_0(f)F(x,f) = \Theta_1(x,f)$.

The next[24] operation, G, of the theory is applied not to the filtered spectra $\Theta_1(x,f)$, but to the corresponding waveforms $\theta_1(x,t)$. This means that we must shift our thinking from the frequency domain to the time domain. (If that seems too much for a theory to require, it may be preferable to transform the operators F into the time domain and let them operate on $\theta_0(t)$. The description of F in the frequency domain was chosen to make direct connection with Békésy's curves.) The operation G can be described in the following way. At each point along x, the wave $\theta_1(\mathrm{x},t)$ is subjected to rectification, the effect of which is to convert the first line of Fig. 7 to the second. The rectification is illustrated as simply clipping off the negative swings of the oscillations. That is an oversimplification but, for the present purposes, a sufficient approximation. After it is rectified, the wave is smoothed by the operation of a "low-pass filter." The smoothed wave, $\theta_2(\mathrm{x},t)$, is shown in the third line of Fig. 7. The wave $\theta_2(\mathrm{x},t)$ is the function that controls the excitation of the auditory neurons at x (i.e., at the jth point on the x dimension of the basilar membrane).

As we enter the nervous system, we must start to distinguish carefully between microscopic and macroscopic levels of description. On the microscopic level, we see individual neurons and their impulses. On the macroscopic level, we see only a level of nervous activity or a local neural flux, which is the sum over a considerable number of neurons, and the integral over a short interval of time, of the discharges of the individual neurons. It will greatly simplify the notation to let the meaning of the spatial coordinates and indexes change a bit as we shift from one level of examination to the other. $\mathcal{G}(\mathrm{x,y,z},t) = \mathcal{G}_{jkl}(t)$ will represent the train of impulses of an individual neuron at the point $(\mathrm{x,y,z}) = (x_j,y_j,z_j)$. At the same time $I(\mathrm{x,y,z},t) = I_{jkl}(t)$ will represent the neural flux in a small region centered upon $(\mathrm{x,y,z}) = (x_j,y_k,z_j)$. If only the x dimension is under discussion, the y and the z will be dropped.

When the excitatory function $\theta_2(\mathrm{x},t)$ is applied to a single neuron, the timing of the impulses that result is dependent upon the interaction of $\theta_2(\mathrm{x},t)$ with the recovery curve $\mu(T)$ of the neuron. The latter specifies the threshold μ of the neuron as a function of time T after firing. It goes to infinity at the instant of discharge and remains there through the short absolutely refractory period, then decreases to the quiescent threshold. It may dip below the quiescent threshold before settling down upon it. The successive recoveries of a hypothetical neuron are shown in line 4 of Fig. 7. The excitation curve is

[24] It is possible that a "sharpening" operation follows immediately after F (before G) and serves in effect to decrease the bandwidths of the cochlear filters. The theory is at present neutral on that point. We shall pass it by for the sake of simplicity.

repeated (dashed) from line 3. Each time $\theta_2(x,t)$ exceeds the threshold curve, the neuron discharges and the recovery cycle begins anew. The impulses are represented schematically in line 5. Impulses of other neurons with similar (but slightly different) recovery curves are shown in lines 6, 7, and 8. The function $I_3(x,t)$ in line 9 is the

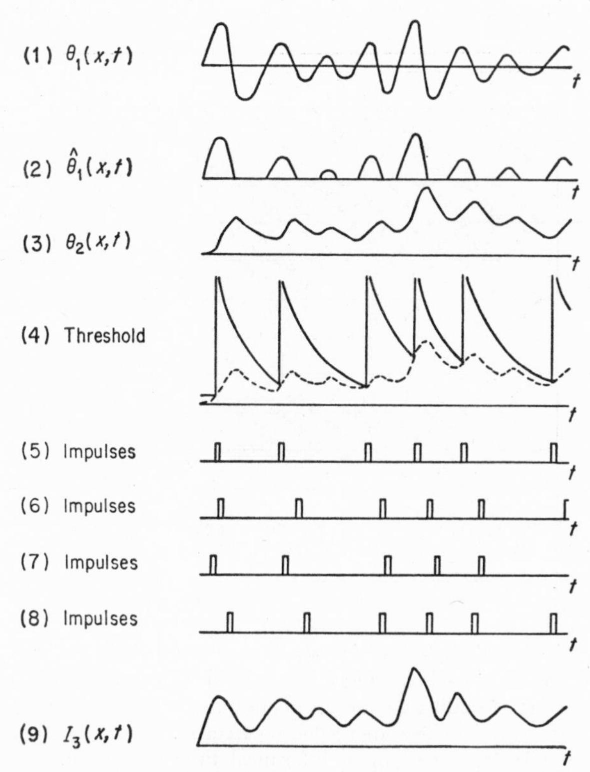

FIG. 7. *Schematic illustration of operation G and formation of the function* $I_3(x,t)$. (1) Stimulus waveform; (2) wave derived by rectification of stimulus; (3) wave derived by smoothing rectified stimulus in a low-pass filter; (4) interaction of the recovery curve of an individual neuron with the rectified and smoothed stimulus waveform, yielding the threshold of the neuron as a function of time; (5) discharges of the neuron; (6,7,8) discharges of neighboring neurons; (9) sum of impulse curves of many neighboring neurons.

smoothed sum of the impulse trains of a fairly large number of neurons such as those of lines 5 through 8.

Note that $I_3(x,t)$ approximates $\theta_2(x,t)$, which in turn is somewhat similar to $\theta_1(x,t)$. Evidently, $I_3(x,t)$ reflects both actual waveform and envelope characteristics of $\theta_1(x,t)$. When the oscillations of $\theta_1(x,t)$ are slow, $I_3(x,t)$ provides information about the timing, as well as the amplitudes, of the individual cycles. When the oscillations of $\theta_1(x,t)$

are fast, the process that produces $I_3(x,t)$—though it does not entirely obscure them—tends to smooth out the oscillations and to reflect mainly the envelope amplitude of $\theta_1(x,t)$. This is the principle of the volley mechanism [92–94], the basis of the representation in neural time domain of stimulus phase and periodicity. The point that is rarely made is that the mechanism is sensitive to both the waveforms

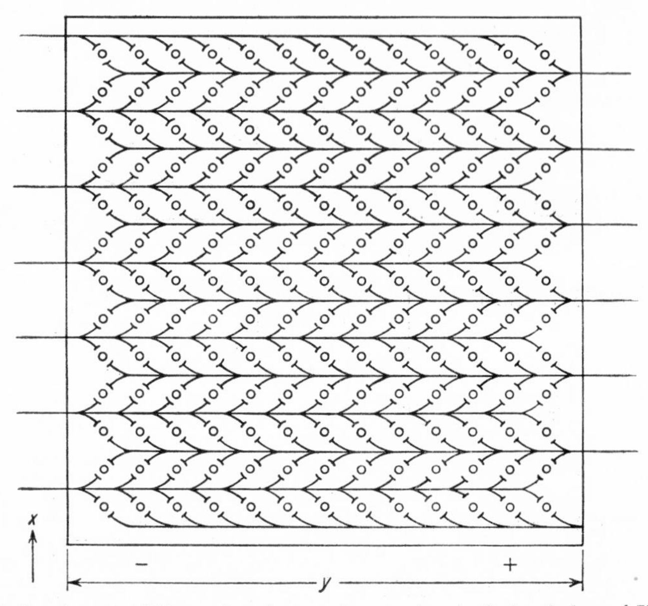

FIG. 8. *Highly schematized illustration of neuronal connections in the basal plane of H.* Neurons enter from left and right cochleas and make synaptic connections with the cell bodies (circles) of neurons ascending in the z dimension of Fig. 5. Temporally coinciding excitations are required to fire an ascending neuron. The y location of ascending activity therefore is dependent upon interaural time difference. This scheme was proposed independently by Wallach [91] and Jeffress [42.]

and the wave envelopes of the oscillatory outputs of the cochlear analyzer.

At the level of the auditory nerve, then, the signal consists (microscopically) of the set of binary time functions $\mathcal{G}_{3j}(t) = \mathcal{G}_3(x,t)$, one of them for each of about 25,000 neurons per nerve, or (macroscopically) of a continuum along the x dimension of smooth time functions $I_3(x,t)$.

It is probable that the next operation in the auditory sequence involves sharpening, but we shall neglect it in hope of keeping the complexity of the story from exceeding all bounds. Let us assume that the signals of the two auditory nerves, or of the second or higher levels of the auditory pathways, are delivered to a space of three dimensions, x, y, and z. The arrangement is shown schematically in Fig. 8. The x dimension is simply an ordinal projection of the cochlear x dimension. In the y dimension, the behavior is that described by Jeffress [42] and Wallach [91] in their place theories of sound localization. The neural signals are kept in their x channels, and corresponding right and left x channels pass each other as they cross the base of block H. The base of block H of Fig. 5 is shown (schematically) in greater detail in Fig. 8. It takes a short time for an impulse to travel across the y dimension. There are many vertically oriented neurons arising from the base plane in H. Whenever impulses meet in adjacent, oppositely directed neurons in the base, the coincidence[25] leads to the firing of a neuron oriented in the z direction. The effect of this coincidence mechanism is to focus activity within the vertical plane midway across the y dimension if the stimulation is the same at both the ears, $\theta_{0r}(t) = \theta_{0l}(t)$. If one ear leads the other, however, the plane of activity is shifted toward the leading ear. If

$$\theta_{0r}(t) = \theta_{0l}(t + T)$$

the active x-z plane of H is the one for which the value of y ($y = 0$ at the midline and increases positively to the right) is $y = vT/2$, v being the velocity of propagation in the y direction. To help ourselves keep track of the signals, we should give a designation to the pattern in the base of block H in Fig. 5. Let us call it $\mathcal{G}_4(x,y,t)$.

Each small circle in Fig. 8 represents the cell body of a neuron that projects upward and forms part of a "neuronal autocorrelator." One such neuron and the other neurons to which it is connected are shown in Fig. 9. The heavy neuron (the one whose cell body is a small circle in Fig. 8) is a "straight through" neuron. Associated with it is a slowly conducting process or (as shown) a chain of neurons that transmits the same sequence of impulses as the straight through neuron, but with a delay τ that increases progressively as the impulses rise through H. For the sake of simplicity, we may assume that τ is proportional to z, and that $z = 0$ is the base plane of H in Fig. 5 and at the bottom of Fig. 9. At many points, the straight through neuron and the delay chain neurons make synaptic connection with neurons that have cell bodies in H and axon terminals in J. We assume that

[25] The geometrical regularity in Fig. 8 is a concession to simplicity. Actually, the neurons of the two oppositely directed sets thread past each other in an arrangement that, on the microscopic level, is random or haphazard. It is, therefore, possible for coincidences between impulses *flowing in the same direction* to produce discharges in the ascending neurons. We assume that some ascending impulses are set up in this way, but that more are produced by coincidences between impulses in oppositely directed neurons.

approximate temporal coincidence of impulses in the two incoming fibers is necessary to produce a discharge of the *H-J* neuron.

It is of interest now to focus attention on a number of *H-J* neurons in the same macroscopic region of *H* and to deduce the activity of the group from the activities of the individuals. The latter fire, we have assumed, whenever there is a temporal coincidence of impulses in the straight through and the delay chain neurons with which they are connected. The probability of a discharge in a particular *H-J* neuron is therefore the probability of a coincidence, which in turn is the product of the two probabilities of discharge, one for the straight through neuron and the other for the delay chain neuron. The probability for the straight through neuron we may assume to be proportional to the intensity $I_4(x,y,t)$. The probability for the delay chain neuron is therefore proportional to $I_4(x, y, t - \tau)$, where τ is the relative time delay at the level of z. The probability of discharge in a particular individual *H-J* neuron is therefore proportional to $I_4(x,y,t) \cdot I_4(x, y, t - \tau)$.

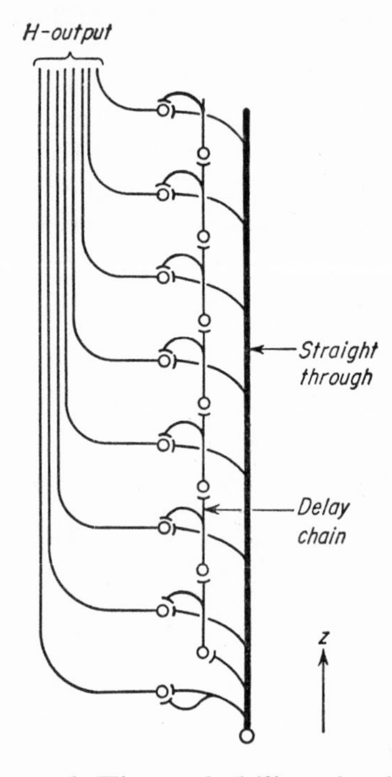

FIG. 9. *Schematic illustration of neuronal autocorrelator.* The straight through neuron is one of the ascending neurons in block *H* of which the cell bodies are shown as circles in Fig. 8. With each straight through neuron is associated a number of delay chain neurons and a number of *H*-output (or *H-J*) neurons. Several or many such networks operate simultaneously and in parallel on inputs that differ only in "microscopic" detail. From the assumption that, for an *H*-input neuron to fire, both fibers impinging upon it must fire within a short interval of temporal integration, it follows that the level of neural flux, regarded as a function jointly of time t and of the spatial coordinate z (which represents time delay τ), is approximately the running autocorrelation function of the macroscopic input. A fuller explanation is given in the text.

To find the function $I_5(x,y,z,t)$ that describes the group of *H-J* neurons that are at or very near the point (x, y, and z), we integrate over an interval of time and over the group of *H-J* neurons. We find that

$$I_5(x,y,z,t) = k \int_{T=-\infty}^{t} I_4(x,y,T) \cdot I_4(x, y, T - \tau) \, dT$$

In the left-hand side, we have called the third variable z instead of τ, since the timelike τ is now represented by the spatial z.

$I_5(x,y,z,t)$ is a running autocorrelation function. It provides a periodicity analysis of the signal $I_4(x,y,t)$. This analysis reveals envelope periodicities as well as periodicities of the original waveform $\theta_0(t)$. As we noted earlier, the envelope properties were introduced into I_3 by the nonlinearity of the neural excitation process. It is important to note that the neural excitation process G follows the mechanical analysis F of the cochlea. The autocorrelational mechanism gets the envelope properties out of the time domain into the place domain.

One phase of the analysis just described must be examined further. It has to do with the fusion—or with the failure to fuse—of the signals from the two ears. If the two patterns entering block H (Fig. 5) are sufficiently simple and similar—as patterns produced by sound reaching the two ears from a single source—activity set up in block H is confined to a single vertical sheet of tissue. The excitations from right and left interact to produce a single, coherent result. On the other hand, if one sound is applied to the right ear and a wholly dissimilar sound is applied to the left, the conditions for orderly reinforcement through right-left coincidence are not met. The signal $I_{3r}(x,t)$ from the right ear, therefore, effects excitation of ascending neurons mainly at the right-hand side of the block, and the signal $I_{3l}(x,t)$ from the left ear effects excitation mainly at the left-hand side of the block. Such patterns are functionally separate and distinct from patterns nearer the middle of the block, patterns produced in large part by coincidences between pulses in the two streams of impulses flowing in opposite directions.

At the output of H (i.e., in the cell bodies and fibers of the H-J neurons), then, we have a time-varying representation in three spatial dimensions of the pair of stimulus waves $\theta_{0r}(t)$ and $\theta_{0l}(t)$. The patterns $I_5(x,y,z,t)$ that correspond to various familiar stimuli could be sketched, but we do not have time now to consider them in detail. The one property that we need to note is that temporally periodic signals produce patterns that are spatially periodic in the z dimension. There is no harm in having such periodicity, but the triplex theory proceeds one more step, and thereby brings the several strata of a periodic pattern together in one place.

The mechanism of this reorganization starts out as a "random each-to-every network" which effects the reorganizing by organizing itself under the influence of stimulation. Assume that each point of H

in Fig. 5 projects[26] to every point of *J*, that a neuron of *J* is excited by coincidences of impulses from two or more of the *H-J* neurons that impinge upon it, and that there is some temporal and spatial spread of excitation. The latter leaves a residual activity in neighboring tissue after a particular pattern of external stimulation subsides. Assume, also, that the synaptic connection between neuron *A* and neuron *B* is strengthened whenever *A* participates in firing *B*, weakened whenever *A* fires but *B* does not.[27] How would *J* behave after the auditory system had been stimulated repeatedly by speech, music, noise, and other familiar sounds?

There is no evident way of handling that question surely other than to construct an analogue and watch it perform. Nevertheless, it seems not too difficult to intuit some parts of the answer. At first, before there is any organization, the whole of *J* is set into greater or less activity by excitation from any part of *H*. The maxima of activity in *J* are scattered haphazardly. Any *H* pattern is randomized or homogenized by the time it reaches *J*. Under the influence of the to some extent orderly stimulation provided by the acoustic environment, however, a correspondingly orderly *H-J* transformation begins to develop. First, the temporal-spatial spread of excitation that we assumed as one of the properties of the tissue favors the location side-by-side of maxima of activity produced by stimuli that frequently occur in close succession. Inasmuch as glissandos are probably the most frequent orderly variations of stimulation, an ordinal[28] representation of stimulus frequency arises. On the framework thus provided, the regular patterns of harmony (in music) and harmonics (in all periodic sounds except pure tones) set up common foci for integral multiples of a given frequency. In this process, the periodically spaced strata of *H* collapse into common foci.

As the *H-J* transformation organizes itself, it becomes a transformation from patterns to points. Each often-repeated pattern in *H* excites most vigorous activity at a particular locus in *J*, but it excites other points, also, to lesser degree. These less strongly excited loci correspond to other patterns of *H* that have common spatial elements

[26] To refine this assumption, we should introduce a constraint upon the randomness corresponding to considerable orderliness in the projection of the *x* dimension. We should say that each point in or near a given *y-z* plane of *H* is connected to every point in or near the corresponding *y-z* plane of *J*.

[27] These assumptions largely parallel those of Hebb's [35, 64] theory of neural organization.

[28] Actually, physical distance in the tissue would provide a metric, and one might argue reasonably that the word *ordinal* is inappropriate, that an interval pitch scale based in a statistical way upon recurrent patterns of auditory stimulation should result.

or that have often been stimulated in close succession. This provides a neural correlate for similarity in which both association and possession of common elements play roles.

The basic condition for the emergence of clear subjective pitch is the activation of an isolated focus of tissue in J. The height Π of the pitch depends upon the location of the focus. The definiteness of the pitch depends upon the degree of isolation, upon the remoteness of the active focus from other active tissue, upon the gradient of the distribution of activity. These characteristics of the patterns of neural activity in J—patterns we may call $I_6(x,y,z,t)$—are related to timbre Υ. Evidently, pitch has to do with the central tendency, timbre with other distribution parameters, of $I_6(x,y,z,t)$. Loudness Λ is assumed to be related to the quantity I_6. Clearly, complex patterns may have several different "loudnesses": There may be an over-all loudness (a triple integral over the entire extents of x, y, and z); there may be almost separate loudnesses for isolated patches of active tissue. Other subjective attributes fit easily into the picture. As we have noted, however, they are *functions* of $I_6(x,y,z,t)$, and not *parts* of it. They do not reside *in* the model as thus far elaborated.

The variables of the theory of pitch perception. In the theory just outlined, we encountered stimulus waveforms and spectra, the waveforms and spectra of mechanical vibrations in the "cochlea," and then a succession of functions describing "neural" activity. The link between the neural activity and the listener's overt response was not formally developed. We shall follow the practice of the earlier sections of the chapter and list the variables under the three headings, giving names to two output variables for the sake of consistency.

1. *Systematic independent variables*

t	Time.
$\theta_0(t)$	Stimulus waveform.
$\Theta_0(f)$	Stimulus spectrum.
r, l	Subscripts denoting right (ear) and left (ear), respectively.

2. *Systematic intervening variables*

x, y, z	Spatial dimensions of the conceptual cochlea and nervous system: x is the dimension into which stimulus frequency is transformed by the mechanical action of the cochlea; y and z are neural dimensions functionally orthogonal to x.

j, k, l	Indexes associated with x, y, and z, respectively.
$\theta_1(\mathrm{x},t) \equiv \theta_{1j}(t)$	Waveform of mechanical vibration in the cochlea at $\mathrm{x} = x_j$.
F	The set of cochlear mechanical transfer characteristics.
$F(\mathrm{x},f) \equiv F_j(f)$	The complex frequency response characteristic of the cochlear filter action between the input and point $\mathrm{x} = x_j$.
$\Theta_1(\mathrm{x},f) \equiv \Theta_{1j}(f)$	Spectrum of mechanical vibration in the cochlea at $\mathrm{x} = x_j$.
$\theta_2(\mathrm{x},t) \equiv \theta_{2j}(t)$	The waveform of the excitation applied to the neurons at $\mathrm{x} = x_j$ on the basilar membrane.
G	The set of transformations inherent in the link between mechanical vibration at various points in the cochlea and excitation of neurons with the same x coordinates.
$\mathcal{g}_3(\mathrm{x},t) \equiv \mathcal{g}_{3j}(t)$	The train (time function) of nerve impulses at $\mathrm{x} = x_j$ in the auditory nerve or its projection to H.
H	The set of transformations effected by the two coincidence analyses. Alternatively, the region in which the coincidence analyses take place.
$\mathcal{g}_4(\mathrm{x},\mathrm{y},t) \equiv \mathcal{g}_{4jk}(t)$	The train of nerve impulses at $\mathrm{x} = x_j$, $\mathrm{y} = y_k$, and $z = 0$ in H.
$\mathcal{g}_5(\mathrm{x},\mathrm{y},\mathrm{z},t) \equiv \mathcal{g}_{5jkl}(t)$	The train of nerve impulses at $\mathrm{x} = x_j$, $\mathrm{y} = y_k$, and $\mathrm{z} = z_l$ in H.
J	The region in which the neurons of the each-to-every network terminate.
$\mathcal{g}_6(\mathrm{x},\mathrm{y},\mathrm{z},t) = \mathcal{g}_{6jkl}(t)$	The train of nerve impulses at $\mathrm{x} = x_j$, $\mathrm{y} = y_k$, $\mathrm{z} = z_l$ in J.
$I(\mathrm{x},\mathrm{y},\mathrm{z},t) \equiv I_{jkl}(t)$	A temporally smoothed space integral of the neural activity in the vicinity of $\mathrm{x} = x_j$, $\mathrm{y} = y_k$, $\mathrm{z} = z_l$ of the tissue denoted by the numerical subscript (not shown).
T	A temporal variable, used to represent time delay or time after a particular event.
$\mu(T)$	Threshold recovery function for a neuron.
v	Velocity of propagation of activity in neural tissue.
τ	A temporal variable, used to represent time delay.

Π	Subjective pitch ("height" of the pitch).
Υ	Subjective timbre.
Λ	Subjective loudness.

3. *Systematic dependent variables*

Ω	A discrete response variable or set of response categories.
Ψ	A continuous response variable.

Mode of definition. In so far as the theoretical structure—the model without its linkages to actual situations—is concerned, the definitions of variables in the theory of pitch perception are quite as abstract as those of the other theories. Formally, the variables have definite mathematical properties, and that is all.

On the stimulus side, the variables are largely the same as the microscopic variables of the other two theories. Although there are none, there is room for macroscopic variables. Generators of complex patterns of sound—noises, musical instruments, even laboratory apparatus—could be handled under that heading. A need for treatment on the macroscopic level appears to exist in the discussion of the self-organization of the each-to-every network, for assumptions concerning the patterns of stimulation applied to the auditory system would have to be made to put the theory into closed form.

The "spatial" intervening variables x, y, and z provide, in conjunction with t (which is assumed to be the same as the independent variable t), a physical space-time in which mechanical and neural processes are assumed to function. There is, of course, no commitment, in the theoretical structure, to any actual location for the spatial dimensions or era for the temporal one. But the intention is of course to appropriate to the theory the familiar physical model that we habitually associate with our actual environment. We do this so naturally that the distinction seems unimportant and, in the present application, probably is.

The intervening variables assigned the symbols θ, Θ, ϑ, and I are defined as functions of the spatial and temporal variables and are therefore localized to one or another of the hierarchy of regions assumed in the theory. The subjective attributes, on the other hand, are essentially "homeless." We may assume that pitch Π and loudness Λ have the properties associated with ratio scales. Timbre Υ is an unanalyzed complex, and all we assume about it is that it is multidimensional.

The output variables Ω and Ψ are included mainly to point up the incompleteness of the theory. They are defined so broadly that one or the other can be identified with any overt response that becomes connected with hearing. We shall use them only in referring to directions in which the theory might proceed.

Initial evidential grounds for assumptions. Among the most important empirical observations that provided the initial evidential basis for the system were those concerning the "missing fundamental" and the "residue." Those observations set in much more dramatic relief a phenomenon that had been discussed in Helmholtz's time as the phenomenon of the "beat note." Since the literature on the latter is voluminous but old and inconclusive, we shall refer to it only by way of secondary sources [8, 36], and proceed at once to examine the more recent and more conclusive evidence.

Fletcher [16, 18] described observations with stimuli consisting of harmonic components such as 400, 500, 600, 700, 800, 900 and 1,000 cycles per second. Listeners reported that the pitch of that complex was of about the same height as the pitch of a 100-cycle pure tone. This result, taken at face value, is obviously incompatible with strict place theory. Activation of places associated with 400, 500, etc., gives rise to a pitch not appropriate to those places. Fletcher explained the phenomenon ("missing fundamental" because, in the stimuli he used, the fundamental was always missing from the series of harmonics) by supposing that the fundamental or common difference component was reintroduced by nonlinear distortion in the part of the auditory process preceding the cochlear frequency analysis (preceding our operation F). That was precisely the explanation invented by Helmholtz to counter Seebeck's observations 80 to 90 years earlier. The question is, is there enough nonlinearity in the auditory process preceding F to introduce a difference frequency component of appreciable magnitude?

Schouten [66–70] made observations somewhat similar to Fletcher's, but he also looked carefully into the question of nonlinear distortion. He produced stimuli consisting of many cosine harmonics[29] of a fundamental frequency, usually 200 cycles per second, and provided a control arrangement with which the listener could neutralize the fundamental component by adjusting its amplitude and its phase. The listener adjusted the controls until he caused to disappear the subjective component that his auditory mechanism analyzed out at the subjective fundamental. When he had completed the adjustment, there remained a subjective pitch of very nearly the same height as the pitch of the fundamental, now missing. The timbre associated

[29] Cosine harmonics are components of the form $|\Theta(n)| \cos [2\pi nft + \phi(n)]$, in which $\phi(n)$ is zero, n is an integer, and f is a constant (the fundamental frequency). In Schouten's experiment, $|\Theta(n)|$ was constant for small n, then declined with increasing n. The over-all sound pressure was held relatively low to avoid nonlinear distortion.

with this pitch was sharper than that of a 100-cycle tone, but the pitch itself (i.e., its "height") was about the same. Schouten ascribed the remaining pitch to a "residue," an unanalyzed subjective component due to the interaction of the remaining harmonics.

In order to obtain further evidence that the fundamental component was indeed missing, Schouten used the "search tone" technique. He introduced another sinusoid into the stimulus pattern, a tone of about 202 cycles per second and of adjustable amplitude. The listener reported no "beats" with any adjustment of the search tone. This supported the conclusion that a pitch ordinarily associated with 200 cycles per second was being heard in the absence of vibration in the cochlea at the (Fourier) frequency of 200 cycles per second.

Finally, Schouten produced the stimulus pattern 200, 400, 600, . . . (fundamental now present) and then shifted it to 240, 440, 640, ... The common difference frequency remained 200. The fundamental went down to 40. But the pitch went up about a semitone.

These observations of Schouten's are extremely damaging to strict place theory. Fletcher's reconciliation, based upon reintroduction of the fundamental or common difference frequency component, is controverted by Schouten's failure to find such a component, and it leads to an incorrect prediction in the case of 240, 440, 640, ...

Equally important as empirical basis for the triplex theory is an observation made by Huggins [39]. He set up an arrangement consisting of a random-noise generator, an "all-pass network," two power amplifiers, and two earphones. The noise was fed through the all-pass network, and one power amplifier and earphone were connected to its input terminals, the other power amplifier and earphone to its output terminals. The all-pass network passed all the audible frequency components without change of amplitude but with a very special shift of phase. In the notation we have been using, if we let the input spectrum be $\Theta_{0r}(f) = |\Theta_{0r}(f)| \cos [2\pi ft + \phi_{0r}(f)]$ and the output spectrum be $|\Theta_{0l}(f)| \cos [2\pi ft + \phi_{0l}(f)]$, then $|\Theta_{0r}| = |\Theta_{0l}|$ is constant over frequency (up as high as the earphones transduce uniformly) and $\phi_{0l}(f) - \phi_{0r}(f)$ is a function of frequency that is constant at 0 radian up to about 570 cycles per second and constant at 2π radians beyond about 630 cycles per second. Between 570 and 630 cycles per second, $\phi_{0l}(f) - \phi_{0r}(f)$ swings smoothly but steeply from 0 to 2π.

The phase pattern of random noise is random to begin with, and no less random after the alteration produced by the all-pass network. It is not surprising, therefore, that $\Theta_{0r}(f)$ heard alone sounds just like $\Theta_{0l}(f)$ heard alone. Listening to the sound from either earphone by itself, one hears the characteristic "shh . . . " of gaussian-process noise. But, when he listens to both earphones at the same time, the listener hears a faint but definite pitch in the midst of the "shh . . . " The pitch is about the same as that of a 600-cycle tone. I have repeated Huggins's observation with phase transitions at other frequencies and of other steepnesses. The pitch, when heard, is always appropriate to the region of the phase transition. The effect does not arise above about 900 or 1,000 cycles per second. It is clearest with phase transitions that go from $\pi/2$ to $3\pi/2$ in a frequency interval of about 30 cycles per second. The pitch that is heard is never very strong. When the phase transition is made too gradual or too steep, the pitch fades into the background noise. Under favorable conditions, however, it is undeniably present.

Besides the experimental observations just mentioned, there were other more or less empirical grounds for setting up the triplex theory. The problems of consonance and of simple harmonic relations (especially the octave) in music have always required *ad hoc* extensions of the standard place and frequency theories. The insistence of some musicians [see 2, 3] that there are two kinds of pitch, or two kinds of pitch perception, appeared to require something that the standard theories did not provide. On the neurophysiological side, it appeared on the basis of limited empirical evidence that one should not expect nerve impulses to retain good synchrony with the stimulus oscillations all the way up the auditory system,[30] and that it would therefore be better to reencode into a spatial dimension the information carried by the fine grain of the temporal patterns of nerve discharge.

Part of the motivation of the triplex theory stemmed from limitations of existing theories. The standard theories restricted themselves essentially to the action of the cochlea (levels F and G in our terms). The place theory simply projected the cochlear analysis upward in the brain, implying only that pitch corresponds in a one-to-one way with locus of activity. The frequency theory attributed everything to the temporal patterns of nerve impulses without saying anything about how the analysis of those patterns was presumed to be made. Fletcher's [18, 20] space-time pattern theory and Wever's [92] resonance volley theory combined the place and frequency principles by adding them together, with greater weight for place as the clue to pitch at low frequency and greater weight for frequency as the clue to pitch at high frequency. But the latter theories stopped at the level of the auditory nerve; they did not discuss how the two

[30] One should not either, on the other hand, all synchrony to be lost, because in a system of successive trigger circuits perturbed by random fluctuations, the degree of synchrony progressively declines toward zero but never reaches zero [53].

clues are blended together or what happens when they refuse to blend. Most other existing theories [4, 79, 92] shared the limitation to the cochlear level.

The principal motivation of the triplex theory was supplied, however, by the difficulties faced by existing theories in explaining the residue phenomenon and Huggins's phenomenon. Since those difficulties have been detailed elsewhere [51], we shall say here only that neither the place principle nor the frequency (periodic-discharge) principle alone, or as combined by Fletcher and Wever, is capable of affording an explanation of Huggins's phenomenon.

We should examine, briefly, the empirical independent and dependent variables of the Schouten and Huggins experiments, and we should ask how they are linked to the systematic independent and dependent variables.

We look, first, at the stimuli. As we have noted, it is difficult to distinguish, when discussing acoustic stimuli, between empirical data language and the language of the theoretical structure. The identifications are so well established that one rarely uses the data language in an article—beyond specifying the type or model numbers of commercial equipment and perhaps presenting schematic diagrams (almost never anything as detailed as wiring diagrams) of special circuits. This may seem at first thought to be contrary to good scientific procedure, this failure to keep the data language and the structure language separated. Actually, however, it could well be an economy of communication essential to effective group enterprise. In producing acoustic stimuli, we take advantage of a highly developed area of classical physics and of an equally developed area of applied electronics and acoustics. And in describing them it is natural to use the mathematical structures that parallel the actual situation so closely.

In Schouten's experiment, the stimuli were produced by an optic (i.e., photoelectric) siren, an amplifier, and a loudspeaker. In Huggins's, the corresponding items were the noise generator, all-pass network, amplifiers, and earphones. But in either case, the proximal stimulus was a pair of sound pressure waves, one in either ear. Through indirect procedure, it is possible to determine rather precisely the detailed courses of the waves in Schouten's experiment, and, if it were very important, the same thing could be done in Huggins's. The data language might then take the form of oscillographic tracings. In Schouten's experiment, it would turn out that we could reproduce the tracing to within the accuracy of the oscillograph from numerical values of $|\Theta(n)|$ plus the form $|\Theta(n)| \cos 2\pi nft$. In Huggins's, it would turn out, because the noise was random, that no two samples of the paired tracings were alike. This would be because the tracings contained information lost in the auditory process; the subjective impression was approximately constant despite the dissimilarity of the tracings. We should, therefore, seek to simplify the representation of the stimulus. Either the data language tends to become abstract when it deals with random noise, or one does not use the data language except to designate the noise generator.

As we turn to inquire into the state independent variables and the dependent variables, we see on the empirical side only instructions such as "What do you hear?" or "Describe how it sounds," and responses such as "I hear a low-pitched tone; it is sharp and buzzy but low," or "There is a faint tone in the noise." Actually, in Huggins's first demonstration, the first listener's response was no more than a smile, and the second listener's response was, "Well, here's the dollar." But the significance of the response has, as we have noted, little to do with its form.

There is nothing in the language of the theoretical structure to correspond to the questions, put by the experimenter, other than the implicit assumption that they somehow connect a verbal mechanism to block J of Fig. 5. Schouten and Huggins might have gained precision and apparent objectivity by supplying their listeners with an oscillator and changing the instruction to, "Adjust the dial until you match the pitch . . . " But that would not have solved the fundamental problem. The criterion of the adjustment, equal pitch, would simply have become part of the experimenter's verbalization instead of the listeners'.

The lack of definiteness about the linkage between systematic and empirical dependent variables disturbs me. I think I see how, in principle, the trouble can be avoided—by assuming no subjective attributes and letting them appear as coherences or natural dimensions in an analysis of a manifold of data. Yet, as a practical matter, there is now no satisfactory working alternative, for the objective procedure would be so time-consuming as not to be feasible.

Construction of function forms. We turn now to the question: what determined the selection of the particular functional or operational interrelations of the systematic variables? This question has already figured in our discussion, but here we shall examine it directly.

The theory of signal detection (as applied to human beings) appropriated a mathematical structure already fully developed in the theory of statistical inference. The selection of function forms was then essentially determined when the selection of the structure was made.

In the theory of pitch perception, there is a concatenation of functions or operations. The form of the first cochlear operation (F) was determined directly by the experiments of Békésy [6]. Looking back beyond those experiments, we see the whole development of linear signal and system analysis. In using sinusoidal test signals and amplitude and phase-against-frequency diagrams, Békésy was employing one of the tools of a highly developed, highly mathematized technology. For convenience in relating the theory to Békésy's observations, we adopted the same tool in describing F. The choice was made only for convenience, however; we could equally well have expressed F as a function of x and τ instead of x and f—or, for that matter, in any other of several equivalent ways of describing linear operators.

The choice of the function form for G, the cochlear excitation transformation, was made in an effort to compromise between simplicity and adequacy of representation. The things required in G were nonlinearity and smoothing. They had to follow F and precede H in order to accord with electrophysiological and psychophysical data. Half-wave rectification is one of the most familiar nonlinear forms and has approximately the required properties. Smoothing of the type provided by a low-pass filter is equally familiar and equally fills its part of the bill. It is possible even now to improve the accuracy of the theory by using more elaborate functions for G, but the increased complexity of description is hardly warranted in this discussion. Actually, the experimental investigation of the excitatory process that intervenes between mechanical analysis and neural transmission is now proceeding rapidly [10], and we shall not have to wait long for a definitive specification of G.

The operations of H and J were selected under a number of influences and constraints. First, there was the desire to work with elementary operations of a type appropriate to neural tissue, i.e., propagation at finite velocity, spatial summation, and temporal summation. Those three operations may be reexpressed as time delay, logical multiplication, and integration with respect to time. Second, there was a need to effect a transformation from the time domain to a spatial dimension. For that transformation, it was natural to try autocorrelation, for in the period immediately following publication of Wiener's *Cybernetics* [95], M.I.T. was fairly bursting with electronic autocorrelators, and autocorrelation required precisely the three elementary operations just mentioned. The binaural coincidence mechanism was borrowed directly from Wallach [91] and Jeffress [42]. In conjunction with the other operations, it offered a way of handling Huggins's phenomenon, and it, too, used only the elementary neural operations. Finally, the H-J transformation (self-organizing network) was selected because it appeared to provide the desired coalescence into a common focus of the multiple strata of activity aroused in *H* by a periodic sound, because it, also, used the three elementary neural operations (plus inhibition, which should be added as a fourth), and because it appeared to offer a number of interesting by-products.

The reasons just given as reasons for selecting the function forms of the triplex theory are more correctly reasons for trying them out. Actually, the process has been to set up informally all the alternative "theories" that appeared intuitively to make any sense at all—see [40], for example. Most of them have, or develop, obvious flaws. Others remain as alternatives. The process of selection is not formal; it is not even formulated. The idea is simply to carry around in your head as many formulations as you can that are self-consistent and consistent with the empirical facts you know. Then, when you make an observation or read a paper, you find yourself saying, for example, "Well, that certainly makes it look bad for the idea that sharpening occurs in the cochlear excitation process." The selection of function forms is thus an informal weeding out of possibilities. Sometimes they are eliminated by particularly relevant evidence. Sometimes they drop out because other function forms with which they have to be combined run into trouble. And sometimes a whole system will fall apart. The triplex theory is simply a combination of function forms that has withstood a few tests.

Measurement of independent and dependent variables. In so far as measurement of the (microscopic) stimulus variables is concerned, the theory of pitch perception takes advantage of the same highly developed technology as the other two theories. Again, there are essentially no difficulties of measurement. When it comes to state variables and dependent variables, on the other hand, the situation confronting the theory of pitch perception is much more complex, and the ways of handling the situation are quite primitive.

The theory, in fact, simply does not attempt to handle in any quantitative way the problem of getting the listener into a state in which he attends to or reports on pitch—or, as we have noted earlier, the problem of connecting the mechanism of response to the auditory "display." In ignoring those fundamental problems, the theory of pitch perception is not alone, but the neglect is more conspicuous in connection with pitch because the operations of the theory are described in a way that could readily lead into a treatment of problems concerning set and the organization of the verbal report. In fact, it is recognized within the theory that those problems are crucial.

Without specifying variables related to the set or state of the listener, it is difficult to discuss the measurement of set or state. We have named dependent variables, but we have done little more than name them. The fact is, simply, that the theory relies naively on the good offices of a verbal mechanism capable of controlling the set and the response of the listener.

The neglect might be less noticeable if the intervening variables were explicitly postulated to connect with the response variables. In order to keep the intervening variables from dangling in mid-air with no output connections, we can suppose that the response mechanism of the listeners is connected to the block J (or to a subsequent projection of J) in such a way as to lead to verbal or other motor responses signifying certain magnitudes or relations in or among the patterns $I_6(x,y,z,t)$. The listener's response, we then assume, reflects with reasonable accuracy the relative (and with some accuracy the absolute) locations of foci of activity along a spatial continuum in J. It does this, however, only when there are few foci of activity. If we assume for convenience that the continuum is the x dimension, we may say that the response mechanism can indicate, for example, that the x coordinate of $I_6(x,y,z,1)$ is greater than the x coordinate of $I_6(x,y,z,0)$—which means that the pitch at time 1 is higher than the pitch at time 0. Alternately, the verbal mechanism may simply post the response $\Omega = C^{\#}$, signifying that the x coordinate is the one associated in past experience with a particular class of sounds made by a piano, and perhaps other classes of sounds with which the same symbol is associated. Such assumptions would get us over to the systematic dependent variables, and the questions of measurement that arise in connection with them are at any rate not philosophical. In the process, we should have either bypassed Π, Λ, and Υ or identified them with functions intervening between $I_6(x,y,z,t)$ and Ψ or Ω.

Formal organization of the system. The triplex theory is obviously less formal than the other two theories we have discussed. It is also less specific in respect of some of the functional linkages within its structure. It does not, for example, specify precisely the transfer characteristic of the smoothing filter in operator G, and it gives only a rough recipe for the H and H-J networks. Even so, it is more widely open to the criticism of speculating too far than to the criticism of not being specific enough.

The reason, apparently, is that the triplex theory is a theory not so much of what the listener does but of how he does it. A trace of the "how" entered the theory of detection. There was practically none in the theory of intelligibility. But the triplex theory is essentially a theory of process.

As is doubtless evident, I favor the concern with process. The process must have a goal or a function, of course, and it must be physically or physiologically reasonable. But the main thing is that it raises or makes contact with potentially substantive questions all along the line. The question of the filter characteristic mentioned in the preceding discussion, for example, is not likely to arise from either of the other two theories. Yet, if there is such a smoothing operation—as evidently there must be—it must play a role in the processes whose over-all effects the other theories describe. Because of its concern with the detailed steps of the over-all transformation from stimulus to response, a "process theory" seems to me to serve as a good framework with which to organize a field or subfield of knowledge. Perhaps even better in the long run, it may serve as a meeting ground for psychological and physiological data.

A feature of process theories related to the last point is that they may go forward on either of two levels. Knowing the properties of the elements of a mechanism, one may hope to deduce the gross behavior. Alternatively, knowing the gross behavior, one may hope to work out the functional details of the mechanism. Further, since the box is not entirely opaque, one may be able to learn rather exactly what is going on in some stages of the process. That then serves to delimit possibilities for the other stages.

In the field of hearing, there has not been a surfeit of factual information on any one level. It is, therefore, reasonable to choose a kind of theory that will accept data from whatever source offers them.

Scope of the system. The system as outlined can be expected to have something to say about the pitch of any sound that is presented to a listener's ear. It is not yet a basis for making quantitative predictions in all instances, but it covers wider ground than most previous theories.

Actually, the main aim of the theory is not to make sharp, quantitative predictions of response to simple stimulus configurations. Rather, it is to provide a basis for understanding the complex and often labile phenomenal appearances of the widest possible variety of sounds. For that reason, it is likely that the theory will bear at least indirectly on many auditory problems not primarily concerned with pitch. The scope of the theory has indefinite bounds. The focus is pitch perception, but it extends out tenuously into other parts of the field of hearing.

Because of its concern with details not treated by other theories, the triplex theory (or parts thereof) may complement other theories formulated wholly on an abstract or stimulus-response basis. There are no essential incompatibilities, for that matter, among the three theories we have considered, and the triplex theory might serve to describe part of the process underlying either or both of the other two.

History of interaction with research. The theory is too new to have been responsible for initiating much research, and, of course, it may turn out never to provide strong research motivation. It is set up in such a way, however, as to relate to a considerable fraction of the work that has been done and continues to be done in the field of psychoacoustics. (In that respect it is different from, for example, the theory of signal detection, TSG, which requires a rather special experimental format.) And, of course, it has exerted very direct guidance over some observations that I, myself, have made.

Actually, the motivation of the observations to be described stemmed in part from the theory and in part from the fact that a compatriot of Schouten's, Hoogland, reported observations that directly questioned the existence of the residue phenomenon and thus appeared to weaken the evidential basis of the theory. In 1953, Hoogland published his thesis, *The Missing Fundamental* [38]. In it, he gave little weight to Schouten's finding that the residue was heard even when the search tone method and the neutralizing method indicated that there was no vibration at the fundamental frequency, and he revived the explanation based upon the reintroduction of the fundamental by nonlinear distortion.

Hoogland's main observations were made with the composite sound produced by five oscillators connected separately to five loudspeakers. The oscillators were set to high-frequency harmonics—e.g., 3,000, 3,100, 3,200, 3,300, and 3,400 cycles per second—of a low-frequency (missing) fundamental. The listener's head was located relative to the loudspeakers in such a way that the five components would add together with equal amplitudes to constitute a periodic complex tone.

In his experiments with sounds of the type just described, Hoogland was able to observe a low-pitched component of sensation when the sound pressure level was high, but reducing the level below that at which nonlinear distortion in the ear is expected to become negligible made the low-pitched component disappear. Hoogland therefore concluded that the missing-fundamental effect is a product of nonlinear distortion, that it is due to excitation in the part of the cochlea that responds mainly to low-frequency sinusoids and not in the part that responds mainly to high-frequency sinusoids. In short, his conclusions supported a strict place theory.

Inasmuch as Hoogland's report more or less neutralized Schouten's evidence, and inasmuch as the strict place theory has such an entrenched position that a competitive theory is lost if it does not have the support of critical and unquestioned evidence, it appeared that what was needed was an independent way of testing the central question—whether or not low pitch can be heard by (or through) the high-frequency channels of the auditory system. A direct way was to saturate the low-frequency channels of the auditory system with low-frequency masking noise, to fill them so full of noise that even a strong low-frequency sinusoid could not be heard at all,[31] and then to observe the subjective impression made by a periodic complex sound consisting only of high-frequency cosine harmonics of a low-frequency missing fundamental.

A series of such signals was therefore prepared and presented, in alternation with segments of low-frequency sinusoids, to 15 individual listeners and to several groups [50]. The fundamental frequency was varied up and down the scale between 150 and 1,300 cycles per second. At each setting of the fundamental frequency, the periodic complex alternated with the sinusoid, the latter being louder because its sound pressure level had intentionally been adjusted high to give it the advantage in the masking test. Then, after the listeners had heard the tonal sounds alone, a low-frequency noise (random noise that had been passed through a filter that attenuated components above 1,000 cycles per second) was added to the tones. The noise masked the sinusoid in each instance unless its frequency was above 1,200 cycles per second—the tone was inaudible as its frequency changed step-by-step from 150 to 1,200 cycles per second, and then it emerged gradually as its frequency moved beyond the cutoff frequency of the noise filter. Throughout the range, however, the periodic complex of high-frequency harmonics was clearly audible, and it had a low pitch.[32] All the listeners (but a few in the group demonstrations who did not get the idea of what to listen for) agreed about that. There is no doubt, in my opinion, that low pitch can be heard when the low-frequency channels of the auditory system are saturated with noise. In fact, independent confirmation came almost at once in a paper by Thurlow and Small [90], which reported quantitative measurements of the masking of similar tones by similar noise.

The foregoing observations supported the residue phenomenon. They were beyond attack on any reasonable basis that appealed to nonlinear distortion, for the low-frequency noise masked a sinusoid of the fundamental (or common difference) frequency that was stronger than the product of any reasonably conceivable nonlinearity. However, they did not account for Hoogland's failure to hear the residue. That was the next item on the program.

[31] To keep in the spirit of TSG, we should say, " . . . that even a strong low-frequency sinusoid had a negligible *d′*."

[32] When high-frequency noise was substituted for the low-frequency noise, the sinusoid became audible and the periodic complex disappeared.

The one thing that Hoogland did not specify or control directly was the phase pattern of the five sinusoidal components that comprised his test signals. He had to accept the phase pattern his oscillators happened to give him, or wait until they drifted into the pattern he wanted—which apparently he did not do. It seemed likely that he did not detect the residue because he did not have the all-cosine phase pattern of Schouten's original experiments, and of the subsequent experiments that confirmed Schouten. The all-cosine phase pattern corresponds to impulsiveness of waveform, and impulsiveness is required, of course, in order to set up volleys of synchronized discharge in the auditory nerve, as required by the theory.

In order to check the hypothesis, a signal-generating arrangement was set up to provide up to eight sinusoidal components in exact harmonic relation and with individual phase controls. When the phases were adjusted for maximum impulsiveness (all-cosine pattern), the residue was quite clear. When the phases were adjusted to minimize the fluctuations of the envelope, the residue became very weak or disappeared. When the phases were set haphazardly, the residue usually was much less pronounced than it was for the all-cosine pattern, but with some "random" adjustments it was fairly strong.

Those observations seemed to offer a reasonable explanation of Hoogland's negative results, though I should admit that I was somewhat concerned about the too frequent appearance of the residue in the observations with random phase settings. In September, 1955, however, I had an opportunity to hear Hoogland's signals in the laboratory at Utrecht and to discuss the problem with Hoogland, Gron, Schouten, and deBoer.[33] After that discussion, it appeared to me that a perhaps equally important factor was Hoogland's and Gron's insistence that the signal level be kept exceedingly low to avoid possible nonlinear distortion. One would not expect very weak signals to produce nonlinear distortion products, but one would not expect them either to set up precisely synchronous discharges in the auditory nerve. Negative results for very weak signals are predicted by either theory; hence, they are not critical. It appears to me now, therefore, that the residue phenomenon is in good standing and that the demonstration of low pitch despite saturation of the low-frequency channels is all the support it possibly needs.

One of the principal bases cited for the duplex theory (precursor

[33] The previous day, I had the pleasure of visiting the Philips Laboratory at Eindhoven and hearing Schouten's demonstrations. They were very convincing. They raised again the question of how in experimental reports to give subjective demonstrations weight proportional to their evident power to convince listeners who actually hear them.

of the triplex theory) was the pitch of periodically interrupted random noise. The reference was to an experiment by Miller and Taylor [57] in which observations were made with noise that was turned on and off abruptly and periodically, at various rates, by an electronic switch. The noise was left on, in successive tests, for various fractions of the total on-off cycle. As explained by Miller and Taylor, the attractiveness of interrupted random noise as a test signal stems from the fact that the shape of the power density spectrum is not changed by the interruptions. It is uniform to begin with, and it remains uniform despite the turning on and off. Therefore, any subjective difference between interrupted and uninterrupted random noise must either be referred to a temporal basis or to nonlinearity in the auditory process.

The most relevant finding of Miller and Taylor's observations was that, when interrupted at rates between about 100 and 250 cycles per second, the random noise had a pitchlike quality. That quality persisted even though the noise was presented at a low sound pressure level. The conclusion was, therefore, that the pitchlike quality was owing to the periodic volleys of impulses in the auditory system, not to activations of the spatial channel (x channel) that would be activated by a sinusoid of frequency equal to the interruption rate.

In my eagerness to accept any evidence that appeared to support the duplex theory, I made an error in explaining how the autocorrelational mechanism would process interrupted random noise. (The duplex mechanism differed from the triplex in not having the binaural coincidence analysis to which we have assigned the y dimension. We may neglect that part of the process because the interrupted noise was presented either to one ear or simultaneously—diotically—to both ears in the observations under discussion.) The question was, what spatial pattern at the output of the autocorrelator (output of H) would be produced by stimulation with random noise turned on and off, for example, 100 times per second and with an on-off ratio of unity. I concluded [48, Fig. 3B] that the pattern would consist of a succession of strata of active tissue, at intervals in the z dimension related to the interruption period ($\frac{1}{100}$ sec), and that each stratum would be approximately uniform in the x dimension because of the uniformity of the power density spectrum of the stimulus. The immediate interpretation, of course, was that the pitch of Miller and Taylor's interrupted random noise was due to the periodic spacing of the strata in the z dimension. Later reflection led me to see, however, that the conclusion and interpretation just described require qualification.

The seriousness of the qualification depends upon the filter characteristics (particularly the damping characteristics and therefore also the bandwidths) associated with the operator $F(x,f)$. In the high-frequency end of the spectrum, where the bandwidths are broad, the picture would be essentially as described. In the low-frequency end, however, the narrow-band cochlear filters would to a considerable extent determine the time function delivered to the autocorrelator. The over-all result would be a complex pattern dominated by parallel strata in the high-frequency zone and converging strata (not spaced in such a way as to correspond to any pattern produced by sinusoidal stimulation) in the low-frequency zone. This still left a basis for pitchlike quality, but it suggested that the pitch should be somewhat obscure when the noise was uniform down to very low frequencies.

The reanalysis just described led to a series of observations on the pitch of interrupted random noise. The first thing was to compare interrupted uniform spectrum noise with interrupted high-pass noise (noise from which the components below 2,500 cycles per second had been removed by a high-pass filter before the interrupting). When the frequency of interruption is low, interrupted high-pass noise has very little power in the vicinity of the interruption frequency and, in any case, there is no concentration of power at the interruption frequency. It turned out that the pitch of the interrupted high-pass noise was considerably clearer than that of the interrupted uniform spectrum noise. The latter, as a matter of fact, had no discernible pitch at all, as far as several volunteer listeners and I could tell, unless the on-off ratio was made lower than unity. With a very low on-off ratio, however, there was no doubt that even the uniform spectrum noise sounded "pitchy." That fact removes some of the uncertainty that appeared to be surrounding the whole question, for Mowbray, Gebhard, and Byham [58] and deBoer [11] reported that they and their listeners could not detect tonality in interrupted uniform spectrum noise, and Garner [27] judged that the whole effect was essentially subjective intermittency and not pitch.[34]

The dependence upon the fraction of the time the interrupted noise was "on" is of course entirely in line with the theory, since short bursts of noise would produce sharp volleys and lead to clear-cut action in the coincidence mechanism. However, the fact that pitchiness increased as on-time fraction decreased, all the way to the point at which the noise burst was turned into a single, sharp pulse, led me

[34] There was even disagreement about the related but less relevant question of the "matchability" of the interrupted random noise. Miller and Taylor found that, up to about 200 interruptions per second, it could be matched in pitch by a sinusoid or square wave, and that the precision of the match, in cycles per second, was about as good as the precision of matching a sinusoid to a square wave. Mowbray, Gebhard, and Byham reported matches, but thought that they were not pitch matches. And deBoer could not even get matches.

to see another possible flaw in the argument. This possible flaw was studied in detail as a thesis project by Cramer [9], and since the results will be presented elsewhere we shall summarize only briefly here.

In short, it is true that the longtime-average power spectrum remains uniform after uniform spectrum noise is interrupted periodically, but the *variance* of the power spectrum is greater at and near integral multiples of the interruption frequency than it is elsewhere. And this nonuniformity of the variance increases with decreasing on-off ratio. It appeared possible, therefore, that the pitch of interrupted random noise was attributable to momentary concentrations of power in the neighborhood of the interruption frequency, and that the perception is explicable in terms of strict place theory. Cramer's thesis work indeed demonstrated the existence of pitches due to fluctuations of the momentary ("running") power density spectrum. But it also demonstrated the existence of another pitchlike quality, separable from the fluctuating pitch. Under favorable conditions, this periodicity-based pitch was audible at interruption rates up at least to 2,000 cycles per second, which is considerably above the upper limit of the pitch but not far above the upper limit of "fusion" reported by Miller and Taylor; the latter was confirmed by Symmes, Chapman, and Halstead [82]. Thus, as matters stand now, it appears that the triplex theory is in line with the observations on the pitch of interrupted random noise. It is reasonable that interrupted noise should have pitch, and also that under some conditions it should be not at all pronounced or even absent.

In his recent thesis, deBoer [11] described a characteristic of the residue phenomenon that at first glance appears to challenge any auditory theory. He used a stimulus generator capable of producing inharmonic complexes of the type we mentioned in connection with one of Schouten's observations, i.e., five or seven sinusoidal components, separated by equal intervals Δf, but not necessarily having frequencies equal to integral multiples of Δf. To understand deBoer's effect, let us assume that there are five cosine components, and let us start with the harmonic pattern, 1,400, 1,600, 1,800, 2,000, and 2,200 cycles per second, for which Δf is 200 cycles per second, and $1{,}800 = 9\,\Delta f$. That has a low pitch, roughly like that of a 200-cycle-per-second tone. Then let us hold the center frequency fixed at 1,800 and increase Δf. In due course we get to another harmonic pattern, 1,350, 1,575, 1,800, 2,025, and 2,250, for which $\Delta f = 225$, and $1{,}800 = 8\,\Delta f$. That has a pitch roughly like that of a 225-cycle-per-second tone. But what about the pitch for intermediate values of Δf? DeBoer reported that the pitch *fell* as Δf was increased from 200 to about 212 cycles per second, and that it was then as though his attention shifted rather suddenly to a new aspect of the sound, for the pitch then jumped to a considerably higher level. As Δf increased further, the pitch fell again, and continued to fall until Δf reached the neighborhood of 237 cycles per second. Then the pitch took another upward jump, after which it again decreased with increasing Δf, and so on. DeBoer quantified the phenomenon by having his subjects match the pitch of the inharmonic complex with a harmonic complex, the value of Δf for the latter being variable and under the control of the subjects.

DeBoer offered two possible explanations for the effect, one based on the spectrum and the other on the waveform. The spectral explanation involves the concept of a pseudofrequency, integral multiples of which approximate the frequencies of the (inharmonic) stimulus components. The best approximating frequency is the one for which the mean square of the weighted differences between its harmonics and the frequencies of the inharmonic components is minimal. The weights may reflect the masking of one component by the others, and the weights are therefore greater for the lower components than for the higher. The pitch heard is assumed to correspond to the pseudofrequency. DeBoer did not suggest an underlying mechanism or process corresponding to this spectral explanation.

For the explanation based upon the waveform of the inharmonic complex, on the other hand, deBoer did suggest a possible basis, and it involved essentially the autocorrelational process of the duplex and triplex theories. Actually, deBoer's main discussion of it related to the waveform and not to neural signals, but he mentioned the possibility that the operations were carried out in the neural tissue. The autocorrelational explanation of the effect is roughly as follows: When the component frequencies are all integral multiples of Δf, the complex wave is periodic. The period is the interval between maxima in the waveform and also the interval between maxima in the autocorrelation function. When Δf is increased slightly beyond the value that produced the periodic, harmonic complex, the average distance between main peaks in the waveform increases. This is perhaps surprising, but nonetheless true. As a corollary, the spacing of the peaks of the autocorrelation function increases also. If one follows the sequence of steps assumed in the triplex theory, he finds that the same thing happens. The theory as described is not sufficiently explicit to permit an exact prediction of the relation between the separation of the strata and Δf, but the direction of the effect is clearly accounted for, and the anomaly is correctly predicted to be small.

Because I have heard deBoer's phenomenon and because it fits the triplex theory so nicely, I am perhaps a bit reluctant to present the next item, which is from experiments made by Goldstein [29, 30, 32]. Goldstein's experiments were designed to check deBoer's observations. Goldstein used a forced-choice, constant method. One of the two stimuli was a segment of a harmonic complex (for example, 1,400, 1,600, 1,800, 2,000, 2,200 cycles per second[35]) with $\Delta f = 200$ cycles per second; the other was a segment of an inharmonic complex (for example, 1,405, 1,605, 1,805, 2,005, 2,205 cycles per second) also with $\Delta f = 200$ cycles per second. The subject had to say which was higher in pitch. Goldstein was one of the listeners, and he found it very difficult to hold a steady set; his judgments do not make orderly psychometric functions. However, the other four subjects did yield rather orderly functions, and they failed to show in any clear or consistent way the anomaly observed by deBoer. Actually, one of the curves for 1.0-msec rise time and all five of the curves for 0.5-msec rise time had reversals, not individually of statistical significance but collectively hard to ignore, at or very near the standard (200 cycles per second) frequency. Goldstein interprets the disagreement between his results and deBoer's as indicating that the [meaning of] "pitch" of the complex stimuli depends upon the set of the listener and upon the psychophysical procedure. Certainly there is such a dependence. When I heard deBoer's demonstration, some minutes passed before I could tell what everyone else was being amazed about. Then, when I finally heard it myself, I could not see how I had ever failed to hear it. More recently, hearing similar signals in Goldstein's setup, I was less confident, again, that I was clear about what I was hearing.

Finally, we come to some physiological observations of a type that bear directly and critically upon specific assumptions of the triplex theory. In addition to his psychophysical tests, Goldstein [30, 32] made electrophysiological observations on the auditory systems of cats, recording responses to complex stimuli both at the cochlea (round window) and at the cerebral cortex (auditory areas I and II in the ectosylvian gyrus). The cortical observations are most relevant.

Using segments of sinusoids of various frequencies, Goldstein determined the frequency response profiles of several small areas on the cortical surface. Then, substituting interrupted random noise for the sinusoids, he observed whether or not the response varied with the interruption frequency. It did not. Then, with the aid of high-pass and low-pass filters, he selected out bands of the interrupted noise and

[35] Actually, Goldstein's signals were made by modulating an 1,800-cycle-per-second carrier by an envelope function having a specified rise time, either 1.0 or 0.5 msec. There were, therefore, other components of lesser amplitude on either side of those whose frequencies are given.

observed the effect upon the cortical response. The "threshold" for the response increased whenever he attenuated the (Fourier) components to which the cortical area had been shown in the sinusoidal tests to be tuned. Evidently the cortical response was governed by the power density spectrum of the interrupted noise, as would be predicted by strict place theory, and not by the periodicity of interruption.

Goldstein made also a few similar tests with bursts of tone similar to the ones he used in his psychophysical tests. The result was again the same; the response was governed by the concentration of power in the spectrum and not by the periodicity of the waveform.

Apparently with even worse effect for the triplex theory, Goldstein used a very sensitive technique to determine to what extent the cortical response followed the periodicity of the stimulus. The assumption, in the theory, of a time-to-place transformation at a subcortical level was motivated largely by the supposition that the fine time detail of the signal would be largely lost or smoothed over by the time the signal reached the cortex. But, by averaging large numbers of cortical responses, with the aid of an electronic computer, Goldstein showed that there was some synchronized response to sharp acoustic impulses even up to 320 pulses per second. More recently, the limit has been pushed up to about 600 per second [31].

A final observation relevant to the theory was made recently by Six [73]. His observations go back to the question of the possible reintroduction of the fundamental or the common difference frequency, into compound sounds that produce the residue phenomenon, by nonlinear distortion. Six measured the electrical response of the guinea-pig cochlea at the low-frequency end and at the high-frequency end. The stimulus components were high in frequency; the difference frequency was low. A component produced by nonlinear distortion was observed when the stimulus was strong, but the low-frequency distortion product was picked up mainly by the electrode at the high-frequency end. This observation, although not crucial, is certainly in line with the triplex theory.

The future of the theory. As explained in the introduction, the later stages of the triplex theory are highly speculative, their aim being to specify, in concrete terms consistent with what is known about the mechanical and neural characteristics of the auditory system, a mechanism that can account for the psychoacoustic facts. It is unlikely that any such structure will remain tenable in detail as relevant data continue to narrow down the range of possibilities. One should not hold too tenaciously to particular parts of the theory, therefore, simply because one put them together and gave them a name. It would not be at all inconsistent with the spirit of the theory, for example, to move the autocorrelational mechanism from subcortical to cortical centers. That is what is suggested by Goldstein's [31] conclusion, " . . . if 'place pitch' and 'periodicity pitch' are brought together in one place in the nervous system, our experimental results indicate that it is probably not at a stage leading to the auditory cortex."

It is, however, as much the responsibility of a speculative theory not to give way too readily to experimental pressure as it is not to be unreasonably inflexible. The immediate question is, what to do in response to Goldstein's electrophysiological findings. To decide upon an answer requires critical examination of the evidence. Examining it critically reveals these facts:

1. The cortical response recorded by Goldstein was an onset, or perhaps sometimes an on-off, phenomenon, and not an enduring correlate of continued stimulation. It was not the kind of thing one would seek as a physiological substratum for pitch, which persists through time. This is of course not a criticism directed at Goldstein, for the onset potential has been used as the response in every electrophysiological experiment on the differential reaction of the cortex to sounds of various frequencies, and I used it myself, though with some misgiving on the present point, in my Ph.D. thesis [47]. Better electrical responses, I think, would be the suppression of spontaneous activity (which does persist to some extent throughout the duration of a tonal stimulus) and the responses of individual neurons recorded with the aid of microelectrodes.

2. Failure to find a differential cortical response to interrupted random noise with unity on-off ratio is not entirely out of line with the psychophysical findings, for there have been more failures to find pitch with such stimuli than successes in finding it.

3. The results obtained with periodically modulated tones were limited apparently to three or four cortical points. The theory does not require that all cortical points show differential response to stimulus periodicity, but only that some of them show it.

4. The finding that the cortical response follows the repetition frequency of periodic impulsive stimuli up to 600 cycles per second must be qualified with the statement that the magnitude of the synchronous response falls off markedly as the repetition frequency increases. Goldstein's graphs show the response at 40 or 50 pulses per second to be only about 20 per cent as great, in peak-to-peak voltage, as the response at 1 pulse per second. At 320 pulses per second, it was only 1 or 2 per cent as great. Intuitively, that behavior seems to correlate better with the subjective impression of intermittency than with the subjective impression of pitch.

The four considerations just outlined lead me, for the time being, to hold onto the notion that a subcortical transformation from periodicity to place may be an important part of the process of pitch perception. On the other hand, Goldstein's observations lead me to prepare myself for substituting the notion that the transformation may be cortical. I was, in fact, already somewhat prepared for that by the results of an experiment, as yet incomplete, by Jenkins [43].

In return for the loan of some equipment, Jenkins agreed to see whether or not pigeons observed the residue phenomenon. Making a suitable translation into the language of differential response, he trained three pigeons as follows:

a. To respond to a 250-cycle-per-second tone but not to a 5,000-cycle-per-second tone.

b. To respond to a 5,000-cycle-per-second tone but not to a 250-cycle-per-second tone.

c. To respond to the harmonics between 3,500 and 7,000 cycles per second derived with the aid of bandpass filters from a periodic train of 250 pulses per second.

He then tested pigeons *a* and *b* on stimulus *c*. Pigeon *b* responded but *a* did not. To pigeon *c* he presented segments of tone from 100 cycles per second to 7,000 cycles per second. The pigeon responded very, very slightly and perhaps not statistically significantly at 250 cycles per second, vigorously at 5,000 cycles per second and neighboring frequencies. Evidently the pigeon, which has no auditory cortex, responds differentially to Fourier frequency but not to periodicity. Jenkins emphasizes, however, that the finding is extremely tentative, and that the observations lead only to the conclusion that the problem may be investigated readily with lower animals. That fact may be important in relation to electrophysiological studies.

Clearly, the future of the triplex theory and alternatives to it are bound up with correlated psychophysical and electrophysiological research. On the psychophysical side, it appears that studies of the latency of the subjective experience of pitch—or perhaps of the duration of stimulation required to set up clear pitch—will be helpful. If there are two mechanisms of pitch, we might expect to find that one requires longer than the other to produce an output. Incidentally, since it is possible in the residue experiments to lead the listener to hear the residue and the fundamental tone (when it is added) separately, one may be able to make a direct subjective comparison of the latencies. On the physiological side, the main thing seems to me to be to find a good electrical correlate of the ongoing auditory process. With such a correlate, it should be possible completely to carry out crucial experiments.

Preparing this discussion has led me to realize that the correlational or coincidence stages of the theory need hardly be distinguished as different from a transformation of the *H-J* type. The latter has built into it the operations of coincidence multiplication and temporal integration, though they were not described precisely in those terms. If we assume—as seems reasonable—that the projections paths (i.e., the interconnecting neurons) are of various lengths, we have a mechanism for differential time delay. The *H-J* transformation thus appears capable of handling binaural coincidence and autocorrelation as well as the other functions ascribed to it. The main difference is that it is represented as a haphazard network of neurons, whereas the representation of the *H* block (Fig. 5) was orderly. It is important to keep in mind that the orderliness was functional, not geographical. In any event, it may be worthwhile to recast the triplex theory by deemphasizing autocorrelation and emphasizing transformations of the *H-J* type. Before that is done, however, it is almost necessary to devise an objective way of studying the behavior of such transformations. The theory will have no substance if the behavior of the structure cannot be described.

PROBLEMS OF SYNTHESIS

As we have seen, our three part theories are quite different from one another in aim and character and content, yet they overlap in several places. Although it seems to me impossible, at this stage, to combine them into a coherent, comprehensive theory, there are several opportunities to improve their compatibility.

Two kinds of "filtering." Perhaps the clearest opportunity is the one provided by the fact that two of the part theories assume that the first main transformation of the stimulus is handled by an array of filters, whereas the third (TSG) postulates a single, sweepable filter.[36] Both conceptions seem to me to be useful. The problem is to combine them in an effective way.

Because it is definitely established on the physiological level that the first significant transformation, the mechanical analysis of the cochlea, is essentially a manifold filtering, I think that we should take that as a point of departure. In doing so, we should keep in mind that the mechanical filter characteristics are broad, that they are not unambiguously bandpass but rather halfway between low-pass and

[36] In another paper, Tanner and Norman [86] suggest that the auditory system may operate in either of two ways. One way involves the single sweepable filter. The other involves a fixed, broad-band channel. The sweepable filter is assumed to be employed in speech perception.

bandpass characteristics, and that they are undoubtedly supplemented by sharpening. To what extent the sharpening is variable and under the control of other parts of the listener's data-processing system is as yet uncertain. I think it is reasonable tentatively to assume that some sharpening is provided by a mechanism of fixed[37] parameters, and that there is delivered to a sensory display surface in the conceptual nervous system a pattern, moving in time, at least one spatial dimension of which represents stimulus frequency. It is difficult to speak clearly about the degree of resolution inherent in such a pattern, for, if the frequency of a stimulus tone were slowly changed, the point of maximum neural activity would move continuously along the dimension representing frequency. In a sense, the resolution of such a representation is limited only by its inherent statistical fluctuations. Neglecting them leads to the conclusion that the resolution in the representation, itself, is infinite, for any change in stimulus frequency, however small, is then seen to produce a shift of the maximum along the continuum of the representation. On the other hand, signals that occur simultaneously in closely neighboring frequency bands certainly interact. If we want to define resolution as the inverse of such interaction, then we must specify the shape of a filter characteristic for each point along the display continuum. We may assume a set of filters with characteristics of approximately the same shape when plotted on the *g* scale, roughly symmetrical and about 0.02 *g*-units wide when the stimulus level is very low, but losing their symmetry as the skirts rise with increasing signal level. The temporal resolution is a little below the limit imposed by the filter bandwidth. One may think of the pattern as having been smoothed by a low-pass filter with a break point somewhere near 10 cycles per second. This filter has gradually sloping skirts; it does not smooth so effectively as to destroy the impact value of strong transient stimuli, but it supplements the action of the bandpass filtering in keeping the main peaks and valleys of the pattern from moving rapidly about on the display surface.

Now, the output mechanism of the observer "sees" the display surface through another filter, which may well have the "sweepable" property assumed in TSG. This filter is not a wave filter, however, for it acts on a pattern displayed spatially. It is therefore more closely related to space domain sharpening mechanisms [40] than it is to filters of the kind we have been discussing. In very rough analogy, one might think of the perceptual system as having a limited number of communication lines with which it can connect itself to the display

[37] The parameters may vary with degree of wakefulness or even with degree of alertness of the auditory system but not, for example, in response to changes in the duration of the signal in a detection test.

surface. Many, or most, of the lines are movable, and the perceptual mechanism can connect so many to one small part of the display area (in order to make statistically very reliable observations of the pattern there) that it is but poorly sensitive to events displayed in other locations. Alternatively, if the problem is to detect a signal of unspecified frequency, the perceptual mechanism might spread its lines sparsely over the whole display region or move them about in a group as rapidly as possible, sweeping the region in the manner envisaged by Tanner, Swets, and Green [89].

The notion of communication lines and moving connections is of course only a rough analogy, but I think it is important to separate in one's thinking the two kinds of filtering. The distinction is not mainly between selectivity of fixed parameters and selectivity under the control of other stages of the system, for the neural stages involved in the first kind of filtering—the time function filtering—may well be to some extent under such control. Rather, the distinction is between the filtering that goes on before the display of the sensory pattern and the filtering that goes on in the examination, by the perceptual mechanism, of the sensory display.

The notion of a sensory display region seems to me to crystallize a distinction between *sensory* and *perceptual* that has waxed and waned throughout the history of psychology. I am not sure that the distinction is useful, but it may be worthwhile to give it a chance to be by making it specific. If one postulates a sensory display region, then all the processes leading up to that region are sensory, and the processes coupling that region with subsequent operators are perceptual. The region need not be continuous in the physical space of the nervous system. It is convenient, however, to suppose that some transformation or disentangling of the neuronal network would bring the neurons functionally concerned with display into physical proximity.

The theory of speech intelligibility that we have described is concerned principally with the first kind of filtering, which we may now call sensory filtering.[38] Presumably the sensory frequency analysis is the main determiner of the importance function. It is what keeps noise in one band from interfering—any more than it does—with the perception of speech in another. It seems to me that the role played in speech perception by the second kind of filtering (perceptual filtering) calls not for a sweeping filter but for the establishment of a selective pattern of connections between the mechanism of apprehension and the sensory display region that will discriminate as much as possible against interference and in favor of the desired speech

[38] However, Tanner, Swets, and Green [89] have outlined a theory of intelligibility based on the second kind of filtering.

signal. In some situations this would call for changing patterns of interconnection, but I see nothing but disadvantage for speech perception if one should introduce a sweeping filter into the system.

In the theory of signal detection, both kinds of filtering have definite roles. In a detection test, the auditory system is certainly operating at a high degree of alertness, and the sensory filtering is providing as sharp an analysis as it can provide. The behavior of the perceptual filter is conditioned by the particulars of the task. If the frequency of the anticipated tone is known, attention is focused upon the appropriate small region of the sensory display. If the frequency is not known, or if the signal is a compound tone or a sound with a continuous spectrum, other behavior is more appropriate. There are interesting experiments to be done in this area.

In the theory of pitch perception, the sensory filtering is handled by the transformations F, G, H, and H-J. The pattern $I_6(x,y,z,t)$ is what is displayed in the display region. The role of the perceptual filter, in the triplex theory, should be to mediate the connection of $I_6(x,y,z,t)$ to the verbal mechanism. There are probably only a few well-developed modes of connection. Having been established under the guidance of a nonhomogeneous verbal community, they vary considerably from person to person. The only point I want to make about them here is that the connections are subject only to gross control through instructions given by the experimenter. They are governed also, and perhaps preponderantly, by "trapping" or "locking" mechanisms at both ends. At the display end, the connections tend to go where there is movement or changing activity. At the verbal end, they go where there are established verbal foci. It is, therefore, very difficult or even impossible for an experimenter to control precisely the judgmental modes of his subjects. If he is interested in a particular problem of sensation or perception, he is likely to have highly developed verbal distinctions (many well-established subfoci) to which connections can be directed by instruction, but run of the mill subjects will not have them. They will respond, all right, but they may respond mainly to features of the sensory display that naturally attract the interconnections and through an inappropriate verbal focus. They will say "higher" or "lower," just as instructed, but the response may not mean what the experimenter intended it to mean, and the results may be either frustrating or misleading unless the experimenter appreciates the true nature of the problem.

The metric of the intensive scale. In the theory of speech intelligibility that we have discussed, the intensive scale is logarithmic. As we noted, that is in line with the widely accepted assumption that the decibel is in some way a natural unit in terms of which to express the power or energy of auditory stimuli, and also, of course, with the Weber-Fechner law. In the theory of signal detection, however, we find that the value of d' for an ideal detector varies directly with $(E/N)^{1/2}$, and experimental evidence indicates that, although a human observer's d' varies more nearly directly with E/N in tests with weak signals, the linear relation with $(E/N)^{1/2}$ comes into effect as soon as the signals are considerably stronger than the noise.

The fact that speech perception is in principle a matter of discrimination, of classifying a signal as being in one or another of a finite member of subsets, suggests that the same intensive metric should appear in both the theory of speech perception and the theory of signal detection. We should keep in mind that the roles played by the metrics are not precisely the same in the two theories as described. (For example, per cent correct detection is related to the intensive variable in a rigidly defined way, whereas per cent articulation is related by a calibration function $A = X(\mathcal{A})$ that is determined empirically for each listening crew.) Nevertheless, it appears worthwhile to examine the possibility of *rapprochement* between the theories in respect of the intensive metric. Force is lent to that idea by the fact that the intensive metric $(\Phi/N)^{1/2}$ suggested for the theory of speech intelligibility by the results of Licklider and Guttman [52] differs from $(E/N)^{1/2}$ only in that one is in a form suitable for indefinitely enduring signals whereas the other is in a form suitable for signals of finite duration.

Probably the best approach is to ask what rationale for selection of an intensive metric exists in the field of speech intelligibility. We should not expect to get very far here, for it is evident at once that the identification of speech sounds is a very subtle process not likely to fall into line with anyone's initial formulation. Yet there does appear to be a need to bring into the field of intelligibility theory some of the thinking from the theory of signal detection in which guidance is provided by study of the theory of an ideal observer.

To simplify matters very greatly, we might restrict our interest to speech contaminated by gaussian-process noise, and we might idealize the problem by considering the task of the observer to be the classification of each received speech element into one of n classes, for each of which he has available a standard or reference pattern identical[39] to the pattern used by the source [49]. Let us assume, even, that

[39] Eventually, of course, we should examine what happens when the listener's patterns are different from the talker's, but let us keep things as simple as possible now. We need complicate the picture only to the extent of assuming (realistically) that the listener has fallible memory for the noise variance and must therefore estimate it from each sample.

the n patterns are orthogonal, mutually uncorrelated. In this particular case, an ideal discriminator might use a process based on product moment correlation. He would segment the noisy incoming signal into elements and correlate the pattern derived from each one with each of the standard patterns. The derived pattern would be quite different from the waveform, of course, because the latter contains much irrelevant information that would obscure the basic correlations. Recent work on mechanical recognition of speech sounds provides a number of interesting leads to follow. Here, however, let us avoid choosing a particular processing schema and assume only that the signal-noise ratio of the reduced patterns is approximately proportional to that (Φ/N) of the unreduced waves.

We have for each elementary speech sound, then, n correlation coefficients. Of them, $n - 1$ differ from zero only because of sampling fluctuations (correlations between standard patterns and the pattern of the noise-contaminated received sample), and one differs from unity only because the correlation has been degraded by the noise. This situation is very closely similar to that existing on the decision axis in the theory of signal detection. The main difference is that the correlation coefficients do not have the distribution characteristics of the logarithm of the likelihood ratio. And that difference can be removed by applying Fisher's [15] z transformation, $z = \tanh^{-1} r$, to the correlation coefficients.

To see what this implies about the intensive metric, we need to ask how ω, the parametric value of z, depends upon Φ/N. Approaching the problem from the point of view of analysis of variance of the received pattern, we note that the square of the correlation coefficient is equal to the ratio of (1) the variance common between the received pattern and the correct standard pattern to (2) the common variance plus the error variance. The common variance is the same thing as the signal variance or signal power, and the error variance is the same thing as the noise variance or noise power. Inasmuch as we are regarding all the quantities as functions of frequency, we are concerned with the signal power density and the noise power density. We have, therefore,

$$\rho^2 = \frac{\Phi}{\Phi + N}$$

and

$$\rho = \left(\frac{\Phi}{\Phi + N}\right)^{1/2}$$

That transforms to

$$\omega = \tanh^{-1} \rho = \tanh^{-1} \left(\frac{\Phi}{\Phi + N}\right)^{1/2}$$

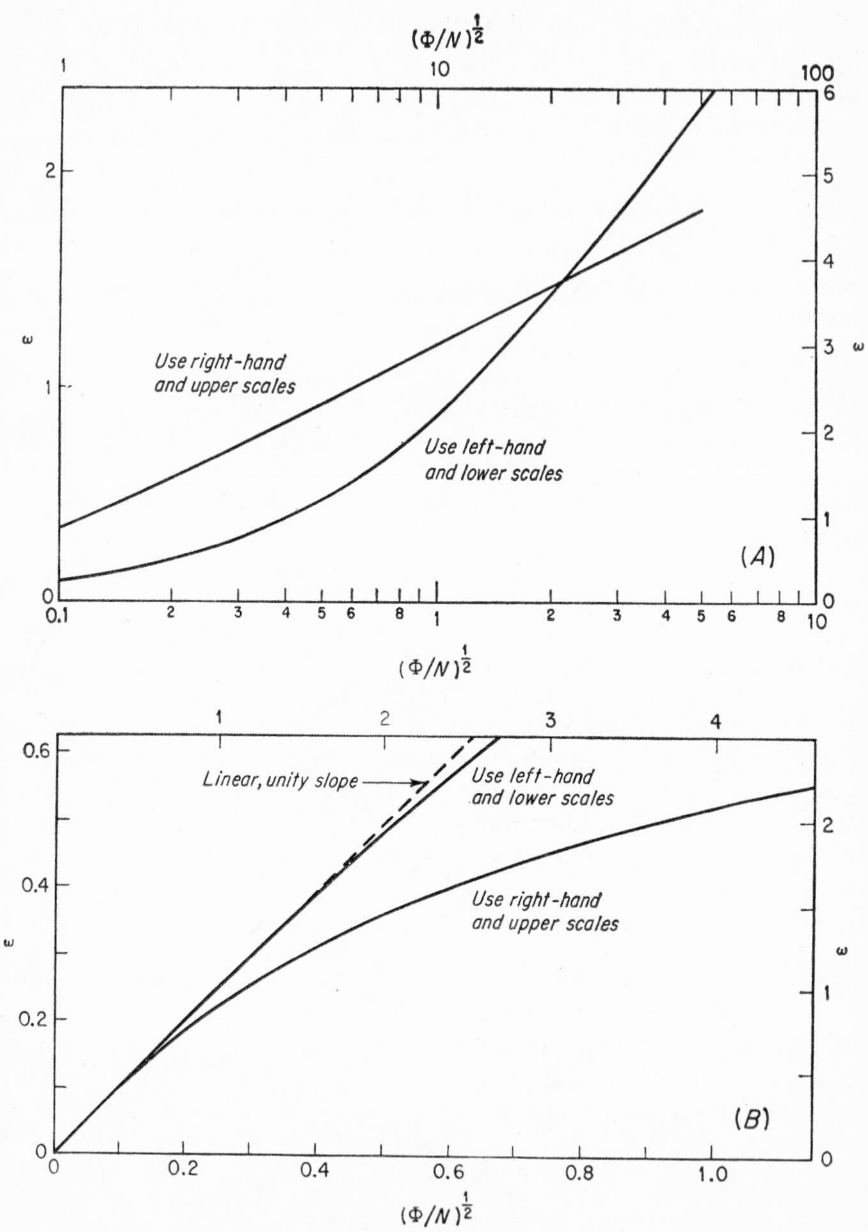

FIG. 10. *Curves showing relations between ω and* $(\Phi/N)^{1/2}$. The quantity ω provides a possible metric for the intensive scale. For low values of ω and $(\Phi/N)^{1/2}$, the relation is approximately linear as shown by the upper curve of the lower graph. For high values of ω and $(\Phi/N)^{1/2}$, the relation is approximately logarithmic, as shown by the upper curve of the upper graph. The transition takes place in the neighborhood of $(\Phi/N)^{1/2} = 1$.

A plot of ω against log $(\Phi/N)^{1/2}$ is shown in Fig. 10*A*; a plot of ω against $(\Phi/N)^{1/2}$ is shown in Fig. 10*B*. Evidently, if ω is basic to the articulation index, the rms pressure metric is appropriate when the value of Φ/N is low, and the logarithmic metric is appropriate when the value of Φ/N is high. In most of the tests that caused difficulty for French and Steinberg's and Beranek's formulas, the speech-noise ratios were low.

The assumptions made in the foregoing discussion were, of course, too unrealistic to support the conclusion that the intensive metric of the theory of intelligibility should be changed. And this is hardly the place to undertake an analysis based upon realistic assumptions, for although it appears to be feasible it would surely become quite involved. Nevertheless, I think that the discussion of the intensive metric may support the notion that the rationale of the theory of signal detection may offer something to the theory of speech intelligibility. In fact, one may see how to go on from the quantity ω, which plays the role of the logarithm of the likelihood ratio, to make use of the a priori information inherent in the listener's knowledge of relative frequencies of speech sounds and in the expectation he has built up out of the past of the received message and other features of the redundant communication situation. There is room, also, for a payoff matrix. It is sometimes observed that people hear what they greatly desire to hear, even though it may have a low probability of being said. Finally, given information about the number of elementary sounds in the ensemble of speech, and about their groupings in phonetic subsets, we might make some progress toward deriving from a rational basis the function $A = X(\mathcal{A})$ that has thus far been based solely on empirical evidence.

The ω transformation of ρ was brought into the discussion only to illustrate an approach, and it may be carrying things too far to ask whether or not it might account for basic phenomena. Nevertheless, it is tempting to examine the implications it seems to have for the theory of differential sensitivity. If the intensive scale has the ω metric, then—other things being equal—signals separated by equal increments of ω should be equally discriminable. From either graph of Fig. 10, therefore, we should be able to derive a statistically based relation covering the same ground as Weber's law. Since the main difficulty encountered by Weber's law is that the first few just noticeable differences (jnds) are larger than predicted by $\Delta\Phi/\Phi$ = const, and since it is obvious that the ω metric will do something toward correcting that difficulty, we may even go so far as to compare the statistically based relation with an experimental curve.

The derivative with respect to ω of the inverse function of Fig. 10*B* is an approximation to the relative size of the jnd in decibels at the corresponding signal level. The inverse function is $20 \log_{10} (\Phi/N)^{1/2}$ or $10 \log_{10} (\Phi/N)$ against ω. If we regard N as the reference value, $20 \log_{10} (\Phi/N)^{1/2} = 10 \log_{10} (\Phi/N)$ is the signal level, and an increment on the abscissa scale of Fig. 10*B* is an increment of signal level

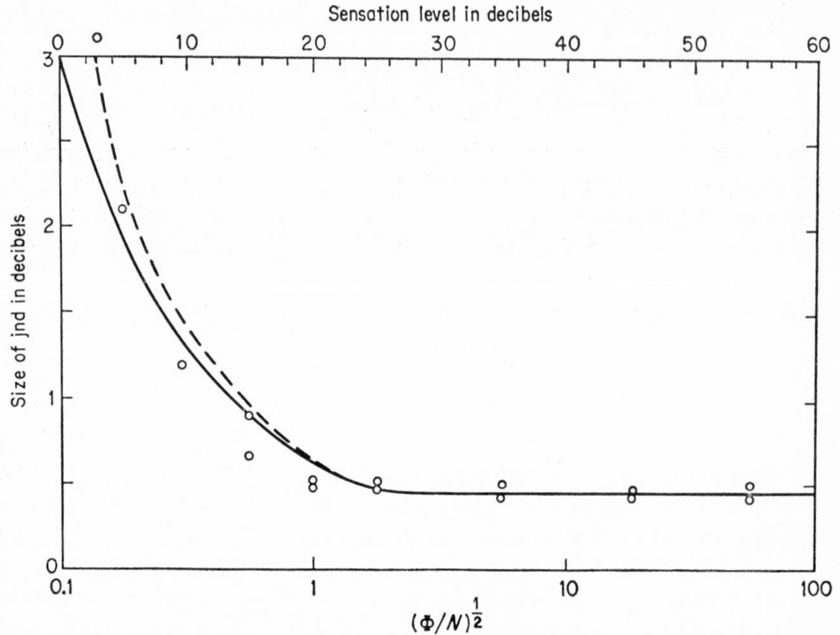

FIG. 11. *Compatibility of the measured just noticeable difference in intensity and the* ω *scale.* The solid curve shows the increments in $(\Phi/N)^{1/2}$, expressed in decibels, that correspond to one-twentieth of one ω unit. The dashed curve is the mean of curves for increments and decrements. The datum points are from measurements of the detectability of changes in the intensity of white noise. Equal discriminability on the ω scale corresponds approximately to equal discriminability in the measurements (if "just noticeable" differences are equally noticeable). Since $\omega \simeq (\Phi/N)^{1/2}$ for weak signals, $(\Phi/N)^{1/2}$ should be 0.05 instead of 0.1 at the "absolute threshold" (0-db sensation level), but the discrepancy is not very serious because the absolute threshold was not measured but estimated from other experiments.

in decibels. The statistical approach prevents our specifying the absolute threshold and the various values of the differential thresholds if we accept the narrow definitions of those terms discussed earlier, but nevertheless we can plot the relative sizes (in decibels) of the equally discriminal increments against the levels of the signals to which the increments are added. That is done in Fig. 11, solid curve. The datum points of Fig. 11 were obtained by G. A. Miller [55] in experiments on the discriminability of changes in the level of random noise.[40] Evidently, the linear-logarithmic metric accounts rather well for the change in discriminatory behavior we encounter as we go from weak to strong signals.

The adequacy of the ω metric for handling the problem of differential sensitivity that has long stood out as the weak spot in Weber's formulation suggests that it be tested experimentally by measuring differential sensitivity in the presence of masking noise. The masking noise would then contribute to N and shift the reference level for the curve of Fig. 11 to a new operating point. A similar suggestion might be made in connection with loudness. At levels well above the background noise, loudness is proportional, not to ω, but to the antilogarithm of ω. (Since ω plays the role of the logarithm of the likelihood ratio, loudness is proportional to the likelihood ratio.) It might be interesting to scale the loudness of signals just emerging from noise.

Process and physiology. One of our three systems is essentially behavioral. One makes reference to the nervous system at one point only, in connection with "neural" noise. The third is not essentially physiological, but it is intended to be compatible with a physiological point of view, and it bases its first main operation upon data nearly physiological in origin. Does the physiological inclination of the third theory stand in the way of blending it with the others?

On the surface, certainly it does. More fundamentally, however, it seems to me that the triplex theory is different in spirit from the others more in its concern with process. The first two theories hold that a particular result or effect is accomplished, and they are not much interested in how. The third (the triplex) theory gets itself so involved in the steps of the process that it becomes a bit vague about the outcome. The difference is especially apparent when we ask what needs to be done next in connection with each system.

The theory of signal detection almost has to depart from its normative model and become more descriptive as it considers the ways in which the actual performance falls short of the ideal. Marill's [54] results indicate, for example, that the human detector is about 13 db below optimal in detecting 1-sec segments of 1,000 cycles per second tone in gaussian-process noise. That leaves a lot of degradation of performance to be explained. It will be necessary to try out a variety of hypotheses, and they will probably take the forms suggested by the names of the "cases" distinguished in the Michigan studies

[40] Recently, Feldtkeller and Zwicker [14] have shown that random noise offers a much more direct approach to the measurement of differential sensitivity than is afforded by tonal stimuli. For that reason, we shall do no more than note that tonal data (e.g., 28) are available for further test of the ω metric.

[25, 59, 60]: "signal known except for phase," "signal one of *M* orthogonal signals known except for phase," etc. Those hypotheses postulate something about the signal ensemble and something about the loss of information during processing. In respect of the latter, they come close to saying that the auditory system derives the signal envelope, losing the fine detail of the oscillations within the envelope. That is not essentially different from what the triplex theory does in operation *G* on high-frequency signals. My point is that as the signal detection theory begins to adjust to data, it will begin to make statements about process, too.

A similar prediction could be made for the theory of intelligibility of speech if it were not for the fact that the latter will have to change in basic essentials—that it will have to reach out beyond the power spectra of speech and interference—to enlarge its scope. As matters stand, it is not clear whether we shall have next another descriptive, behavioral theory or a rational, process theory. Surely, however, it will involve a more detailed specification of speech and interference. The recent work of Miller and Nicely [56], based on the linguists' concept of distinctive features [41, Jakobson, Fant, and Halle], affords a good starting point. It will be difficult to develop a comprehensive theory on that basis without postulating definite steps in the processing of the recovered signals.

If the theories do develop concerns for process, then the question of physiological connections will arise. Probably the well-established facts of cochlear analysis will be appropriated by the theories. It would be extremely helpful to have some physiological answers also to questions about neural parts of the auditory process. For example, does speech perception involve the same neural tissue as the perception of musical sounds? That certainly has a bearing on synthesis. It may be a long time, however, before there are physiological data directly relevant to the decision process or to discrimination among speech sounds.

Essential components of a composite theory. At this stage, it is clear that we cannot synthesize a composite theory. It is tempting, nevertheless, to select a few parts that seem especially attractive, and it is impossible to avoid noting again a few gaps.

First, it will almost surely be helpful to have a well-coordinated dual system for specifying the stimuli. For the microscopic level, the available techniques and language are adequate. For the macroscopic level, we now have "trials" and related paraphernalia and we have auditory objects such as voices, words, clarinets, and fire engines; the former are artificial, and the systematic status of the latter is not clear.

Last, and closely related to the first, we need a way of handling the connection of the listener's reporting mechanism to his auditory mechanism.

Connecting the listener's responses to the macroscopic description of the stimuli, and thus in a sense completing the loop around the listener, we have the payoff matrix. It promises to be an exceedingly valuable tool.

And within the listener we have (1) the picture given us by Békésy of the mechanical action of the cochlea, (2) a rapidly developing understanding of the peripheral excitation process, (3) the concept of "critical bands"—of a system consisting of partially overlapping but otherwise functionally insulated frequency channels, (4) the concept of the residue, (5) the Jeffress-Wallach mechanism of binaural interaction, and (6) the family of concepts relating to optimal observers. A broad theory of hearing would have to have more ingredients, but I should like it to include most of those just listed.

REFERENCES

1. Anon. Suggested discussion topics for contributors of systematic analyses. American Psychological Association Study of Psychological Science, Project A, 1955. (Mimeographed) (See Appendix of this volume.)

2. Bachem, A. Various types of absolute pitch. *J. acoust. Soc. Amer.*, 1937, **9**, 146–151.

3. Bachem, A. Tone height and tone chroma as two different pitch qualities. *Acta Psychol.*, The Hague, 1950, **7**, 80–88.

4. Békésy, G. von. Current status of theories of hearing. *Science*, 1956, **123**, 779–783.

5. Békésy, G. von, & Rosenblith, W. A. The early history of hearing—observations and theories. *J. acoust. Soc. Amer.*, 1948, **20**, 727–748.

6. Békésy, G. von, & Rosenblith, W. A. The mechanical properties of the ear. In S. S. Stevens (Ed.), *Handbook of experimental psychology.* New York: Wiley, 1951. Chap. 27. (References to the relevant series of Békésy's papers are given in this chapter.)

7. Beranek, L. L. The design of speech communication systems. *Proc. Inst. Radio Engrs*, 1947, **35**, 880–890.

8. Boring, E. G. *A history of experimental psychology.* (2d ed.) New York: Appleton-Century-Crofts, 1950.

9. Cramer, E. The pitch of periodically spaced pulses of random polarity. Unpublished senior thesis, Massachusetts Institute of Technology, June, 1955.

10. Davis, H. The excitation of nerve impulses in the cochlea. *Ann. Otol. Rhinol. Laryngol.*, 1954, **61**, 469–481.

11. deBoer, E. *On the "residue" in hearing.* Doctoral dissertation,

Univer. of Amsterdam, 'S-Gravenhage, The Netherlands: Excelsior Publishers, 1956.

12. Egan, J. P. Articulation testing methods. *Laryngoscope,* 1948, **58,** 955–991.

13. Egan, J. P., & Wiener, F. M. On the articulation efficiency of bands of speech in noise. *J. acoust. Soc. Amer.,* 1946, **18,** 435–441.

14. Feldtkeller, R., & Zwicker, E. *Das Ohr als Nachrichtenempfänger.* Stuttgart: S. Hirzel Verlag, 1956.

15. Fisher, R. A., & Yates, F. *Statistical tables for biological, agricultural, and medical research.* London: Oliver and Boyd, 1953.

16. Fletcher, H. Loudness, pitch, and timbre of musical tones and their relation to the intensity, the frequency, and the overtone structure. 1934, *J. acoust. Soc. Amer.,* 1934, **6,** 59–69.

17. Fletcher, H. The mechanism of hearing as revealed through experiment on the masking effect of thermal noise. *Proc. nat. Acad. Sci.,* 1938, **24,** 265–276.

18. Fletcher, H. Auditory patterns. *Rev. mod. Phys.,* 1940, **12,** 47–65.

19. Fletcher, H. Perception of speech sounds by deafened persons. *J. acoust. Soc. Amer.,* 1952, **24,** 490–498.

20. Fletcher, H. *Speech and hearing in communication.* New York: Van Nostrand, 1953.

21. Fletcher, H., & Galt, R. H. Perception of speech and its relation to telephony. *J. acoust. Soc. Amer.,* 1950, **22,** 89–151.

22. Fletcher, H., & Munson, W. A. Loudness, its definition, measurement and calculation. *J. acoust. Soc. Amer.,* 1933, **5,** 82–108.

23. Fletcher, H., & Munson, W. A. Relation between loudness and masking. *J. acoust. Soc. Amer.,* 1937, **9,** 1–10.

24. Fourier, J. B. J. *Théorie analytique de la chaleur.* Paris: Didot, 1822.

25. Fox, W. C. "Signal detectability: a unified description of statistical methods employing fixed and sequential observation processes," Tech. Report No. 19, Electronic Defense Group, Dept. of Electrical Engineering, Univer. of Michigan, Ann Arbor, Mich., Dec., 1953.

26. French, N. R., & Steinberg, J. C. Factors governing the intelligibility of speech sounds. *J. acoust. Soc. Amer.,* 1947, **19,** 90–120.

27. Garner, W. R. Hearing. In C. P. Stone (Ed.), *Annual review of psychology.* Vol. 3, Annual Reviews, Inc., Stanford, Calif., 1952.

28. Garner, W. R., & Miller, G. A. The masked threshold of pure tones as a function of duration. *J. exp. Psychol.,* 1947, **37,** 293–303.

29. Goldstein, M. H., Jr. Representation of some periodic stimuli in the bifrequency plane. *J. acoust. Soc. Amer.,* 1956, **28,** 153 (abstract).

30. Goldstein, M. H., Jr. A study of certain nonlinear characteristics of the auditory nervous system. Unpublished doctoral dissertation, Massachusetts Institute of Technology, 1957.

31. Goldstein, M. H., Jr. Personal communication, 1957.

32. Goldstein, M. H., Jr., & Kiang, N. Y. Electrical responses from the

cat's auditory nervous system to certain repetitive stimuli. *J. acoust. Soc. Amer.,* 1956, **28,** 757 (abstract).

33. Green, D. M. Personal communication, 1956.

34. Hawley, M. E. Personal communication, 1955.

35. Hebb, D. O. *The organization of behavior.* New York: Wiley, 1949.

36. Helmholtz, H. L. F. *Sensations of tone.* A. J. Ellis (Trans.) New York: Longmans, Green, 1930.

37. Hirsh, I. J., Reynolds, E. G., & Joseph, M. Intelligibility of different speech materials. *J. acoust. Soc. Amer.,* 1954, **26,** 530–539.

38. Hoogland, G. A. *The missing fundamental.* Doctoral dissertation, Univer. of Utrecht. Utrecht, The Netherlands: Druckerij Fa. Schotanus en Jens, 1953.

39. Huggins, W. H. Personal communication, 1953.

40. Huggins, W. H. & Licklider, J. C. R. Place mechanisms of auditory frequency analysis. *J. acoust. Soc. Amer.,* 1951, **23,** 290–299.

41. Jakobson, R., Fant, C. G. M., & Halle, M. "Preliminaries to speech analysis: the distinctive features and their correlates," Tech. Report No. 13, Acoustics Laboratory, Massachusetts Institute of Technology, Jan., 1952.

42. Jeffress, L. A. A place theory of sound localization, *J. comp. physiol. Psychol.* 1948, **41,** 35–39.

43. Jenkins, H. M. Personal communication, 1956.

44. Kryter, K. D. "Speech communication in noise," Tech. Report AFCRC-TR-54-52, Operational Applications Laboratory, Air Force Cambridge Research Center, Bolling Air Force Base, Washington, D.C., May, 1955.

45. Kryter, K. D. On predicting the intelligibility of speech from acoustical measures. *J. Speech Hearing Disorders,* 1956, **21,** 208–217.

46. Kryter, K. D. Variables affecting speech communication in noise (in preparation).

47. Licklider, J. C. R. An electrical investigation of frequency localization in the auditory cortex of the cat. Unpublished doctoral dissertation, Univer. of Rochester, 1942.

48. Licklider, J. C. R. A duplex theory of pitch perception. *Experientia,* 1951, **7,** 128–134.

49. Licklider, J. C. R. On the process of speech perception. *J. acoust. Soc. Amer.,* 1952, **24,** 590–594.

50. Licklider, J. C. R. "Periodicity" pitch and "place" pitch. *J. acoust. Soc. Amer.,* 1954, **26,** 945 (abstract).

51. Licklider, J. C. R. Auditory frequency analysis. In Colin Cherry (Ed.), *Information theory.* New York: Academic Press, 1956.

52. Licklider, J. C. R. & Guttman, N. Masking of speech by line-spectrum interference. *J. acoust. Soc. Amer.,* 1957, **29,** 287–296.

53. Licklider, J. C. R., Webster, J. C., & Hedlun, J. M. On the frequency limits of binaural beats. *J. acoust. Soc. Amer.,* 1950, **22,** 468–473.

54. Marill, T. "Detection theory and psychophysics." Tech. Report No.

319, Research Laboratory of Electronics, Massachusetts Institute of Technology, Oct., 1956.

55. Miller, G. A. Sensitivity to changes in the intensity of white noise and its relation to masking and loudness. *J. acoust. Soc. Amer.*, 1944, **19**, 609–619.

56. Miller, G. A., & Nicely, P. E. Analysis of perceptual confusions among some English consonants. *J. acoust. Soc. Amer.*, 1955, **27**, 338–352.

57. Miller, G. A., & Taylor, W. G. The perception of repeated bursts of noise. *J. acoust. Soc. Amer.*, 1948, **20**, 171–182.

58. Mowbray, G. H., Gebhard, J. W., & Byham, C. L. Sensitivity to changes in the interruption rate of white noise. *J. acoust. Soc. Amer.*, 1956, **28**, 106–110.

59. Peterson, W. W., & Birdsall, T. G. "The theory of signal detectability," Tech. Report No. 13, Electronic Defense Group, Dept. of Electrical Engineering, Univer. of Michigan, Ann Arbor, Mich., June, 1953.

60. Peterson, W. W., Birdsall, T. G., & Fox, W. C. The theory of signal detectability. Inst. Radio Engrs *Transactions on Information Theory,* Sept., 1954, Vol. PGIT-4.

61. Pickett, J. M., & Kryter, K. D. "Prediction of speech intelligibility in noise," Tech. Report AFCRC-TR-55-4, Operational Applications Laboratory, Air Force Cambridge Research Center, Bolling Air Force Base, Washington, D.C. June, 1955.

62. Pollack, I. Effects of high pass and low pass filtering upon the intelligibility of bands of speech in noise. *J. acoust. Soc. Amer.*, 1948, **20,** 259–266.

63. Pollack, I. On the effect of frequency and amplitude distortion on the intelligibility of speech in noise. *J. acoust. Soc. Amer.*, 1952, **24,** 538–541.

64. Rochester, N., Holland, J. H., Haibt, L. H., & Duda, W. L. Tests on a cell assembly theory of the action of the brain, using a large digital computer. Inst. Radio Engrs *Transactions on Information Theory,* 1956, Vol. IT-2, pp. 80–93.

65. Schafer, T. H., Gales, R. S., Shewmaker, C. A., & Thompson, P. O. The frequency selectivity of the ear as determined by masking experiments. *J. acoust. Soc. Amer.*, 1950, **22**, 490–496.

66. Schouten, J. F. The perception of subjective tones. *Proc. Konink. Nederlandsche Akad. Wetenschappen,* 1938, **41**, 1086–1093.

67. Schouten, J. F. The perception of pitch. *Philips Tech. Rev.*, 1940, **5**, 286–294.

68. Schouten, J. F. Synthetic Sound. *Philips Tech. Rev.,* 1939, **4**, 167–173.

69. Schouten, J. F. The residue and the mechanism of hearing. *Proc. Konink. Nederlandsche Akad. Wetenschappen,* 1940, **43**, 991–999.

70. Schouten, J. F. The residue, a new component in subjective sound analysis. *Proc. Konink. Nederlandsche Akad. Wetenschappen,* 1940, **43,** 356–365.

71. Shannon, C. E. *The mathematical theory of communication.* Urbana, Ill.: Univer. Illinois Press, 1949.

72. Sherwin, C. W., Kodman, F., Jr., Kovaly, J. J., Prothe, W. C., & Melrose, J. Detection of signals in noise: a comparison between the human detector and an electronic detector. *J. acoust. Soc. Amer.,* 1956, **28,** 617–622.

73. Six, P. D. *De cochleaire verschiltoon.* Doctoral dissertation, Univer. of Amsterdam. Amsterdam: Jacob van Campen Press, 1956.

74. Smith, M., & Wilson, E. A model of the auditory threshold and its application to the problem of the multiple observer. *Psychol. Monogr.,* **67,** 1953.

75. Stevens, S. S. Mathematics, measurement, and psychophysics. In S. S. Stevens (Ed.), *Handbook of experimental psychology.* New York: Wiley, 1951, Chap. 1.

76. Stevens, S. S. Measurement of loudness. *J. acoust. Soc. Amer.,* 1955, **27,** 815–829.

77. Stevens, S. S. On the averaging of data. *Science,* 1955, **121,** 113–116.

78. Stevens, S. S. Calculation of the loudness of complex noise. *J. acoust. Soc. Amer.,* 1956, **28,** 807–832.

79. Stevens, S. S., & Davis, H. *Hearing: its psychology and physiology.* New York: Wiley, 1938.

80. Stevens, S. S., & Volkmann, J. The relation of pitch to frequency. *Amer. J. Psychol.,* 1940, **53,** 329–353.

81. Stevens, S. S., Volkmann, J., & Newman, E. B. A scale for the measurement of the psychological magnitude pitch. *J. acoust. Soc. Amer.,* 1937, **8,** 185–190.

82. Symmes, D., Chapman, L. F., & Halstead, W. C. The fusion of intermittent white noise. *J. acoust. Soc. Amer.,* 1956, **28,** 106–110.

83. Tanner, W. P. Jr. "Psychophysical application of the theory of signal detectability" (reprinted from Minutes of Armed Forces–NRC Vision Committee, Nov. 13, 1953). Engineering Research Institute, Dept. of Electrical Engineering, Univer. of Michigan, Ann Arbor, Mich. 1954.

84. Tanner, W. P. Jr. Theory of recognition. *J. acoust. Soc. Amer.,* 1956, **28,** 882–888.

85. Tanner, W. P. Jr. Personal communication, 1956.

86. Tanner, W. P. Jr., & Norman, R. Z. The human use of information, II: signal detection for the case of an unknown signal parameter, Inst. Radio Engrs *Transactions on Information Theory,* Sept., 1956, Vol. PGIT-4.

87. Tanner, W. P. Jr., & Swets, J. A. "A new theory of visual detection," Report 1970-5-S, Electronic Defense Group, Dept. of Electrical Engineering, Univ. of Michigan, Ann Arbor, Mich., Feb. 1954.

88. Tanner, W. P. Jr., & Swets, J. A. The human use of information, I: signal detection for the case of the signal known exactly, Inst. Radio Engrs *Transactions on Information Theory,* Sept. 1954. Vol. PGIT-4.

89. Tanner, W. P. Jr., Swets, J. A., & Green, D. M. "Some general properties of the hearing mechanism," Tech. Report No. 30, Electronic De-

fense Group, Dept. of Electrical Engineering, Univ. of Michigan, Ann Arbor, Mich., Mar., 1956.

90. Thurlow, W. R., & Small, A. M. Jr. Pitch perception for certain periodic auditory stimuli, *J. acoust. Soc. Amer.*, 1955, **27,** 132–137.

91. Wallach, H. Personal communication, 1942.

92. Wever, E. G. *Theory of hearing*. New York: Wiley, 1949.

93. Wever, E. G., & Bray, C. W. The nature of acoustical response: the relation between the sound frequency and the frequency of impulses in the auditory nerve, *J. exp. Psychol.,* 1930, **13,** 373–387.

94. Wever, E. G., & Bray, C. W. Action currents in the auditory nerve in response to acoustical stimulation. *Proc. nat. Acad. Sci.,* Wash., 1930, **16,** 344–350.

95. Wiener, N. *Cybernetics*. New York: Wiley, 1948.

96. Zwicker, E., Flottrop, G., & Stevens, S. S. Critical bandwidth in loudness summation. *J. acoust. Soc. Amer.,* 1957, **29,** 548–557.

COLOR THEORY[1]

C. H. GRAHAM
Columbia University

[1] The preparation of this manuscript was supported by a contract between the Office of Naval Research and Columbia University. Reproduction in whole or in part is permitted for any purpose of the United States Government.

This article is adapted from a forthcoming book on vision by Clarence H. Graham and associates to be published by John Wiley & Sons, Inc.

INTRODUCTION

This account of color vision and color theory will adhere to the following outline. (1) An account will first be given of certain discriminations whose data stand as especially significant tests of color theory. Considered in the discussion will be such topics as hue discrimination, luminosity, saturation, complementary colors, and the two-color threshold. (2) The topic of color mixture will, because of its extensive historical, experimental, and theoretical background, be taken up in a separate section. The treatment will, to a considerable extent, follow that of Le Grand [115], and to a lesser extent, that of Wright [202, 203]. (3) A general theoretical section will follow the discussion of color mixture. This section will involve short descriptions of the Young-Helmholtz and Hering theories. These descriptions will be followed, in their appropriate places, by considerations of (*a*) examples of variations of the Young-Helmholtz theory and (*b*) a quantitative account based on the Hering hypothesis.[2] (4) A final section will present some analytic and methodological aspects of the general topic of color theory as taken up in (1), (2), and (3).

It is sufficient to say that the position is taken, in the present statement, that some of the factual content of color vision must be described before its topical form can be discussed. An inclusive description of color has not been always available in readily understandable form, but it is worth noting that several excellent accounts [115, 198, 101, 202, 203] have appeared in the recent past. In any case, the present account will offer more than the usual amount of factual description and possibly less "methodological" discussion than might seem desirable to some psychologists.

[2] The discussion of color here presented probably involves insufficient attention to the data of color blindness. However, some consideration of this topic is taken up in the section on color theories.

The section on color mixture will contain information on the history of color theory; it will also present something of what can be said about the systematic and formal nature of color theory. In particular, it will be shown there that, in the study of color vision, theory and experimental observation have progressed simultaneously in a mutually interacting manner. Many of the results that we now think of as quite empirical would have remained unformulated and inexpressible in the absence of a theoretical account; theory language has become data language. Conversely, the theoretical account could not have advanced in the absence of appropriate empirical evidence such, for example, as has established the trichromatic nature of vision.

It should be mentioned and underlined in connection with color mixture that this topic is, at the moment, in a period of change. Concepts which from the beginning have been accepted as basic seem now to be under searching inquiry. Despite this fact, the reader need not be deterred from considering what the data and theories of color mixture have been and what direction they may take in the future. These matters will be taken up in the discussion of the topic.

It will become clear in our discussion that various aspects of color theory exist at various distances from the realm of data language. At one level, we find a condition of theory in which ("tested" or "proved") theoretical concepts are so inextricably intertwined with empirical data that the latter would be relatively meaningless in the absence of the former. At another level, we find a condition in which theoretical concepts exhibit a more general but also (usually) a more tentative nature. As an example of the first condition may be cited the existence of such empirical quantities as the trichromatic coordinates which owe their strategic value and a good deal of their meaning to the representational characteristics of the chromaticity diagram. At a more tentative, general level might be included accounts that involve representations in color-brightness space or theories that describe how color depends on the action of physiological mechanisms.

Both abstract mathematical and mechanical types of theory have been applied to the area of color. For example, the accounts in terms of color-brightness space [167] are of the former type whereas Hecht's hypothesis [55, 58], based on principles of receptor activity, represents the latter type. Within the categories of color theory may be found some relatively positivisitic descriptions that attempt, with a minimum (but still very considerable amount) of theory, the practical task of representing colors and their difference thresholds in appropriate numerical form [96, 119, 120]. Accounts of the latter sort are balanced by descriptions that were intended to develop rigorously from a minimum set of theoretical assumptions [67, 156].

Before considering specific topics, we may, with profit, take up certain terms that will be used throughout our discussion.[3]

Most data of color vision represent discriminations, that is, relations between configurations of luminous flux and appropriate values or aspects of a subject's responses. [On the stimulus-response relations of the psychophysical experiment, see 29, 30, 31, 32.] It might conceivably be possible to get along without such words as "color," "brightness," "saturation," or "hue," provided that we could specify the end terms of a given discrimination. Experience, however, shows that, even if we could always (as we cannot) express uniquely the energy relations that correlate with a given response (and vice versa), the use of such terms would be excessively cumbersome. For this reason, such words as "hue," "saturation," "brightness," and "color" will be used in the present discussion. We shall not argue the question of whether these names are labels, intervening variables, or hypothetical constructs [129, 6].

Consider, first, the use of the term "hue." This term (*a*) represents an inferred effect (behavioral, physiological, or mathematico-representational) taken to exist between events (2) and (3) or (*b*) is the label for the relation between (2) and (3) within the sequence: (1) instructions to a subject (who has had a past history with the vocabulary represented in the instructions), (2) the presentation of radiant energy to the subject, and (3) the subject's responses. It turns out as a matter of empirical fact that wavelength is the appropriate aspect of energy in (2) for hue discrimination.

The dependence of hue discrimination (as manifested by the subject's responses) on wavelength may have been established early in such observations or experiments as the ordering of stimuli by a subject when he is instructed to arrange colors on the basis of hue. The subject is said to discriminate differences in hue when, to take one concrete example, he gives one response (for example, a hue name) to a radiant flux of one narrow wavelength band and another response to flux of a different wavelength. Another type of correlated observation involves the subject's giving (*a*) one response ("No, there is no difference in hue") to a small difference between wavelengths of a pair of stimuli and (*b*) another response ("Yes, there is a difference in hue") to a larger difference. The threshold wavelength difference is evaluated at the appropriate frequency of occurrence of the two responses.

It will be observed that the word "hue" comes into play at least twice in the sequence of events (1), (2), and (3) above. (*a*) It occurs as

[3] The book *Science of Color* [14] gives an excellent discussion of terms that are useful and important in the study of color vision.

part of the instructions (as in the statement "Arrange these colors on the basis of hue"); and (*b*) it is either the term for the inferred effect between (2) and (3), or it is a label for the dependence of (3) on (2). (A full account of the total situation would probably require the additional consideration of (*c*) the role of the word "hue" in the language repertory of the subject who must respond to the instructions.)

The word "hue" used in the instructions (and reacted to by the subject) is analytically a different word from the word applied to the discrimination. The difference in the two words is comparable to the difference discussed by Bergmann and Spence [7] when they contrast the "social" language of the subject and the experimenter in an experiment with the metalanguage of the experimenter as a scientist. Possibly, the difference could be specified by the use of subscripts, as in "hue_i" and "hue_t", where the former word represents the term in the instructions, and the latter, the term applied to the discrimination. The former term controls a subject's activity; it "tells him what to do"; it may imply little or no theoretical context. The latter term involves whatever significances may be attached to it by its ramifying empirical and theoretical connections.

Considerations comparable to those holding for the word "hue" exist with respect to "saturation." The term represents the inferred effect between a stimulus variable and differential responses (or the relational label) that exists when a subject is instructed to order colors on the basis of, for example, "paleness of color." (Here the word "saturation" is not used in the instructions; rather a denotative aspect, "paleness of color," is stated.) It has been found that colorimetric purity is an important (but possibly not an exclusive) stimulus variable in this type of experiment. (Colorimetric purity specifies monochromatic light as a percentage of the total of monochromatic and white light.) The subject does not give different names to different colorimetric purities but he can indicate the existence of differences.

Differences in brightness may be discriminated by processes analogous to those holding for hue discrimination. The subject, under instructions to arrange stimuli according to differences in "brightness" or to "indicate brightness differences," gives different responses (for example, the words "dim" or "bright") to different luminances, or he may differentially signal a difference between luminances. Such discriminations are said to be brightness discriminations. The word "brightness" appears in the double sense characteristic of the word "hue."

The word "color" represents a generic type of discrimination based on a combination of wavelength, colorimetric purity, and luminance. The subject, properly instructed, can respond by naming different colors or with such differential "judgmental" responses as "Same color" or "Different."[4]

"Chromaticness" represents another generic type of discrimination based on a combination of wavelength and colorimetric purity. (It is thus a combination of hue and saturation with brightness constant and removed from consideration.) It (chromaticness) is a correlate of chromaticity, where chromaticity represents values of hue and saturation matches charted on a chromaticity diagram. (The method and significance of the charting will be discussed later.)

The main emphasis in what follows will be upon a description of some basic empirical and theoretical concepts in the area of color. Critical comments will not usually be presented systematically, except in the last section. Consequently, the presentation will lack systematic form. It will, however, have the advantage of remaining closely tied to subject matter. Discussions of color theory require just such a close association of methodology with theory and data, for color is an area whose empirical and formal structures have not always been clearly delineated by expositors.

DISCRIMINATIONS THAT DEPEND ON WAVELENGTH

Color names. During a child's early life, various stimuli come to control different responses, depending upon the conditions of rein-

[4] The discussion of names for stimulus-response relations omits important problems of the context, experimental, verbal, and logical, that "surrounds" each name. The term "brightness," for example, may be taken to represent a relation between luminous flux and a subject's responses, but the question arises as to what characteristics differentiate "brightness" responses from other responses. The difference depends on the experimenter who provides a basis for difference by his method of categorizing the response. He "accepts" only "appropriate" or "meaningful" responses and categorizes them in terms of the statements he and other scientists may make about the conditions of luminous fluxes and responses that are correlated with them. The instructions given a subject restrict his ensuing responses; his "universe" of available behaviors is reduced. In the case of animals, restriction of responses is determined by the apparatus and procedures used. The apparatus partially determines the type of operant elicited [159], and the subsequent conditions of food presentation (reinforcement or nonreinforcement) determine the relative strengths of responses to different stimuli.

In the case of the term "brightness," significant statements concern an array of interrelated concepts based on the observable responses to luminance. Included among these concepts, for example, may be the notion of a "dim-bright" dimension that endows the concept of "brightness" with the concept of quantity. Or, in the view of another experimenter, the concept of nerve impulse frequency may be related to "brightness." In any case, the problem of words as labels, intervening variables, or hypothetical constructs becomes a question of what usage the experimenter or theorist allows himself or is allowed. Certainly, such terms as "color," "saturation," etc., cannot, as hypothetical constructs, remain invariant; their significances or tested associations must change as theory changes.

forcement that prevail during the child's development of the conditioned discriminations.[5] For example, a child gives the word "green" in the presence of a specifiable set of wavelengths and in the presence of a parent's reinforcing approval.[6] "Naming a color" means that, at a later time and in the presence of such wavelengths, the person will continue to give the reinforced response. If the person says "green" to light of wavelength 530 mμ, such a response obtains social approval; it is the "correct" response [160].

The color names that a normal individual gives in the presence of various wavelengths are usually "correct;" that is, they "agree" with the responses of other people. (They would not be reinforced if they did not.) Stated in another way, this means that a given narrow band of wavelengths provides a high frequency of occurrence of a given ("correct") form of response. With a change in wavelength, there may be a change in frequency of that response, very often to zero, with the concurrent appearance of a new ("correct") response at a high frequency.

In establishing a curve between spectral wavelength and frequency of naming responses one would not ordinarily examine the behavior of such terms as *khaki* or *aquamarine*. In fact, it would be assumed that such terms would neither be applicable to narrow wavelength bands (i.e., monochromatic lights)[7] nor appropriate objectives for study in many experiments on color discrimination. For various reasons then, theoretical or otherwise, instructions given to a subject in a naming experiment are usually restrictive; and in experiments on the so-called "psychologically unique" colors four responses only may be given by the subject: "red," "yellow," "green," and "blue" [16, 17].

Judd [97] has presented average wavelength settings for 10 different hues throughout the spectrum based on the data of 26 investigators. The color names that follow are presumed to be applicable

[5] A reinforcement may be defined as a member of a class of agents (food, water, etc.) which, when presented an appropriate interval after a response to a stimulus, causes, in successive trials, a strengthening of the response.

A conditioned discrimination may be defined as the increase in strength of the response to one stimulus and the decrease in strength of a response to another stimulus brought about by reinforcing the response in the former case and withholding reinforcement in the latter case. The discrimination consists in the fact that the animal responds to one stimulus and does not respond to the other [cf., e.g., 159].

[6] A "parent's reinforcing approval" consists of certain responses that the parent makes in response to the child's behavior as "stimuli." The parent's responses might consist of smiling, speaking (in words that could be established as being "secondary" reinforcers), patting, and possibly, the giving of food.

[7] Light given by a narrow band of wavelengths (a band so narrow that its light is, for practical purposes, considered homogeneous as to wavelength) is sometimes termed monochromatic light. We shall frequently employ the term in this sense.

to the hues listed by Judd; each color name is associated with its average wavelength setting. The color names and their associated average wavelength settings are as follows: red (a color bluer than the longest visible wavelength), computed as the complementary[8] of λ521 mμ; reddish-orange, computed as the complementary of 499 mμ; orange, 598 mμ; yellowish-orange, 589 mμ; yellow, 577 mμ; greenish-yellow, 566 mμ; green, 512 mμ; blue-green, 495 mμ; blue, 472 mμ; purplish-blue, 439 mμ.

It would be desirable to have frequency distributions for different color names but these do not seem to be available. It might be inferred that such distributions would behave in the following manner. (We shall here only consider distributions for the names, "yellow," "orange," and "red.")

It is assumed that subjects rarely say "yellow" to a homogeneous light of 570 mμ. As wavelength increases, the frequency of occurrence of "yellow" increases and near 575 mμ it occurs almost all of the time. Near 580 mμ it decreases in frequency and rarely occurs by 590 mμ. Concurrently with the drop in frequency of "yellow," there is a rise in the frequency of a new response, "orange." The frequency of this response rises from a low value near 590 mμ and reaches a maximum by about 600 mμ. A high frequency is maintained to about 610 mμ; thereafter the frequency drops rapidly. The frequency of the response "red" increases from a low value near 610 mμ and reaches a maximum by about 640 mμ. The response "red" is maintained at a high frequency of occurrence to the long wavelength limit of the visible spectrum. The sum of the frequencies in all frequency distributions must be 100 per cent at any wavelength.

The number of color-naming responses that a subject could give to the regions of the visible spectrum might be specified in terms of the separate frequency distributions that would be ascertainable in an exhaustive investigation. Undoubtedly many variables could influence the total number of response distributions and the range of each. Among the probably influencing factors are (a) the different parameters of the stimulus (its area, luminosity, etc.), (b) the instructions given the subject, and (c) the past history of the subject in respect to color naming. Of course photopic levels of intensity are presupposed.

It is not surprising that certain peoples of the world do not have as large a repertory of color responses as do members of Western civilizations. Rivers [154] tested the color responses of two tribes of Papuans, of some natives of the island of Kiwai, and of members of

[8] The topic of complementary colors will soon be discussed. The complementary of a given wavelength is that wavelength (or purple, a mixture of blue and red) that mixes with the given wavelength to give white.

several Australian tribes. Australian tribesmen from the region of Seven Rivers had only three color responses: one for red, purple, and orange; another for white, yellow, and green; and a third for black, blue, and violet. The other groups also had curtailed repertories. For a related discussion of color names of nine Indian cultures of northwestern America, see [152].

Rivers's result probably means no more than that few color responses were ever reinforced in the early lives of his individual subjects. As Myers [133] says: "Language affords no safe clue to sensibil-

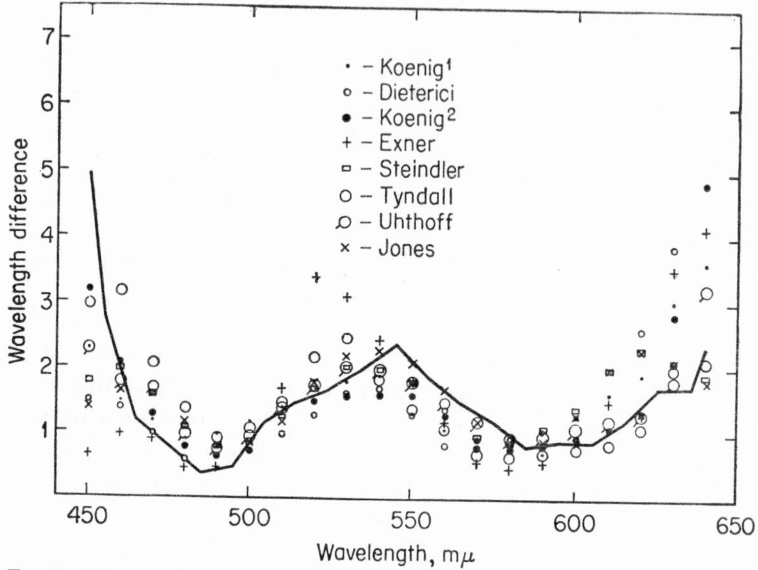

FIG. 1. Thresholds for hue discrimination at various wavelengths as given by the data of eight experimenters. *From Judd* [95].

ity. A color name occurs when it is needful. When it is needless it will not be formed, be the sensibility to that color ever so great." A manifestation of this principle is shown by the fact that Eskimos have many more verbal responses for snow than we do [105].

Hue discrimination. Experiments on hue discrimination thresholds have the following characteristics. A subject regards a photometric field, with half-fields A and B, under instruction to say when a color difference exists between the two half-fields. Field A is filled with the homogeneous light of a very narrow wavelength band. Field B is also filled with homogeneous light whose wavelength may be changed continuously from that of the standard in field A. The fields should be equated in luminance to insure that the subject does not discriminate on a basis of brightness. (This condition is a very important requirement. Small differences in the luminances of the two fields can provide an erroneous result such as has, in fact, occurred in some experiments. Thresholds in the blue are particularly susceptible to this sort of error.) The hue discrimination threshold $\Delta\lambda$ given by such an experiment is the wavelength difference $\lambda_A - \lambda_B$ existing between the two monochromatic lights at the response criterion of threshold. When this general procedure is carried out for many wavelengths λ throughout the spectrum, we obtain a hue discrimination curve.

Figure 1 shows the data on normal subjects of eight experimenters assembled in one graph by Judd [95]. The graph shows that the hue discrimination threshold $\Delta\lambda$ is at a minimum near 480 mμ; thereafter it passes through a maximum near 540 mμ and through a second

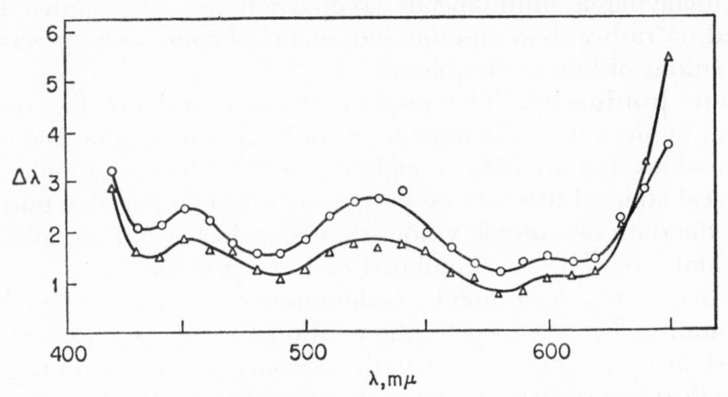

FIG. 2. Hue discrimination data of Laurens and Hamilton [113] for their own eyes. *Adapted from* [113].

minimum near 600 mμ. The threshold is large at the extremes of the spectrum. The spread of data shown in Judd's graph is not surprising. Presumably it is the sort of result that can be expected for data obtained under different conditions.

Figure 2 shows the data of Laurens and Hamilton [113] for their own eyes. As a matter of detail it must be pointed out that a secondary maximum appears in the blue that has no obvious counterpart in Judd's graph. In addition, the data are in accord with results by Steindler [165] and Jones [92] in showing a secondary hump in the orange and red near 600 to 620 mμ. The results differ from the findings of König and Dieterici [110] and Wright and his collaborators [203], which do not show the latter hump.

The significance of the hue discrimination data has been well put from a descriptive point of view by Wright [203] who says:

> The curves as a whole have the characteristics that might be anticipated from a qualitative examination of the spectrum. The part of the spectrum

where a minimum exists must obviously occur where there is a rapid change of hue; thus in the yellow where the colour turns redder on one side and greener on the other, in the blue-green where it turns bluer on one side and greener on the other, in the violet where it becomes redder or bluer, minimum steps would be expected. But beyond 0.61μ the colour changes steadily to a deeper and deeper red, and in the green where there is only a gradual change to either a blue-green or yellow-green, the discrimination is poorer and the step consequently greater.

The hue discrimination threshold is much smaller than the minimum wavelength difference required for the differential naming of colors. In a word, the subject can see differences in hue when he cannot report different color names. It is for this reason that hue discrimination (involving a simultaneous comparison of wavelengths) is depended on rather than absolute judgments of color when precise discriminations of hue are required.

Cone luminosity. The present section considers the data of spectral luminosity at photopic levels of illumination, that is daylight illuminations that are high enough to provide colors by stimulation of the foveal cones. Little will be said, except for comparative purposes, about the data of scotopic vision, that is, vision at dim illuminations where only the rods are stimulated and vision is colorless.

In line with a suggestion by Goldhammer [25], relative luminosity (or visibility) V_λ is defined by the relation $V_\lambda = B_\lambda/KE_\lambda$, where E_λ is the radiance at a given wavelength necessary to provide a luminance B_λ equal to a standard. A plot of V_λ against wavelength gives us the luminosity curve. K is a constant whose values depend upon the units of B_λ and E_λ: it has a value such that when V_λ is at its maximum value, unity, $B_\lambda/E_\lambda = K$.

It is of considerable interest that the rod luminosity values for the different spectral wavelengths can be shown theoretically by Beer's law to be very nearly proportional to the absorption coefficient[9] of

[9] By Beer's law, if I_a is the absorbed energy, I the incident energy, a the concentration of visual purple, and ϵ the absorption coefficient, then

$$I_a = I(1 - e^{-\epsilon a}) \tag{a}$$

This expression expands into the series

$$e^{-\epsilon a} = 1 - \epsilon a + \frac{\epsilon^2 a^2}{1 \cdot 2} \cdots \tag{b}$$

On dropping all but the first two terms and substituting them in (a) we get

$$\epsilon = \frac{I_a}{I \cdot a} \tag{c}$$

The absorption coefficient is (approximately) inversely proportional to the incident energy required for a threshold effect [59].

visual purple [59]. By analogy, as we shall see, the curves for the hypothetical fundamental processes in the cones are often taken to represent the absorption spectra of the sensitive materials.

Gibson and Tyndall [24] made some recommendations and computations concerning the photopic luminosity curve. The computations were accepted as the official data of the average observer by the Commission Internationale de l'Éclairage (CIE)[10] at the sixth Congrès International de l'Éclairage.

In making their computations, Gibson and Tyndall [24] first examined their own data and then those of Hyde, Forsythe, and Cady [78], Coblentz and Emerson [13], Nutting [138], Reeves [153], Ives [88], and So [162]. Data from all these experiments represent results on more than 300 subjects. The data of Gibson and Tyndall and Hyde, Forsythe and Cady—the latter augmented by some data obtained by Hartman [52] in the blue region of the spectrum—were obtained by the method of making heterochromatic comparisons at small steps of wavelength difference (that is, by the step-by-step method). The remaining data were obtained by the flicker method. The latter method involves the adjustment of the luminance of a comparison light until flicker is minimized during the alternation of the comparison with the constant standard light.

The curve giving the CIE luminosity data is presented in Fig. 3. The figure presents the 1924 CIE Photopic Luminosity Function for the Standard Observer, and for comparison, a set of luminosity data approved by the CIE (International Commission on Illumination, 1951) as applying to the rod vision of young eyes.[11] The maximum of each curve, V_{max} $(=K)$, is arbitrarily set at unity (i.e., $\log V_{max} = \log K = 0$).

The maximum of the scotopic curve is at about 507 mμ. The curve of the photopic function has a maximum at about 555 mμ; luminosity values drop on either side of the maximum to low values in the red and blue.

[10] In America the Commission has usually been known as the International Commission on Illumination, abbreviated ICI. However, the designation CIE is official.

[11] The data of Fig. 3 are given in terms of the logarithm of the reciprocal of energy (relative to the maximum) for the fovea and the periphery. The relative energy values must be considered as those existing at the cornea when the retina is stimulated. For luminosity values based on retinal energies, the values shown in Fig. 3 must be corrected [cf., e.g., 62] for: (1) light lost by reflection from the cornea; and (2) the spectral transmittance of light by the refractive media of the eye—the data of Ludvigh and McCarthy [117] are especially useful for the latter correction. Finally it may be desirable to compute luminosity in terms of quanta; the number of quanta corresponding to energy for a given wavelength may be calculated. The relative number of quanta at various wavelengths is directly proportional to wavelength for a given energy.

The luminosity data of Wald [187] have been extended into the infrared by Griffin, Hubbard, and Wald [45]. Near 1,000 mμ the threshold for both periphery and fovea is more than a million times higher than it is for 700 mμ. Goodeve [26] has shown that aphakic eyes (lacking the crystalline lens) can, because of the absence of the ultraviolet absorbing lens, respond to energy of wavelengths down to 320 mμ in the ultraviolet.

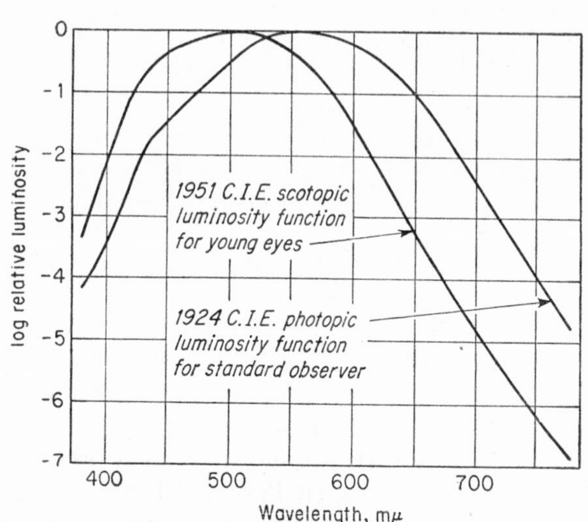

FIG. 3. Log relative luminosity for the rods and cones. The curve to the right is the 1924 CIE photopic luminosity function for the Standard Observer. The curve to the left is the 1951 CIE scotopic luminosity function for young eyes. The curves are so adjusted that maximum visibility for each is set at unity.

In the light of recent evidence, the CIE photopic luminosity values in the blue seem to be too low [cf., e.g., 179] and a reexamination of the curve, particularly in the blue, will probably be made soon [5].

Figure 4 presents data by Hsia and Graham [74] on five color-normal subjects. In their experiment, the area of stimulation was a circular patch 42′ in diameter, exposed centrally for 4 msec under conditions of foveal dark adaptation. The difference between the log luminosity values at 550 mμ and 415 mμ is, for the averaged data, about 1.8 log units. Wald's data [187] give a somewhat higher value, about 2.2 log units. Stiles's results [169] seem to show a difference of about 1.7 log units, and those of Hurvich and Jameson [75], about the same. These figures are to be contrasted with the difference represented on the CIE curve, about 2.7 log units. It is clear that the CIE curve underestimates luminosity[12] in the blue by a considerable amount.

Not only is the luminosity in the blue higher than the values specified by the CIE curve, but the segment below about 460 mμ shows a

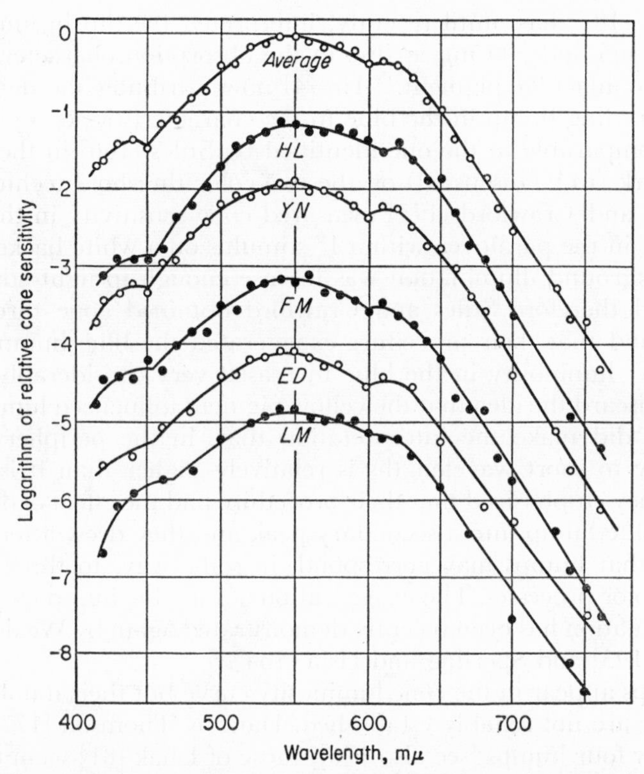

FIG. 4. Logarithm of relative cone sensitivity as a function of wavelength. The stimulus is a centrally viewed round field 42′ in diameter, appearing for a duration of 4 msec. The topmost curve includes the averaged data for the five subjects whose individual data are given in the lower curves. Each successive curve is lowered through one logarithmic unit for clarity of presentation. *From Hsia and Graham* [74].

"hump" such as the one indicated for the data of Hsia and Graham, Fig. 4, and in the results of Wald [187], Stiles [169], Hurvich and

[12] In this connection it is worth observing that the data of both Coblentz and Emerson [13] and Gibson and Tyndall [24] give considerably smaller differences between the logarithms of luminosities at 555 mμ and 415 mμ than the one given by the CIE curve. Thus, the CIE curve does not contain, in the blue, data from experiments which contributed to the rest of the curve. As Thomson points out [176] its values in the blue are those of one investigator, Hartman [52].

Jameson [75], Ishak [81], Thomson [177], Weale [192], and others, including Gibson and Tyndall [24]. A question arises in this connection. Is the hump a "true" hump due to heightened sensitivity, or is it the return to normal (at short wavelengths) from a depressed sensitivity in the spectral region from about 465 to 500 mμ?

Wald [187] has, until recently, interpreted the dip in luminosity between 465 and 500 mμ as due to the absorption characteristics of the yellow macular pigment.[13] He [4] now attributes the depression and succeeding hump in the blue to the characteristics of a violet receptor comparable to the one identified by Stiles [166] in the course of his work (to be discussed) on the two-color threshold technique.

Stiles and Crawford [175] measured cone sensitivity in the fovea and at 5° in the parafovea with a 1° stimulus on a white background. The background illumination was intense enough to light-adapt the rods, and therefore Stiles and Crawford obtained cone thresholds. They found that their procedure exaggerated the blue hump in the periphery; luminosity in the blue increased very considerably. They did not discard the idea that the yellow pigment influenced luminosity, but they did make the interpretation that, in the periphery, cone sensitivity to short wavelengths is relatively higher than it is in the fovea. They emphasized that their procedure had the effect of developing the blue hump into a secondary peak and they drew attention to the fact that humps may correspond, in some way, to three fundamental color processes. The exaggeration of the blue hump by peripheral stimulation has been recently demonstrated again by Weale [192]; see also [193] and Sperling and Hsia [164].

Humps appear in the cone luminosity curve but their number and character are not reliably established. Data by Thomson [177] probably show four humps [see also 176]; those of Ishak [81] seem to indicate two humps in the blue region. The results of Walters and Wright [190], Sloan [161], Hsia and Graham [74], and Hurvich and Jameson [75] indicate that at least one hump appears in the red. Crozier [15] presents a curve with very marked irregularities. Individual differences among subjects in these matters are probably considerable. Results

[13] Walls and Mathews [188] maintain, against Wald's original position, that the central fovea is not pigmented. If pigment exists, it exists in insignificant amounts, and in any case, as experiments on Maxwell's spot [125; see also 130] tell us, it may not exist at all in a central region having a diameter of about half a degree. Maxwell's spot is an entoptic phenomenon ascribed to the yellow pigment. Maxwell, who first described the effect, interpreted it as due to a decreased effectiveness of blue light in stimulating the cones because of absorption by the overlying yellow pigment. The result would be that the pigment is seen entoptically as a dark region outlined against a bright blue background. Walls and Mathews give an excellent history of research on the yellow pigment, including evidence on its histology and biochemistry.

obtained by Göthlin [27; see also 28] on the Rayleigh equation for 100 normal subjects show a considerable range in the proportion of the red to green necessary to match a yellow on Göthlin's anomaloscope. This finding, which is in accord with unpublished observations by Hsia and Graham, indicates that differences exist in the degree of red sensitivity and green sensitivity exhibited by normal subjects. On this basis, it might be supposed that humps, depending upon differential sensitivities, would vary considerably from subject to subject.

The CIE luminosity curve for the Standard Observer is a representational scheme that by no means represents all the data of cone luminosity; in fact, the shape and position of the luminosity curve depend upon a considerable number of controlling variables. For example, an increase in stimulus area results, even within an anatomically homogeneous area of the retina, in a decrease in threshold for a given wavelength [see, e.g., 33]. In addition, with small foveal areas, the shape of the luminosity curve depends upon the position of stimulation within different parts of the fovea [197, 179].

The reciprocity law, $B \cdot \tau$ = const, for the duration and luminance of lights required to produce a constant effect, probably applies to light of all wavelengths [155]; for values of τ less than a critical duration τ_c the radiance of a given wavelength must be increased when its duration of exposure is decreased if the same constant effect (threshold, for instance) is to be achieved under the changed conditions of stimulation.

The shape of the luminosity curve depends on the intensity level of the criterion effect and on the degree of light adaptation that exists when the subject makes his observations [161]. For a size of stimulus that fell within the rod-free area, Sloan found that, under conditions of dark adaptation, the photopic luminosity curve changes shape with change in intensity level; in particular, the position of maximum luminosity changes from about 555 to 540 mμ for intensities below 0.2 meter-candle; at intensities above this level and under conditions of light adaptation, the wavelength of maximum luminosity remains near 555 mμ. In a similar type of experiment, Walters and Wright [190] found that the maximum of the luminosity curve shifts slightly toward the blue as luminance of the matching field decreases. Hurvich and Jameson [75] found a similar shift of the maximum into the blue as dark adaptation increases.

If the area of stimulation includes both cones and rods, the luminosity curve may be taken to represent cone function at high intensities and rod function at low intensities. The maximum of luminosity passes from about 555 mμ at photopic intensities to about 500 mμ at scotopic [161].

Changes in shape of the function also occur as intensity level increases; the luminosity curve becomes asymmetrical, exhibiting a broadening on the long-wave side [161]. In conditions of light adaptation provided by an illuminated surround, a decrease in intensity causes the reverse of a Purkinje effect; there is a shift of the maximum to 580 mμ [161].

Hurvich and Jameson [76; see also 90] examined the influence of different levels of adapting luminances due to white, blue, green, yellow, and red adapting-surround fields. They found that chromatic adaptation provides a relative decrement in the luminosity for wavelengths that correspond to the chromatic adaptation. In general, "luminosity functions applying to the chromatically adapted observer may depart considerably from the standard luminosity function" [76].

The condition of light adaptation (and conversely, dark adaptation) may be determined by other factors than prevailing illumination, as, for example, by the duration of dark adaptation following exposure to a preadapting light. An example of this effect in selecting the class of receptor to be studied may be cited in the case of an experiment by Wald [187]. See also Graham, Brown, and Mote [34] for a similar method that used light adaptation to restrict stimulation to the foveal cones. Wald presented a stimulus, 1° in diameter, in a position 8° above the subject's fovea. By restricting threshold determinations to the temporal interval covered by the cone plateau of the dark adaptation curve, Wald was able to obtain cone thresholds in the periphery. Continued dark adaptation, of course, brought in rods, and determinations after about ten minutes in the dark involved thresholds for rods that were far below cone thresholds.

The ratio of rods to cones stimulated depends upon a number of factors among which are the size of stimulus area, the intensity of stimulus, the retinal region stimulated, the density of rods and cones in the stimulated area, the wavelength of light, the duration of dark adaptation, and the type of receptor available for stimulation at that duration. Information on these factors will become increasingly important theoretically to refine and augment the implications of the Duplicity theory [59].

Complementary colors. Complementary colors are those pairs of colors that mix to match a given white standard in ascertainable proportions. Table 1 lists complementary pairs, together with their respective retinal illuminances, required to match a white light of 75 trolands. The data are Hecht's [58] computations of Sinden's [158]. The table presents no complementaries for wavelengths between 570.5 and 496 mμ; in fact, no single wavelength will provide white when it is added to a wavelength in the range between the latter two wavelengths. It will be shown later, when we consider Grassman's laws, color mixture, and the chromaticity diagram, that the complementaries of these intervening wavelengths are not spectral colors. The complementaries lie, in fact, in the purples, colors that are mixtures of red and blue.

Many experiments have been aimed at determining complementary pairs. Priest [146] has combined data based on the determinations of Helmholtz, von Kries, von Frey, König, Dieterici, Angier, and Trendelenburg, as presented by Nagel [68] in the third edition of

TABLE 1. SPECTRAL COMPLEMENTARIES AND THEIR RETINAL ILLUMINANCES TO MATCH A WHITE OF 75 TROLANDS*

Complementaries		Retinal illuminances	
λ_1	λ_2	$(RI)_1$	$(RI)_2$
650	496	31.6	43.4
609	493.5	39.3	35.7
591	490	50.3	24.7
586	487.5	55.4	19.6
580	482.5	62.0	13.0
578.5	480.5	64.2	10.8
576.5	477.5	65.8	9.2
575.5	474.5	67.7	7.3
574	472	69.0	6.0
573	466.5	70.6	4.4
572	459	72.1	2.9
570.5	443	73.2	1.8

* Data from R. H. Sinden, Studies based on spectral complementaries, *J. opt. Soc. Amer.*, 1923, **7**, 1123–1153, as computed by S. Hecht, Vision: II. The nature of the photoreceptor process, in C. Murchison (Ed.), *Handbook of general experimental psychology*, Worcester, Mass., Clark Univ. Press, 1934. Pp. 704–828.

Helmholtz (vol. 2), and finds that the relation between the complementary wavelengths corresponds to a rectangular hyperbola having the equation $(530 - f)(f_c - 608) = 220$, where f is wave frequency per 10^{-12} second and f_c is that of its complementary. Southall [69] presents Grunberg's formulation in a footnote in Helmholtz (vol. 2). This formulation is in terms of wavelengths λ and λ' of the complementary pairs. It is expressed as follows: $(\lambda - 559)(498 - \lambda') = 424$; $(\lambda > \lambda')$. These empirical relations are of some interest but they have an uncertain significance.

The white given by a mixture of complementaries may be thought of as a limiting case of saturation changes (see the following section) that occur when colors are mixed. When two lights close to each other in the spectrum are mixed, the color of the mixture corresponds to a wavelength intermediate between the two lights; that is, the dominant wavelength of the mixture (the wavelength matched by the mixture) lies between the two lights. It is to be noted, however, that under these circumstances, the mixture differs from the intermediate wavelength by the fact that the mixture seems to be paler or less saturated than the intermediate wavelength. As the two lights to be mixed become more and more separated in the spectrum, the mixture becomes less saturated until finally it gives only a white. An account of the decrease in saturation of the mixture (as contrasted with the saturation of the matching intermediate wavelength) is given by the geometrical representation of the chromaticity diagram, which will be taken up later.

Jameson and Hurvich [91], working within the framework of an opponent-colors theory of vision, determined the chromatic responses for the four "cancellation" stimuli, red, yellow, green, and blue. The cancellation stimuli for the two observers were slightly different; for H, they were 467, 490, 588, and 700 mμ; for J, 475, 500, 580, and 700 mμ.

The cancellation stimuli were chosen (except for λ700 mμ) on the basis of the "psychological uniqueness" of their colors. Since "unique" red is theoretically extraspectral, the 700 mμ stimulus was taken as a representative of red in the realm of real colors. ("Unique" stimuli are not essential; in fact, they were used by Jameson and Hurvich only to simplify analysis.)

Consider now how the experiment is performed. A subject views a mixture of the cancellation stimulus and another wavelength. The subject can manipulate the energy of the cancellation stimulus until a point is reached where he states "No trace of the complementary of the cancellation stimulus is detectable in the mixture." At this point the log energy of the cancellation stimulus is recorded. When this operation is performed a number of times for not too widely spaced wavelengths, one can obtain a curve such as the one marked g in Fig. 5. The log chromatic valence values on the curve are the energies of λ700 mμ required to produce the statement of "no appearance of green." At the different wavelengths indicated, the "green component" in each color for low wavelength is "cancelled" by the "red" of λ700 mμ. The g curve gives the results for wavelengths that exhibit measurable g valences. The other curves b, y and r are determined by finding the cancellation energies for, respectively, 588, 467, and 490 mμ. Cancellation of the y component in, say, 550 mμ takes place when the cancellation stimulus 467 mμ is added to 550 mμ in such amount that "no trace of yellow is left." (Nor, of course, must there be an "excess of blue" due to 467 mμ. Under these circumstances, the subject reports a "neutral hue.")

The result of the procedure is the four curves of Fig. 5, one for each cancellation stimulus. (The *r* curve has two widely separated

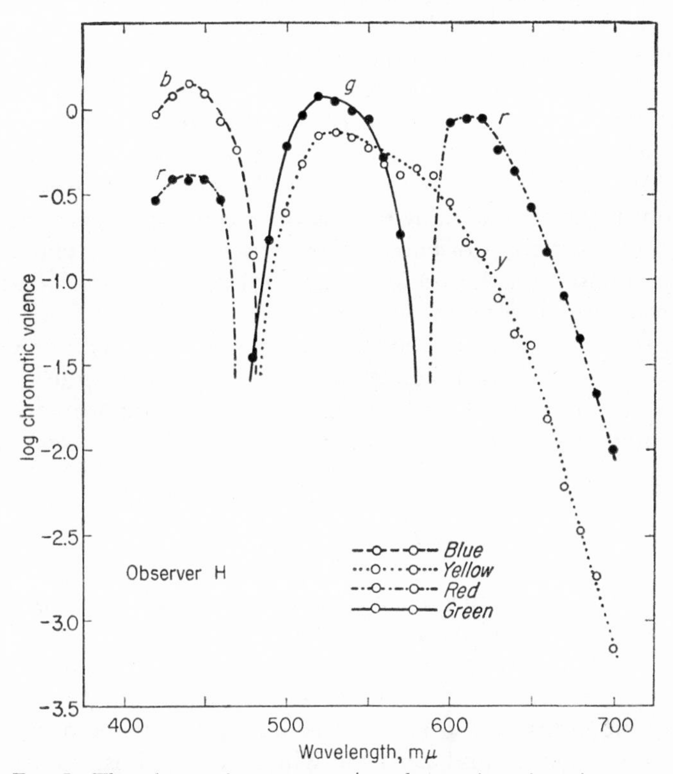

Fig. 5. The chromatic response (or chromatic valence) curves for subject H in the experiment by Jameson and Hurvich [91]. The form of each chromatic curve is measured directly by the relative log energy of the opponent "cancellation" stimulus at each wavelength. In the case of the blue function, for example, the chromatic response values are given by the "cancellation" energies of the fixed opponent yellow stimulus; in the case of the red curve, by the cancellation energies of the fixed opponent green stimulus, etc. *From Jameson and Hurvich* [91].

branches, one at the long-wave end, the other at the short-wave end of the spectrum.)

Since it is assumed that equal amounts of the opponent hue responses (*y* and *b* or *r* and *g*) are present in a truly complementary mixture, the measured relative energy ratios of the components of a mixture of opponent stimulus pairs may be used to adjust the paired chromatic valence curves. This adjustment positions the *Y* curve with respect to the *B*, and the *R* with respect to the *G*. It does not place the yellow-blue pair in relation to the red-green pair. This is done by determining (for a given luminance level) the wavelengths at which, for example, the sensations of yellow and red are equal. The *Y* and *R* curves are adjusted to intersect at this wavelength.

Saturation and colorimetric purity. If a subject, rated normal as to color vision, is instructed to arrange a set of similarly colored cards according to some such characteristic as degree of "paleness of color" he will produce an orderly array, even though the cards are photometrically equated in luminance. A similar or slightly different set of instructions given to a number of people will probably result in the same general ordering of cards. The arrangement, the experimenter will say, is based on the subject's discrimination of saturation differences between the colors of the samples.

The stimulus terms of the saturation relation have not yet been finally specified in a completely satisfactory manner. One important stimulus variable in saturation discrimination is colorimetric purity p. Colorimetric purity is defined for a mixture of a spectral color and white as

$$p = \frac{B_\lambda}{B_W + B_\lambda} \tag{1}$$

where B_λ is the luminance of a spectral color and B_W the luminance of the white with which it is mixed. (The colorimetric purity of a color composed of mixed spectral colors is the p value of a mixture of white and a single spectral color that matches the mixture of spectral colors.) The definition of purity in (1) is such that p has a value of 1.0 for any spectral color alone, and zero for white alone; thus, by definition, purity varies between the limits of zero and 1.0.

A subject can not only discriminate saturation differences for the same dominant wavelength; he can also make the discrimination as between wavelengths. For example, a subject will ordinarily say that a yellow, whose luminance is equated to that of a blue, is less saturated than the blue. In a word, spectral colors also seem to exhibit differences in saturation. It is not possible on the basis of Eq. (1) to assign different values of colorimetric purity to different spectral colors, for by the definition, a value of unity is attributed to all spectral colors. This fact raises an obvious difficulty to considering saturation to be monotonically related to colorimetric purity for different wavelengths.

Precise experiments on colorimetric purity have ordinarily employed two photometric fields. Both fields are initially equal in luminance, B, and spectral composition; they contain either (1) a white alone ($B = B_W$), or (2) a white mixed with a given amount of a spectral color ($B = B_\lambda + B_W$). Under either condition, it is possible to determine a just discriminable difference Δp in purity between two fields. In the first case, (1), where we find the first discriminable step Δp_1 from white,

$$\Delta p_1 = p_1 - p_0 = \frac{B_{\lambda_1}}{B_{W_1} + B_{\lambda_1}} \tag{2}$$

In this expression, the first term p_1 is the only effective one since, for white, $p = p_0 = 0$. Successive discriminable differences in purity are given by

$$\Delta p_n = p_n - p_{n-1} = \frac{B_{\lambda_n}}{B_{W_n} + B_{\lambda_n}} - \frac{B_{\lambda_{n-1}}}{B_{W_{n-1}} + B_{\lambda_{n-1}}} \tag{3}$$

In experiments on colorimetric purity it is usually important to add B_λ in such a way that the total luminance of the field ($B = B_W + B_\lambda$) is maintained constant. This procedure requires that when B_λ is increased, B_W must be decreased by the same change in luminance. For a series of determinations of discriminable differences in purity, luminance remains constant, that is, $B_W + B_\lambda = B = const.$ Since this is so, the denominators of both quotients on the right hand side of (3) are constant and equal, and, in general,

$$\Delta p_n = \frac{\Delta B_n}{B} \tag{4}$$

where $\Delta B_n = B_{\lambda_n} - B_{\lambda_{n-1}}$

The first discriminable difference ($\Delta p_1 = \Delta B_1/B$) is usually called the least or minimum colorimetric purity. Its reciprocal is often used as an index of saturation for different wavelengths.[14]

The experiment of Priest and Brickwedde [149] provides a good example of work on least perceptible colorimetric purity. Data were obtained on 10 subjects. The white used was Abbott-Priest sunlight [147], representing a color temperature of approximately 5000°K. Observations were made through an artificial pupil of 3 mm, a 4° field at about 80 trolands being observed in a large surround of about 10 trolands. Figure 6 presents log Δp_1 as a function of wavelength. It may be observed that the lowest value of least perceptible colorimetric purity occurs in the blue, the threshold rising with increasing wave-

[14] The reciprocal of Δp_1 is the ratio of maximum colorimetric purity (=1.0) to least colorimetric purity. The larger the ratio, the smaller the percentage the least colorimetric purity is of the maximum. A low threshold (i.e., a low percentage value) might represent a high strength of "saturation producing effect." In this matter, too, we are faced with difficulties arising from the fact that colorimetric purities of 100 per cent do not correspond to the same saturation for various wavelengths.

length until it reaches a maximum at about 570 mμ; it drops thereafter to a final intermediate value in the red.

Other authors who have determined least perceptible colorimetric purities by adding spectral lights to white include Purdy [151], Martin, Warburton, and Morgan [122], Wright and Pitt [207], Nelson [134], Grether [44], and Chapanis [11]. Grether [44] investigated the saturation function for chimpanzees as well as man and found similar curves for the two organisms. Chapanis tested color-blind individuals as well as two normal persons.

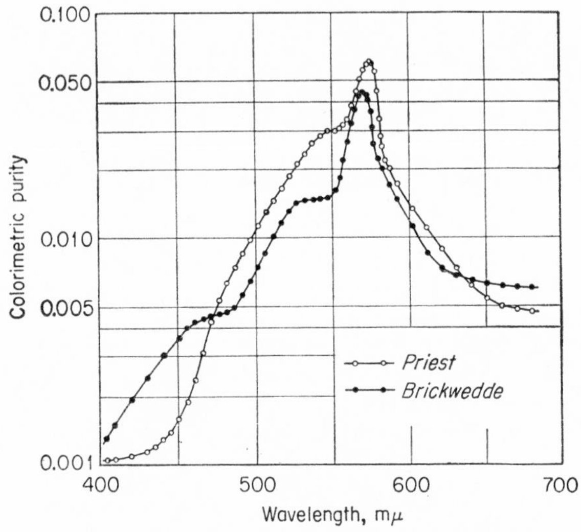

FIG. 6. The individual data of Priest and Brickwedde in their experiment on least colorimetric purity. *From Hecht* [58]; *data from Priest and Brickwedde* [149].

The results of all of these investigators are, in general, similar to those of Priest and Brickwedde. Least colorimetric purity has low values in the short- and long-wave regions of the spectrum; the maximum occurs in the spectral region from 560 to 580 mμ. When the reciprocal of least colorimetric purity $1/\Delta p_1$ is taken as an index of saturation, then saturation exhibits a maximum in the blue region of the spectrum, a minimum in the yellow near 570 mμ, and an intermediate value in the red.

Jones and Lowry [93] determined the number of steps in colorimetric purity that exist between a white of 5200°K and each of eight spectral colors. They found that the number varied from 23 steps at 440, 640, and 680 mμ to 16 at 575 mμ. Results by Martin, Warburton, and Morgan [122] also show the dependence of number of steps on wavelength. Using a probably smaller field (2°) than Jones and Lowry's, they found (for a white of color temperature 4800°K) that the number of steps varies from about 5 to 6 near 565 mμ to something like 20 to 25 in the blue and red regions of the spectrum. On the assumption that the just discriminable steps in purity represent equivalent increments (or decrements) in saturation, Jones and Lowry's results, and even more strikingly, those of Martin, Warburton, and Morgan support the contention that spectral colors do vary in saturation.

One other fact should be mentioned concerning the data of Jones and Lowry and an observation that is supported by some results of Wright and Pitt [206]; the decrement in purity $-\Delta p_n$ in the change from a spectral color to one just tinged with white varies much less with wavelength than does Δp_1, the change from a white to one just tinged with the spectral color. Wright and Pitt have suggested that initial states of adaptation might account for the different results in the two cases. (See [77] to be discussed in a later section.)

It is interesting to observe that the curve relating discriminable steps of purity to wavelength is, in general, similar in shape to the curve of the reciprocal of least colorimetric purity plotted against wavelength, and both exhibit some similarity to the curve for flicker-photometer frequency as a function of wavelength [Troland, 181, 183]. (Flicker-photometer frequency is the lowest rate of alternation per second of a color with a white which suffices to eliminate flicker.) The minimum flicker rate occurs at about 570 mμ, the wavelength at which the maximum value for least colorimetric purity occurs.

The data on complementary colors can be treated from the point of view of saturation relations. (In this connection, see Hecht's discussion [58] of Sinden's data on complementary pairs.) In particular, it will be worth while to consider Jameson and Hurvich's [91] treatment of chromatic responses as relating to their four "cancellation" stimuli. They assume that saturation discrimination can be calculated from their data on the assumption that the threshold increment in a given spectral light varies inversely with the ratio of chromatic to achromatic plus chromatic components $B_\lambda/(B_W + B_\lambda)$ in the response to that light. The measured chromatic response functions of, for example, Fig. 5 are assumed to provide the independent measure of chromatic excitation, and the measured luminosity functions [90] on the same two observers provide an independent measure of the achromatic response, i.e., the relative luminosity of each wavelength. The logarithms of the ratio of chromatic to achromatic effect at each wavelength are presented for subjects H and J in the lowest two curves in

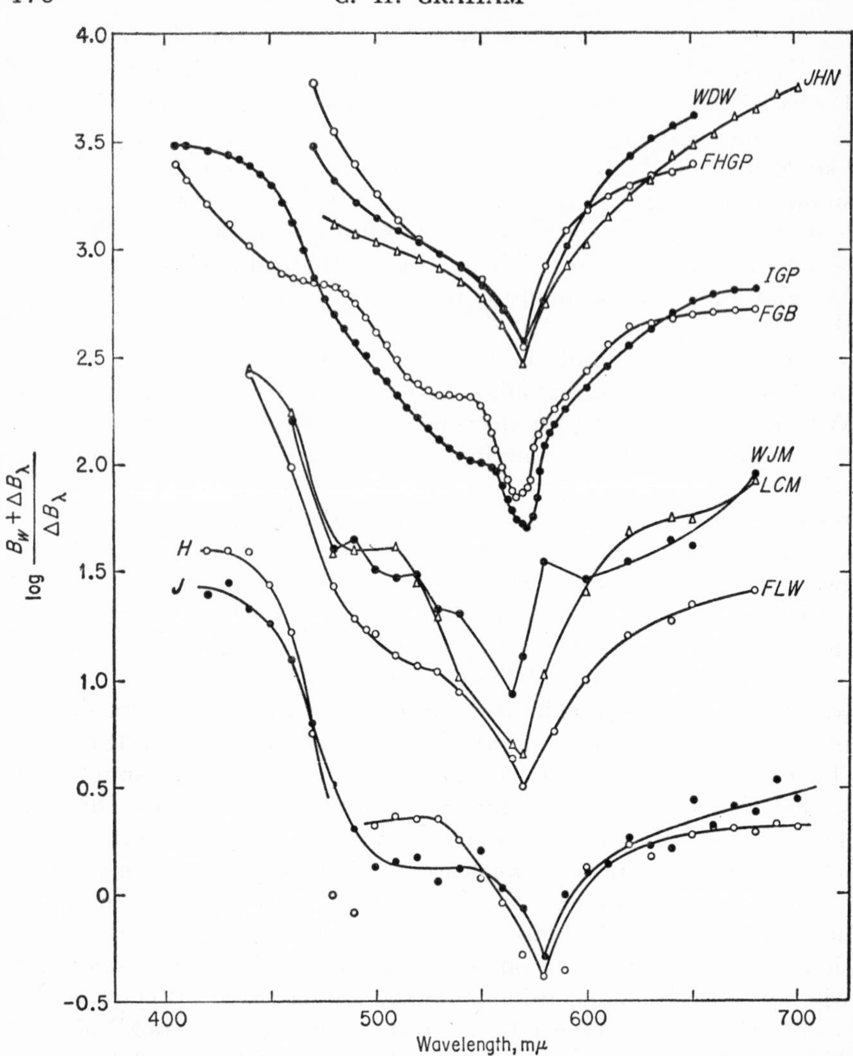

Fig. 7. The saturation discrimination curves obtained by Wright and Pitt [207], Nelson [134], Priest and Brickwedde [149], and Martin, Warburton and Morgan [122], respectively. The bottom curve represents saturation discrimination computed as the ratio of chromatic to achromatic components by Jameson and Hurvich [91] in their experiment on chromatic valences determined by the cancellation procedure. *From Jameson and Hurvich* [91].

Fig. 7. In general, it seems that the computations of Jameson and Hurvich in regard to saturation gave results similar to those obtained on subjects in the experiments of Wright and Pitt [207], Nelson [134], Priest and Brickwedde [149], and Martin, Warburton, and Morgan [122].

The two-color threshold. In 1939, Stiles [166, 169, 170, 171] presented data on the spectral sensitivities of rods and cones obtained by means of a two-color threshold technique. The quantity measured was the increment threshold U_λ of a small test stimulus, of wavelength λ, presented in the form of a flash on a larger adapting field of wavelength μ and energy W_μ.[15] The diameter of the adapting field was about 10°, and each side of the square test field subtended about 1.0°. Conditions of exposure were such that the test field was presented for 0.063 sec once every 3.6 sec. The subject was dark adapted before each series of determintions [166].

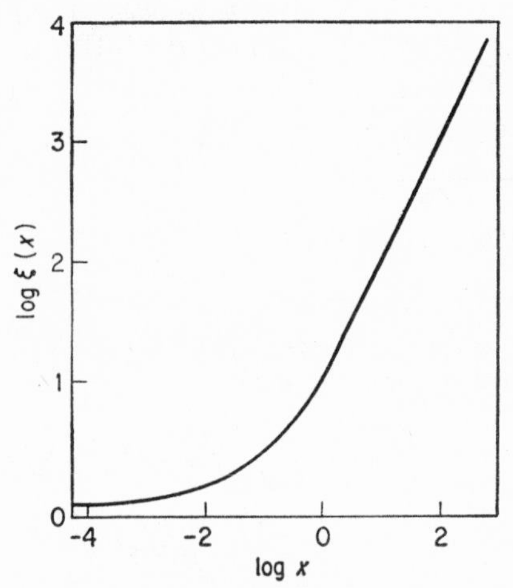

FIG. 8. Stiles's theoretical $\xi(x)$ curve. *Adapted from Stiles* [166, 170].

A number of considerations led Stiles to estimate a type of theoretical relation, called the $\xi(x)$ function, that should exist between log U_λ and log W_μ for a single color mechanism with unique spectral sensitivity [166, 170]. Such a curve, shown in Fig. 8, has, for fixed λ and μ, a finite threshold value of U_λ as W_μ approaches zero, while at moderately high values of W_μ, U_λ increases regularly with W_μ, in fact, proportionally if Weber's law holds. The theoretical curve is fairly well reproduced in the results for brightness discrimination when $\lambda = \mu$. Under circumstances of similarly colored test and back-

[15] U'_λ = the flux of radiant energy of wavelength λ in ergs/sec received by the eye during the stimulus flash, divided by the angular area of the stimulus in square degrees. W_μ is a comparable quantity for the field providing wavelength μ. U_λ is defined as the threshold value of U'_λ for seeing the test field on the adapting field. U'_λ and W_μ are, for convenience, referred to as the energies of the test and adapting stimuli respectively.

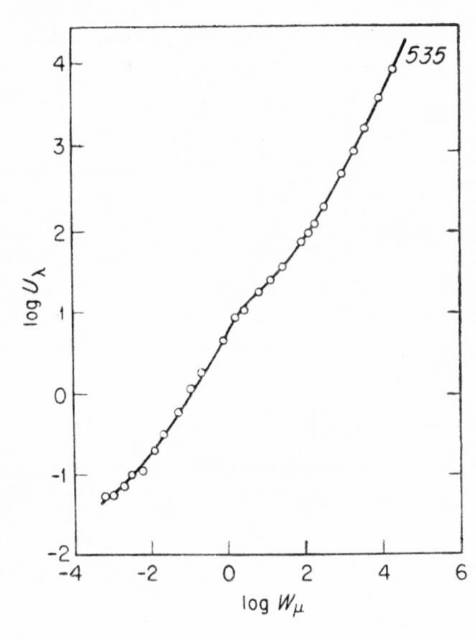

Fig. 9. Intensity discrimination thresholds when both test and background areas are filled with light of wavelength 535 mμ. Log U_λ is plotted against log W_μ. The curve represents rod function at low values of log W_μ and cone function at high values. *From Stiles's* [170] *presentation of data from Hecht, Peskin, and Patt* [61].

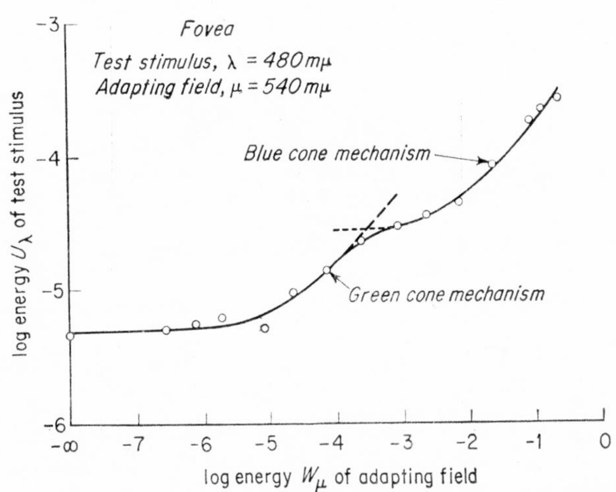

Fig. 10. The threshold of the test stimulus as a function of the energy of the adapting field for two different wavelengths in foveal vision: $\lambda = 480$ mμ, $\mu = 540$ mμ. *From Stiles* [170].

ground areas, U_λ varies with W_μ in the manner described in Fig. 9 which represents results obtained by Hecht, Peskin, and Patt [61] for wavelength 535 mμ. The brightness discrimination curve is composed of two branches, one representing rods at low values of W_μ, and the other, cones at high values of W_μ. Each branch is a simple rising function; the two functions meet at the rod-cone "break."

The situation is different when λ and μ are not the same (i.e., $\lambda \neq \mu$). Under these circumstances, the foveal curve for U_λ vs. W_μ shows, for some combinations of wavelengths, a division into two or more component branches. An example of such behavior is exhibited in Fig. 10 [170] which shows how the threshold for a blue test stimulus ($\lambda = 480$ mμ) varies as a function of the intensity of a green adapting field ($\mu = 540$ mμ). (The same general type of relation exists for all conditions of stimulation for which λ lies between 460 and 510 mμ and μ is less than 530 mμ. Weaker effects are obtained with a yellow test stimulus and a deep red adapting field.) The two divisions of the curve are interpreted as due to the fact that one cone mechanism gives way to another as intensity is raised, just as rods give way to cones with increasing intensity as in Fig. 9. Thus each branch in a foveal U_λ vs. W_μ curve presumably represents the activity of a group of color receptors of a single type. From a consideration of the position of such curves it is possible to estimate the spectral sensitivity functions of the different types of foveal receptors.[16]

From an analysis of measurements made on his own eye Stiles has derived the cone spectral sensitivity curves shown in Fig. 11 [166, 170].

The curves on the right (S_μ, B_μ, G_μ, R_μ) represent spectral sensitivities to the adapting effect of the field, those on the left (s_λ, b_λ, g_λ, r_λ), threshold

[16] Each foveal curve having separate branches seems to be made up of simple component curves, each of which has the shape of $\xi(x)$. The following displacement rules apply for different colors of test area and adapting field: (1) for every pair of wavelengths λ, μ, the curve of each component of the log U_λ vs. log W_μ curve will have the same shape but will assume different positions with respect to the axes. (2) When the wavelength of the test stimulus is changed from λ_1 to λ_2, the curve is translated parallel to the axis of log U_λ by the amount log $(s_{\lambda_1}/s_{\lambda_2})$, i.e., by the logarithm of the ratio of the spectral luminosities. (3) When the wavelength of the adapting field is changed from μ_1 to μ_2, the curve is translated parallel to the axis W_μ by the amount log (S_{μ_1}/S_{μ_2}). S_{μ_1} and S_{μ_2} are the reciprocals of the intensities of adapting field required to provide a U_λ that has a value 10 times the "absolute" threshold [170]. (By "absolute" threshold is meant the value of U_λ that exists when no background W_μ is present.)

The methods required to determine the spectral sensitivity functions b_λ to R_μ of Fig. 11 [166, 169] may be illustrated by two examples [170]. "Assuming that for a deep red test stimulus, say $\lambda > 650$ mμ, the absolute threshold of the 'red' mechanism is materially lower than those of the 'green' and 'blue' (say less than one-fifth), then for an adapting field of any wavelength the initial (low intensity) portion (say from the absolute threshold to five times the absolute threshold) of the observed (U_λ vs. W_μ) curve will coincide with the 'red' component curve. The position of the latter along the axis of log W_μ is obtained therefore for all values of μ and hence the function R_μ is determined. Again, for a test stimulus of wavelength between 460 and 510 mμ and for an adapting field of wavelength greater than 530 mμ, the (U_λ vs. W_μ) curve can be represented by two components. From the position of these two components considerable sections of the b_λ, B_μ, g_λ, G_μ curves can be determined."

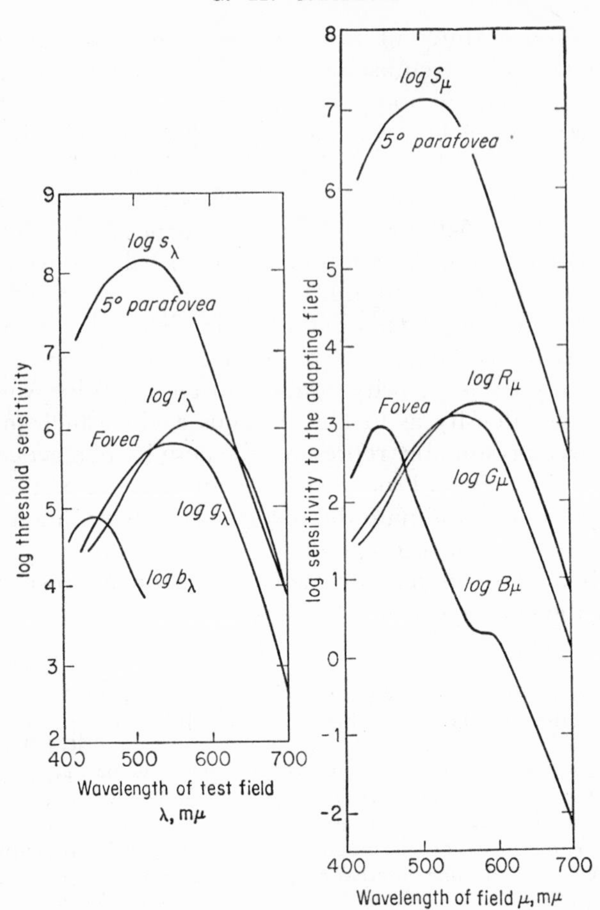

FIG. 11. The spectral sensitivities of the cones determined by the two-color technique. The figure to the left represents threshold sensitivities for the test stimulus; the curve to the right, sensitivities for the adapting effect of the field. In each figure, the upper curve represents the sensitivity curve for the 5° parafoveal rod mechanism; the lower group of curves, the foveal cones. *From Stiles* [169].

sensitivities (S_μ). It will be noted that the threshold (s_λ) and adapting sensitivities of the 5 degree-parafoveal rods are also included in the figure. No corrections for macular or lens pigmentation have been applied. According to the results summarized in Figure [11], the threshold spectral sensitivity curve of cone vision is the resultant of three curves with maxima at about 440 mμ, 540 mμ, and 590 mμ respectively. . . . Another point which should be noticed is that the ratio of the threshold and field sensitivities taken at the same wavelength has different values for the different mechanisms. We have,

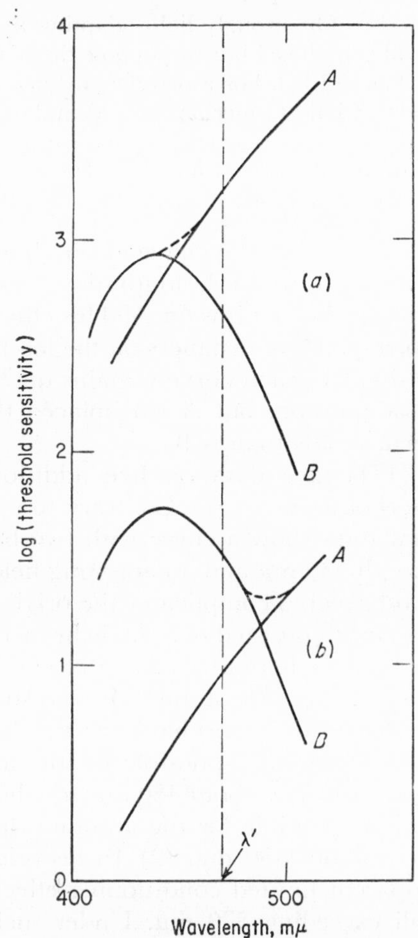

FIG. 12. Stiles's scheme to account for the way in which light adaptation modifies the cone luminosity curve. *From Stiles* [169].

approximately, for $\lambda = \mu$,

$$\frac{r_\lambda}{R_\mu}:\frac{g_\lambda}{G_\mu}:\frac{b_\lambda}{B_\mu}:\frac{s_\lambda}{S_\mu} = 6:5:1:0.1$$

The different values of the ratios indicate that the sensitivities of the three mechanisms change relative to each other at threshold under conditions of increased light adaptation. The significance of the change may be understood in terms of the following analysis [169]:

Suppose for simplicity that there are only two cone mechanisms A and B, and that their respective sensitivity curves for the fully dark-adapted fovea are as shown in Fig. [12]. On strongly light-adapting the fovea, both component sensitivities will be reduced but we suppose the reduction is much less for (B) as shown in Fig. [12(b)]. For a wavelength such as λ' the threshold sensitivity corresponds initially to mechanism (A) and finally to mechanism (B) and we may expect that by determining the variation of the threshold sensitivity as the adapting intensity is increased from zero, some indication of the transition may be obtainable.

It will be observed that, in the change from dark to light adaptation, the ratio of sensitivity in dark adaptation to sensitivity in light adaptation is smaller for B than it is for A. This effect is indicated, for example, by the corresponding distances on the log threshold sensitivity axis at λ'. The shape of each curve remains unchanged under the two conditions of adaptation, but A is displaced through a greater distance on the vertical axis than is B.

Later reports [171] give data on five additional subjects and provide two new sets of findings. (1) Contrary to results obtained on himself, Stiles's new data show a curve with two branches for a test stimulus of wavelength 430 mμ and an adapting field of 600 mμ. The presence of the two branches complicates the original picture where, for Stiles alone, the curve consisted of a single branch. Stiles concludes that the two-branch curve is representative of curves for short-wave test stimuli and long-wave field stimuli. It may be generated from component curves due to three mechanisms: π_1, the original "blue" mechanism; π_2, a mechanism responsible for the absolute threshold when the test stimulus is below about 450 mμ; π_4, the original "green" mechanism which is responsible for the absolute threshold when the test stimulus exceeds about 450 mμ. (2) In his original experiments Stiles found an apparent limited conditioning effect for wavelengths of adapting stimuli exceeding 570 mμ. Under such conditions, the "blue" branch conformed to a cone curve only over a short range of intensities above the absolute threshold; beyond this point the threshold U_λ remained practically unchanged. When, in the later experiments, a high intensity of yellow adapting field was made available, curves obtained for a blue test stimulus on a yellow field show that the previously noted flat region is only the initial part of a third, high intensity branch.

The new results [171] have caused Stiles to change his ideas about his original three spectral sensitivity curves. Now it seems that five mechanisms are needed; they are given the noncommittal names of π_1, π_2, π_3, π_4, and π_5. Figure 13 gives tentative spectral sensitivity curves for all these mechanisms except π_2 whose spectral sensitivity curve is not well established. (Note that the graph gives a plot in terms of wave number, i.e., $1/\lambda$, rather than wavelength.)

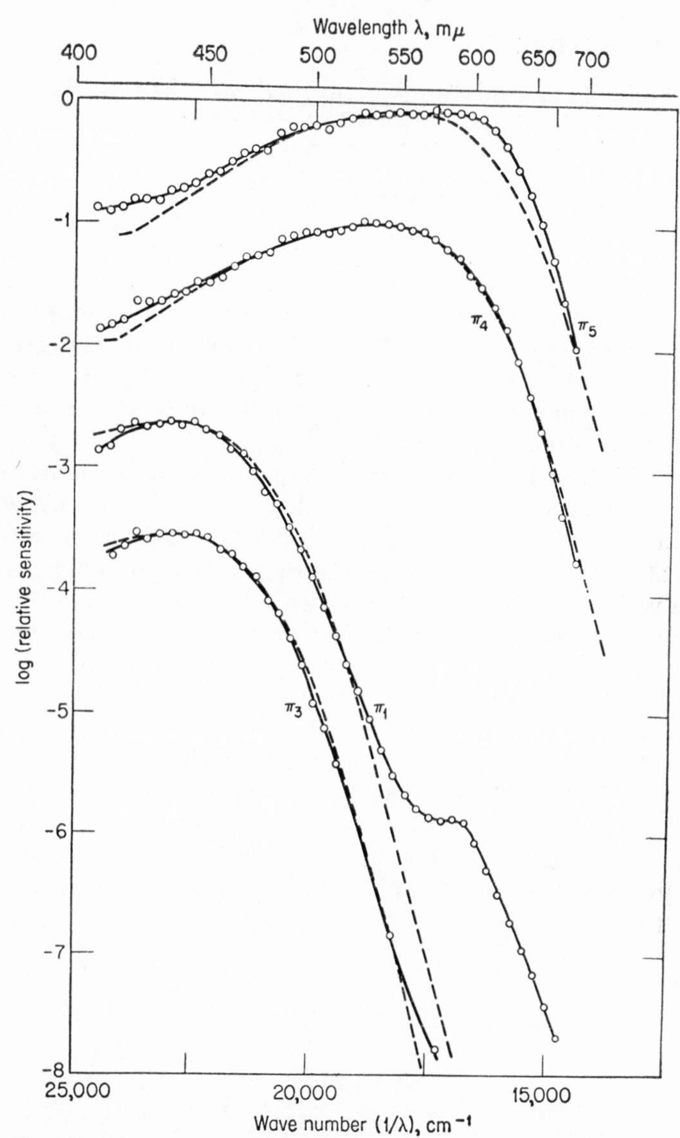

FIG. 13. The relative field sensitivity curves of π_1, π_3, π_4, and π_5 corrected for optic media and macular pigment absorption—the corrections are based on the results of Ludvigh and McCarthy [117], Wald [187], and Wright [204]. The dotted curve is the rod sensitivity curve appropriately displaced to apply to each π function on the argument that the spectral sensitivity of each may correspond to the spectral absorption of rhodopsin (a single pigment) with maximum displaced. *From Stiles* [171].

COLOR MIXTURE

The topic of color mixture is concerned with the problem of how a subject's discriminations change when different colors are added by physical superposition or temporal mixture.

The case of physical superposition is illustrated by the overlapping of differently colored light beams falling on a common surface. The essential thing in superposition is that different wavelengths, irrespective of source, become physically added.

Temporal mixture involves another type of color addition. It is the type that occurs when a subject views differently colored sectors on a disc rotating at a speed above fusion frequency. Mixture is provided by the "fusion" of the different colors. In this connection, see the later description of Guild's experiment [49].

Color mixture by "subtraction" is entirely different from color mixture by superposition or temporal mixture [63, 64, 69, vol. 2]. The final color given by subtraction is due to those wavelengths that remain after successive selective absorptions by the colored media through which the light passes.[17]

Some general characteristics of color mixture. This section is meant to provide a rapid short summary of some basic characteristics of color mixture. The introduction will be followed, in succeeding sections, by discussions of more specific issues.

First, let it be noted that one wavelength distribution can be matched against another, properly chosen, not only with respect to brightness but also with respect to hue and saturation. Colorimetric equations represent the appropriate quantities involved in such a match. "Contrary to what appears to be sometimes believed, it is *not* possible to place on one side of a photometric field a mixture of three

[17] The mixing of pigments provides an example of subtraction; the mixture does not give the same color that would result from superposition of the light rays reflected from the two pigments individually. Helmholtz [64; 69, vol. 2] was the first to clarify the nature of subtractive mixture. He described it in the following terms: "Now if a uniform mixture of two coloured powders merely reflected light from its outer surface, this light would really be the sum of the two kinds of light obtained from each powder separately. But, as a matter of fact, most of the light is reflected back from the interior, and the behavior is just like that of a mixture of coloured liquids or of a series of coloured glasses. This light has had to pass on its way particles of both sorts, and so it contains merely such rays as were able to get through both elements. Thus, most of the light reflected from a mixture of coloured powders is due, not to an addition of both colours, but to a subtraction. . . ." The color of the mixture is determined by the rays that remain after absorption by the various particles. It was a failure to understand the principle of subtractive mixture that vitiated many of the interpretations of workers before Helmholtz.

given monochromatic lights which would match exactly all the monochromatic lights of the spectrum placed on the other side of the field in turn" [142]. However, it is always possible to match two *mixtures* in appearance, each mixture being composed of *two* appropriately chosen monochromatic lights. The matching is brought about by adjusting the intensities of three of the four monochromatic lights (i.e., the three primaries) until the two mixtures are indistinguishable.

The following generalization seems to cover all cases of color matches. "Any existing light (monochromatic or mixed) can be matched (a) either against white light, (b) or against a monochromatic light, (c) or against a purple light, that is, a light made of a mixture of extreme spectral red and extreme spectral blue light, (d) or against a mixture of white light plus a monochromatic light, or plus a purple light" [142]. According to this statement, mixtures that match a given light may be composed of more than two monochromatic lights, as in the case where a purple (red plus blue) is mixed with another wavelength, or when a given wavelength is mixed with white. However, if we refer to (a) monochromatic lights, (b) mixtures that match monochromatic lights, (c) purples, (d) white, and (e) mixtures of lights in categories (a), (b) or (c) with white, as all being colors of the same class, then it can be said that no new colors are added to the class when two or more such colors are mixed.

Let us say that we wish to mix light of wavelength C with one light of an invariant set of three lights, A, B, and D, in such a way that C plus one of the set will match the mixture of the remaining two. A, B, and D are known as primaries. (For purposes of the present discussion A, B, and D are taken to be monochromatic lights. It will be shown later that wavelength mixtures can also be used as primaries.) When C is mixed with one of the set A, B and D, it plus the selected member of the set can, in fact, match the mixture of the remaining two. Such a match can always be made except for one condition, namely, that an individual member of the set A, B, and D is a match for a mixture of the other two members.

A, B, and D are arbitrarily chosen. They are not unique; any of an infinite number of wavelengths may comprise the set. For convenience, primaries are usually limited to radiations in the red, green, and blue. A, B, and D may be mixed with any wavelength C of the spectrum with assurance that some two mixtures, each composed of two wavelengths, can be matched with respect to luminosity and hue. Of course, C cannot always be mixed with the same primary. The appropriate primary to accompany C depends upon the wavelength of C; sometimes it is A, sometimes B, and sometimes D.

The result of the "two-against-two" match may be expressed in the form of the equation

$$cC = aA + bB + dD \tag{5}$$

where a, b, and d represent the respective numbers of unit quantities, A, B, and D of the three primaries, and the coefficient of C is c, the number of units of C. As will be seen later, when A, B, and D are monochromatic lights, one of the coefficients a, b, or d must be negative. The primary possessing the negative coefficient is the one that is mixed with C. When C is not a monochromatic light, Eq. (5) still holds except that the terms may be but are not necessarily positive. Equation (5), which expresses the relation of a standard light to three other lights, represents the fact of visual trichromaticity.

The additivity of heterochromatic luminances. The homochromatic luminances of identical colors add to give a total luminance equivalent to their sum. A similar rule, known as Abney's law [2, 1], has been applied to heterochromatic luminances; it says that the luminance of a mixture of differently colored lights is equal to the sum of the luminances of the components. Abney's law has provided the basis for defining heterochromatic luminance by the expression

$$B = K \int V_\lambda E_\lambda \, d\lambda \tag{6}$$

where B is luminance; V_λ, the relative luminosity at wavelength λ; E_λ, the "energy" distribution of the light—here to be specified most appropriately as a radiance (power per unit solid angle per unit area) and in any other particular case to be interpreted as the applicable physical measure; and K, a constant that allows for differences in the units of B and E_λ. (The limits of the integral are essentially determined by V_λ, which approaches zero at each end of the visible spectrum.) The equation implies that the luminance of a given monochromatic light is proportional to the luminosity, V_λ, of the light and the radiance E_λ.

Abney's law has not, in general, been fully supported by subsequent work. In fact, it is questions about Abney's law that lie at the root of a present-day crisis in colorimetry [103]. The deficiencies of Abney's law have been known for a long time, but they have been tolerated or evaded until recently.

As long ago as 1912, Ives's investigations [82, 83, 84, 85, 86] gave data on heterochromatic luminance matches by the flicker, step-by-step, and direct comparison methods that did not, as Dresler [19] points out, consistently support the precise additivity of luminances; the greatest deviations from additivity occur with the direct comparison method. Piéron [141] found that the luminances of two complementary monochromatic lights may have a sum that exceeds the luminance of their white mixture by 34 per cent. Le Grand and Geblewicz [116] found that, with high luminances and large areas in the periphery, monochromatic luminances were underestimated in comparison with a white light. Dresler [19] has shown that Abney's rule is approximately valid if heterochromatic matches are made by flicker photometry and for small differences of stimulus wavelength. It has often been thought that the deviations from additivity shown particularly by the method of direct comparison are due to the fact that saturation effects become confused with brightness effects. In any case, we may take it that, at best, Abney's law does not hold generally; if it holds at all, it holds only under very precisely specified conditions. It is sufficient to say here that the method of resolving the crisis provoked by the intrusion of difficulties surrounding Abney's law cannot be foreseen. For this reason, the present account of color mixture will adhere to an exposition of old principles. The reader is warned, however, that events of the near future will require close attention, for the next few years will probably see considerable changes in the topic of color mixture. Further reference to the crisis in colorimetry will be made in the last section of the paper dealing with methodological considerations.

Newton's and Grassman's formulations. The first fruitful scheme for systematizing the data of color mixture was presented by Newton [135, 136]. Newton's ideas did not arise as the culmination of a long historical development. Rather, they seemed to be an imaginative "leap in the dark," an unashamed speculation. Newton recommended that colors be arranged in a circle, white being placed in the center, with the spectral colors (from red through orange, yellow, green, blue, indigo, and violet) around it; the more desaturated a color, the closer was to be its position to the center. Newton had the idea of representing the quantity of a given color by a small circle drawn about the position of the color on the large circle; the area of the small circle was taken to be proportional to the quantity of the color. (The small circle may be thought of as equivalent to a small weight placed at the color's position.) Newton then stated that the position of a mixture of colors can be determined by calculating the center of gravity of the weights of the individual components. Newton's choice [9] of a circle probably did not provide an accurate scheme, and in addition, he had no way at that time of specifying quantity of a color. Nevertheless, Newton's account contains, within the scope of its implications, all the principles of color mixture laid down in improved form by Grassman [43] 150 years later.

Grassman's laws constitute a set of statements that describe some relations of color vision. When first presented, some of these statements were regarded by Grassman as necessary assumptions to the formulation of a mathematical basis for Newton's center-of-gravity method of symbolizing color mixture in a plane; others were regarded as necessary consequences of the assumptions and the accepted geometric arrangement of color symbols. The laws and many of their implications are best understood in terms of their underlying geometry; the principles of their geometry will become clearer when we take up the chromaticity diagram, the modern development of Newton's closed figure.

Grassman's laws are here stated in the sometimes paraphrased views of different authors. (Grassman labeled his assumptions clearly but he was not always so explicit about labeling their formal consequences. As a result an author may have to give an independent interpretative exposition of the laws.)

1. Any mixed color, no matter how it is composed, must have the same appearance as the mixture of a certain saturated color with white [64; 69, vol. 2].

2. When one of the two kinds of light that are to be mixed together changes continuously, the appearance of the mixture changes continuously also [64; 69, vol. 2].

a. For every color there can be found another complementary or antagonistic color which, if mixed with it in the right proportion, gives white or gray, and if mixed in any other proportion, an unsaturated color of the hue of the stronger component [180].

b. The mixture of any two colors that are not complementaries gives an intermediate color, varying in hue with the relative amounts of the two original colors and varying in saturation with their nearness or remoteness in the color series [180].

3. The mixture of any two combinations which match will itself match either of the original combinations, provided that the illumination of the colors remains approximately the same [180].

4. The total intensity of the mixture is the sum of the intensities of the lights mixed [43].

Laws 1, 2, and 3 were taken by Grassman to be assumptions necessary to formalize Newton's arrangement of color symbols. Laws 2*a* and 2*b* were consequences of assuming 1 and 2. Law 4 provided a basis for the center-of-gravity method.

Since they were first advanced, the laws have probably undergone several changes in status. Originally conceived as mathematical assumptions, they and their attendant geometrical arrangement quickly became hypotheses to be tested and now constitute part of a usable (if not final) complex of relations existing among geometrical theory, mathematical assumption, experimental data, and verbal account. They are important elements in the pattern of color theory.

Chromatic flux, tristimulus value, and distribution coefficient. A recent systematic account by Le Grand [115] treats, on an empirical basis and in a context that is independent of geometrical considerations, several topics included by and related to the chromaticity diagram and Grassman's principles. Le Grand's treatment will not be taken up here but one of its basic concepts must be considered, that is, the concept of chromatic flux. The term *chromatic flux*, introduced by Le Grand (following a suggestion by P. Fleury), specifies the quantitative variable involved in the addition of colors. Le Grand recognizes that stimuli for color usually involve extended sources; hence, radiance is the appropriate energy specification. However, for reasons not gone into here, Le Grand usually specifies the energy variable in terms of radiant flux (power), Φ, which for given circumstances is proportional to radiance. The associated luminous variable is luminous flux F.

Chromatic fluxes are proportional to the quantities known as *tristimulus values*. The latter term is a more flexible one in the sense that relative, rather than absolute, quantities are implied. Certain workers prefer to apply the term *tristimulus value* to mixed lights only. Others apply it to denote mixed and monochromatic lights. In the case of monochromatic light, the term *distribution coefficient* is synonymous with *tristimulus value*.

We shall here deal with the case of monochromatic primaries. A later discussion will deal with mixed primaries.

Consider three monochromatic radiations λ_1, λ_2, and λ_3 which are primaries, arbitrarily chosen except for the previously stated condition that no two of the radiations will, when mixed, match the third in color. The three radiations represent respectively radiant fluxes Φ_1, Φ_2, and Φ_3.

To the radiant fluxes Φ_1, Φ_2, and Φ_3 of these primaries correspond the luminous fluxes:

$$F_1 = KV_1\Phi_1 \qquad F_2 = KV_2\Phi_2 \qquad F_3 = KV_3\Phi_3 \tag{7}$$

K is the coefficient of maximum luminosity (685 lumens per watt), and V_1, V_2, V_3 are the relative luminosity factors of the primaries λ_1, λ_2, and λ_3.

For the three primaries, the corresponding chromatic fluxes Γ_1, Γ_2, and Γ_3 are defined as

$$\Gamma_1 = \frac{\Phi_1}{\phi_1} \qquad \Gamma_2 = \frac{\Phi_2}{\phi_2} \qquad \Gamma_3 = \frac{\Phi_3}{\phi_3} \tag{8}$$

ϕ_1, ϕ_2, and ϕ_3 designate three radiant fluxes chosen arbitrarily as unit energies of the primaries. (The units of flux are not ordinarily given in watts; they are usually defined in terms of some convenient empirical reference.) In terms of the above development we can write

$$\Gamma_1 = \frac{F_1}{L_1} \qquad \Gamma_2 = \frac{F_2}{L_2} \qquad \Gamma_3 = \frac{F_3}{L_3} \tag{9}$$

where the L with subscript 1, 2, or 3 designates the luminous unit of the appropriate primary. These units are related to radiant energy units by the expressions

$$L_1 = KV_1\phi_1 \qquad L_2 = KV_2\phi_2 \qquad L_3 = KV_3\phi_3 \tag{10}$$

The trichromaticity of vision. It has been previously stated to be an experimental fact that vision is trichromatic in nature. It can also be shown on the theoretical side that trichromaticity follows from Grassman's laws in a manner that will not be developed here. For a general discussion of this topic see Le Grand [115, pp. 130–146].[18]

In terms of the system of symbols generally used throughout this discussion, Eq. (5) can be written

$$\Gamma_S L_S = \Gamma_1 L_1 + \Gamma_2 L_2 + \Gamma_3 L_3 \tag{11}$$

when Γ_S, Γ_1, Γ_2, and Γ_3 are substituted for c, a, b, and d and L_S, L_1, L_2, and L_3 for C, A, B, and D. In Eq. (11), the coefficients have the meaning of chromatic fluxes, rather than tristimulus values, as in (5). The same convention respecting the negative sign holds in Eq. (11) as in (5).

It is necessary at this point to define Γ_S. Up to the present we have only defined chromatic fluxes for primaries, but by analogy with colorimetric equations expressible in luminances we shall agree that the chromatic flux Γ_S is equal numerically to the sum of the chromatic fluxes of the component primaries. That is,

$$\Gamma_S = \Gamma_1 + \Gamma_2 + \Gamma_3 \tag{12}$$

In general, we should wish the relation

$$\Gamma_S = \frac{F_S}{L_S} \tag{13}$$

to hold for a light S that is either monochromatic or mixed. (The relation has an analogue in Eq. (9) for monochromatic primaries.) Equation (13) expresses the relation between Γ_S and the luminous flux

[18] The English translation of Le Grand's book appeared just before the proofs of this article became available. Y. Le Grand, *Light, colour and vision*, translated by J. W. T. Walsh, F. R. W. Walsh, and R. W. G. Hunt, New York, Wiley, 1957. The translation introduces considerable changes in nomenclature.

F_S for light S. Hence, L_S, the unit of luminous flux of S, is defined as the quantity that makes Eq. (13) true:

$$L_S = \frac{F_S}{\Gamma_S} \tag{14}$$

By an expression for Abney's law—in a form different from (6)—

$$F_S = F_1 + F_2 + F_3 \tag{15}$$

On the basis of the expressions in (9) and (13)

$$L_S = \left(\frac{\Gamma_1}{\Gamma_S}\right) L_1 + \left(\frac{\Gamma_2}{\Gamma_S}\right) L_2 + \left(\frac{\Gamma_3}{\Gamma_S}\right) L_3 \tag{16}$$

Trichromatic coordinates. Very often, in practical work, one need only know the relative values of the primaries used to match a given light. A number of writers, including Wright [203], Le Grand [115], and Judd [101, 102] have discussed the nature and derivation of the quantities known as the trichromatic coordinates, sometimes termed the trichromatic coefficients [203] or chromaticity coordinates [102]. The use of these coefficients in connection with practical problems of colorimetry and the practical representation of color make them of considerable systematic importance.

The trichromatic coordinates γ_1, γ_2, and γ_3 [115] may be defined as follows:

$$\frac{\gamma_1}{\Gamma_1} = \frac{\gamma_2}{\Gamma_2} = \frac{\gamma_3}{\Gamma_3} = \frac{1}{\Gamma_1 + \Gamma_2 + \Gamma_3} = \frac{1}{\Gamma_S} \tag{17}$$

or, otherwise stated,

$$\gamma_1 = \frac{\Gamma_1}{\Gamma_S} \qquad \gamma_2 = \frac{\Gamma_2}{\Gamma_S} \qquad \text{and} \qquad \gamma_3 = \frac{\Gamma_3}{\Gamma_S} \tag{18}$$

In these terms, Eq. (16) may be rewritten as

$$L_S = \gamma_1 L_1 + \gamma_2 L_2 + \gamma_3 L_3 \tag{19}$$

Since, by Eq. (12) $\Gamma_S \equiv \Gamma_1 + \Gamma_2 + \Gamma_3$ then

$$\gamma_1 = \frac{\Gamma_1}{\Gamma_1 + \Gamma_2 + \Gamma_3} \qquad \gamma_2 = \frac{\Gamma_2}{\Gamma_1 + \Gamma_2 + \Gamma_3} \qquad \text{and} \qquad \gamma_3 = \frac{\Gamma_3}{\Gamma_1 + \Gamma_2 + \Gamma_3} \tag{20}$$

From the foregoing expressions it follows that

$$\gamma_1 + \gamma_2 + \gamma_3 = 1 \tag{21}$$

that is, the sum of the trichromatic coordinates is unity. The trichromatic coordinates of each primary indicate what percentage that primary contributes to the total chromatic flux (taken as unity) of the three primaries in matching a given color.

The trichromatic coordinates are important in geometrical representations of color and owe their significance to the existence of color charts, most importantly, the chromaticity diagram.

The chromaticity diagram. The chromaticity diagram is now used in preference to Maxwell's equilateral color triangle [123]. The representation of hue and saturation on the chromaticity diagram, a right-angled triangle, is mathematically simpler than it is in the case of the equilateral triangle.

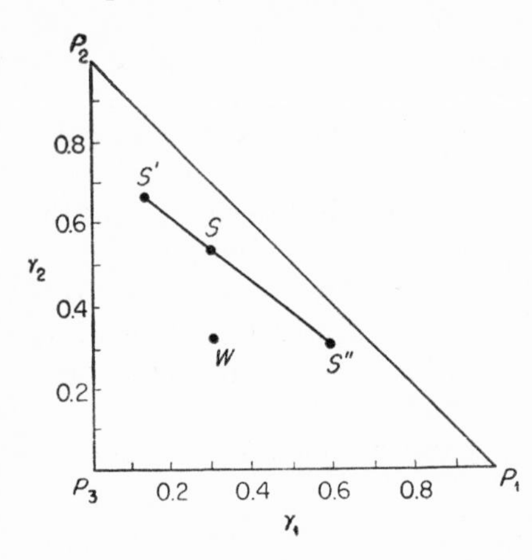

FIG. 14. Geometrical representation of two colors S′ and S″ and their mixture S on the chromaticity diagram.

Consider the unit Eq. (19). This equation tells us that one luminous unit of S is matched by the sum of three products, each one representing a trichromatic coordinate times the luminous unit of the associated primary. It is possible to fix the position of any color in the chromaticity diagram when any two of the coordinates γ_1, γ_2, or γ_3 are known. The third coordinate is fixed by virtue of the fact that Eq. (21) $\gamma_1 + \gamma_2 + \gamma_3 = 1$; it must be the difference between unity and the sum of the other two. This general type of relation is fundamental to the chromaticity diagram, an example of which is shown in Fig. 14. In the diagram, values of γ_1 are recorded on the horizontal axis and values of γ_2 on the vertical axis. The values of γ_1 and γ_2 vary between zero and 1.0.

The chromaticity diagram gives a geometrical representation of many quantitative facts of color mixture. For example, we can plot on the diagram two points located, respectively, at (γ_1', γ_2') and (γ_1'', γ_2''), to represent two colors S′ and S″. In the diagram the point representing S, the mixture of S′ and S″, lies on the straight line S′S″. Furthermore, in line with Newton's and Grassman's ideas, if m luminous units of S′ are mixed with n units of S″, $m + n$ units of S result, while the position of S with respect to S′ and S″ is such that $S'S/SS'' = n/m$. S is then located at a point analogous to the center of gravity lying between weights m and n placed at S′ and S″ respectively. For mixtures of three colors, S may be considered to be at the center of gravity of a system of weights assumed placed at S′, S″ and S‴. A case of special interest concerns the color white, which is usually specified as placed at the center of gravity of a system of three equal weights located at the apices of the chromaticity diagram and representing primaries P_1, P_2, and P_3.

An infinity of chromaticity diagrams can be drawn depending upon the primaries P_1, P_2, and P_3 that are used to establish a match with a given color. (In what follows, P_1 may be taken completely to represent the "red" primary; P_2, the "green"; and P_3, the "blue.") In addition, the chromaticity diagram will depend also upon the reference units of the system. The latter units are usually described in terms of the coordinates specified to produce a given white light. (See a later section of this article on transformations of units and primaries.) A white light may be defined in terms of the energy distribution of a tungsten lamp of given color temperature, an equal energy stimulus, or some equally specifiable radiation. In any case, a different chromaticity diagram will be needed for each set of primaries and associated units. It is nevertheless important to realize that the same colors may be represented in different diagrams by appropriate transformations from one system of primaries and units to another.

The spectrum locus of the chromaticity diagram. For its most effective use and interpretation, the chromaticity diagram requires that the color of each spectral wavelength be positioned precisely. The path of the points of such colors on the diagram is called the spectrum locus. The positions of the different colors corresponding to the spectral wavelengths are determined by the appropriate γ_1 and γ_2 values ascertained in standard color mixture experiments such as those of Guild [49] and Wright [200]; our present discussion will rely on the data of the latter investigator.

By determining the trichromatic coordinates based on mixtures of wavelengths 650 mμ, 530 mμ, and 460 mμ as primaries, Wright was able to plot the spectrum locus for his particular primary set. Figure 15 presents the chromaticity diagram with the spectrum locus.

It will be noticed [in Fig. 15] that the curve is everywhere either straight or convex, but never concave. From this it follows that the colour resulting from the mixture of any two wavelengths must lie either on the locus or within the area bounded by the locus, but never outside it. This applies even more strongly when several radiations are combined; hence it happens that the area included by the spectrum locus and the straight line joining its red and violet extremities defines the region on the chromaticity chart outside which no homogeneous or heterogeneous physical stimulus will be located . . .

It will be seen that the locus from the extreme red end of the spectrum to the green is very nearly straight. This means that the spectral orange, yellow and yellow-green radiations can be very closely matched by a mixture of monochromatic red and green stimuli. On the other hand, in the blue-green region the locus is steeply curved and lies well beyond the line P_3P_2;

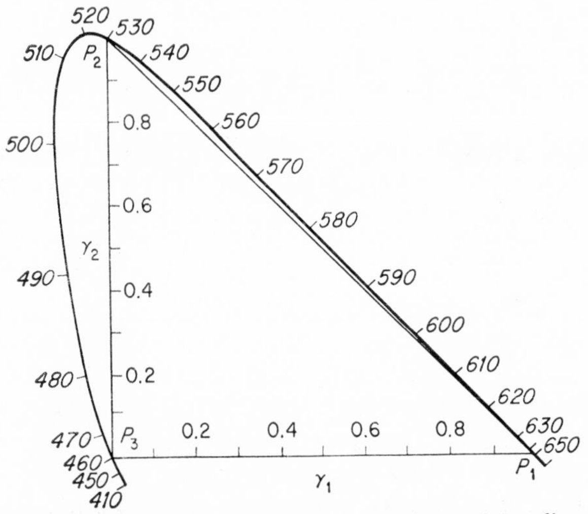

FIG. 15. The spectrum locus in the chromaticity diagram. The diagram is in terms of the trichromatic coordinates obtained by Wright for primaries 650, 530, and 460 mμ. *After Wright* [203].

this indicates that mixtures of P_3 and P_2 are more desaturated than the spectral blue-green radiations. No additive combination of P_1, P_2 and P_3 will produce an adequate match of a spectral blue-green radiation (nor, in fact, of any other spectral radiation, since the spectrum locus lies wholly outside the triangle $P_1P_2P_3$) and to measure M, [Fig. 16], a suitable amount of P_1 must first be mixed with it. When sufficient of P_1 has been added, the mixture will have moved along the line MP_1 until a point such as P will be reached lying inside $P_1P_2P_3$. P can then be matched by a positive mixture of P_1, P_2 and P_3 and subsequently the amount of P_1 which has been added can be measured. By subtraction, the negative amount of P_1 in M can be derived and hence the unit equation for M alone can be calculated [203]. (Wright's symbols have been changed in the above quotations to accord with the present text.)

It is, of course, possible to obtain a mixture of a given wavelength and a combination of wavelengths. In particular, the case of white is of considerable importance. Let it be assumed that coordinates of a given white have been specified and the white takes its position at W in Fig. 17. A mixture of W and λ on the spectrum locus results in S, the position of the mixture of the two. S lies on a line joining W and λ. The percentage distance of S along line $W\lambda$ is described as *excitation purity*, p_e, defined by the ratio WS/Wλ. If $(\gamma_{1W}, \gamma_{2W})$ are coordinates of W,

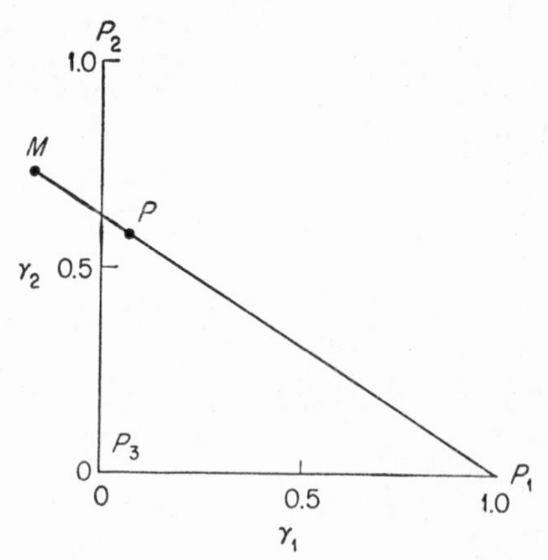

FIG. 16. The specification of a color lying outside the triangle $P_1P_2P_3$. It is required that a certain amount of P_1 be added to M until a point P lying inside the triangle results from the mixture. *After Wright* [203].

$(\gamma_{1S}, \gamma_{2S})$ coordinates of S and $(\gamma_{1\lambda}, \gamma_{2\lambda})$ coordinates of λ, excitation purity is given by

$$p_e = \frac{\gamma_{1S} - \gamma_{1W}}{\gamma_{1\lambda} - \gamma_{1W}} = \frac{\gamma_{2S} - \gamma_{2W}}{\gamma_{2\lambda} - \gamma_{2W}} \tag{22}$$

the equivalent expressions existing by virtue of the ratio of corresponding sides in similar triangles. The fully desaturated white W represents zero purity, and a color on either the spectrum locus or the line of purples that connects extremes of the spectrum represents a purity of 1.0.

It must be pointed out that excitation purity p_e is different from colorimetric purity [14], for which we have earlier reserved the symbol p. It has been shown that colorimetric purity has a definite meaning in terms of operations that are not at all connected with the chromaticity diagram. Nevertheless, it will be shown later that colorimetric purity can be referred to variables on the chromaticity diagram of the XYZ system of colorimetry.

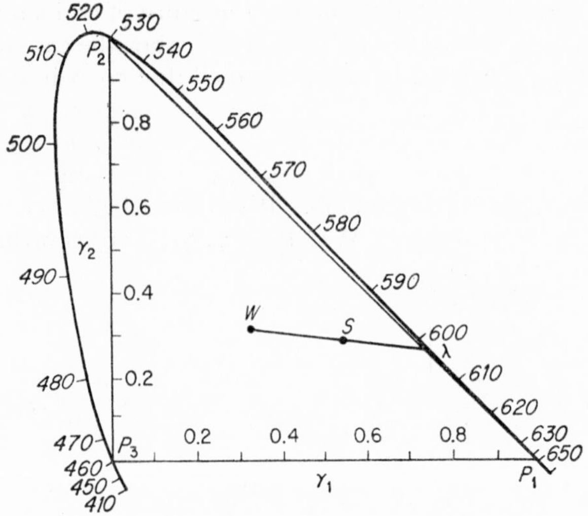

FIG. 17. The representation of a color in terms of dominant wavelength and purity. *After Wright* [203].

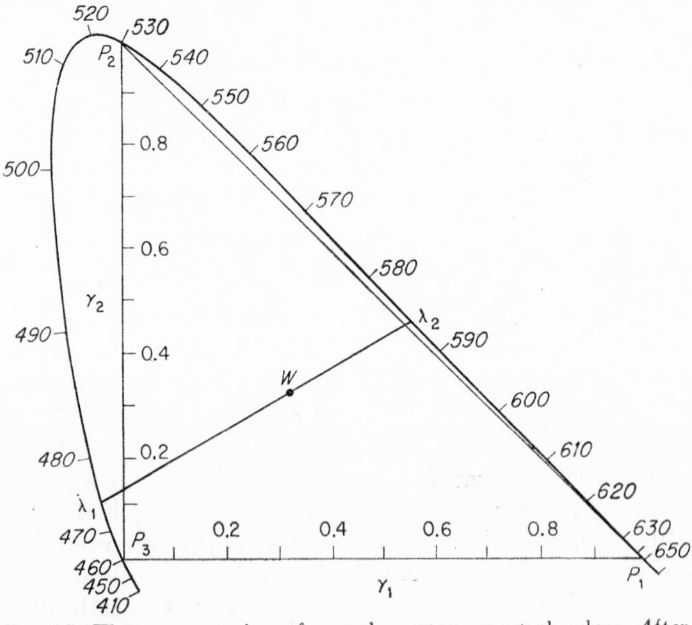

FIG. 18. The repesentation of complementary spectral colors. *After Wright* [203].

Both types of purity assign colors on the spectral locus the same maximum value of 100 per cent, while the value of zero is applied to a reference white. Because of the fact that all spectral wavelengths are defined as having 100 per cent purities, neither type has an unequivocal correlation with saturation. We know that spectral colors do, in fact, exhibit different degrees of saturation.

Complementary colors are readily represented in the chromaticity diagram (Fig. 18). In the chromaticity diagram the intersections of the spectrum locus by a straight line passing through W specifies λ_1 and λ_2, complementary pairs located at the two points of intersection. All complementary pairs of wavelengths may be specified by the intersections of the spectrum locus by straight lines passing through W. No spectrum locus exists near the γ_1 coordinate axis; this means that complementaries for wavelengths between about $\lambda = 595$ mμ and $\lambda = 570$ mμ must, for Wright's conditions, be appropriate mixtures of primaries 460 mμ and 650 mμ. In a word, they are purples; they are represented by the straight line connecting the spectral extremes. Specific wavelength values of the complementaries will depend on the physical characteristics of the chosen white stimulus.

Distribution coefficients. Let us define three quantities called distribution coefficients. These coefficients are written like the trichromatic coordinates except for the fact that each is surmounted by a horizontal bar. The distribution coefficients are defined by

$$\bar{\gamma}_1 = \frac{\gamma_{1\lambda} V_\lambda}{L_\lambda} \qquad \bar{\gamma}_2 = \frac{\gamma_{2\lambda} V_\lambda}{L_\lambda} \qquad \text{and} \qquad \bar{\gamma}_3 = \frac{\gamma_{3\lambda} V_\lambda}{L_\lambda} \tag{23}$$

in which, in line with Eq. (19),

$$L_\lambda = \gamma_1 L_1 + \gamma_2 L_2 + \gamma_3 L_3 \tag{24}$$

The distribution coefficients are a set of tristimulus values for monochromatic lights.

It will be the purpose of the following discussion to state the significance of the distribution coefficients and their use in computations that involve, not percentage values of component chromatic flux as in the case of the trichromatic coefficients, but rather, the component chromatic flux attributable to each primary in matching light from a source S of known energy distribution.

The distribution coefficients differ from the trichromatic coordinates in two details. First, distribution coefficients apply only to monochromatic radiations; the trichromatic coefficients apply to all light. Second, whereas the sum of the trichromatic coefficients is unity, the sum of the distribution coefficients is $\Delta\Gamma_\lambda / \alpha E_\lambda \, \Delta\lambda$, that is,

$$\Delta\Gamma_\lambda = (\alpha E_\lambda \, \Delta\lambda)(\bar{\gamma}_1 + \bar{\gamma}_2 + \bar{\gamma}_3) \tag{25}$$

This equation[19] says that the sum of the respective distribution coefficients for the three primaries is proportional, by way of a constant $1/(\alpha E_\lambda \Delta\lambda)$, to the elementary chromatic flux $\Delta\Gamma_\lambda$ corresponding to the energy E_λ of a narrow wavelength band $\Delta\lambda$ centering on λ. α is a constant that depends on the way E_λ is measured. E_λ is constant for a given λ but varies from wavelength to wavelength depending on the energy distribution of the source. For an equal energy spectrum, E_λ = const.

The relations existing among the elementary resultant chromatic flux $\Delta\Gamma_\lambda$, the elementary component fluxes $\Delta\Gamma_1$, $\Delta\Gamma_2$, and $\Delta\Gamma_3$, and the distribution coefficients may be written[20]

$$\begin{aligned} \Delta\Gamma_1 &= (\alpha E_\lambda \gamma_{1\lambda} \Delta\lambda)(\bar{\gamma}_1 + \bar{\gamma}_2 + \bar{\gamma}_3) \\ \Delta\Gamma_2 &= (\alpha E_\lambda \gamma_{2\lambda} \Delta\lambda)(\bar{\gamma}_1 + \bar{\gamma}_2 + \bar{\gamma}_3) \\ \Delta\Gamma_3 &= (\alpha E_\lambda \gamma_{3\lambda} \Delta\lambda)(\bar{\gamma}_1 + \bar{\gamma}_2 + \bar{\gamma}_3) \end{aligned} \tag{26}$$

[19] The relationship expressed in (25) can be demonstrated in the following way. Add the three terms for $\bar{\gamma}_1$, $\bar{\gamma}_2$, and $\bar{\gamma}_3$ in Eq. (23) and

$$\bar{\gamma}_1 + \bar{\gamma}_2 + \bar{\gamma}_3 = \frac{V_\lambda}{L_\lambda} \tag{23a}$$

Equation (6) can be written in such units that α can be substituted for K; and F, for B. Consequently $\Delta F_\lambda = \alpha V_\lambda E_\lambda \Delta\lambda$, and

$$\Delta\Gamma_\lambda = \frac{\Delta F_\lambda}{L_\lambda} = \frac{\alpha V_\lambda E_\lambda \Delta\lambda}{L_\lambda} \tag{23b}$$

it is thus seen that $V_\lambda/L_\lambda = \Delta\Gamma_\lambda/\alpha E_\lambda \Delta\lambda$; whence, in view of (23a), Eq. (25) follows.

[20] On analogy with Eq. (17),

$$\frac{\Gamma_1}{\gamma_1} = \frac{\Gamma_2}{\gamma_2} = \frac{\Gamma_3}{\gamma_3} = \Gamma_\lambda$$

It follows that, for the elementary chromatic fluxes at the wavelength of each primary,

$$\Delta\Gamma_1 = \gamma_{1_\lambda} \Delta\Gamma_\lambda \qquad \Delta\Gamma_2 = \gamma_{2_\lambda} \Delta\Gamma_\lambda \qquad \text{and} \qquad \Delta\Gamma_3 = \gamma_{3_\lambda} \Delta\Gamma_\lambda \tag{25a}$$

Equations (26) follow from Eqs. (25) and (25a), i.e.,

$$\Delta\Gamma_1 = \gamma_{1_\lambda} \Delta\Gamma_\lambda = (\alpha\gamma_{1_\lambda} E_\lambda \Delta\lambda)(\bar{\gamma}_1 + \bar{\gamma}_2 + \bar{\gamma}_3) \tag{26a}$$

Similar equations exist for $\Delta\Gamma_2$ and $\Delta\Gamma_3$

It may be demonstrated from Eqs. (25a) that, since $\gamma_1 + \gamma_2 + \gamma_3 = 1$,

$$\Delta\Gamma_1 + \Delta\Gamma_2 + \Delta\Gamma_3 = \Delta\Gamma_\lambda$$

For all wavelengths of light in source S, by Eqs. (25a),

$$\Gamma_1 = \Sigma\, \Delta\Gamma_1 = \Sigma\gamma_{1_\lambda} \Delta\Gamma_\lambda$$

In terms of Eq. (23b) of footnote 19,

$$\Gamma_1 = \sum \frac{\alpha\gamma_{1_\lambda} V_\lambda E_\lambda \Delta\lambda}{L_1\gamma_{1_\lambda} + L_2\gamma_{2_\lambda} + L_3\gamma_{3_\lambda}}$$

Analogous relations hold for Γ_2 and Γ_3, with appropriate substitution of γ_{2_λ} and γ_{3_λ} for γ_{1_λ}. The calculation of the chromatic fluxes of light S reduces to the calculations of the sums

$$\Gamma_i = \Sigma\alpha\bar{\gamma}_i E_\lambda \Delta\lambda \tag{26b}$$

Finally, another relation concerning the distribution coefficients may be considered. From the definition of the distribution coefficients in (23), it may be demonstrated that

$$\bar{\gamma}_1 L_1 + \bar{\gamma}_2 L_2 + \bar{\gamma}_3 L_3 = V_\lambda \tag{27}$$

the sum of the products of distribution coefficients and their corresponding luminous units equals relative luminosity at a given wavelength.[21] Each ordinate of the luminosity curve can be split into three component parts [203] corresponding to the three terms on the left-hand side of Eq. (27). These parts represent the amounts $L_1\bar{\gamma}_1$, $L_2\bar{\gamma}_2$, and $L_3\bar{\gamma}_3$ of each of the primaries which, when mixed together, match V_λ units in both color and brightness. L_1, L_2, and L_3 are the luminous units of the respective primaries based upon some appropriate colorimetric system (e.g., the "white" system, in which the three units, considered as making equal color contributions to a white mixture, are specified in terms of luminous flux).

Some data of color mixture. The first data on color mixture were obtained by Maxwell in a series of experiments between 1852 and 1860 [123, 124, 126]. In the course of his experiments, Maxwell not only determined quantitative laws of color mixture [124, 126] for the first time but he also developed [cf. 126] the Maxwellian view system for visual observation and the method of mixing colors on the rotating wheel [123, 124]. On the theoretical side, he [123, 127], together with Helmholtz [63], reestablished Thomas Young's trichromatic theory [208] and advocated the equilateral triangle [123] as a substitute for Newton's color circle in the geometrical representation of color. The equilateral triangle has, in its various modifications, played an important role in mathematical descriptions of color.

Maxwell's results on the mixture of colors [124] by means of rotating disks need not be considered here, nor, is it, in fact, necessary to describe in detail his work with spectral colors [126]. It is sufficient to say that, in the latter researches, his apparatus consisted of a dark box with three slits in one wall; the widths and positions of the slits could be varied. Light entered the box by way of the slits, traversed a pair of prisms and then the resulting (nearly) monochromatic beams, controlled in intensity and wavelength by the widths and positions of the slits, were focused on the eye by a lens. To the eye it appeared that a vertical edge of the nearer prism bisected the field of the lens, one half of the field being filled with a mixture of the monochromatic radiations from the prism. White light could be admitted along another optical path so as to fill the half-field of the lens not already

[21] This is most readily demonstrated by multiplying the left and right members of the three Eqs. in (23) by, respectively, L_1, L_2 and L_3, and summing the products.

filled by light from the prism. The subject was required to vary the widths of the three slits until the mixture gave a match for the white light. Maxwell's primaries were wavelengths 631, 529, and 457 mμ [9].

Maxwell's method of determining the spectrum locus for his equilateral triangle was indirect. He first determined the slit widths required for each primary in order to have his white matched in brightness and color. Following each such match, he changed the wavelength of one of his monochromatic lights and determined the slit widths required to match his white. By eliminating the white term in the resulting two equations, it was possible to establish an equation that specified the amount of a selected monochromatic light in terms of the other three. When this procedure of matching white was followed for 14 wavelength triads in the case of one subject and

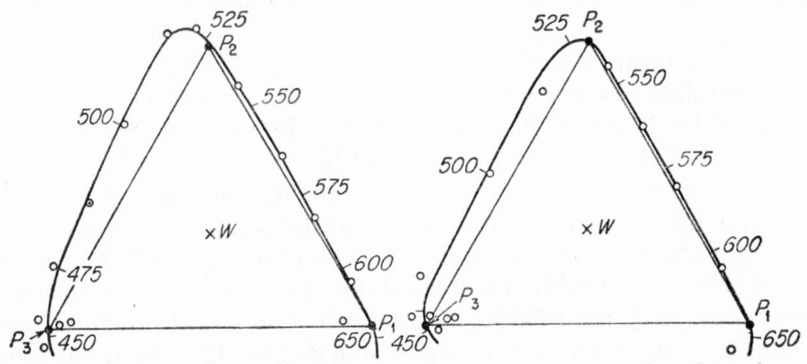

Fig. 19. The spectral loci for Maxwell's two subjects represented on his color triangle. The point W represents sunlight. Maxwell's primaries were 631, 529, 457 mμ. *From Le Grand* [115].

13 in the case of the other, Maxwell could, by eliminating the term for white from appropriate pairs of equations, obtain an equation for each selected color of the spectrum in terms of the three primaries.

Maxwell's data are not precise by modern standards, but they do involve matters of considerable historical interest and it is for this reason that the spectrum locus as he determined it for two subjects is presented in Fig. 19 taken from Le Grand [115]. The spectrum locus based on Maxwell's data is exterior to his color triangle; in consequence, one of his three trichromatic coordinates for any spectral color must be negative.

Maxwell's observations were followed by the improved experiments of König and Dieterici [111]. These experimenters, using the Helmholtz color mixer, determined trichromatic coordinates for two normal subjects and seven persons who exhibited three different types of color blindness. Other determinations were made by Abney [1], following König and Dieterici. Neither König and Dieterici nor Abney had available the technical refinements of modern research; their total of three subjects in both experiments was not sufficient to provide definitive data. Nevertheless, the data of König and Dieterici and Abney provided the basis for the excitation curves [182] that served as standard for nine years before the CIE recommendations were made in 1931 [79].

The change in standards proposed in 1931 was due in large part to the results of Wright [200, 201] and Guild [49] who independently reported experiments that have, until the present, provided us with our most precise data on color mixture.

Wright's work. Wright's experiments constituted a great advance over the work of earlier experimenters. Not only did Wright determine the trichromatic coordinates [200, 203] for the wavelengths of the spectrum in terms of his three spectral primaries, but he also determined the contributions of his primaries to the luminosity provided by each wavelength of a reference light source; in a word, he determined the distribution coefficients [201, 203] and the part contributions to luminosity. The latter quantities might, on analogy with their use in spectral mixture curves [203], be called spectral mixture coefficients.

Wright's experiments were made possible by his development of a colorimeter [cf. 203]. The colorimeter was a double monochromator system with a nearly complete absence of scattered light. The field of observation was a square 2° on a side. In the upper part of the field, three monochromatic primaries (P_1 = 650 mμ, P_2 = 530 mμ, and P_3 = 460 mμ) could be superposed, while in the lower half, any one of the three primaries could be added to any monochromatic band; the latter two radiations were taken from a second spectrum. In this general optical system, lights of fairly high intensities (about 100 trolands) could be obtained, except in the extreme violet.

Wright did not initially specify his luminous units by the usual convention that equal chromatic fluxes of the primaries are taken to give white. Rather, he chose units of his primaries P_1 and P_2 according to the convention that equal chromatic fluxes of the primaries were produced when they matched the yellow radiation of λ_4 = 582.5 mμ (plus a small, unrecorded amount of P_3). The unit of the primary P_3 was taken as equal to the chromatic flux of P_2 when the two matched λ_5 = 494 mμ (plus an unrecorded amount of P_1). The choice of λ_4 and λ_5 was based on instrumental considerations.

Wright's convention possesses an important advantage. If two subjects differ only with respect to the absorption characteristics of their ocular media (primarily the yellow pigment), their trichromatic coordinates for spectral colors will not differ, for the qualities of all spectral colors, including the primaries and λ_4 and λ_5, are unchanged by the presence of a filter. On the other hand, the position of white in the chromaticity diagram will vary from subject to subject.

Wright's determinations of the trichromatic coordinates for 10 subjects are given in Fig. 20.

By illuminating the lower half of the visual field with his source S_B of white light,[22] Wright could determine the trichromatic coordinates for white. For 36 subjects, the average trichromatic coordinates for white were as follows: $\gamma_1 = 0.243$, $\gamma_2 = 0.410$, $\gamma_3 = 0.347$. These coefficients probably vary as a function of the subject's age. The spectrum locus of Wright's data is plotted in Fig. 21. The triangle

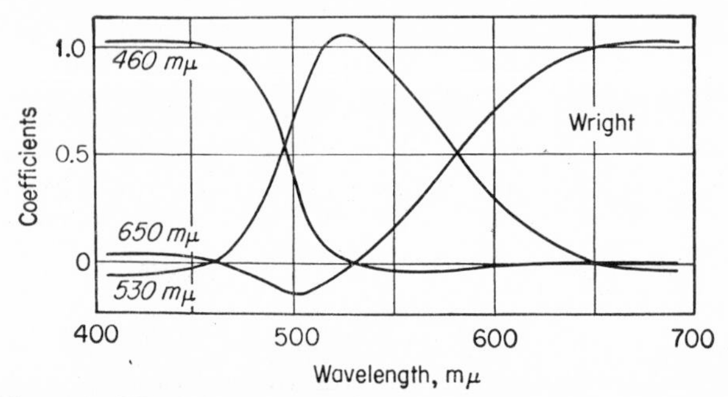

FIG. 20. Wright's average determinations of the trichromatic coordinates for 10 subjects. His primaries were 460, 530, and 650 mμ. *From Hecht's figure* [58] *of Wright's data* [200].

encompasses the white points for 36 subjects, the 10 who participated in the complete determinations and 26 who only matched λ_4 and λ_5 against the white stimulus.[23]

Wright [201, 203] next recomputed his original data in such a way that his trichromatic coordinates were based on the conventional white system,[24] i.e., for white, $\gamma_1 = \gamma_2 = \gamma_3 = 0.333$. Following the change in units, Wright determined L_1, L_2, and L_3 for primaries P_1, P_2, and P_3, preparatory to computing the distribution coefficients. Flicker measurements of his primaries against the white reference source S_B showed,

[22] Illuminant B of color temperature 4800°K [see Appendix I in 202].

[23] The point W represents the position of white for an equal energy spectrum calculated on the basis of the distribution coefficients. The coordinates are, respectively, 0.228, 0.390, and 0.382.

[24] The resulting trichromatic coordinates are the ones given in Wright [203]. The trichromatic coordinates for Wright's original units are given (as computations) in Le Grand [115, p. 155].

with seven subjects, that the luminous units were, respectively, $L_1 = 0.385$, $L_2 = 1.000$, and $L_3 = 0.0372$.

The specific steps involved in computing the distribution coefficients and fractional contributions to luminosity from the trichromatic coordinates are as follows: (1) At each wavelength multiply γ_1, γ_2, and γ_3 by V_λ/L_λ, where V_λ is the CIE luminosity value corrected for the S_B spectrum and $L_\lambda = \gamma_1 L_1 + \gamma_2 L_2 + \gamma_3 L_3$ in Eq. (24). This computation gives $\bar{\gamma}_1$, $\bar{\gamma}_2$, and $\bar{\gamma}_3$, the respective distribution coefficients

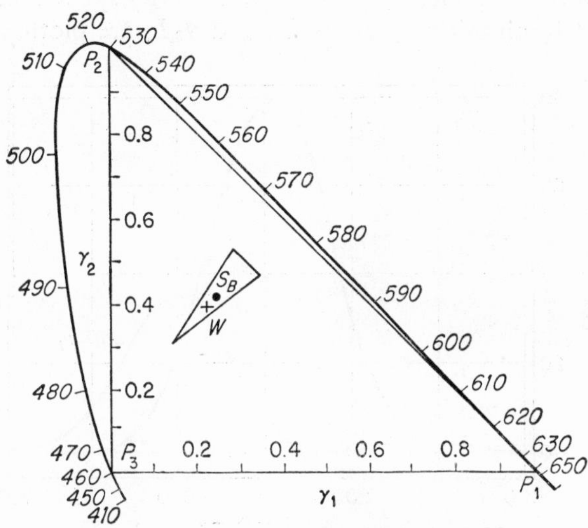

FIG. 21. The spectrum locus of Wright's data and the average and scatter of white points for 36 subjects. *After Le Grand* [115] *and Wright* [203].

in Eqs. (23) for luminosity in the S_B spectrum. (2) Multiply $\bar{\gamma}_1$ by L_1, $\bar{\gamma}_2$ by L_2, and $\bar{\gamma}_3$ by L_3 in order to compute the part luminosities $\bar{\gamma}_1 L_1$, $\bar{\gamma}_2 L_2$, and $\bar{\gamma}_3 L_3$ in Eq. (27),

$$\bar{\gamma}_1 L_1 + \bar{\gamma}_2 L_2 + \bar{\gamma}_3 L_3 = V_\lambda \tag{27}$$

for the S_B spectrum.

We are interested in finding the distribution coefficients for luminosity of the equal energy spectrum. (We shall refer to it as V_{λ_e}.) The relation between V_{λ_e} and V_λ is given by

$$V_{\lambda_e} = V_\lambda \left(\frac{E_{\lambda_e}}{E_\lambda}\right) \tag{28}$$

where E_λ and E_{λ_e} are the energies at wavelength λ in, respectively, the spectrum of source S_B and in the equal energy spectrum.

E_{λ_e} is constant and may be taken to be unity, in which case

$$\bar{\gamma}_{1_e} L_1 + \bar{\gamma}_{2_e} L_2 + \bar{\gamma}_{3_e} L_3 = V_\lambda \quad (29)$$

where $$\bar{\gamma}_{1_e} = \frac{\bar{\gamma}_1}{E_\lambda} \qquad \bar{\gamma}_{2_e} = \frac{\bar{\gamma}_2}{E_\lambda} \qquad \text{and} \qquad \bar{\gamma}_{3_e} = \frac{\bar{\gamma}_3}{E_\lambda} \quad (30)$$

Each distribution coefficient for the S_B spectrum must be divided by E_λ (the energy of wavelength λ in the S_B spectrum) in order to obtain the distribution coefficients for the equal energy spectrum.

The part luminosities $\bar{\gamma}_{1_e} L_1$, $\bar{\gamma}_{2_e} L_2$, and $\bar{\gamma}_{3_e} L_3$ are plotted in Fig. 22.

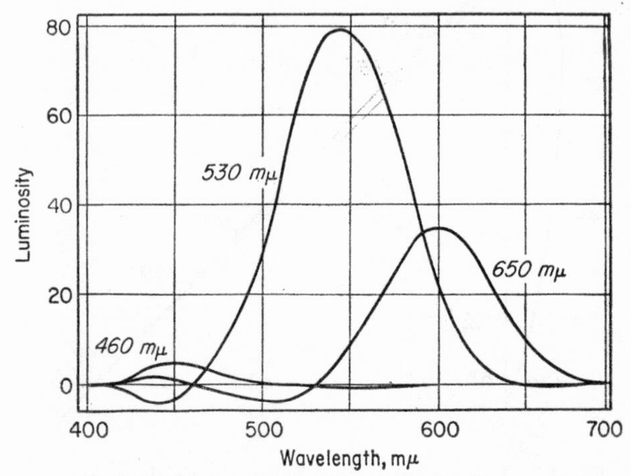

FIG. 22. The products of the three distribution coefficients and their respective luminous units add to give the luminosity of an equal energy spectrum. *From Hecht's discussion* [58] *of Wright's data* [201, 203].

The figure indicates the way in which each primary contributes its part relative luminosity to the total relative luminosity V_{λ_e} in the equal energy spectrum.

Changes of system. The trichromatic coordinates of a given color depend upon two factors, the primaries that are used to match the color and the luminous units of the primaries. A change in either factor changes the system of specifying colors, but it is important to realize that appropriate transformations allow one to calculate coordinates in the new system from a consideration of the old. [For a more extended treatment of the subject matter of the section, see an article by Howett and Graham, 73.]

Changes in the luminous units of the primaries. First, consider what happens if, for a given set of primaries, we change the luminous units.

Suppose that the three chromatic fluxes Γ_1, Γ_2 and Γ_3 required to match the chromatic flux Γ_S of any light S are changed to amounts Γ'_1, Γ'_2, and Γ'_3 by virtue of a change from the "old" luminous units, L_i, to the "new" ones, L'_i. The component luminous fluxes F_1, F_2, and F_3 of the light S are of course unaffected by the shift from the "old" to the "new" units. Therefore, $F_1 = \Gamma_1 L_1 = \Gamma'_1 L'_1$, and similar relations apply to F_2 and F_3. It follows that

$$\Gamma'_1 = \frac{L_1\Gamma_1}{L'_1} \qquad \Gamma'_2 = \frac{L_2\Gamma_2}{L'_2} \qquad \text{and} \qquad \Gamma'_3 = \frac{L_3\Gamma_3}{L'_3} \tag{31}$$

Usually, we shall be interested in the relations among the trichromatic coordinates rather than the chromatic fluxes. By (31),

$$\gamma'_1 = \frac{\Gamma'_1}{\Gamma'_1 + \Gamma'_2 + \Gamma'_3} = \frac{\dfrac{L_1}{L'_1}\cdot\Gamma_1}{\dfrac{L_1}{L'_1}\cdot\Gamma_1 + \dfrac{L_2}{L'_2}\cdot\Gamma_2 + \dfrac{L_3}{L'_3}\cdot\Gamma_3}$$

On dividing numerator and denominator by $\Gamma_1 + \Gamma_2 + \Gamma_3$, we obtain

$$\gamma'_1 = \frac{\dfrac{L_1}{L'_1}\cdot\gamma_1}{\dfrac{L_1}{L'_1}\cdot\gamma_1 + \dfrac{L_2}{L'_2}\cdot\gamma_2 + \dfrac{L_3}{L'_3}\cdot\gamma_3}$$

Similarly,

$$\gamma'_2 = \frac{\dfrac{L_2}{L'_2}\cdot\gamma_2}{\dfrac{L_1}{L'_1}\cdot\gamma_1 + \dfrac{L_2}{L'_2}\cdot\gamma_2 + \dfrac{L_3}{L'_3}\cdot\gamma_3} \tag{32}$$

and

$$\gamma'_3 = \frac{\dfrac{L_3}{L'_3}\cdot\gamma_3}{\dfrac{L_1}{L'_1}\cdot\gamma_1 + \dfrac{L_2}{L'_2}\cdot\gamma_2 + \dfrac{L_3}{L'_3}\cdot\gamma_3}$$

Since the actual sizes of the units L_i and L'_i are often not known, a change of units is most often made indirectly. The most frequent method is simply to assign a new set of trichromatic coordinates to a particular light, choosing the new values according to convenience, or some theoretical assumption.

Let γ_{W1}, γ_{W2}, and γ_{W3} be the original trichromatic coordinates of some particular reference light. (The W subscripts are used because the reference light is usually white, although it does not have to be.) Let γ'_{W1}, γ'_{W2} and γ'_{W3} be the "new" coordinates chosen for the reference light. On the assumption that the change in coordinates for this reference light is the result of a change in the units of the primaries, we can derive a formula for the "new" coordinates of any light S in terms of its "old" coordinates and the "new" and "old" coordinates of the reference light.

The "new" and "old" chromatic fluxes of the reference light (and any other light) must satisfy Eqs. (31), since we are assuming that the change in the coordinates of the reference light is due to a change in units. Then

$$\Gamma'_{W1} = \frac{L_1}{L'_1} \cdot \Gamma_{W1} \qquad \Gamma'_{W2} = \frac{L_2}{L'_2} \cdot \Gamma_{W2} \qquad \text{and} \qquad \Gamma'_{W3} = \frac{L_3}{L'_3} \cdot \Gamma_{W3} \tag{33}$$

Hence

$$\frac{L_1}{L'_1} = \frac{\Gamma'_{W1}}{\Gamma_{W1}} \qquad \frac{L_2}{L'_2} = \frac{\Gamma'_{W2}}{\Gamma_{W2}} \qquad \text{and} \qquad \frac{L_3}{L'_3} = \frac{\Gamma'_{W3}}{\Gamma_{W3}} \tag{34}$$

Now define

$$\begin{aligned} K_W &= \Gamma_{W1} + \Gamma_{W2} + \Gamma_{W3} \\ K'_W &= \Gamma'_{W1} + \Gamma'_{W2} + \Gamma'_{W3} \end{aligned} \tag{35}$$

Using Eqs. (20), we may then write

$$\gamma_{W1} = \frac{\Gamma_{W1}}{K_W} \qquad \gamma'_{W1} = \frac{\Gamma'_{W1}}{K'_W} \tag{36}$$

or

$$\Gamma_{W1} = K_W \gamma_{W1} \qquad \Gamma'_{W1} = K'_W \gamma'_{W1} \tag{37}$$

Hence

$$\frac{\Gamma'_{W1}}{\Gamma_{W1}} = \frac{K'_W}{K_W} \cdot \frac{\gamma'_{W1}}{\gamma_{W1}} \tag{38}$$

and analogous expressions hold for $\frac{\Gamma'_{W2}}{\Gamma_{W2}}$ and $\frac{\Gamma'_{W3}}{\Gamma_{W3}}$.

Thus, from (34) we have

$$\frac{L_1}{L'_1} = \frac{K'_W}{K_W} \cdot \frac{\gamma'_{W1}}{\gamma_{W1}} \qquad \frac{L_2}{L'_2} = \frac{K'_W}{K_W} \cdot \frac{\gamma'_{W2}}{\gamma_{W2}} \qquad \text{and} \qquad \frac{L_3}{L'_3} = \frac{K'_W}{K_W} \cdot \frac{\gamma'_{W3}}{\gamma_{W3}} \tag{39}$$

Substituting these expressions for all the $\frac{L_i}{L'_i}$ in Eqs. (32), we obtain, for γ'_i, the formula

$$\gamma'_1 = \frac{\frac{K'_W}{K_W} \cdot \frac{\gamma'_{W1}}{\gamma_{W1}} \cdot \gamma_1}{\frac{K'_W}{K_W} \cdot \frac{\gamma'_{W1}}{\gamma_{W1}} \cdot \gamma_1 + \frac{K'_W}{K_W} \cdot \frac{\gamma'_{W2}}{\gamma_{W2}} \cdot \gamma_2 + \frac{K'_W}{K_W} \cdot \frac{\gamma'_{W3}}{\gamma_{W3}} \cdot \gamma_3}$$

which reduces to
$$\gamma_1' = \frac{\frac{\gamma_{W1}'}{\gamma_{W1}} \cdot \gamma_1}{\frac{\gamma_{W1}'}{\gamma_{W1}} \cdot \gamma_1 + \frac{\gamma_{W2}'}{\gamma_{W2}} \cdot \gamma_2 + \frac{\gamma_{W3}'}{\gamma_{W3}} \cdot \gamma_3}$$

Similarly
$$\gamma_2' = \frac{\frac{\gamma_{W2}'}{\gamma_{W2}} \cdot \gamma_2}{\frac{\gamma_{W1}'}{\gamma_{W1}} \cdot \gamma_1 + \frac{\gamma_{W2}'}{\gamma_{W2}} \cdot \gamma_2 + \frac{\gamma_{W3}'}{\gamma_{W3}} \cdot \gamma_3} \tag{40}$$

and
$$\gamma_3' = \frac{\frac{\gamma_{W3}'}{\gamma_{W3}} \cdot \gamma_3}{\frac{\gamma_{W1}'}{\gamma_{W1}} \cdot \gamma_1 + \frac{\gamma_{W2}'}{\gamma_{W2}} \cdot \gamma_2 + \frac{\gamma_{W3}'}{\gamma_{W3}} \cdot \gamma_3}$$

Changes in the primaries: the coordinates of a color specified with respect to new primaries as computed from the coordinates of that color with respect to old primaries. In addition to changing units one can also change primaries. Appropriate algebraic transformations are required, for example, when it is desired to compare readings that involve different primaries, or when it becomes necessary to compare results obtained with arbitrary primaries with results that hold for a standard system.

It is to Ives [87, 89] and Guild [46, 47] that we owe much of our methodology for making algebraic and geometric transformations from one system of primaries to another. See also Southall [163], Le Grand [115], Judd [101], and especially, Wright [202] for some valuable additional considerations.

The problem is this: we are given that γ_1, γ_2, and γ_3 are the trichromatic coordinates of a light S with respect to three primaries P_1, P_2, and P_3, having luminous units L_1, L_2, and L_3, respectively. In equation form, this relationship can be expressed as Eq. (19):

$$L_S = \gamma_1 L_1 + \gamma_2 L_2 + \gamma_3 L_3$$

We wish to determine the trichromatic coordinates of S with respect to a new set of primaries, P_4', P_5', and P_6', having luminous units L_4', L_5', and L_6', respectively. In other words, we wish to determine γ_4', γ_5', and γ_6' in the equation

$$L_S' = \gamma_4' L_4' + \gamma_5' L_5' + \gamma_6' L_6' \tag{41}$$

The L' terms of Eq. (41) represent units in the "new" $P_4'P_5'P_6'$ system as contrasted with the unprimed L terms of Eq. (19), which represent units in the "old" $P_1P_2P_3$ system. The differentiation of units in the two systems by means of primes is maintained throughout this chapter. The luminous unit represented by any L term refers to light of the same spectral composition as the L' term with the same subscript. In general, the magnitudes of corresponding L and L' terms are unequal, so that, for example, L'_S of Eq. (41) would not equal L_S of Eq. (19) except by an unusual coincidence.

The luminous units of the old primaries given in terms of the luminous units of the new primaries. The simplest method for making the necessary transformations applies when we have the information represented by the following equations, in which L_1, L_2, and L_3 are the same $P_1P_2P_3$ units as in Eq. (19), and L'_4, L'_5, and L'_6, the same $P'_4P'_5P'_6$ units as in Eq. (41):

$$\begin{aligned} L_1 &= a_{14}L'_4 + a_{15}L'_5 + a_{16}L'_6 \\ L_2 &= a_{24}L'_4 + a_{25}L'_5 + a_{26}L'_6 \\ L_3 &= a_{34}L'_4 + a_{35}L'_5 + a_{36}L'_6 \end{aligned} \tag{42}$$

It is worth pointing out that the sum of the transformation coefficients, the a_{ij} terms in each of Eqs. (42), is not in general equal to unity because of the fact that the units on the two sides of each equation are in different systems.

The information required for Eqs. (42) is characteristically present in such a practical colorimetric situation as the following: A given apparatus is standardized in terms of three arbitrary primaries and their associated units which may be specified in terms of some convenient settings on the apparatus. Experimental data obtained with such an apparatus are expressed in terms of the "working primaries" of the system. In our present situation we may think of these as the "old" primaries of the $P_1P_2P_3$ system. For many purposes, results in such terms as these are useful, but in other circumstances it may turn out that a transformation of the data to a standard system of primaries, the "new" (or, in the present instance, $P'_4P'_5P'_6$) system, may become necessary in order to specify the data of the colorimeter in terms of standard values. Under such circumstances one may specify the standard equations for the old primaries in terms of the new primaries, as in Eqs. (42).

The problem of describing the old primaries in terms of the new is not always easily solved; in most concrete experimental situations the converse account is more readily obtainable. The fact is that the method of describing the old primaries in terms of the new is a very special one that, at some stage, requires elaborate measurements; in particular, it requires a calibration of the working primaries in terms of the reference primaries. It is obvious that at this stage, the old (working primary) units are, in fact, the new units of the given operation and the new units are, in reality, the old (reference) units. It will not do here to labor the methodological problems underlying this type of computation, for Guild [46] has discussed them in considerable detail. It now remains only to consider the mathematical basis of the computations.

It has been said that the corresponding L and L' terms of Eqs. (19) and (41) are not, in general, equal. In particular, L'_S of (41) is not equal to L_S of (19). Thus their ratio c defined by the equation

$$cL'_S = L_S \tag{43}$$

is not, in general, equal to 1.

On substituting in (19) the equivalents of L_S, L_1, L_2, and L_3 in Eqs. (42) and (43) we obtain

$$cL'_S = a_4L'_4 + a_5L'_5 + a_6L'_6 \tag{44}$$

where

$$\begin{aligned} a_4 &= a_{14}\gamma_1 + a_{24}\gamma_2 + a_{34}\gamma_3 \\ a_5 &= a_{15}\gamma_1 + a_{25}\gamma_2 + a_{35}\gamma_3 \\ a_6 &= a_{16}\gamma_1 + a_{26}\gamma_2 + a_{36}\gamma_3 \end{aligned} \tag{45}$$

If we divide both sides of (44) by c, we obtain our sought-for Eq. (41),

$$L'_S = \gamma'_4L'_4 + \gamma'_5L'_5 + \gamma'_6L'_6$$

where $\gamma'_4 = a_4/c$; $\gamma'_5 = a_5/c$; and $\gamma'_6 = a_6/c$. Since (41) is a unit equation, $\gamma'_4 + \gamma'_5 + \gamma'_6 = 1$, or

$$a_4 + a_5 + a_6 = c \tag{46}$$

Hence,

$$\begin{aligned} \gamma'_4 &= \frac{a_4}{a_4 + a_5 + a_6} \\ \gamma'_5 &= \frac{a_5}{a_4 + a_5 + a_6} \\ \gamma'_6 &= \frac{a_6}{a_4 + a_5 + a_6} \end{aligned} \tag{47}$$

Thus, to obtain the coordinates γ'_4, γ'_5, γ'_6 when the coordinates γ_1, γ_2, γ_3 and the quantities a_{ij} of Eqs. (42) are given, two steps are sufficient:

1. Substitute the given quantities directly in Eqs. (45) to obtain a_4, a_5, a_6.
2. As indicated by Eqs. (47), a_4, a_5, and a_6 should be added together and each one divided by the sum to give γ'_4, γ'_5, and γ'_6.

There is some interest to be found in the explicit form of the transformation (i.e., the result of substituting the expressions of (41) in the final Eq. (43), although it is not convenient for computational purposes. These explicit equations are:

$$\begin{aligned} \gamma_4' &= \frac{a_{14}\gamma_1 + a_{24}\gamma_2 + a_{34}\gamma_3}{k_1\gamma_1 + k_2\gamma_2 + k_3\gamma_3} \\ \gamma_5' &= \frac{a_{15}\gamma_1 + a_{25}\gamma_2 + a_{35}\gamma_3}{k_1\gamma_1 + k_2\gamma_2 + k_3\gamma_3} \\ \gamma_6' &= \frac{a_{16}\gamma_1 + a_{26}\gamma_2 + a_{36}\gamma_3}{k_1\gamma_1 + k_2\gamma_2 + k_3\gamma_3} \end{aligned} \tag{48}$$

where

$$k_1 = a_{14} + a_{15} + a_{16} \qquad k_2 = a_{24} + a_{25} + a_{26} \qquad k_3 = a_{34} + a_{35} + a_{36} \tag{49}$$

It is to be noted that these equations, representing the transformation of trichromatic coordinates from one system of primaries to another, are not *linear* transformations (as are those between the tristimulus values or distribution coefficients), but are rather *linear fractional* transformations.

Luminous units of the new primaries given in terms of the old. The previously described method of specifying a luminous unit of an old primary in terms of the units of new primaries provides a mathematically simple method of transforming results from one set of primaries to another. On the other hand, it has been stated that the method has severe practical limitations [46]. In particular, difficulties arise if there does not exist, for the wavelengths of the spectrum, a table (or its graphic equivalent) of trichromatic coordinates referred to the new primaries. An elaborate series of measurements and computations [46] might be required to circumvent the difficulty, and it is fortunate that the problem may be eliminated by the use of a second mathematical method. The second method is mathematically more elaborate than the first, but it eliminates many difficulties of physical procedure. In essence, the method specifies the luminous units of the new primaries in terms of the old. As contrasted with the information presented in Eqs. (42) we now have

$$\begin{aligned} L_4 &= \gamma_{41}L_1 + \gamma_{42}L_2 + \gamma_{43}L_3 \\ L_5 &= \gamma_{51}L_1 + \gamma_{52}L_2 + \gamma_{53}L_3 \\ L_6 &= \gamma_{61}L_1 + \gamma_{62}L_2 + \gamma_{63}L_3 \end{aligned} \tag{50}$$

where the γs are all trichromatic coordinates whose subscripts refer in each case, first to the color whose unit appears on the left side, and second to the particular primary whose unit the coordinate multiplies. If P_4, P_5, and P_6 are monochromatic, the coefficients γ_{ji} of (50) can be read directly from the table of trichromatic coefficients relative to the "old" primaries P_1, P_2, P_3.

If we solve the Eqs. (50) for L_1, L_2, and L_3 in terms of L_4, L_5, and L_6, we obtain

$$\begin{aligned} L_1 &= \gamma_{14}L_4 + \gamma_{15}L_5 + \gamma_{16}L_6 \\ L_2 &= \gamma_{24}L_4 + \gamma_{25}L_5 + \gamma_{26}L_6 \\ L_3 &= \gamma_{34}L_4 + \gamma_{35}L_5 + \gamma_{36}L_6 \end{aligned} \tag{51}$$

where the γs are again trichromatic coordinates, but now relative to the "new" primaries P_4, P_5, P_6. The subscripts, as before, refer first to the color on the left side and second to the appropriate primary on the right side. These coordinates are, of course, different from those of (50) and may be distinguished by the fact that in (51) the first subscript is smaller than the second, while in (50) the reverse is true. In general, any γ_{ij} in (51) is not the same quantity as its corresponding γ_{ji} in (50). The expressions for the values of the coordinates in (51) in terms of the coordinates of (50) are as follows:

$$\begin{aligned} \gamma_{14} &= \frac{1}{D}(\gamma_{52}\gamma_{63} - \gamma_{53}\gamma_{62}) \qquad \gamma_{15} = \frac{1}{D}(\gamma_{43}\gamma_{62} - \gamma_{42}\gamma_{63}) \\ \gamma_{16} &= \frac{1}{D}(\gamma_{42}\gamma_{53} - \gamma_{43}\gamma_{52}) \\ \gamma_{24} &= \frac{1}{D}(\gamma_{53}\gamma_{61} - \gamma_{51}\gamma_{63}) \qquad \gamma_{25} = \frac{1}{D}(\gamma_{41}\gamma_{63} - \gamma_{43}\gamma_{61}) \\ \gamma_{26} &= \frac{1}{D}(\gamma_{43}\gamma_{51} - \gamma_{41}\gamma_{53}) \\ \gamma_{34} &= \frac{1}{D}(\gamma_{51}\gamma_{62} - \gamma_{52}\gamma_{61}) \qquad \gamma_{35} = \frac{1}{D}(\gamma_{42}\gamma_{61} - \gamma_{41}\gamma_{62}) \\ \gamma_{36} &= \frac{1}{D}(\gamma_{41}\gamma_{52} - \gamma_{42}\gamma_{51}) \end{aligned} \tag{52}$$

In these equations, D is the determinant of the coordinates in (50), i.e.,

$$D = \gamma_{41}\gamma_{52}\gamma_{63} + \gamma_{42}\gamma_{53}\gamma_{61} + \gamma_{43}\gamma_{51}\gamma_{62} - \gamma_{43}\gamma_{52}\gamma_{61} - \gamma_{41}\gamma_{53}\gamma_{62} - \gamma_{42}\gamma_{51}\gamma_{63} \tag{53}$$

The transition from (50) to (51) represents a change of primaries without a change in the sizes of the units of any of the colors. As long as we are dealing with a system having these same unit sizes, we shall write the colors being used as primaries, e.g., $P_4P_5P_6$, without primes; and similarly the units L_4, L_5, and L_6 will be written without primes. When we are dealing with systems with the same unit sizes as the "new" $P'_4P'_5P'_6$ system, we shall write the primaries and units *with* primes, so that, for example, one could refer to the $P'_1P'_2P'_3$ system with units L'_1, L'_2, L'_3. It is to be noted that, e.g., $P_4P_5P_6$ refers to the same colors as $P'_4P'_5P'_6$, the primes of the latter indicating only that the unit sizes of the two systems are unequal.

The units L_4, L_5, and L_6 of (51) are units in the "old" (unprimed) system. The next step will be to specify the corresponding units, L'_4, L'_5, and L'_6 in the "new" (primed) system. One may employ many different methods for choosing unit values in a new system of primaries, but, in practice, the most frequently used device seems to be that of arbitrarily assigning coordinates to a particular reference color W. (For example, it is common practice to specify that one of the standard white sources is matched by equal chromatic fluxes from the three new primaries; i.e., the trichromatic coordinates are all equal to 0.3333.) The reference source is here denoted by W because a white is usually chosen, but such a choice is not necessary. The steps of specifying the new units may be described for the most general case as follows.

Let the trichromatic coordinates of a reference source W be γ_{W1}, γ_{W2}, γ_{W3} in the $P_1P_2P_3$ system and γ'_{W4}, γ'_{W5}, γ'_{W6} in the $P'_4P'_5P'_6$ system. Let the units of W in the two systems by L_W and L'_W respectively.

Then
$$L_W = \gamma_{W1}L_1 + \gamma_{W2}L_2 + \gamma_{W3}L_3 \tag{54}$$

and
$$L'_W = \gamma'_{W4}L'_4 + \gamma'_{W5}L'_5 + \gamma'_{W6}L'_6 \tag{55}$$

On substituting in (54) the values for L_1, L_2, and L_3 given by (51) and regrouping terms, we obtain

$$\begin{aligned} L_W = (\gamma_{W1}\gamma_{14} + \gamma_{W2}\gamma_{24} + \gamma_{W3}\gamma_{34})L_4 \\ + (\gamma_{W1}\gamma_{15} + \gamma_{W2}\gamma_{25} + \gamma_{W3}\gamma_{35})L_5 \\ + (\gamma_{W1}\gamma_{16} + \gamma_{W2}\gamma_{26} + \gamma_{W3}\gamma_{36})L_6 \end{aligned} \tag{56}$$

If we now define the quantities γ_{W4}, γ_{W5}, and γ_{6W} as follows:

$$\begin{aligned} \gamma_{W4} &= \gamma_{W1}\gamma_{14} + \gamma_{W2}\gamma_{24} + \gamma_{W3}\gamma_{34} \\ \gamma_{W5} &= \gamma_{W1}\gamma_{15} + \gamma_{W2}\gamma_{25} + \gamma_{W3}\gamma_{35} \\ \gamma_{W6} &= \gamma_{W1}\gamma_{16} + \gamma_{W2}\gamma_{26} + \gamma_{W3}\gamma_{36} \end{aligned} \tag{57}$$

Eq. (56) may be written

$$L_W = \gamma_{W4}L_4 + \gamma_{W5}L_5 + \gamma_{W6}L_6 \tag{58}$$

The light W is thus analyzed into the three new primaries $P_4P_5P_6$, where the luminous units of P_4, P_5, and P_6 are the same as the units of

P_4, P_5, and P_6 in the old $P_1P_2P_3$ system. We now want to relate (58) to (55).

The relation between (58) and (55) involves a simple change of units for which we can use formulas (32), so that

$$\gamma'_{W4} = \frac{1}{K}\left(\frac{L_4}{L'_4} \cdot \gamma_{W4}\right)$$
$$\gamma'_{W5} = \frac{1}{K}\left(\frac{L_5}{L'_5} \cdot \gamma_{W5}\right) \qquad (59)$$
$$\gamma'_{W6} = \frac{1}{K}\left(\frac{L_6}{L'_6} \cdot \gamma_{W6}\right)$$

where
$$K = \frac{L_4}{L'_4} \cdot \gamma_{W4} + \frac{L_5}{L'_5} \cdot \gamma_{W5} + \frac{L_6}{L'_6} \cdot \gamma_{W6} \qquad (60)$$

It can be shown that the quantity K drops out at a stage preceding the final formula and so need not be calculated.

If we substitute in (51) the values for L_4, L_5, and L_6 obtained by solving Eqs. (59) for these quantities, we obtain equations expressing L_1, L_2, and L_3 as linear functions of L'_4, L'_5, and L'_6; in other words, we obtain equations of the form of (42). The final solution, then, develops exactly as given in Eqs. (43) to (47). The quantities a_4, a_5, and a_6 of (47) turn out to have the following values:

$$a_4 = \frac{\gamma'_{W4}}{\gamma_{W4}}(\gamma_{14}\gamma_1 + \gamma_{24}\gamma_2 + \gamma_{34}\gamma_3)$$
$$a_5 = \frac{\gamma'_{W5}}{\gamma_{W5}}(\gamma_{15}\gamma_1 + \gamma_{25}\gamma_2 + \gamma_{35}\gamma_3) \qquad (61)$$
$$a_6 = \frac{\gamma'_{W6}}{\gamma_{W6}}(\gamma_{16}\gamma_1 + \gamma_{26}\gamma_2 + \gamma_{36}\gamma_3)$$

When Eqs. (61) are expressed entirely in terms of quantities assumed to be directly given in the present method, it can be seen that the quantity D of (52) and (53) appears as a factor in each numerator and denominator, and hence, like K of (59) and (60) drops out and need not be calculated.

We are now ready to describe the specific steps to be used to obtain the "new" coordinates γ'_4, γ'_5, and γ'_6, under the assumption that we are given the "old" coordinates γ_1, γ_2, and γ_3, the coordinates γ_{ji} of Eqs. (50), the "old" coordinates γ_{W1}, γ_{W2}, and γ_{W3} of the reference source, and the "new" coordinates γ'_{W4}, γ'_{W5}, and γ'_{W6} of the reference source. They are as follows:

1. Calculate the quantities γ_{ij} as given in Eqs. (52), *disregarding the factors* $1/D$.[25]

2. Calculate the quantities γ_{W4}, γ_{W5}, and γ_{W6} as given in Eqs. (57), using the values for the γ_{ij} calculated in step 1.

3. Substitute the values calculated in 1 and 2, in addition to the appropriate given quantities, into Eqs. (61) to obtain a_4, a_5, and a_6.

4. Obtain γ'_4, γ'_5, and γ'_6 from a_4, a_5, and a_6 as indicated by Eqs. (47).

Methods based on other sets of initial data. We have considered here only the two commonest methods of specifying the units of one set of primaries in terms of the units of another set of primaries. Such specification is a prerequisite for transformations of trichromatic coordinates from one system of primaries to another. The sets of Eqs. (42) and (50) represent two of a total of eight different possible such sets. The units on the left sides of the equations can be either those of the old primary colors, as in (42), or of the new primary colors, as in (50). These units on the left may be given in either the old (unprimed) system, as in both (42) and (50), or in the new (primed) system. And, finally, the units on the right may also be in either the unprimed system, as in (50), or the primed system, as in (42). These three criteria permit of two cubed or eight possible combinations.

Each of the eight methods requires somewhat different algebraic manipulation, generally similar to the sort of processes employed in the two methods we have discussed. Some require considerably more mathematical manipulation than others, and some may also require more experimental work than others. The decision as to which method to use will, in each individual case, be dictated by considerations of available apparatus, required experimental procedure, total time available, and similar factors.

Guild's work. Guild [49] determined, for seven subjects, the trichromatic coordinates of wavelengths throughout the spectrum in terms of three primaries that were not monochromatic. The primaries were provided by means of the following device [48]. Three openings covered by red, green, and blue filters, respectively, appeared in an opaque screen. The area of each opening could be varied independently of the other two. A rotating prism collected light from each opening in turn and presented the light, mixed as a fusion of successive

[25] The quantities so calculated are no longer really γ_{ij} but are actually $D \cdot \gamma_{ij}$. Hence the sum of the three quantities for any value of i is not 1, but D. This, rather than Eq. (49), is the easiest way to obtain the value of D if it is desired, but it is not necessary for the purposes of the calculation. However, since the sum D of the three quantities should be the same for all three values of i, it is worth expending the small effort of finding the sums in order to have a check on the calculations.

presentations, to the eye. Colors produced by the monochromatic bands of a monochromator could be placed beside the mixed light of the primaries, and the proportions of the latter required to match the color of each narrow spectral region could be determined.

The spectrum locus for Guild's primaries is presented in Fig. 23. The figure shows that the primaries were equivalent to dominant wavelengths of 630, 542, 460 mμ, the latter two having purities slightly less than unity. The position of the reference white S_B is indicated at $\gamma_1 = \gamma_2 = \gamma_3 = 0.333$ in the diagram.

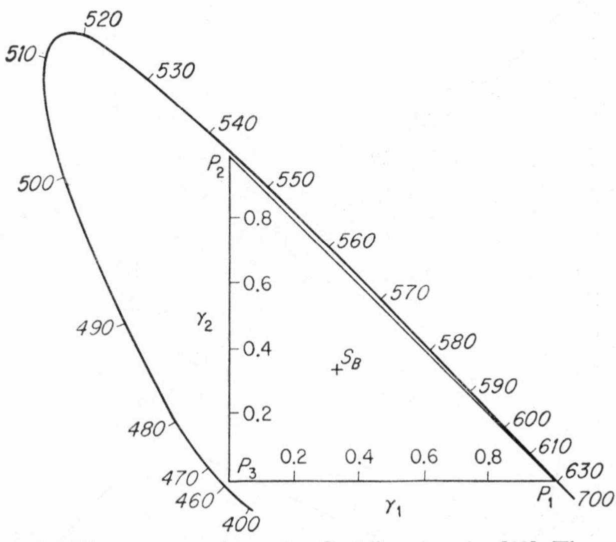

FIG. 23. The spectrum locus for Guild's primaries [49]. The reference white S_B is placed at $\gamma_1 = \gamma_2 = \gamma_3 = 0.333$.

The CIE Standard Observer for Colorimetry. Some time before 1931 the National Physical Laboratory adopted a set of primaries as standards for colorimetric specification [49]. These primaries, consisting of the monochromatic radiations of wavelengths 700, 546.1, and 435.8 mμ, were chosen because of their availability and convenience. Wavelengths 546.1 and 435.8 mμ are lines of the mercury arc, while wavelength 700 mμ represents a color that remains constant throughout the long wavelength end of the spectrum [189].

These primaries were accepted as standards by the Eighth Session of the Commission Internationale de l'Éclairage in 1931. At that time the newly obtained results of Wright and Guild were averaged after each had been transformed to a system based on the recommended primaries; this system is called the RGB system. Wright's and Guild's averages were modified slightly to obtain smooth curves and to place source W, the light given by the equal energy spectrum, at the center of the chromaticity diagram. Recomputed in this manner the data turned out to give closely similar sets of trichromatic coordinates.

The international XYZ system. The RGB system, adopted as the system specifying the Standard Observer for Colorimetry, could have been used as a basis for general colorimetric specification. However, it soon became obvious that a different system would be desirable, one, for example, that would be based on the RGB data as standard but

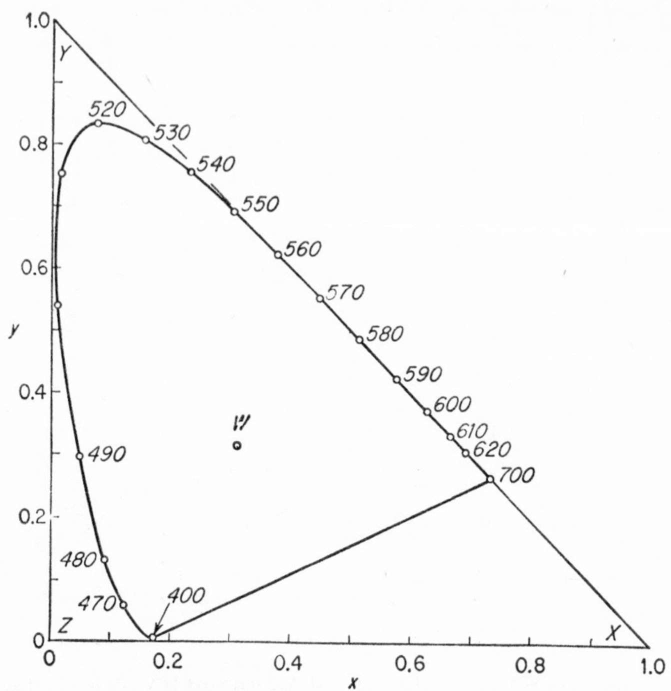

Fig. 24. Chromaticity diagram for the XYZ system. *After Hardy* [51] *and Le Grand* [115].

which would nevertheless exhibit certain other desirable characteristics. In particular, it was felt that the new system should not contain negative coefficients. Meeting this requirement would mean, of course, that colorimetrists would be dealing with imaginary primaries, but it was felt that this disadvantage would be outweighed by the gain in freedom from computational error and the increase in simplicity of calculations. For these reasons, the international XYZ system was established, largely under the influence of Judd [94].

A recent publication [103] indicates certain questions that have arisen in connection with the 1931 CIE Standard Observer. They concern the nature of color mixture functions for large (10°) areas and the need for more information on the validity of Abney's law, which has been reported many times to be invalid. It can be foreseen that new data may change our basic attitude with respect to the 1931 CIE Standard Observer. At the time of writing this paper, the new data of Stiles [173, 174] on color mixture for 2° and 10° fields have just come to the writer's attention as well as a personal communication on a failure of Abney's law from Dr. H. G. Sperling. The experimental data of both investigators have a direct connection with the problems raised by Judd [103].

The chromaticity diagram for the XYZ system is shown in Fig. 24. Its side XY is tangent to the spectral locus in the red, and side XZ is very nearly tangent to it at about λ503 mμ. Colors, including primaries, that are represented as lying outside the boundary of real colors, i.e., the spectrum locus, are imaginary. The drawing of sides XY and YZ tangent (or nearly so) to the spectrum locus minimizes possibilities for imaginary colors within and keeps the spectrum locus inside the triangle XYZ.

The XYZ system makes use of the strange, but useful, convention that zero luminous units are ascribed to primaries X and Z. The equal energy source W is assigned to the center of the XYZ chromaticity diagram. The unit equations defining the primaries X, Y and Z in the RGB system are as follows:

$$\begin{aligned} L'_x &= 1.2750L'_r - 0.2778L'_g + 0.0028L'_b \\ L'_y &= -1.7392L'_r + 2.7671L'_g - 0.0279L'_b \\ L'_z &= -0.7431L'_r + 0.1409L'_g + 1.6022L'_b \end{aligned} \tag{62}$$

In line with our earlier convention, we use primes to differentiate units in the old (RGB) system and the new (XYZ) system. However, because the remainder of the discussion concerns itself almost exclusively with the XYZ system, we shall put the primes on the RGB units, so that the appearance of all the XYZ equations will be simplified.

The points that represent primaries X and Z are on what Schrödinger [157] and Judd [94] have called the alychne. The alychne is a straight line on the chromaticity diagram for which all points have luminous units of zero. Consequently the primaries X and Z must be regarded as mathematical abstractions whose employment is justified only as a useful convention.

The equation for the alychne can be developed as follows. For the unit of color L'_c written in terms, not of the original symbols L'_r, L'_g, and L'_b, but rather, their numerical values $L'_r = 1$, $L'_g = 4.5907$, and $L'_b = 0.0601$,

$$L'_c = r + 4.5907g + 0.0601b \tag{63}$$

by analogy with Eq. (19). The symbols r, g, and b represent the trichromatic coordinates of the RGB system.

For the alychne, $L'_c = 0$; hence

$$r + 4.5907g + 0.0601b = 0 \tag{64}$$

In the RGB system, $r + g + b = 1$; hence $1 - r - g$ may be substituted for b and Eq. (64) becomes

$$0.9399r + 4.5306g + 0.0601 = 0 \tag{65}$$

This equation, a straight line, is the equation of the alychne, points on which have luminous units of zero. See [202] for a more comprehensive treatment. Substitution of the coordinates for X and Z in the RGB system given by (62) in Eq. (65) shows that they satisfy the relation; hence $L'_x = L'_z = 0$. It is also demonstrable that colors having luminous units of zero in the RGB system have luminous units of zero in the XYZ system. Hence $L_x = L_z = 0$.

As Le Grand [115] points out, the concept of stimuli with zero or negative luminous fluxes implies nothing mysterious; such stimuli come into existence when the convention of writing negative chromatic fluxes is accepted. Such a concept seems to be appropriate for chromaticity relations; it would be out of place for luminosity relations.

There are great advantages in a system in which two of the primaries have luminous units of zero. For example, the amount of light represented in a color equation is given directly by the coefficient of L_y. Thus in the equation

$$L_\lambda = xL_x + yL_y + zL_z \tag{66}$$

when $L_x = L_z = 0$, L_λ becomes

$$L_\lambda = yL_y \tag{67}$$

In (66), x, y, and z represent the trichromatic coordinates of the XYZ system. Under these circumstances y is directly proportional by way of L_y to the unit L_λ in (67).

Trichromatic coordinates. Equations (48) provide the basis for obtaining the trichromatic coordinates x, y, and z of the XYZ system from a consideration of the coordinates r, g, and b of the RGB system. The appropriate transformation equations are:

$$\begin{aligned} x &= (0.4900r + 0.3100g + 0.2000b)\frac{1}{K} \\ y &= (0.1770r + 0.8124g + 0.0106b)\frac{1}{K} \\ z &= \qquad\qquad (0.0100g + 0.9900b)\frac{1}{K} \end{aligned} \tag{68}$$

where $$K = 0.6670r + 1.1234g + 1.2006b \tag{69}$$

These equations were obtained on the basis of the following standard reference values of r, g, and b for primaries X, Y and Z [where r, g, and b are the appropriate values of γ_{ji} of (50)]:

for X, $r = 1.2750, \quad g = -0.2778, b = 0.0028;$
for Y, $r = -1.7392, g = 2.7671, \quad b = -0.0279;$
for Z, $r = -0.7431, g = 0.1409, \quad b = 1.6022.$

[See also Eq. (62).] The values of r, g, and b are those given by Le Grand [expressions following his Eq. (101)] for the old RGB coordinates of the new primaries X, Y, and Z. [See the transformation method applicable to (50).]

Equations (68) and (69) reduce to an expression similar to Le Grand's Eq. (102), in which $1 - r - g$ is written for b. Results computed by the two methods show agreement to the third decimal place.

Distribution coefficients of the XYZ system. An equation analogous to (27) may be written

$$V_\lambda = \bar{x}L_x + \bar{y}L_y + \bar{z}L_z \tag{70}$$

where $\bar{x}$, $\bar{y}$, and $\bar{z}$ are the distribution coefficients for the XYZ system. When, in Eq. (70), $L_x = L_z = 0$

$$V_\lambda = \bar{y}L_y \tag{71}$$

This result means that the distribution coefficient $\bar{y}$ is directly proportional to V_λ as λ varies. The plot of V_λ against λ is the equal energy luminosity curve; hence $\bar{y}_\lambda$ plotted against λ is the same curve with ordinates multiplied by $1/L_y$. Since the scale of luminosity values can be arbitrarily determined, L_y can be assigned a value of unity, in which case the plot of $\bar{y}$ against λ is also the equal energy curve. On the condition that $L_y = 1$, Eq. (67) becomes

$$y = L_\lambda \tag{72}$$

For this case, and on analogy with Eq. (23),

$$\bar{x} = \frac{xV_\lambda}{y} \qquad \bar{y} = V_\lambda \qquad \bar{z} = \frac{zV_\lambda}{y} \tag{73}$$

The formulas in (73) give the coefficients of distribution when the luminosity function V_λ is known. The coefficients of distribution $\bar{x}$, $\bar{y}$, and $\bar{z}$ are shown in Fig. 25, where they are referred to as tristimulus values.

Tristimulus values. In Eq. (11), written

$$\Gamma_1L_1 + \Gamma_2L_2 + \Gamma_3L_3 = \Gamma_SL_S$$

the chromatic fluxes Γ_1, Γ_2, and Γ_3 can be referred to as tristimulu values of S, as can also any convenient triad of numbers proportiona to them [115]. Similarly in the XYZ system the tristimulus values denoted by X, Y, and Z, specify the component chromatic fluxes of given stimulus when the stimulus is computed to be matched by mixture of primaries X, Y, and Z. The tristimulus values may b determined. For X, one weights the distribution coefficient $\bar{x}$, at eac wavelength of the stimulus, by the relative energy at that wavelengt and sums $\bar{x}E_\lambda$ over wavelength. For Y and Z, the corresponding sum-

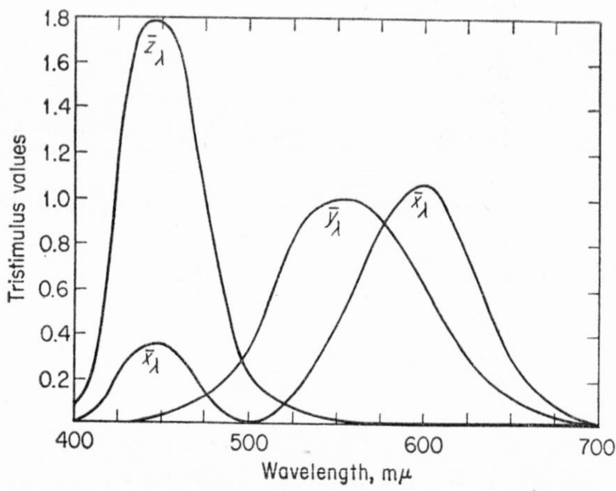

FIG. 25. The distribution coefficients (or tristimulus values) for an equal energy spectrum on the XYZ system. *From Judd* [102].

mations involve the distribution coefficients $\bar{y}$ and $\bar{z}$. Thus, on analogy with Eq. (26b), see footnote 20,

$$X = \Sigma\alpha\bar{x}E_\lambda\,\Delta\lambda \qquad Y = \Sigma\alpha\bar{y}E_\lambda\,\Delta\lambda \qquad \text{and} \qquad Z = \Sigma\alpha\bar{z}E_\lambda\,\Delta\lambda \quad (74)$$

in which α is a factor that depends on the unit of E_λ. For convenience, we may obtain a relative measure involving E_λ at constant wavelength intervals $\Delta\lambda$, with $\alpha\Delta\lambda$ set equal to unity. Under these circumstances

$$X = \Sigma\bar{x}E_\lambda \qquad Y = \Sigma\bar{y}E_\lambda \qquad \text{and} \qquad Z = \Sigma\bar{z}E_\lambda \quad (75)$$

When the stimulus being matched is monochromatic, the tristimulus values and distribution coefficients are identical, with E_λ being given a value of unity.

Colorimetric purity and excitation purity. Let O in Fig. 26 represent the position of a reference white (e.g., the equal energy source) in the XYZ system. Its coordinates are (x_0, y_0), M is the point with coordinates (x, y) representing a given light and L, with coordinates (x_λ, y_λ), is a point on the spectrum locus. Points O, L, and M fall on the same straight line.

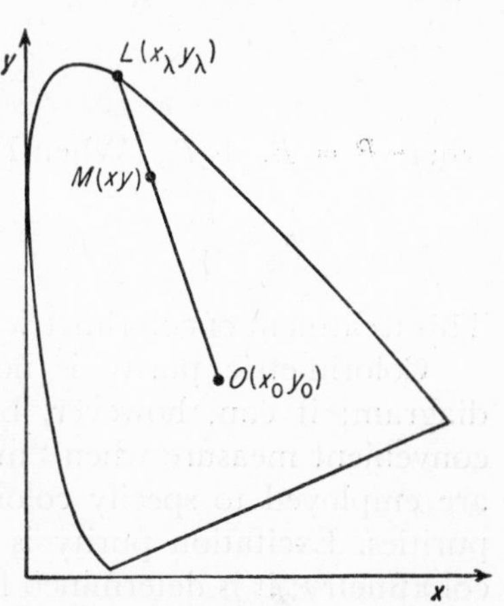

FIG. 26. Representation of dominant wavelength and excitation purity in the XYZ system. *From Le Grand* [115].

Excitation purity p_e may be represented in Fig. 26 according to the definition in Eqs. (22):

$$p_e = \frac{OM}{OL} = \frac{x - x_0}{x_\lambda - x_0} = \frac{y - y_0}{y_\lambda - y_0} \tag{76}$$

with the x and y terms of the present equation substituted for the γ terms in (22). The color at M can be thought of as a mixture of the colors at L and O. By the center-of-gravity rule, the corresponding chromatic fluxes Γ_λ and Γ_O are related so that

$$\frac{OM}{ML} = \frac{\Gamma_\lambda}{\Gamma_O} \tag{77}$$

Hence it follows that

$$p_e = \frac{OM}{OM + ML} = \frac{\Gamma_\lambda}{\Gamma_\lambda + \Gamma_O} = \frac{\Gamma_\lambda}{\Gamma} = \frac{X_\lambda + Y_\lambda + Z_\lambda}{X + Y + Z} \tag{78}$$

where X, Y and Z are chromatic fluxes in the XYZ system. The definition of trichromatic coordinates in Eq. (17) tells us that

$$\frac{x}{X} = \frac{y}{Y} = \frac{z}{Z} = \frac{1}{X + Y + Z} \tag{79}$$

and, in particular, that

$$\frac{Y}{y} = X + Y + Z \tag{80}$$

Similarly

$$\frac{Y_\lambda}{y_\lambda} = X_\lambda + Y_\lambda + Z_\lambda \tag{81}$$

Excitation purity is given when, in line with (78), (81) is divided by (80). Hence

$$p_e = \frac{Y_\lambda}{Y} \cdot \frac{y}{y_\lambda} \tag{82}$$

By the definition of colorimetric purity in Eq. (1)

$$p = \frac{B_\lambda}{B}$$

where $B = B_\lambda + B_W$. When Y_λ is taken equal to B_λ and Y equal to B,

$$p = \frac{Y_\lambda}{Y} = \frac{y_\lambda}{y} p_e = \frac{y_\lambda}{y}\left(\frac{y - y_0}{y_\lambda - y_0}\right) = \frac{y_\lambda}{y}\left(\frac{x - x_0}{x_\lambda - x_0}\right) \tag{83}$$

This treatment of colorimetric purity follows Le Grand's [115] outline.

Colorimetric purity is not given directly by the chromaticity diagram; it can, however, be computed. Colorimetric purity is a convenient measure when "monochromatic-plus-white" colorimeters are employed to specify colors by their dominant wavelengths and purities. Excitation purity is useful in modern methods of indirect colorimetry; it is determined from the trichromatic coordinates. Both colorimetric purity and excitation purity exhibit similar limitations in their correlations with saturation.

THEORIES OF COLOR VISION

A color theory, ideally, should describe all the phenomena of color vision within a coherent set of relations. Judged by historical precedent, it should also probably be quantitative in form. Color theories in the past have been important in shaping the substance of the field, and despite the fact that no completely satisfying account exists at present, the search for appropriate theory continues vigorously.

A considerable number of theories of color exist over and above the level represented by, for example, the chromaticity diagram, in itself an important theoretical construct. In general, these theories may, with few exceptions, be classified as in the tradition of either Thomas Young or Ewald Hering. The name of the former is associated with trichromatic theories of color, and the name of the latter, with theories that emphasize the role of opponent color processes. Certain theories, called stage or zone theories, combine both influences.

The present section will consider first the nature of some theories in the Young tradition and secondly some theoretical ideas in the Hering tradition.

The trichromaticity of color and Young's ideas. In 1801 Thomas Young in his Bakerian Lecture [208] to the Royal Society suggested that since "it is almost impossible to conceive each sensitive point on the retina to contain an infinite number of particles each capable of vibrating in perfect unison with every possible undulation it becomes necessary to suppose the number limited, for instance, to the three principal colors, red, yellow and blue." In 1802 Young [209] revised his estimate of the basic colors because an error was discovered in Wollaston's description of the spectrum. The basic colors now became red, green, and violet.

Young's ideas were forgotten for about 50 years. They were rediscovered by Maxwell [123] and Helmholtz [63] at nearly the same time. Maxwell's data on color mixture [124, 126] provided some of the most important supporting evidence for Young. Helmholtz accepted Young's hypothesis after some hesitation and went on to examine its implications in such detail until his death in 1894 [see 64, 67] that his name is often bracketed with Young's.

Young's theory, or rather the Young-Helmholtz development of it, depends in a most important manner upon the data of color mixture. Maxwell's experiments [124, 126] on mixture verified the essential trichromaticity of color vision, i.e., the fact that a spectral color can be represented as mathematically equivalent to a mixture of three primaries, one (in the case of spectral primaries) having a negative coefficient. The fact of trichromaticity was readily assimilated with the idea of three principal colors, and so trichromatic theory was established on a relatively firm foundation.[26]

The essential aspect of the Young-Helmholtz theory exists in the concept of three sets of sensory mechanisms, cones and their connections, whose quantitative characteristics provide a basis for the different discriminations of color vision [115]. (1) Each sensory mechanism is presumed to have a given sensitivity curve which presents $\bar{j}_i$, sensitivity or response, at each spectral wavelength for each of the three mechanisms. (2) The total response in each mechanism is $J_i = \int \bar{j}_i E_\lambda \, d\lambda$. (3) Color is a function of the relative values of the three responses J_1, J_2, and J_3. (4) Brightness is a function of the three responses. The simplest but not, it must be emphasized (in view of recent questions concerning the validity of Abney's law), the only possible combination of responses is represented by the quantity $(J_1L_1 + J_2L_2 + J_3L_3)$, where the L_i are constants comparable to the luminous units of colorimetric equations.

As stated by Le Grand [115]:

> It is seen immediately on the one hand that Abney's and Grassman's laws result from the linear character of the accepted equations and reciprocally necessitate such a character; on the other hand, in line with their expressions, the J_i represent the tristimulus values of a colorimetric system in which the J_i would be the primaries, the $\bar{j}_i$, the distribution coefficients and the L_i

[26] It seems needless to point out that the trichromaticity of vision, as embodied in the data of "two-against-two" matches, is a fact that does not depend on theory for its validity.

the luminous units. In order that this system will coincide with experimental systems, for example with the XYZ system, it is necessary and sufficient that linear transformations exist among the tristimulus values, or what amounts to the same thing, among the distribution coefficients.

(In the above quotation the symbol J has been substituted for Le Grand's G.) In these terms, one can write:

$$\begin{aligned} \bar{j}_1 &= a_{1x}\bar{x} + a_{1y}\bar{y} + a_{1z}\bar{z} \\ \bar{j}_2 &= a_{2x}\bar{x} + a_{2y}\bar{y} + a_{2z}\bar{z} \\ \bar{j}_3 &= a_{3x}\bar{x} + a_{3y}\bar{y} + a_{3z}\bar{z} \end{aligned} \tag{84}$$

and, for spectral luminosity, in the ideal case

$$\bar{j}_1L_1 + \bar{j}_2L_2 + \bar{j}_3L_3 = V_\lambda = \bar{y} \tag{85}$$

Young's theory presumes that one set of a possible infinity of sets of primaries can be found that will describe the characteristics of the hypothetical sensory mechanisms. Such a system of primaries constitutes a set of so-called fundamentals. The fundamentals must be linearly related to the basic data of color mixture, for example, the data of the XYZ system. Since, however, an infinity of primaries can describe the data of color mixture, other criteria than color mixture must be used to make a choice of the fundamentals.

Most workers in the Young tradition are loath to accept fundamentals that involve negative quantities (presumably on the basis that, since the fundamentals probably represent absorption curves, negative quantities become embarrassing). If all-positive curves are required, then the fundamentals must represent the effects of imaginary primaries (though not, theoretically, imaginary absorption curves). Another criterion usually applied to the fundamentals is the requirement that $J_1 = J_2 = J_3$ for the production of white. This restriction is widely accepted but not logically necessary; it derives from the convention of placing a reference white in the center of the chromaticity diagram by assigning to it the coordinates $x = y = z = 0.333$.

Fundamentals based on considerations of color blindness. Considerable effort has been devoted to the search for appropriate fundamentals. Judd [101] gives an important list of fundamentals, as presented in Table 2, not only for theories of the Young-Helmholtz type but also for those of the Hering and zone type. The list of limitations in the table may be subject to revision in the light of more recent data: for example, the experiment of Graham and Hsia [35, 36] may be interpreted as favoring, with complications, Young's idea of luminosity loss in dichromatic vision. Among the sets of fundamentals proposed, many were established to meet requirements imposed by the data of color blindness,[27] and our first consideration of fundamentals will take up some that lean heavily on this criterion.

Since the time of König, theoretical ideas concerning dichromatic vision have followed either of two general lines of thought: (1) Young's idea [208] that dichromatic vision is produced by loss or suppression of one of the three fundamental processes; or (2) Leber's [114] and Fick's idea [22] that dichromatic vision (deuteranopia in particular) can be attributed to a "fusion" of the red and green fundamentals.[28] The

[27] The various classes of color-blind individuals may be described as follows:

1. Individuals with normal color vision are called *trichromats*. They can match a mixture of a given wavelength and a spectral primary against a mixture of two spectral primaries.

2. *Dichromats* can match a spectral color by a mixture of two spectral colors.

The majority of dichromats are "red-green" blind. They "confuse" red, yellow, and green.

The red-green variety of dichromats may be subdivided into two types. One is the *protanope* who shows greatly reduced sensitivity to long wavelengths in the red end of the spectrum. The other class is the *deuteranope*. The deuteranope's spectral sensitivity curve is not defective in the red. Both classes have it in common that they "confuse" red, yellow, and green.

A third, rare class of dichromats consists of *tritanopes* who confuse blue and green, as do *tetartanopes* who comprise an even rarer class. Unlike other dichromats who can match a single small region of the spectrum by white, the *tetartanopes* can match two regions of the spectrum by white.

3. *Anomalous trichromats* are persons who, despite the fact that they confuse parts of the spectrum, still need three primaries to match any single wavelength. They form intermediates of all grades between dichromats and trichromats; they may be (*a*) *protanomalous*, (*b*) *deuteranomalous*, or (*c*) *tritanomalous* depending on which type of dichromat they resemble.

4. Totally color-blind people, *monochromats*, are those who can make no color discriminations at all. They match any wavelength by the proper adjustment of the luminance of a white light or any other wavelength.

Comment: tritanopia of central vision in normal subjects. An interesting series of experiments starting with one by König [108] showed the existence of so-called "tritanopia" in normal subjects when small areas of test object (up to about 20′ diameter) are viewed in the fovea. Normal subjects under these circumstances match any radiation with two monochromatic lights; protanopes and deuteranopes match any radiation with only one monochromatic light. See the later experiments by Willmer [195, 196], Thomson and Wright [178], and researches cited in Hillmann, Connolly, and Farnsworth [72] as well as Burnham and Newhall [10].

[28] Ladd-Franklin [23] attributes Fick's ideas to Helmholtz. She says:

"Fick's explanation was, in reality, first suggested by Helmholtz, although Helmholtz himself seems to have forgotten the fact. The passage in question occurs in the Nachträge to the first edition of the *Physiological Optics*, p. 848: 'Man könnte denken . . . dass die Gestalt der Intensitätscurven, Fig. 119, für die drei Arten lichtempfindlicher Elemente sich änderte, wobei dann eine viel grössere Veränderlichkeit in dem Verhalten der objectiven Farben gegen das Auge eintreten könnte.' "

TABLE 2. SUMMARY OF A FEW OF THE BETTER-KNOWN VISUAL THEORIES

Name	Anatomical location	Fundamental colors	Relation to Standard Observer	Chief limitation
Young, three components	Cone pigments	Red Green Violet	$+3.1956X + 2.4478Y - 0.6434Z$ $-2.5455X + 7.0492Y + 0.4963Z$ $+5.0000Z$	Fails to explain dichromatic vision as intended.
Helmholtz, three components	Cone response	Red Green Violet	$+0.070X + 0.945Y - 0.015Z$ $-0.460X + 1.359Y + 0.101Z$ $+1.000Z$	Fails to explain color perceptions of protanopes and deuteranopes.
Dominator-modulator, late König	Cone response	Red Green Violet	$+1.000Y$ $-0.460X + 1.359Y + 0.101Z$ $+1.000Z$	Fails to explain color perceptions of protanopes and deuteranopes.
Ladd-Franklin, three components, early König	Cone response	Red Green Blue	$-3.7656X + 1.4635Y - 0.2291Z$ $-1.3973X + 6.1289Y + 0.2683Z$ $+5.0000Z$	Implies that the blue function has a negative luminosity for normals and deuteranopes, positive for protanopes.
Hering, opponent colors	Optic nerve	Red-green Yellow-blue White-black	$+1.000X - 1.000Y$ $+0.400Y - 0.400Z$ $+1.000Y$	Fails to give an account of protanopia and tritanopia.
Von Kries-Schrödinger, zone or stage	Cone response Optic nerve	Red Green Blue Green-red Blue-yellow White-black	$+3.7656X + 1.4635Y - 0.2291Z$ $-1.3973X + 6.1289Y + 0.2683Z$ $+5.0000Z$ $-3.537X + 3.196Y + 0.341Z$ $+1.341X - 5.884Y + 4.542Z$ $+1.000Y$	Implies that the blue function has a negative luminosity for normals and deuteranopes, positive for protanopes; fails to give an account of tritanopia.

Adams, zone or stage	Cone pigments	Red	$+3.1956X + 2.4478Y - 0.6434Z$	Explanations of protanopia and tritanopia based on subsidiary assumptions.
		Green	$-2.5455X + 7.0492Y + 0.4963Z$	
		Violet	$+5.0000Z$	
	Cone response*	Red	$+1.000X$	
		Green	$+1.000Y$	
		Blue	$+1.000Z$	
	Optic nerve*	Red-green	$+1.000X - 1.000Y$	
		Blue-yellow	$-0.400Y + 0.400Z$	
		White-black	$+1.000Y$	
Müller, zone or stage	Cone pigments	Red	$+3.1956X + 2.4478Y - 0.6434Z$	Implausible explanation of protanopic luminosity by resort to luminosity of the *yR* cone response and luminosity-inhibiting action of the *bG* cone response, both of which disappear with the *yR-bG* cone response to produce protanopia.
		Green	$-2.5455X + 7.0492Y + 0.4963Z$	
		Violet	$+5.0000Z$	
	Cone response*	*yR-bG*	$+5.741X - 4.601Y - 1.140Z$	
		gY-rB	$-0.932X + 2.750Y - 1.819Z$	
		Luminosity	$+1.000Y$	
	Optic nerve*	Red-green	$+6.325X - 6.325Y$	
		Yellow-blue	$+2.004Y - 2.004Z$	
		White-black	$+1.000Y$	

* The theory allows for a nonlinear dependence of the responses upon the stimulus in addition to the linear dependence indicated here.

SOURCE: D. B. Judd, Basic correlates of the visual stimulus, in S. S. Stevens (Ed.), *Handbook of experimental psychology*, New York, Wiley, 1951.

fundamentals that have historically developed from the first approach are called König-type fundamentals. Those that have developed from the second type are called Leber-Fick–type fundamentals.

It may be said at once that both types of fundamentals have been based on interpretations of dichromatic vision that are subject to revision. A consideration of some possible directions of revision will be taken up as part of the discussion that follows.

König-type fundamentals. An important set of fundamentals, called *Grundempfindungen*, was proposed by König [107] and by König and Dieterici [111]. The set consisted of three curves based on algebraic transformations of color mixture equations. The curves represented

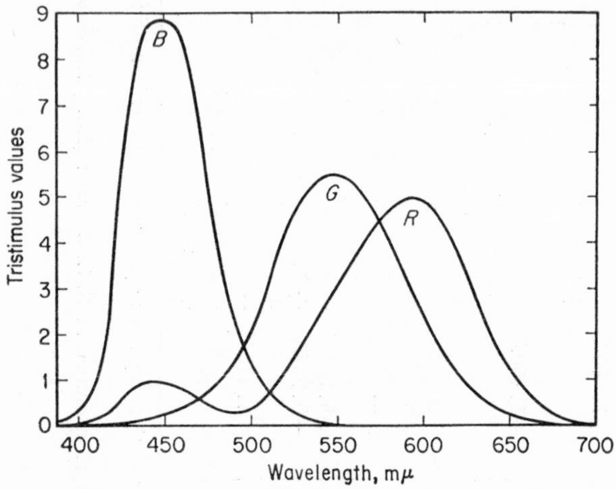

Fig. 27. Judd's representation of König-type fundamentals [107]. Tristimulus values are shown as functions of wavelength. *From Judd* [101].

positive values of coefficients that could be used to describe the data of protanopes and deuteranopes as well as normal subjects. Protanopes were presumed to lack the *R* ("red") fundamental, and deuteranopes, the *G* ("green"). The type form of the *Grundempfindungen* is illustrated in Fig. 27 which gives Judd's [101] representation. Note that the *R* and *G* curves cross near 470 mμ.

A second set of fundamentals was proposed by König [109]. On the basis of some observations by Pitt [144] on the color confusions of dichromats, Judd [98] derived a set of fundamentals comparable to König's second set. Judd's set is represented in Fig. 28. The fundamentals W_d, W_p, and K follow König's nomenclature of W for "warm" colors and K for "cold" (kalt). W_d, W_p, and K taken together represent the normal observer. W_d and K taken in combination represent the deuteranope, and W_p and K account for the protanope. These fundamentals may be represented in terms of $\bar{x}$, $\bar{y}$, and $\bar{z}$ as follows:

$$\begin{aligned} W_d &= \bar{y} \\ W_p &= -0.460\bar{x} + 1.359\bar{y} + 0.101\bar{z} \\ K &= \bar{z} \\ L_1 &= 1 \qquad L_2 = L_3 = 0 \end{aligned} \tag{86}$$

In order that W_d, W_p, and K add to give luminosity, the respective areas of the curves must be multiplied by the units of luminous flux L_1, L_2, and L_3, according to Eq. (85). For the present case, $L_1 = 1$. It is

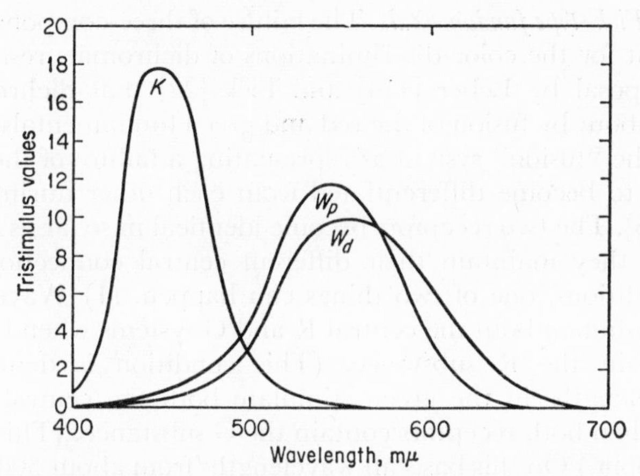

FIG. 28. Judd's set [98, 101] of fundamentals comparable to those of König's second set [109].

supposed that the "red" process W_d has the form of the CIE luminosity curve $\bar{y}$ and, in the normal subject, completely accounts for luminosity. The function W_p is taken to represent the luminosity curve for the protanope, and the curve W_d, the curve for the deuteranope as well as the normal.

Le Grand [115] suggests that the zero values of L_2 and L_3 in Judd's formulation provide difficulties for an interpretation of luminosity. He suggests a change in formulation whereby $L_1 = 0.868$, $L_2 = 0.132$, and $L_3 = 0$, with appropriate changes in the distribution coefficients. Under these circumstances, complete blindness would not result (as it would for Judd) in the case of a protanope where the fundamental carrying all of the luminosity is lost. [See also 100.]

Zero values of units (as in the formulations of Judd and Le Grand) might conceivably provide a permissible mathematical basis for the data of color mixture but it would be hard to advocate the biological mechanisms (color without brightness) that they imply.

The König-type theory can tell us what stimuli are confused by a dichromatic subject. It does not tell us what colors are seen and named by a subject who is dichromatic in one eye. Such a subject can compare what he sees in his color-blind eye with what he sees in his normal eye. König-type theories ascribe protanopia to absence of a red process and deuteranopia to absence of a green process. On this basis a unilateral protanope should see green, violet, and their mixtures, and a deuteranope, violet, red, and their mixtures. In fact, however, it is commonly accepted that both types of dichromats see blue and yellow [99].

Leber-Fick–type fundamentals. The failure of three-components theory to account for the color discriminations of dichromats resulted in an early proposal by Leber [114] and Fick [22] that dichromatism is brought about by fusion of the red and green fundamentals. One may think of the "fusion" system as representing a failure of the R and G receptors to become differentiated from each other during development [188]. The two receptors become identical in so far as absorption goes, but they maintain their different central connections. Under these conditions, one of two things can happen. (1) Wavelengths in the red stimulate both the central R and G systems when both receptors contain the R substance. (This condition is deuteranopia.) (2) Wavelengths in the green stimulate both the central R and G systems when both receptors contain the G substance. (This condition is protanopia.) On this basis all wavelengths from about 500 mμ to the red end of the spectrum are named yellow by the protanopic or deuteranopic subject. The fusion idea has the advantage that it seems to account for the color names of unilaterally color-blind people.

Pitt [143], in performing his experiments on the luminosity of dichromats, anomalous cases, and normal subjects, followed the practice of plotting each luminosity curve with its maximum set at 100 per cent. Such a practice precludes the comparison of absolute luminosities among the different classes of subject, and it also masks such differences of shape among the curves as would be apparent if luminosities were based on an absolute measure. In any case, Pitt's result seemed to verify the long-held opinion that the luminosity curve of deuteranopes is similar to the curve for normal people (see Fig. 29). This interpretation no doubt influenced Pitt [144] to interpret his data on the color confusions of dichromats in terms of his specific version of Leber-Fick–type theory, i.e., protanopia is due to loss of the red process whereas deuteranopia is due to the green mechanism's taking on the absorption characteristics of the red. (The interpretation that protanopia is a loss of the red process causes a difficulty that does not arise in conventional Leber-Fick theory. Pitt cannot account for the yellow seen by the protanope in the absence of red.)

Pitt's set of fundamentals based on his work [144] on the color confusions of dichromats, was represented originally in terms of

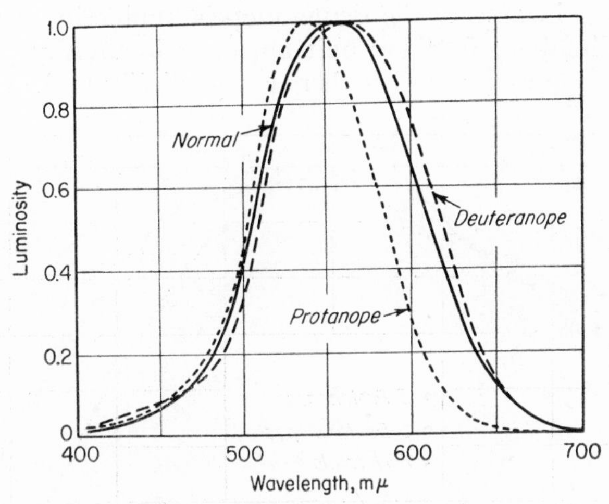

FIG. 29. Luminosity curves for protanopes, deuteranopes, and normal subjects with each maximum set at 100 per cent. *From Hecht and Hsia's* [60] *representation of Pitt's data* [143].

Wright's system [203]. It has been represented (on the XYZ system) by Le Grand [115] as follows:[29]

$$\begin{aligned} \bar{j}_1 &= 0.606\bar{x} + 0.516\bar{y} - 0.122\bar{z} \\ \bar{j}_2 &= -0.466\bar{x} + 1.375\bar{y} + 0.090\bar{z} \\ \bar{j}_3 &= \bar{z} \\ L_1 &= 0.434 \qquad L_2 = 0.564, \qquad L_3 = 0.002 \end{aligned} \tag{87}$$

A main difference between the König-type and Leber-Fick–type fundamentals lies in the relative magnitude of the L_i in Eq. (85). As shown, for example, in Eqs. (86) for the König-type fundamentals, L_1 has a much greater magnitude than L_2. This means that the brightness contribution to luminosity of W_p is greater than that of W_d. In the case of the Fick-type fundamentals, the brightness contributions of J_1 and J_2 are nearly equal, as shown in Eqs. (87), where $L_1 = 0.434$, $L_2 = 0.564$, and $L_3 = 0.002$.

[29] Le Grand has also presented his own modification of Pitt's fundamentals; it is similar enough to Pitt's own so that it need not be taken up here. It is interesting, too, that Wright's fundamentals [203], obtained by means of estimates of invariant hues during chromatic adaptation, are not inconsistent with those of Pitt.

Deuteranopes, however, will show little luminosity loss with the Fick-type fundamentals. In the normal eye, $L_2 + L_1 = 0.998$. In the deuteranopic eye, where L_2 becomes L_1, $L_2 = 0$, and the contribution of L_1 is doubled. Under these circumstances $2L_1 = 0.868$, or the area under the deuteranope's curve is about 90 per cent of normal. The resulting loss in area of the deuteranope's luminosity curve is relatively small (about 0.04 log unit on a log luminosity plot) under these circumstances, and since there is a small shift to the red, the loss

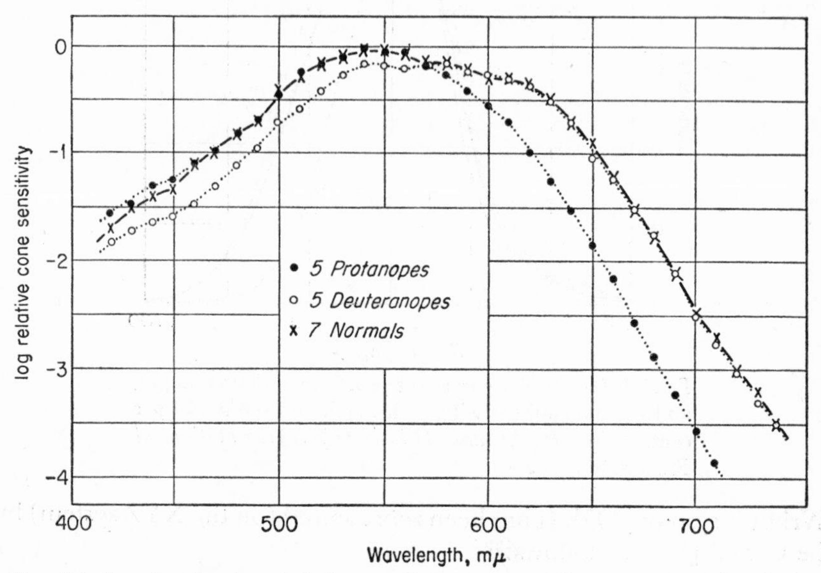

FIG. 30. Log luminosity (relative to the maximum for normal subjects) for protanopes, deuteranopes, and normal persons. The protanopes show a luminosity loss in the red and the deuteranopes in the green and blue.

is not easily ascertainable. This line of reasoning is in line with Pitt's interpretation [143] of deuteranopic luminosity.

Recent results on the visual responses of dichromats and their theoretical implications. It has been widely accepted that Leber's and Fick's ideas on color blindness have two great advantages: they account for (1) the colors seen by dichromats and (2) the presumed similarity of the luminosity curve of deuteranopes to that of normals. In recent years the facts of dichromatic vision that seemed to require Leber's and Fick's "fusion" system have been reexamined by Hecht and Hsia [60], Graham and Hsia [35, 36], and Graham, Hsia, and Berger [37]. (See also Graham and Hsia, *Science*, 1958, **127,** 675-682.)

Graham and Hsia [35] determined the absolute energy threshold throughout the spectrum for three groups of subjects, seven normal persons, five protanopes, and six deuteranopes. By this procedure they were able to eliminate problems of interpreting luminosity values when the maximum of each group's luminosity curve was set at 100 per cent [e.g., 143]. When absolute rather than relative energies were plotted, a loss of luminosity was found for the protanopes and five out of six deuteranopes as compared with normals. The results are seen in Fig. 30 where the data for the normal subjects are contrasted with those of the protanopes and deuteranopes. The deuteranope loses luminosity in the green and blue, the protanope in the red.

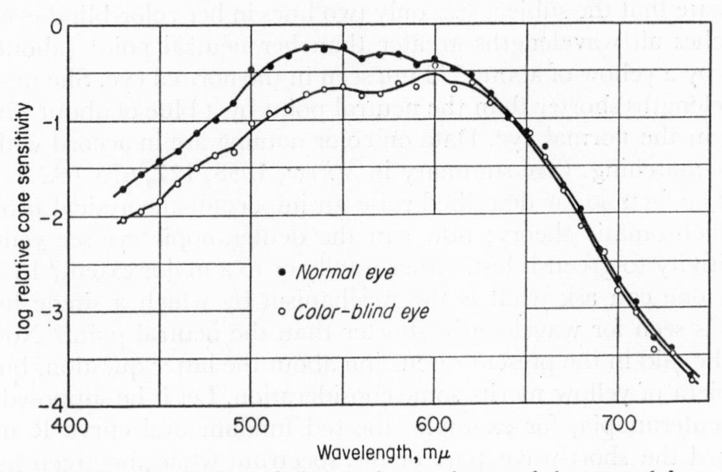

FIG. 31. Log luminosity relative to the maximum of the normal for a unilaterally color-blind subject. The type of color blindness evidenced in the color-blind eye has some of the characteristics of deuteranopia. As in the data of Fig. 30, a luminosity loss appears in the blue and green. *Note added in press:* Figure 30 refers to an experiment by Y. Hsia and C. H. Graham, *Proc. nat. Acad. Sci.,* 1957, **43,** 1011–1019. (In the 1957 article the deuteranopic data referred to 6 rather than 5 subjects.) Figure 31 applies to an experiment by C. H. Graham and Y. Hsia, *Proc. nat. Acad. Sci.,* 1958, **44,** 46–49.

In another experiment, Graham and Hsia [36] examined absolute luminosity for a subject with normal vision in her right eye and predominantly deuteranopic vision in her left.[30] The normal eye of this unilaterally color-blind subject was considerably more sensitive in the blue and green than the corresponding color-blind eye (Fig. 31). Both eyes seemed to be equally sensitive to the red. Data on flicker [37] and binocular brightness matches (in preparation) showed that the luminosity losses exhibited by the unilaterally color-blind subject continued to exist at intensities well above threshold.

[30] The subject is a true dichromat; she is not an anomalous case. She can match any spectral color by a mixture of two monochromatic primaries.

Another matter of theoretical importance concerned the colors seen by the unilaterally color-blind subject in her color-blind eye (Graham, Sperling, Hsia, and Coulson; in preparation). An experiment on binocular color-matching was performed by means of an apparatus, essentially a mirror stereoscope, that was so arranged as to provide slits of spectral colors in the left and right eyes. The subject viewing them could see them side by side, the slit on the left side being vertical and the slit on the right, horizontal. The slits were so arranged that their images did not appear to intersect. The results of the experiments indicate that the subject sees only two hues in her color-blind eye. She matches all wavelengths greater than her neutral point (about 502 mμ) by a yellow of about 570 mμ seen in the normal eye. She matches wavelengths shorter than the neutral point by a blue of about 470 mμ seen in the normal eye. Data on color naming are in accord with her color-matching. (See summary in *Science*, 1958, **127**, 675–682.)

The facts so far described raise an important theoretical problem for dichromatic theory; how can the deuteranopic eye see yellow if sensitivity to green is lost, either totally or to a major extent? In addition, one can ask what is the mechanism by which a single hue of blue is seen for wavelengths shorter than the neutral point? Nothing will be said in the present discussion about the latter question, but the problem of yellow merits some consideration. Let it be supposed that in deuteranopia, for example, the red fundamental curve R moves toward the short-wave part of the spectrum while the green fundamental curve G moves toward the red. The curves in their new positions must meet at least two requirements. (1) Their constant ratio of ordinates must be such that their luminous fluxes mix to match the single hue, 570 mμ. (2) The ordinate values of the transposed curve must sum to give normal luminosity in the range of wavelengths embraced by the curves.

Curves of the sort described predict, as does Fick-Leber theory, that a wavelength which stimulates the now identical G and R substances will give yellow, for although both fundamentals have the same absorption spectrum they are connected centrally with different R and G mechanisms. By virtue of the fact that, at any wavelength, the sum of the two ordinates of the average curves equals the sum of the ordinates of the normal R and G curves, luminosity is maintained as in the normal eye.

The formulation accounts for the case of a deuteranope who shows no luminosity loss. A luminosity loss can be introduced by multiplying the ordinates of the average curves by the appropriate percentage values to specify luminosity remaining after the proper degree of loss has been specified. A luminosity curve for deuteranopes can be constructed in this manner; in fact, this type of analysis can be applied in the case of protanopes.

Implications of some physiological research. *Granit's work.* The physiological investigations of Granit [38, 39, 40, 42] have given data of considerable theoretical significance. Some aspects of the results might be interpretable in a context of trichromatic theory and other aspects, in a context of opponent-colors theory. In a sense then, the results are neutral as to theory. They must, nevertheless, be considered as establishing some limiting conditions whose place in theory must be understood.

Granit recorded the electrical responses in single or grouped optic nerve fibers and ganglion cells in the retinas of various animals in response to lights of different wavelengths. The recording was done with microelectrodes. The thresholds for the responses observed are functions of wavelength. In the case of animals that have rods, the spectral sensitivity curves, representing in each case the reciprocal of energy plotted against wavelength, are broad curves. In shape and in position of their maxima, they agree, within the limits of minor deviations, with the absorption curve of visual purple. Such broad-band curves seem to represent the sensitivity of the rods; they are termed scotopic dominator curves by Granit [40].

The snake eye contains only cones. Records of the threshold responses of single units in such an eye give a broad-band curve with a maximum at 560 mμ. Such a curve may also be observed in, for example, the frog or cat eye after the activity of rods has been minimized by previous light adaptation. The resulting curve was called the photopic dominator by Granit [38].

A different sort of curve was observed in about 64 per cent of the isolated units studied in the light-adapted cat's eye. In these cases the dominator curve is not seen, but one finds narrow-band curves with maxima at about 450, 540, and 610 mμ. These curves are called modulator curves. They appear in recordings from the eyes of many animals, e.g., frogs, snakes, etc. The eyes of pigeons are rich in cones, and the cones are associated with oil droplets which act like filters. In any case, the modulators of the pigeon are especially narrow curves [18] which exist in addition to the photopic dominator.

Certain animals (e.g., the tench and the carp) have a scotopic visual violet system (with an absorption maximum at about 440 mμ) rather than a visual purple system. Such animals show photopic dominator curves with a maximum at about 610 mμ. The pure cone eye of the tortoise, *Testudo*, has a photopic dominator curve that is similar in position to that of animals with the visual violet system [40].

It is Granit's idea [see, e.g., 40, p. 298] that the photopic dominator curve may be attributed to the combined action of several modulator curves. He discusses various types of interlinkage between color sensitive receptors that are attached to a single nerve fiber and thinks of the dominator curve as resulting from the interaction of modulators. At a more complex level, photopic visibility and hue discrimination may be explainable in terms of combinations of modulators.

It is probable that the photopic and scotopic dominators which between them carry the Purkinje effect are responsible for nothing but the average spectral distributions of scotopic and photopic brightnesses. The photopic dominator may be thought of as corresponding to Hering's achromatic black-white process (which will be discussed later). On the other hand, the modulators probably provide the cues for wavelength discriminations. In general, the modulator curves seem to fall into three spectral regions, 440 to 470 mμ, 520 to 540 mμ, and 580 to 610 mμ, albeit marked variations in the shape and position of the curves occur within the three regions. Wavelengths within the preferential ranges produce deviations from the usual dominator response by activating modulator responses. See also Ekman [20].

The relations of the dominator-modulator theory to the data of color vision are discussed in Granit's 1947 account. There Granit shows how modulators may combine to reproduce the human photopic luminosity curve [see 38, Fig. 13] and he suggests a dominator-modulator account of hue discrimination and luminosity. Hue discrimination is best in spectral regions where differences in the slopes of overlapping modulator curves are great. Mechanisms of color blindness are also discussed [40].

Le Grand [115] does not believe that the modulator-dominator theory explains trichromaticity. The data on modulators and dominators may seem to imply a need for a polychromatic theory of the sort advanced by Hartridge [54].[31] Le Grand asks if the narrow curves

[31] Hartridge's support of a polychromatic theory is based on such evidence as the fact, first observed by Holmgren in 1884 and then by Fick in 1889, (see the discussion in Hartridge, 54), that a small white stimulus moving slowly over the retina is seen as having different colors at different positions [53]. On the basis of a number of experiments, Hartridge concludes that there are seven types of color receptors. (The polychromatic theory has received little support because the problem of evaluating the influence of eye movements arises and a special "cluster" hypothesis requires verification.)

Shortly before this article was sent to press a series of studies by G. Svaetichin appeared in *Acta Physiologica Scandinavica*, 1956, **39**, Supplementum 134, 3–112. Svaetichin (pp. 19–46) recorded electrical responses which he presumed were obtained from single cones and not from nerve fibers or ganglion cells. The responses were recorded by means of electrodes with tips less than 0.1 μ in diameter. Recordings were made on the *Mugil* genus of teleost fish from the Venezuelan coast. Earlier experiments had

of the modulators are not due to neural interaction, for Granit [41] has shown that red and green stimuli interact in the same element. Granit believes that such an interpretation is premature [42].

Rushton's work. Rushton has developed an important technique for measuring the absorption of cone pigments in intact eyes. The method involves measuring, in an ophthalmoscope, the light reflected from the back of the eye in the foveal region as a fraction of the light entering the eye. The ratio of light emerging from the eye to light entering the eye depends on the absorption that takes place during the double passage of the light rays through the cones. With proper controls, the double density of the retinal pigments can be determined (W. A. H. Rushton, Paper 1 in *Proceedings of the Symposium on Visual Problems of Color*, London, Her Majesty's Stationary Office, 1958. See also *Nature*, 1957, **174**, 571–6).

Rushton examined the bleaching and regeneration of cone pigments in color-blind and normal human subjects. Protanopes seem to

---

shown that the cone response is a graded response; it does not follow the all-or-none law. The magnitude is dependent upon the intensity of stimulation primarily. Svaetichin found that there seemed to be three fundamentally different types of curves (representing response as a function of wavelength) in different parts of the spectrum. These three types of curves he called the L-type, the R-G type, and the Y-B types. The L-type curve exhibits an increased intracellular negativity (i.e., a hyperpolarization potential) in response to any wavelength of the spectrum. The R-G curve shows depolarizing responses, i.e., increased intracellular positivity, for wavelengths up to about 580 mμ; thereafter, the graded cone response becomes a hyperpolarization. The Y-B response shows hyperpolarization for wavelengths up to about 580 mμ; thereafter, in the long-wave region, the response is a depolarizing response. The amplitude of the Y response was always less than the corresponding amplitude of the B response. It will be observed that the sign of the potential of short and long wavelengths is reversed for the R-G and for the Y-B responses. Svaetichin interprets the R-G and Y-R responses as due to recording from twin cones. The L-type response, he says, is presumably obtained from a single cone. Twin cones are interpreted as producing potentials of opposite sign. Svaetichin thinks of them as the receptor bases for the kind of mechanism postulated by Hering's theory (to be discussed). The L-type cone is taken to be Hering's photopic luminosity process.

Later work (MacNichol, Macpherson, and Svaethichin, Paper 39 in *Proceedings of the Symposium on Visual Problems of Color*, London, Her Majesty's Stationery Office, 1958) indicates, contrary to original interpretations, that the R-G and Y-B types of response curves are obtained from the bipolar cell layer while the L type of curves is obtained from the synaptic endings of cones and horizontal cells.

Absorption measurements of individual visual cells have been made with a photographic method by Denton and Wyllie (*J. Physiol.*, 1955, **127,** 81) and by Dobrowolski, Johnson, and Tansley (*J. Physiol.*, 1955, **130,** 533). Hanaoka and Fujimoto (*Jap. J. Physiol.*, 1957, **7,** 276), using a microspectrophotometric method, found, in single cones of the carp eye, five types of narrow-band difference spectra, reminiscent of Granit's modulator curves, with maxima distributed through the spectrum. A few cones were found to contain two photopigments. Broad rod curves occur with maxima near 525 mμ).

have only one pigment in the fovea. The normal fovea contains two visual pigments, one like that of the protanope and another more sensitive to red. The deuteranope has both normal pigments but with a greater preponderance of red. (A pigment especially responsive to blue may exist, but its absorption is not determinable by Rushton's method.)

Rushton's work, the implications of which are not fully elaborated here, may constitute one of the most important recent contributions to color theory. It provides a method that may establish on an objective basis the nature of the fundamental cone pigments in the normal and color-blind human eye.

Quantitative theories of color vision. The discussion that follows deals with four different examples of quantitative theorizing in color vision. The treatments[32] are those of Helmholtz, Stiles, Hecht, and Hurvich and Jameson, respectively. It would be wrong to suppose that any of the accounts gives final statements of the quantitative relations of color vision. Nevertheless, each exhibits worthwhile features and so merits consideration.

The Helmholtz line-element. Helmholtz wrote his quantitative treatment of color discrimination[33] shortly before his death in 1894. The precise hypothesis [65, 66, 67], has not had lasting value as a plausible description of data, but its treatment of data in the mathematics of a brightness-color space has had a persisting effect.

General formulation. In developing his theory Helmholtz [66] asked the question: Can hue be discriminated on the basis of gradations in the intensity of three fundamental processes R, G, and B that are evoked whenever the cones are stimulated by light?

Let dS be the magnitude of a "step in sensation," while dS_R, dS_G, and dS_B are the "steps" attributable to the respective fundamentals. dS can only vanish if dS_R, dS_G, and dS_B all vanish; hence, when $dS = 0$, it is necessary that $dS_R = dS_G = dS_B = 0$. In addition dS cannot be

[32] The mathematical symbols used by the individual authors are, with some exceptions, maintained in the present treatment even though they may differ from the symbols used generally in this book. The attempt to impose uniformity would probably necessitate the total recasting of the systems of symbols used in the different mathematical accounts.

[33] It appears in the second edition of the *Handbuch der Physiologischen Optik* [67] but is missing from the third edition [68]. The editors of the latter edition (Nagel, Gullstrand, and von Kries) used the first edition as their basic source in the preparation of the third edition. They discarded the second edition on the ground that some of its materials, including the present treatment of color, had not favorably withstood the test of the intervening 13 years. Southall's English translation [69], based as it is upon the third edition, also lacks a description of Helmholtz's treatment of color. Peddie's book [140] gives the best account that is available in English. Unfortunately, it lacks references to the original literature.

negative. An appropriate function that fulfills these conditions is

$$(dS)^2 = (dS_R)^2 + (dS_G)^2 + (dS_B)^2 \tag{88}$$

In basing an account of color discrimination upon (88), it will be necessary to specify "sensation" in terms of the intensities x, y, z of the respective processes R, G, and B [65].

The unmodified form of Fechner's law, that is, $dS_R = k\frac{dx}{x}$, is sufficiently exact for most cases, but Helmholtz [65, 66; 140] gives a more elaborate generalization, in which

$$dS_R = HX\frac{dx}{x} \qquad dS_G = HY\frac{dy}{y} \qquad dS_B = HZ\frac{dz}{z} \tag{89}$$

as required in special cases. In these equations,

$$H = 1/(1 + lx + my + nz)$$

and the quantities l, m, n are small constants. The "dazzle" term H can be used to account for the upward trend of the intensity discrimination curve at high intensities. The terms X, Y, Z are

$$X = \frac{kx}{a + x} \qquad Y = \frac{ky}{b + y} \qquad Z = \frac{kz}{c + z} \tag{90}$$

where a, b, and c are constants that refer to estimated amounts of "retinal self-light" (a phenomenon probably accountable for the augmented values of the Weber fraction in intensity discrimination at low levels). When the dazzle term H is equal to unity and the terms of (89) are substituted appropriately in Eq. (88), we obtain an expression comparable to the one discussed by Stiles [169]:

$$3\delta s^2 = \left(\frac{\delta x}{a + x}\right)^2 + \left(\frac{\delta y}{b + y}\right)^2 + \left(\frac{\delta z}{c + z}\right)^2 = 3F^2 \tag{91}$$

where F is a constant. Stiles says:

> It is customary to regard the quantity δs defined in [the latter equation] as the length of the line-element in a non-Euclidean space of co-ordinates x, y, z. In this so-called brightness-colour space, the points corresponding to any pair of just-distinguishable light patches are the same elementary distance F apart. . . . The factor 3 is introduced so that F has a simple physical meaning.

Intensity of colors. The descriptive expressions so far presented enable us to express the intensity of a color of any composition in R, G, and B. If we change the total luminance of a color by a certain percentage, then the intensities of the component processes R, G, and B

are changed by the same percentage, and dx/x, dy/y, and dz/z have the same value, $d\epsilon$, for example. Thus from Eqs. (88) and (89),

$$dS = H(X^2 + Y^2 + Z^2)^{1/2}\, d\epsilon \tag{92}$$

At very high intensities, X, Y, and Z approximate a constant value k and (92) becomes [65, 140]

$$dS = H(3k^2)^{1/2}\, d\epsilon \tag{93}$$

When H is taken as unity, $dS = 0.0176$ as computed by Helmholtz [66] from the data of König and Dieterici [110]. Helmholtz used the value of 0.0176 in his theoretical calculations on hue discrimination.

Similar colors. The difference between two similar, adjacent colors may be varied by changing the intensities of R, G, and B which exist in amounts x, y, z and $x + dx$, $y + dy$, $z + dz$ respectively [66, 140]. We may, for example, keep the latter set fixed while we alter the magnitude of each component in the set x, y, z in the same ratio, say $(1 + p):1$. (Under these circumstances, the color provided by the effects of x, y, and z remains constant.) By experiment we may adjust p so that the difference between the two colors is minimized. The two patches then provide a pair of similar colors. The differences of their fundamental process intensities are $dx - px$, $dy - py$, $dz - pz$.

By Eqs. (88) and (89), the square of the "step of sensation" is (for $H = 1$)

$$(dS)^2 = X^2\left(\frac{dx - px}{x}\right)^2 + Y^2\left(\frac{dy - py}{y}\right)^2 + Z^2\left(\frac{dz - pz}{z}\right)^2 \tag{94}$$

The problem now is to determine p, so that dS may be a minimum. We have therefore to differentiate the right-hand side with regard to p, and equate the result to zero. This gives

$$p(X^2 + Y^2 + Z^2) = X^2\frac{dx}{x} + Y^2\frac{dy}{y} + Z^2\frac{dz}{z} \tag{95}$$

and, inserting this value of p in the previous expression, we find

$$(X^2 + Y^2 + Z^2)(dS)^2 = X^2Y^2\left(\frac{dx}{x} - \frac{dy}{y}\right)^2 + Y^2Z^2\left(\frac{dy}{y} - \frac{dz}{z}\right)^2 + Z^2X^2\left(\frac{dz}{z} - \frac{dx}{x}\right)^2 \tag{96}$$

The result is quite independent of the units in which x, y, and z are measured, and Helmholtz also points out that the only presumption involved is that X, Y, and Z are expressed relatively in the same units as x, y, and z. In the special case in which the light is strong enough, X, Y, and Z each have the constant value k, and we get

$$(dS)^2 = \frac{k^2}{3}\left[\left(\frac{dx}{x} - \frac{dy}{y}\right)^2 + \left(\frac{dy}{y} - \frac{dz}{z}\right)^2 + \left(\frac{dz}{z} - \frac{dx}{x}\right)^2\right] \tag{97}$$

In either form the expression is that for the magnitude of the difference of colour sensation between two near colours of different colour tones which have been made as similar as possible to one another by suitable regulation of their brightness [140; Eqs. (95), (96), and (97) have been renumbered.]

The curves of the fundamental color processes. König and Dieterici [111] had, as a consequence of their early work on color mixture, derived a set of three curves, the *Elementarempfindungen*, to represent the data of color mixture.[34] König and Dieterici did not believe that the *Elementarempfindungen* gave precise accounts of the luminosities of the three fundamental processes, and for this reason they made some transformations of the *Elementarempfindungen* that resulted in the three curves which they called the *Grundempfindungen*. When Helmholtz [66, 67, 140] wished to account for the data of König and Dieterici [110] on hue discrimination, he assumed three new fundamentals. These fundamentals were computed [66] from Eq. (97) written in the form

$$\frac{dS}{k} = \frac{\delta\lambda}{\sqrt{3}}\left[\left(\frac{1}{x}\frac{dx}{d\lambda} - \frac{1}{y}\frac{dy}{d\lambda}\right)^2 + \left(\frac{1}{y}\frac{dy}{d\lambda} - \frac{1}{z}\frac{dz}{d\lambda}\right)^2 + \left(\frac{1}{z}\frac{dz}{d\lambda} - \frac{1}{x}\frac{dx}{d\lambda}\right)^2\right]^{1/2} \quad (98)$$

It was Helmholtz's idea that

> . . . the equation can only give correct values for the changes of wavelength $\delta\lambda$ corresponding to a given change dS in sensation, which is brought to a minimum by suitable regulation of the light strength, provided that x, y, z represent the absolute fundamentals. These unknown fundamentals are . . . linearly related to any experimentally used set [140].

Helmholtz employed the set established by König and Dieterici [111]. The problem was then to determine those values of x, y, and z (as linear transformations of König and Dieterici's coefficients) that will make dS/k in (98) a constant when appropriate values of $\delta\lambda$, x, y, z and $dx/d\lambda$, $dy/d\lambda$, and $dz/d\lambda$ are substituted therein.

Figure 32 shows a full line drawn as a fit for the hue discrimination data of König and Dieterici [110]. The dotted line is the theoretical curve. The ordinates give the threshold changes in wavelength $\delta\lambda$, and the abscissas, the values of λ.

Figure 33 gives the graph of Helmholtz's fundamentals derived as linear transformations of König and Dieterici's *Elementarempfindungen*. These coefficients provided the theoretical curves of Fig. 32. The three

[34] The *Elementarempfindungen* were similar to the excitation curves which were adopted as standard by the Optical Society of America in 1922. The excitation curves were derived by Weaver [182] who, in fact, obtained them by recomputing and averaging the data of König and Dieterici together with those of Abney [58].

curves of Fig. 33 represent the theoretical absorptions of the fundamentals at the different wavelengths of the visible spectrum. Stiles [167] and Hecht [55] have pointed out that the curves obtained by Helmholtz are probably neither correct nor useful. In particular, each curve in the Helmholtz formulation has the undesirable characteristic of exhibiting two maxima.

Unconsidered details of theory. It will not do here to consider further details of the Helmholtz line-element treatment of color phenomena, for example, such a concept as shortest color lines. Stiles's theory, described in the next section, has many elements in common with the

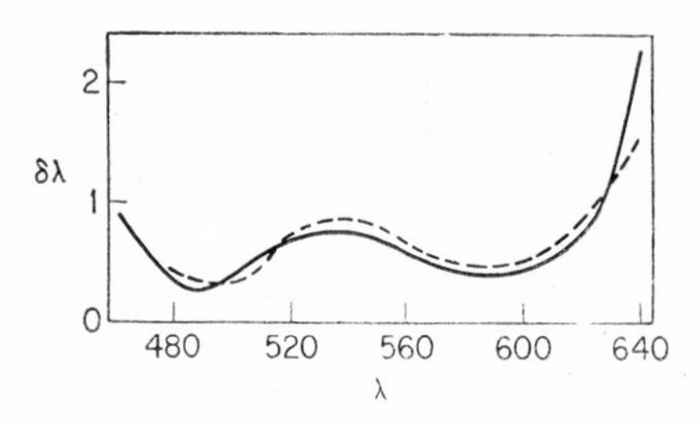

FIG. 32. Helmholtz's theoretical treatment [66, 67; 140] of König and Dieterici's data [110] on hue discrimination. *Modified from Helmholtz* [66].

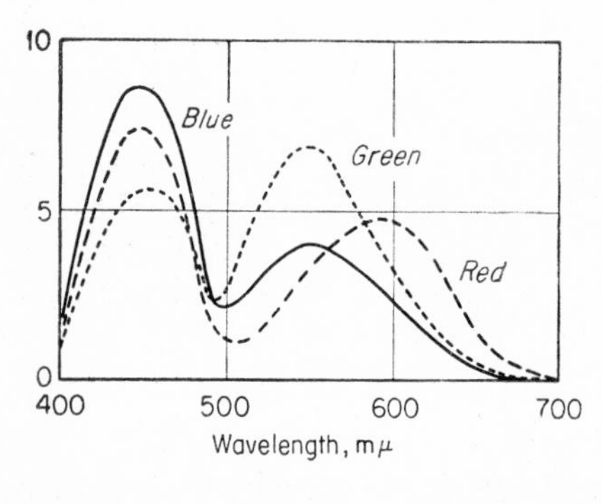

FIG. 33. Helmholtz's fundamentals [66, 67; 140] designed to account for hue discrimination. *From Hecht* [55].

Helmholtz account, and we may gain a more profitable idea of the line-element theory as a type by moving directly to a consideration of Stiles's formulation.

Stiles's modification of Helmholtz's line-element. (Stiles [167] formulated his line-element theory of trichromatic visual processes before he had the benefit of his later data on the two-color threshold [171], data that implied the need for a five- or seven-receptor color mechanism. Since the theory of 1946 is not in accord with later research, its importance may be largely historical. Despite this possibility, it may be regarded as an improvement over the Helmholtz line-element, and it is certainly worthy of consideration from a methodological point of view and as a possible basis for a modified account.

The changes made by Stiles as extensions and improvements of Helmholtz's account consisted of the following steps:

1. First, he substituted for Helmholtz's double-peaked fundamental curves his own curves, R_λ, G_λ, B_λ, based on a fit of the experimental data obtained by the two-color technique. (See the discussion centering about Fig. 11.) These functions, R_λ, G_λ, B_λ, are linear forms of the CIE distribution coefficients $\bar{x}$, $\bar{y}$, $\bar{z}$. Using the coefficients of the CIE Standard Observer [79], one obtains an appropriate linear representation of R_λ, G_λ, B_λ as follows:

$$\begin{aligned} R_\lambda &= 661\bar{x} + 1260\bar{y} - 112\bar{z} \\ G_\lambda &= -438\bar{x} + 1620\bar{y} + 123\bar{z} \\ B_\lambda &= 0.708\bar{x} + 417\bar{z} \end{aligned} \tag{99}$$

The agreement of these transformations with the empirical curves R_μ, G_μ, and R_μ is shown in Fig. 34 [166]. Their agreement, when appropriate multiplying constants are introduced, with curves r_λ, g_λ, and b_λ is also demonstrated. To a fair approximation R_λ, G_λ, and R_λ seem to describe the experimentally determined form of Stiles's fundamental curves.

2. Second, Stiles used a relation to describe the dependency of $1/U_\lambda$ on W_μ that was different from the Fechnerian relation called for in Helmholtz's account. Stiles refers to his relation, discussed earlier (see Fig. 8), as $\xi(p)$; it is a curve, selected by trial as applicable to any one of the component branches of the experimental curves relating log $(1/U_\lambda)$ to log W_μ in the two-color threshold experiments. The positions on the graph at which component curves of this shape had to be placed to yield a resultant curve agreeing with the experimental curve were determined for the various combinations of λ and μ used.

> The common shape of the component curves was represented as a function $\xi(p)$ . . . defined so that $\xi(p) = 1$ for $p = 0$, $\xi(p) = 0.1$ for $p = 1$ . . . . The expression for a particular component, say the "red" component, then took the form
>
> $$\log\ (1/U_{\lambda_r}) = \log\ [r_\lambda \xi(R_\mu W_\mu)] \tag{100}$$
>
> where for given λ and μ the constants r_λ and R_μ fix the position of the curve in the diagram [167]. [Equations of this section are renumbered.]

3. Finally, Stiles pointed out that the ratios R_λ/r_λ, G_λ/g_λ, B_λ/b_λ are not equal: B_λ/b_λ is greater than the other two, for reasons that were pointed out in the consideration of the two-color threshold. (See, for example, the discussion that centers about Figs. 11 and 12.) Different effects of light adaptation occur in the three fundamental processes. If $\mu = \lambda$, the curves for, respectively, $-\log\ (1/U_{\lambda_r})$, $-\log\ (1/U_{\lambda_g})$,

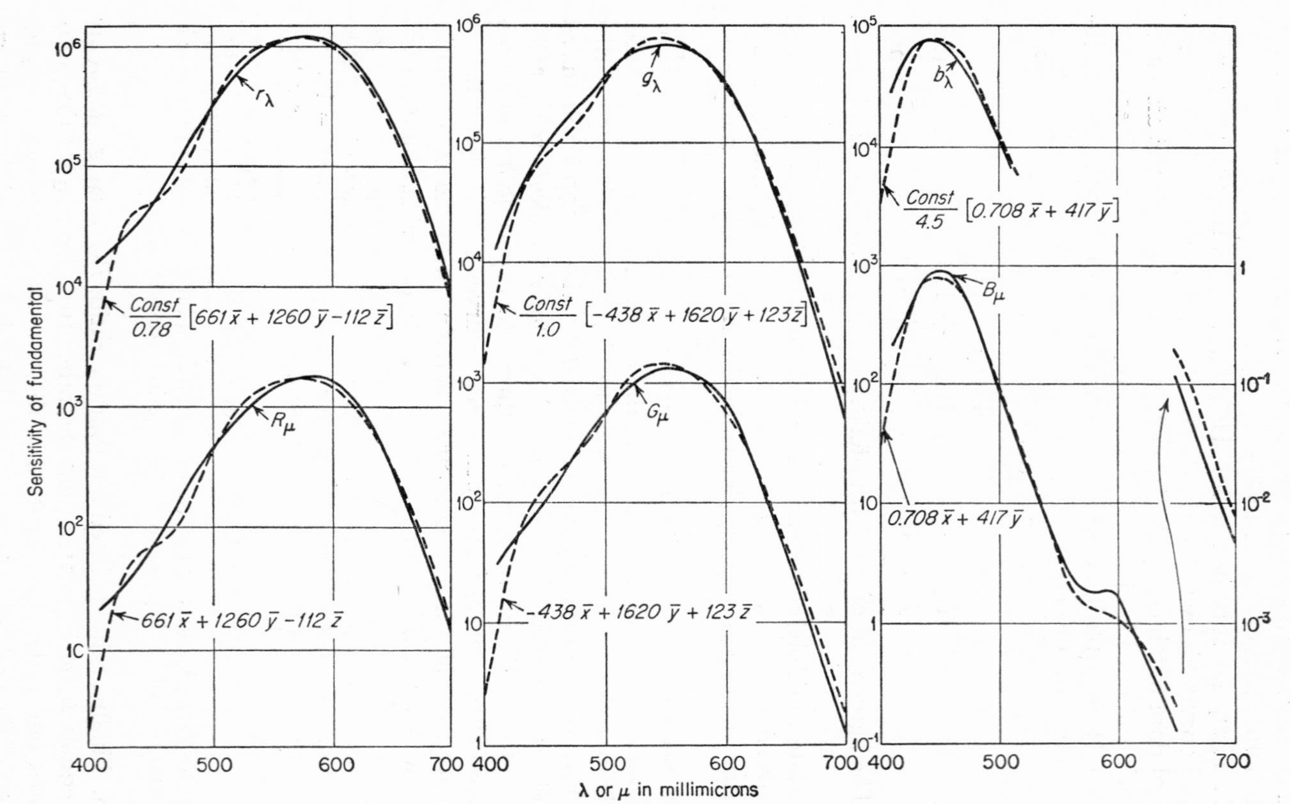

FIG. 34. Stiles's R_λ, G_λ, B_λ functions (dashed lines) as fits (by way of area-adjusting constants in the case of r_λ, g_λ, and b_λ) for the r_λ, . . . B_μ functions obtained with the two-color threshold technique. *Based on Stiles* [167].

and $-\log(1/U_{\lambda_b})$ against $\log W_\mu$ do not tend to a common line at high intensities. Said in another way: the minimum Weber ratios, U_{λ_r}/W_μ, etc., are, contrary to Helmholtz's account, different for the three primaries.

It is a consequence of Stiles's modifications that the three mechanisms add up to a slightly smaller extent than is required by the sum of Helmholtz's squares relation.

The modified line-element. Stiles's tentative line-element for application to any pair of just distinguishable light patches, P′ and P, having absolute energy distributions $W_\lambda\, d\lambda$ and $W'_\lambda\, d\lambda$, respectively, is formulated as follows. Let

$$\zeta(p) = 9\xi(p) \qquad R = \int W_\lambda R_\lambda\, d\lambda \qquad \text{and} \qquad \delta R = \int (W'_\lambda - W_\lambda) R_\lambda\, d\lambda \tag{101}$$

G, δG, B, and δB are defined similarly to R and δR, R_λ, G_λ, B_λ are the fundamental curves testable by the two-color threshold technique and defined by Eqs. (99).

Introduce the quantities ρ, γ, and β proportional to the limiting (Weber) fractions of the three mechanisms,

$$\rho:\gamma:\beta = \frac{R_\lambda}{r_\lambda}:\frac{G_\lambda}{g_\lambda}:\frac{B_\lambda}{b_\lambda} = 0.78:1:4.46 \tag{102}$$

and satisfying

$$\frac{1}{\rho^2} + \frac{1}{\gamma^2} + \frac{1}{\beta^2} = 1 \tag{103}$$

so that $\frac{1}{\rho^2} = 0.612$, $\frac{1}{\gamma^2} = 0.369$, $\frac{1}{\beta^2} = 0.0185$. The proposed line-element is then

$$\delta s^2 \equiv \left[\frac{\delta R}{\rho}\zeta(R)\right]^2 + \left[\frac{\delta G}{\gamma}\zeta(G)\right]^2 + \left[\frac{\delta B}{\beta}\zeta(\beta)\right]^2 = F^2 \tag{104}$$

which reduces at high intensities to

$$\delta s^2 \equiv \left[\frac{1}{\rho}\frac{\delta R}{R}\right]^2 + \left[\frac{1}{\gamma}\frac{\delta G}{G}\right]^2 + \left[\frac{1}{\beta}\frac{\delta B}{B}\right]^2 = F^2 \tag{105}$$

where F is a constant [167]. [Equations have been renumbered.]

If the patches P and P′ have the same *relative* energy distributions, their intensities may be specified by their total energies T' and T (or by their total energies weighted according to any function of wavelength, such as the visibility curve). Their Weber fraction is given by

$$\frac{\delta T}{T} = \frac{\delta R}{R} = \frac{\delta G}{G} = \frac{\delta B}{B}$$

Thus, by Eq. (105), $\delta T/T = F$ at high intensities; F is seen to be the limiting Weber fraction for any pair of patches of the same relative energy distribution. A value of $F = 0.01$ was used by Stiles in applying his theory to data.

Step-by-step luminosity curve. In order to provide a luminosity curve by the step-by-step method, a subject first views two juxtaposed patches which exhibit slightly different wavelength distributions. The intensity of one patch is then varied until the subject signals that the intensity differences between the two patches is a minimum. If the color difference is small enough, the two patches are just indiscriminable at this minimum setting of the intensity difference.

Stiles [167] first presents a general formulation of the application of the line-element to the step-by-step luminosity data obtained with pairs of patches of nearly the same color. The minimum value of δs^2 is reached when, with the intensity of one patch being varied while its color is maintained constant,

$$0 = \frac{\delta R}{R}\left[\frac{R}{\rho}\zeta(R)\right]^2 + \frac{\delta G}{G}\left[\frac{G}{\gamma}\zeta(G)\right]^2 + \frac{\delta B}{B}\left[\frac{B}{\beta}\zeta(B)\right]^2 \tag{106}$$

Only first-order quantities are retained in this equation.

In the special case of monochromatic patches of wavelengths λ, $\lambda + \delta\lambda$ and energy intensities W_λ, $W_\lambda + \delta W_\lambda$ (a case that is of most immediate relevance), Stiles's general equation reduces to

$$-\frac{\delta W_\lambda}{W_\lambda} = \delta\lambda\left[\frac{C_r^2}{R_\lambda}\frac{dR_\lambda}{d\lambda} + \frac{C_g^2}{G_\lambda}\frac{dG_\lambda}{d\lambda} + \frac{C_b^2}{B_\lambda}\frac{dB_\lambda}{d\lambda}\right] \tag{107}$$

where

$$C_r^2 = \frac{\left[\frac{R}{\rho}\zeta(R)\right]^2}{\left[\frac{R}{\rho}\zeta(R)\right]^2 + \left[\frac{G}{\gamma}\zeta(G)\right]^2 + \left[\frac{B}{\beta}\zeta(B)\right]^2} \tag{108}$$

and C_g^2, C_b^2 are similarly defined. By successive applications of this equation, one can determine the energies of a series of monochromatic patches whose wavelengths increase in small steps from the blue to the red, during which process each patch remains matched in brightness to its neighbor. The reciprocal of the energy of each patch plotted against wavelength gives a step-by-step visibility curve. The shape of the curve depends on the intensity level specified, for example, by the energy value of the maximum.

At high intensity levels C_r^2, C_g^2, C_b^2 tend to $1/\rho^2$, $1/\gamma^2$, $1/\beta^2$, respectively, and the luminosity curve approaches a limiting form

$$V_\lambda = \frac{\text{const}}{W_\lambda} = \text{const}\,(R_\lambda^{1/\rho^2} G_\lambda^{1/\gamma^2} B_\lambda^{1/\beta^2}) \tag{109}$$

When the necessary computations, involving R_λ, G_λ, and B_λ values at different wavelengths are made, it turns out that the theoretical values probably provide an acceptable fit for the step-by-step luminosity data of Gibson and Tyndall [24] on 52 subjects. Helmholtz's double-peak primaries cannot be used to describe such data.

At low intensities near foveal threshold a new limiting form of the luminosity curve would apply; i.e.,

$$V_\lambda = \text{const}\sqrt{\left(\frac{R_\lambda}{\rho}\right)^2 + \left(\frac{G_\lambda}{\gamma}\right)^2 + \left(\frac{B_\lambda}{\beta}\right)^2} \tag{110}$$

Lowering the intensity level increases slightly the luminosities in the orange, red, and blue spectral regions.

No determinations of the foveal luminosity curve by the step-by-step method have been made near threshold, and so the second limiting form cannot as yet be tested against data.

Nonadditivity of small-step luminance. According to Stiles's formulation, luminances of differently colored but equally bright lights are not additive. Abney's law is not presumed to hold. Let $P(R,G,B)$ represent the brightness of a light in terms of the intensities of fundamental processes integrated over the wavelength band of the stimulus. According to the line-element theory

$$P(R,G,B) = P_r(R) + P_g(G) + P_b(B) \tag{111}$$

where

$$P_r(R) = \int^R \frac{dR}{R}\left[\frac{R\zeta(R)}{\rho}\right]^2 \tag{112}$$

and P_g, P_b are similarly defined.

To estimate the magnitude of the breakdown in the additive law, we will use for $P(R,G,B)$ the form to which it reduces at high intensities, namely,

$$\log_e\left[R^{1/\rho^2}G^{1/\gamma^2}B^{1/\beta^2}\right] \tag{113}$$

If lights 1 and 2 have the same small-step brightness

$$R_1{}^{1/\rho^2}G_1{}^{1/\gamma^2}B_1{}^{1/\beta^2} = R_2{}^{1/\rho^2}G_2{}^{1/\gamma^2}B_2{}^{1/\beta^2} \tag{114}$$

and the equality of brightness still holds if their intensities are changed by the same factor, α say, since

$$(R_1\alpha)^{1/\rho^2}(G_1\alpha)^{1/\gamma^2}(B_1\alpha)^{1/\beta^2} = (R_2\alpha)^{1/\rho^2}(G_2\alpha)^{1/\gamma^2}(B_2\alpha)^{1/\beta^2} \tag{115}$$

But if lights 1 and 2 each match light 3 in brightness, the mixture of 1 and 2 will not in general match light 3 increased to double its original intensity, since

$$(R_1 + R_2)^{1/\rho^2}(G_1 + G_2)^{1/\gamma^2}(B_1 + B_2)^{1/\beta^2} = (2R_3)^{1/\rho^2}(2G_3)^{1/\gamma^2}(2B_3)^{1/\beta^2} \tag{116}$$

is not in general true. The discrepancy may be expected to be greatest when the colours of 1 and 2 are most widely different, and it is estimated that about the worst case arises with monochromatic lights in the blue (<470 mμ) and red (>680 mμ). The colour of light 3 is immaterial.

This prediction should be given extensive experimental test. The specification that Abney's law *not* be adhered to is interesting in view of recent developments that cast doubt on the validity of that rule [103]. Whether or not such a development as Stiles's may be appropriate is, of course, open to test.

Hue discrimination.

The hue limen, or the difference of wavelength of two just-distinguishable monochromatic patches of equal brightness, is obtained from relations (104) and (106) by the substitutions

$$R = W_\lambda R_\lambda,\ \delta R = R_\lambda \delta W_\lambda + W_\lambda \frac{dR_\lambda}{d\lambda}\,\delta\lambda, \text{ etc.}$$

On eliminating W_λ, the equation for the hue limen λ takes the form:

$$F^2 = \delta\lambda \left[\left\{ \frac{C_r^2 - 1}{R_\lambda}\frac{dR_\lambda}{d\lambda} + \frac{C_g^2}{G_\lambda}\frac{dG_\lambda}{d\lambda} + \frac{C_b^2}{B_\lambda}\frac{dB_\lambda}{d\lambda} \right\}^2 \left\{ \frac{R}{\rho}\,\zeta(R) \right\}^2 + \text{two similar terms} \right] \quad (117)$$

At high intensities this reduces to

$$F^2 = \delta\lambda^2 \left[\left\{ \frac{1/\rho^2 - 1}{R_\lambda}\frac{dR_\lambda}{d\lambda} + \frac{1/\gamma^2}{G_\lambda}\frac{dG_\lambda}{d\lambda} + \frac{1/\beta^2}{B_\lambda}\frac{dB}{d\lambda} \right\}^2 1/\rho^2 + \text{two similar terms} \right] \quad (118)$$

The equation used by Helmholtz is a special case of (118) when ρ, γ, β, are made equal [167].

Figure 35 presents the application (heavy ruled line) of Eq. (117) to five experimental curves portrayed by Wright and Pitt [205] at an average intensity level of 70 photons. It may be seen that the hue discrimination thresholds of the theoretical curve fall consistently below the thresholds of the experimental curves in the blue. Some of the discrepancy between theory and observation may be attributable to the fact that it was necessary to use intensity levels in the blue (below 480 mμ) that were only about 5 per cent as high as those in other spectral regions. In any case, the agreement between theory and observation is not encouraging.

Color limens. When two differently colored patches having the same brightness are just distinguishable, they specify a general color limen. Such color limens are conveniently displayed in the CIE (x,y) chart by drawing ellipses about various points in the chart; each point through which the curve passes specifies a color that is just distinguishable from the central color at the crossing point of the major and minor axes [118]. Experimental observations of this sort have been made by MacAdam. MacAdam determined, for one subject, complete ellipses for 25 fixed colors distributed over the CIE chart.

Stiles [167] has computed theoretical ellipses based on line-element considerations and compared them with the data of MacAdam. The methods used by Stiles in computing the ellipses will not be here described. The data obtained on MacAdam's single subject, who was tested over a wide range of colors, show some similarity between theory and data. The orientations of the theoretical and experimental el-

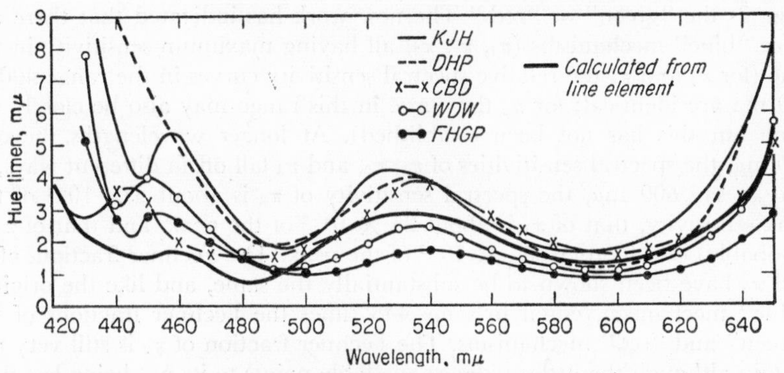

Fig. 35. Stiles's formulation of hue discrimination, Eq. (117), applied to the data of Wright and Pitt [205]. *From Stiles* [167].

lipses correspond well and their areas show some correlation. However, the axis ratios of the ellipses show no relationship. A second subject tested by MacAdam underwent tests on a limited number of colors. The second subject gave only fragmentary data that cannot be used except to indicate that the ellipses of different subjects show different characteristics.

Stiles's comment on the modified line-element. Stiles gives the following evaluation of his line-element model.

To be satisfactory, the line-element (104) with a particular numerical determination of R_λ, G_λ, B_λ, ρ, γ, β, F, and $\zeta(p)$ should reproduce the colour-matching values, the step-by-step visibility curve, the increment and colour limens and possibly some other visual properties of a particular eye. . . . Certain main features of the experimental results are reproduced. . . . For the restricted group of colour-limen measurements . . . the case of MacAdam's subject P.G.N. [shows] that complete agreement could not be reached by any change in which the fundamental response functions R_λ, G_λ, B_λ remained always positive, linear forms in the C.I.E. distribution coefficients. . . . Our conclusion must be that the modified line-element, constructed to suit measurements of increment limens, leads to the right kind of step-by-step visibility curve, but is in difficulties when applied to measurements of colour limens.

A communication to the writer has this to say about the relation between the early line-element hypothesis and its connection with the later work [171] that seems to call for five- or seven-receptor theory.

The line-element theory has to be reconsidered in the light of the later threshold work. . . . The measure of success of the line-element theory turned on the recognition of a major difference in the Fechner fractions of the "blue" mechanism, on the one hand, and of the "green" and "red" mechanisms, on the other, the "blue" having a Fechner fraction some 4–5 times as large as the "green" or "red." The new work has indicated that there are three "blue" mechanisms (π_1, π_2, π_3) all having maximum sensitivity in the blue (for π_1 and π_3 the relative spectral sensitivity curves in the range 400 to 500 mμ are identical; for π_2 the curve in this range may also be closely the same but this has not been established). At longer wavelengths, beyond 500 mμ, the spectral sensitivities of π_1, π_2, and π_3 fall off in different ways, so that at say 600 mμ, the spectral sensitivity of π_3 is about 5×10^{-4} of the peak sensitivity, that of π_1 is about 25×10^{-2} of the peak, and that of π_2 is (probably) of the order of 1×10^{-1} of the peak. The Fechner fractions of π_1 and π_3 have been shown to be substantially the same, and like the original "blue" mechanism, equal to some 4–5 times the Fechner fractions of the "green" and "red" mechanisms. The Fechner fraction of π_2 is still very uncertain although the little evidence available points to its not being less than those of π_1 and π_3. If it has in fact the same or a greater Fechner fraction than these mechanisms, the line-element theory can cope with π_1, π_2, and π_3 without serious difficulty. If it should have the same Fechner fraction as the "green" or "red" mechanisms, then the line-element theory would be in trouble and would, I think, be untenable [172].

Hecht's theory. Hecht's theory [55, 56, 57, 58] is different from the line-element type of theory. Stated in (probably) oversimplified form, one can say that, whereas the line-element type is concerned with an isomorphic relation between visual data and a mathematical space (little reference being made to intervening relations), Hecht's theory is a mathematical account of component physiological processes.

The nature of the theory. The theory supposes

. . . that there are . . . three kinds of cones present in the retina, and that in the fovea they exist in approximately equal numbers. The sensations which result from the action of these three cones are qualitatively specific and may be tentatively described as blue, green, and red respectively. Thus a given cone, which contains a photosensitive substance whose spectral absorption is greater in the blue, or in the green, or in the red, is joined to a nerve fiber which is so connected with the brain that, when the photosensitive substance in the cone is changed by light and starts an impulse in the nerve, the nerve will register respectively blue or green or red in the brain. It should be emphasized that, regardless of the method used for starting this impulse, and regardless of the wavelength of the stimulating light, and indeed regardless of the nature of the photosensitive substance, an impulse proceeding along a "blue" nerve will register blue in the brain, a "green" nerve green, and a "red" nerve red [58].

The essential element of the theory consists of the three curves, labeled R_0, G_0, and V_0 in Fig. 36. V_0, G_0, and R_0 may be considered as

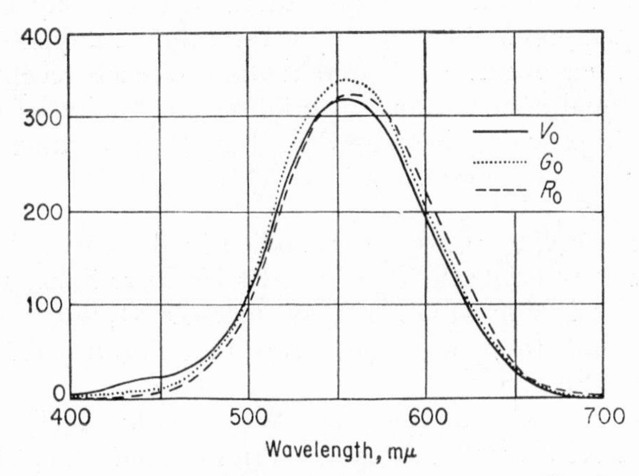

FIG. 36. Hecht's fundamental response curves V_0, G_0, and R_0. *From Hecht* [58].

mathematical curves from which certain color functions may be derived. They may also be thought of theoretically as the luminosity curves of three species of cones.

The abscissas are wave-lengths. The ordinates are the reciprocals of the energies required at the different wave-lengths to produce the same intensity of sensation in a given species of cone. This means that if we could investigate separately the activity, say of the red cones alone, and were to measure the energy required to produce the same red sensation qualitatively and quantitatively with different wave-lengths in the spectrum, then the reciprocals of these energies would yield a curve such as the R_0 curve in [Fig. 36]. The same holds for the other two curves. The ordinates are therefore brightness values.[35] If what has been found for visual purple . . . holds for the sensitive substances in the cones, then the curves in [Fig. 36] are very nearly the absorption spectra of the three sensitive materials [58].

[35] That is, they are for an equal energy spectrum, for which E_λ is constant through the spectrum.

The V_0, G_0, R_0 curves were chosen as functions which would effec tively predict several sets of color vision data. A study of differen properties of color vision first disclosed some conditions which th curves should meet. First, certain of the curves should cross at wave lengths that correspond to the neutral points of color-blind individual (i.e., the wavelengths seen as white by dichromats). Second, th ordinate values on the curves should add at any wavelength to give th appropriate luminosity value. Third, it was felt that it would b desirable to have equal areas under the curves. (The equal area represent equal available totals of brightness integrated throug wavelength; and these equal quantities, in turn, may be taken t stand for equal populations among the three different types of recepto The equal areas mean equal contributions of each receptor type t color and equal contributions to brightness.) Finally, of course, th curves should provide a basis for describing the experimentally deter mined relations of color vision.

These requirements are all embodied in the curves[36] of Fig. 36 The curves were originally described by Hecht as linear transforma tions of the excitation curves [182; see footnote 34] but, as used in th present account, they are derived from the XYZ distribution coeffi cients.[37] (See Fig. 25.)

The manner of obtaining these was as follows. (1) The value $\bar{x}$, $\bar{y}$, and $\bar{z}$ were corrected for Abbot-Priest sunlight [58, 145, 147] b multiplying each at 10 mμ steps by E_λ, the relative energy of Abbot Priest sunlight for the appropriate wavelength. (2) Each $\bar{x}E_\lambda$ value wa multiplied by a constant k so that the sum of the $k\bar{x}E_\lambda$ values over th range 400 to 700 mμ was equal to the mean area of Hecht's V_0, G_0, an R_0 curves. (These latter curves are in fact slightly different in are though they were meant to be equal.) (3) The procedure was carrie out for $k'\bar{y}E_\lambda$ and $k''\bar{z}E_\lambda$ values. The values $k\bar{x}E_\lambda$ are denoted by $\dot{\bar{x}}$; th values $k'\bar{y}E_\lambda$ are designated by $\dot{\bar{y}}$; and the values $k''\bar{z}E_\lambda$ are designate by $\dot{\bar{z}}$. (4) The problem is to specify R_0, G_0, and V_0 in terms of $\dot{\bar{x}}$, $\dot{\bar{y}}$, an $\dot{\bar{z}}$. As calculated in this manner the curves $\dot{\bar{x}}$, $\dot{\bar{y}}$, and $\dot{\bar{z}}$ and R_0, G_0, and V

[36] Hecht labels his all-positive, hence imaginary, fundamentals R_0, G_0, and V_0 They follow an earlier set V, G, R [55]. The reason for labeling one of the primaries V rather than B is that "violet seems to act as a unitary thing in color mixture and hu discrimination. . . . Nevertheless . . . blue . . . is a unique sensation, wherea violet is a color blend. . . . It is for this reason that I spoke . . . of a blue receivin cone" [55]. Hecht spoke of a blue receptor but a violet primary because of the fac that König's tritanopes failed to show a neutral point at the supposed crossing of I and G curves in the violet end of the spectrum.

[37] The author is indebted to Dr. Eda Berger and Dr. Gerald Howett for th computations.

meet the requirement that both sets are specified relative to the same source of Abbot-Priest sunlight, R_0, G_0, and V_0, represented by Hecht's curves are, to a good approximation, linear transformations of $\mathring{x}$, $\mathring{y}$, and $\mathring{z}$, according to the equations:[38]

$$\begin{aligned} R_0 &= .0736\mathring{x} + .9458\mathring{y} - .0230\mathring{z} \\ G_0 &= -.0461\mathring{x} + 1.0625\mathring{y} + .0065\mathring{z} \\ V_0 &= -.0275\mathring{x} + .9947\mathring{y} + .0165\mathring{z} \end{aligned} \tag{119}$$

Color mixture. The curves V_0, G_0, and R_0 are shown, to a good approximation, to be linear transformations of $\mathring{x}$, $\mathring{y}$, and $\mathring{z}$. Therefore, they describe the *XYZ* data of color mixture, $\mathring{x}$, $\mathring{y}$, and $\mathring{z}$ being obtained by correcting $\bar{x}$, $\bar{y}$, and $\bar{z}$ for Abbot-Priest sunlight. The variables R_0, G_0, and V_0 can in appropriate combination predict to a considerable degree of precision the data of color mixture.

Luminosity. The curves V_0, G_0, and R_0 give, each, at any wavelength, that part of the total luminosity V_λ that can be attributed to the respective fundamental; therefore, the luminosity, V_λ, is obtained by adding the coefficients at any wavelength. If Eqs. (119) be added, we get

$$R_0 + G_0 + V_0 = 3\mathring{y} \tag{120}$$

If we divide both sides of (120) by 3 so as to make the area of the luminosity curve equal to the area of R_0, G_0, or V_0, we get

$$V_\lambda = \frac{R_0 + G_0 + V_0}{3} = \mathring{y} \tag{121}$$

The sum of R_0, G_0, and V_0 in appropriate units gives $\mathring{y}$, the CIE luminosity function corrected for Abbot-Priest sunlight.

Brightness and white. Total brightness at a given wavelength is described by the sum of $V_0 + G_0 + R_0$. The brightness of the "white" component of a light is equal to three times the value of the lowest coefficient because "white" is produced when $V_0 = G_0 = R_0$. The brightness of the "color" part is the difference between the total brightness $V_0 + G_0 + R_0$ and three times the lowest fundamental. Figure 36 shows that for $\lambda < 550$ mμ, the lowest fundamental is R_0;

[38] The least squares fit for Eqs. (119) gives coefficients slightly different from those represented. In order, the least squares coefficients are:

.0595	.9454	−.0158
−.0606	1.0641	+.0123
−.0353	.9888	+.0304.

The coefficients of Eqs. (119) were adjusted from the above values to satisfy the condition (120).

"color" is then given by $V_0 + G_0 - 2R_0$. For $\lambda > 550$ mμ the lowest coefficient is V_0, and "color" is given by $G_0 + R_0 - 2V_0$. The same type of analysis applies also to a mixture of lights of different wavelengths. It shows that, in comparing the "relative values of the color-producing portion and of the white-producing portion of most wavelengths . . . the latter is by far the largest magnitude of the two in relation to total brightness. In other words, speaking as a rough approximation, the brightness of a color is largely determined by its white-producing capacity" [58].

Saturation. Total luminosity minus "white" luminosity gives "color" luminosity for each wavelength λ. The saturation of each wavelength may be thought of as the ratio of "color" luminosity to total luminosity, that is,

$$S_{\lambda<550} = \frac{V_0 + G_0 - 2R_0}{V_0 + G_0 + R_0} \tag{122}$$

and

$$S_{\lambda>550} = \frac{G_0 + R_0 - 2V_0}{V_0 + G_0 + R_0} \tag{123}$$

for the respective spectral regions $\lambda < 550$ mμ and $\lambda > 550$ mμ.

Priest and Brickwedde's experiment [148, 149] on colorimetric purity was used by Hecht to test his quantitative formulation of saturation. (Note that his definition of colorimetric purity is not the conventional one.)

In these experiments

. . . let B_λ be the brightness of the homogeneous light which needs to be added to secure a just-perceptible color; let B_w be the brightness of the constant white field, and let P_λ be the minimum-perceptible colorimetric purity. Then the equation

$$P_\lambda = \frac{B_\lambda}{B_w} \tag{124}$$

represents the definition of least-perceptible colorimetric purity. Since the amount of "color" added is assumed constant, the brightness B_λ which has to be added to furnish this "color" is inversely proportional to the saturation S_λ. This may be written as

$$B_\lambda = \frac{k}{S_\lambda} \tag{125}$$

and can be introduced into Eq. (124). The equation now becomes

$$P_\lambda = \frac{K_p}{S_\lambda} \tag{126}$$

in which $K_p = k/B_w$ since B_w is kept experimentally constant. In other words, the minimum perceptible colorimetric purity as determined by Priest and

Brickwedde is inversely proportional to the saturation as determinable from the values of the (fundamentals) V_0, G_0 and R_0 [58]. [In this quotation equation numbers have been changed.]

Figure 37 shows the average data of Priest and Brickwedde contrasted with results obtained from V_0, G_0, and R_0 in terms of Eqs. (122), (123), and (126), where $K_p = .001$. There is considerable resemblance between the theoretical and experimental curves [58]. Hecht points out that a new set of fundamentals, V'_0, G'_0, and R'_0, slightly different

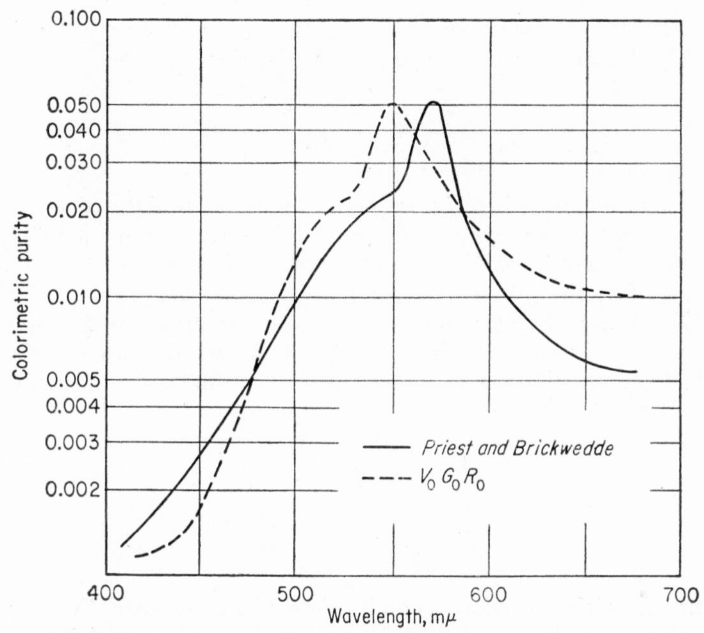

FIG. 37. Least perceptible colorimetric purity as given by the averaged data of Priest and Brickwedde [149]. *From Hecht* [58].

from V_0, G_0, and R_0, could provide an almost exact fit for Priest and Brickwedde's averaged data.

Wavelength discrimination. Hecht derives hue discrimination relations from his V_0, G_0, and R_0 functions in terms of the idea, similar to Helmholtz's, that spectral hue changes are connected with differential changes in certain properties of the three color receptors.

Suppose that a minimum change in the appearance of the spectrum depends on the rates of change $dV_0/d\lambda$, $dG_0/d\lambda$, and $dR_0/d\lambda$ in relation to one another. Figure [36] shows that when $\lambda < 550$ mμ, the rate of change of V_0 relative to that of R_0 is

$$\frac{dV_0}{d\lambda} = \frac{dR_0}{d\lambda} \tag{127}$$

and the rate of change of G_0 relative to that of R_0 is

$$\frac{dG_0}{d\lambda} - \frac{dR_0}{d\lambda} \tag{128}$$

The difference between the two expressions in (127) and (128) is

$$\frac{dH}{d\lambda} = \frac{d(V_0 - G_0)}{d\lambda} \tag{129}$$

and represents the way in which the appearance H of the spectrum for $\lambda < 550$ mμ changes with the wave-length λ in terms of the relative changes of V_0, G_0 and R_0. By the same process we may derive expression

$$\frac{dH}{d\lambda} = \frac{d(R_0 - G_0)}{d\lambda} \tag{130}$$

for $\lambda > 550$ mμ.

In order to relate these ideas to the quantitative data of wavelength discrimination, we must remember that what is measured is not a differential, but a finite distance in wave-length $\Delta\lambda_c$ necessary for a minimal difference in appearance ΔH. Since this difference in appearance, ΔH, is minimal, it may be considered as constant, and possibly corresponds to a constant difference in the number of cones of each species functional for the two wave-lengths. Converting differentials to finite differences and writing $\Delta H = K_H$, we change Eqs. (129) and (130) into

$$\Delta\lambda_c = K_H \frac{\Delta\lambda}{\Delta(V_0 - G_0)} \tag{131}$$

$$\Delta\lambda_c = K_H \frac{\Delta\lambda}{\Delta(R_0 - G_0)} \tag{132}$$

in terms of which the experimentally determined distance $\Delta\lambda_c$ along the spectrum required for a minimal difference in the appearance of the spectrum is proportional to the distance $\Delta\lambda$ which one has to move on the curves in Figure [36] to yield a constant value of $\Delta(V_0 - G_0)$ or $\Delta(R_0 - G_0)$ [58].[39] [Equations and figures of this quotation have been renumbered.]

The results of the necessary computations applied to the hue discrimination data from Laurens's eye and Hamilton's eye [113], made at constant brightness, are shown in Fig. 38. The figure shows that the theoretical curve derived from the fundamentals V_0, G_0, and R_0 is about as well correlated with either set of data as either set is with the other. K_H is here taken to be 0.35. The data of Laurens and Hamilton are in qualitative agreement with the theory. Hecht explains that a small alteration in the slope of the V_0, G_0, and R_0 curves would result

[39] A more complete discussion of the method for relating theory to data is given by Hecht [58, pp. 812 ff.].

in an exact reproduction of an individual set of hue discrimination data, for example, those on Laurens's eye.

General considerations. The type of theory advocated by Hecht exhibits many desirable features. For one thing, it formulates "mechanisms," and despite whatever may be said to the contrary, it is a fact that a considerable number of investigators feel at home with this sort of account.

It is pretty certain that, at the time of his death, Hecht had given up his belief in the validity of the V_0, G_0, and R_0 curves. [See 60.] By then it had become clear that these fundamentals could not account

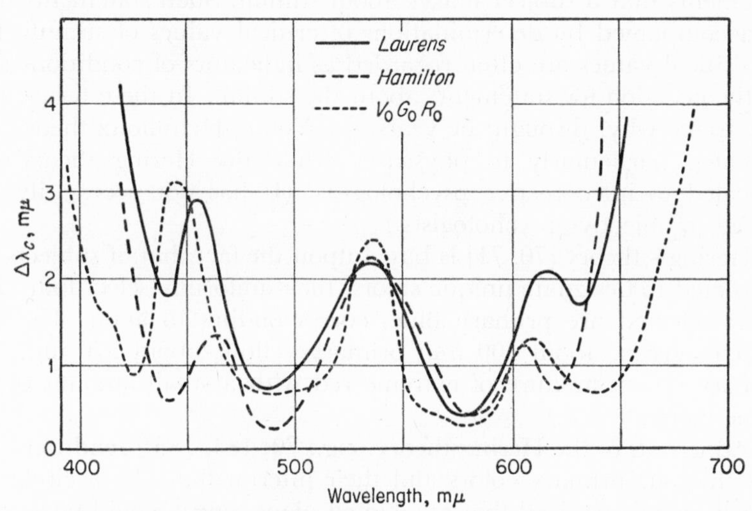

FIG. 38. Wavelength discrimination for measurements on the eyes of Laurens and Hamilton [113] and as derived theoretically from V_0, G_0, and R_0. *From Hecht* [58].

for many aspects of color vision, particularly the data of color blindness. It is clear, too, that these $V_0G_0R_0$ fundamentals could not now handle easily new data that have accumulated in several areas (e.g., the two-color threshold). Whatever direction color theory will take in the future, it will have to consider many more data than were available at the time of Hecht's formulation [55].

Hering's theory. Experimental work along lines influenced by the Young-Helmholtz theory has, in general, been concerned with stimulus thresholds or matches that are based on judgments of equality or difference. Little attention has been paid to qualitative estimates or "introspective reports" about stimuli presented in the absence of a standard for comparison. In work relating to the Hering theory, however, considerable attention has been paid to psychological variables.

Emphasis, for example, has often been placed on absolute judgments in the absence of a standard stimulus. The subject may be asked to vary the relative intensities of two "opposed" colors until he says that the mixture does not exhibit the hue of either component. The criterion of "lack of either component" corresponds to no operation on stimuli; it may be thought of as subjective, that is, understandable in terms of statements bearing no environmental referents. As contrasted then, with the Young-Helmholtz tradition, which emphasizes the effects of the subject's adjustments on physically specifiable differences between stimuli, the Hering tradition places importance on the statements that a subject makes about stimuli. Such statements may be accompanied by determinations of critical values of stimuli, but the critical values are often regarded as indicators of conditions that set the occasion for statements about the stimuli. In these terms, it is easy to see why, through the years, the Young-Helmholtz theory has appealed particularly to physicists, while the Hering theory has appealed to introspective psychologists. (It has not necessarily appealed to objective psychologists.)

Hering's theory [70, 71] is based upon the fact that, if subjects are instructed to designate unique colors, they uniformly select four. The colors selected are primary blue, corresponding to about 470 mμ; primary green, about 500 mμ; primary yellow, about 570 mμ; and primary red, a mixture of extreme red with a small amount of extreme violet.

Adherents of the Hering theory [e.g., 70; 184, 185]; tend to represent the four primary colors and their intermediates by a circle, although it is recognized that any closed plane figures could be used; a rectangle, in particular, might have advantages [185]. In the case of the circle, the "opponent" primary colors can be represented as opposite each other at a separation of 180°, primary red being opposite primary green, and primary blue, opposite primary yellow. Colors intermediate between the primaries are also brought into opposition. The circle represents hue and saturation in the manner of plane color diagrams; the third dimension represents brightness (or brilliance).

Coincidence with the vertical axis means that the sensation is colorless, whereas the segment's moving out along a radial line corresponds to increasing saturation. Every radial line represents a definite ratio between two compatible (primary) colors, i.e., a definite hue. The nuance, finally, is represented by the segment's position relative to the horizontal plane, i.e., by the ratio of its parts above and below, or W:B. The white and black components, however, cannot go below their respective minimal values (W_i or B_i) which are fixed by the intrinsic gray. Brilliance is determined by the achromatic component, which in turn is quantitatively and qualitatively dependent on the state of adaptation and to some extent also on the retinal region. In addition, the color component, depending on its hue and saturation, has probably a modest influence on the brilliance of the total sensation. Thus red and yellow seem to have a brightening effect, green and blue a specific darkening effect [185].

For this reason, red and yellow have sometimes been called the "warm" colors, while green and blue have been called the "cold" colors. Darker shades favor in general the impression of increased saturation, lighter shades, less saturation. The maximum saturation is less at high and low brightness than it is at medium brightness.

The primary colors have some important properties. In particular, (1) they do not, unlike their intermediates, change their hue when their brightnesses change, and (2) they exhibit and maintain a standard "opposition" relation for an achromatic effect and in simultaneous contrast. Intermediate colors do not maintain these invariant characteristics.

Hering's theory was based on the mutually antagonistic properties exhibited by the primary pairs, red and green, yellow and blue, and white and black. The properties of each pair depended upon antagonistic subprocesses in the white-black achromatic process, the red-green process, and the yellow-blue process. The white subprocess opposed the black; the red opposed the green; and the yellow, the blue. Hering [70, 71] originally characterized the antagonistic subprocesses as manifesting assimilation and dissimilation. The white, red, and yellow subprocesses were considered to be dissimilative "breakdown" processes, whereas the black, green, and blue subprocesses were thought of as assimilative "build-up" processes. Each single subprocess could produce its associated primary color: red, green, yellow, or blue. Intermediate hues, however, depend upon the interaction between processes of assimilative and dissimilative components. Violet, for example, depends on a combination of dissimilative red with assimilative blue.

Since assimilation and dissimilation are mutually exclusive in the red-green substance and the yellow-blue substance, in any one substance there is simply less or more of either process. Hering had to imagine, however, that in the white-black substance both processes may go on together. . . . The brightness of a gray, he asserted, must depend upon the ratio of assimilation in the white-black substance to the total of assimilation and dissimilation taken together. . . . Thus "middle gray" is experienced when assimilation and dissimilation equal each other in the white-black substance. This point is very important, for, if assimilation and dissimilation were mutually exclusive in the white-black substance, as they were said to be in the other two substances, then, instead of middle gray at the point of equilibrium for all three substances, one should see nothing at all [8].

The action of light, according to Hering and his followers, depends not only on its physical characteristics but also upon the condition of the visual mechanism. In line with this principle a change in hue as a function of brightness (the Bezold-Brücke effect) can be ascribed to conditions of adaptation, as in Hurvich and Jameson's account [77] which follows. Simultaneous color contrast is described in terms of antagonistic processes set up in areas adjacent to a stimulated zone. The physical addition of complementary lights results in addition of brilliance but a compensation or subtraction process causes opponent colors to cancel each other in such a way that the resulting mixture, white, "contains no trace of either of the components."

The first quantitative statement of an opponent-colors theory has recently been presented by Hurvich and Jameson [77]. For the first time one may now trace the interconnections of such an account within a system of explicit relations.

Hurvich and Jameson's theory. Logarithmic chromatic response (or valence) curves for subject H in Jameson and Hurvich's experiment [91] are given in Fig. 5. The results shown in Fig. 5 may be converted into arithmetic units, and the opponent members of each chromatic pair (*r* and *g*, *bl* and *y*) given arbitrary positive and negative signs to correspond with their opponent characteristics (i.e., *bl* and *g* are designated as negative, *r* and *y* as positive). The result of this treatment is a function similar to that shown in Fig. 39. The curves of Fig. 39 were derived by Judd [101] from the average color mixture values for the CIE Standard Observer, according to the equations

$$\begin{aligned} y - bl &= 0.4Y - 0.4Z \\ r - g &= 1.0X - 1.0Y \end{aligned} \qquad (133)$$

In Eqs. (133), $y - bl$ and $r - g$ are differences between chromatic responses specified in terms of the tristimulus values X, Y, and Z. In Eqs. (133) the chromatic responses ($r - g$ and $y - bl$) do not represent the initial effect of light; rather, they are taken to be the result of differences in neural excitation that depend on differences in photochemical processes. Since the chromatic responses depend on the differential effects in photochemical absorption, a quantification of an opponent-colors theory requires a postulated set of spectral absorption functions.[40] The functions selected by Hurvich and Jameson were

[40] The requirement of more than one set of specifying relations is characteristic not only of the Hering opponent-colors theory, but also of all so-called stage or zone

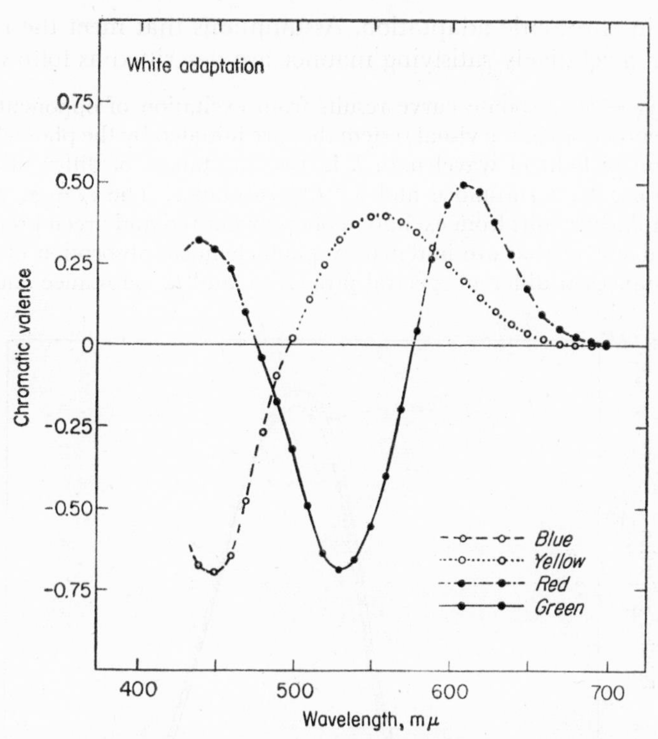

FIG. 39. Chromatic response curves for the CIE Standard Observer as derived by Judd [101]. *From Hurvich and Jameson* [77].

derived from CIE color mixture data transformed to meet a number of requirements. (1) The functions had to provide a basis for the chromatic response curves of Fig. 39; that is, simple combinations of these receptor functions had to yield chromatic response curves (for monochromatic lights) of the forms:

$$\begin{aligned} y_\lambda - bl_\lambda &= 0.4\bar{y}_\lambda - 0.4\bar{z}_\lambda \\ r_\lambda - g_\lambda &= 1.0\bar{x}_\lambda - 1.0\bar{y}_\lambda \end{aligned} \tag{134}$$

(2) They had to predict a considerable change in chromatic response with a change in chromatic adaptation. (3) They had also to provide a basis for luminosity and predict a small change in luminosity with a

theories. These theories give separate accounts of the processes at various stages or levels of the visual mechanism (e.g., receptors, retina, optic nerve fibers, etc.). The von Kries [112], Schrödinger [156], Müller [132], and Adams [3] theories are good examples of complex stage theories. They all use Hering's idea of opposing components in the description of the final stage.

change in chromatic adaptation. Assumptions that meet the requirements in a relatively satisfying manner are described as follows:[41]

The $y_\lambda - bl_\lambda$ response curve results from excitation of opponent yellow and blue processes in the visual system that are initiated by the photochemical absorption of light of wavelength λ in two substances of different spectral properties, a "*Y*" substance and a "*Bl*" substance. The $r_\lambda - g_\lambda$ response curve similarly results from excitation of opponent red and green processes in the visual system that are initiated by photochemical absorption of light in two substances of different spectral properties, an "*R*" substance and a "*G*"

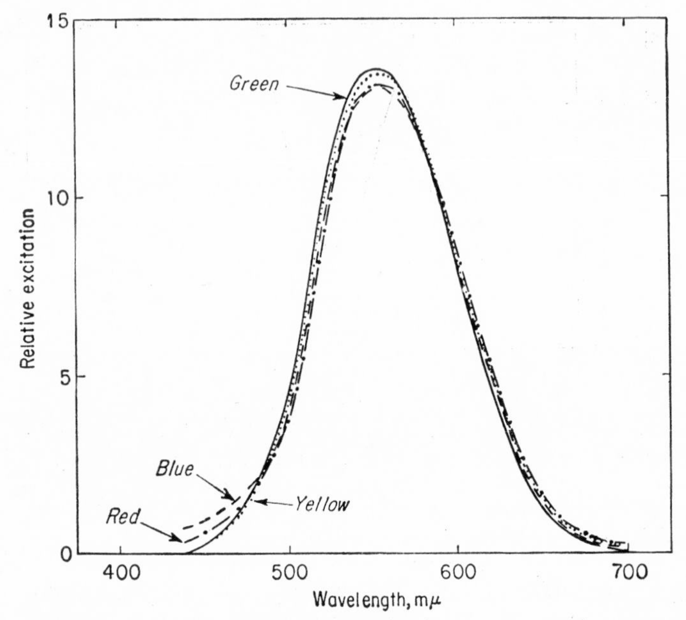

FIG. 40. Spectral distribution curves for four receptor substances. *From Hurvich and Jameson* [77].

substance. The excitations in the *R*, *G*, *Y*, and *Bl* substances (decomposition reactions) combine in a specified way to activate a white process in the visual system, and the activities involved in the reformation of these four substances (*Bl*, *G*, *Y*, and *R*) are also combined in a specific way to activate an opponent, black process. The white-black response ($w - bk$) is, like the chromatic responses, assumed to represent the residual of excitations, in this case in the opponent white and black processes. This achromatic response is assumed to have the same form as the spectral luminosity function, and to be the basic

[41] Throughout the discussion of this section the symbols *bl* and *Bl* are used for Hurvich and Jameson's *b* and *B* in order to maintain *B* as the symbol for luminance ("brightness"). The changed symbols are used without further notice in quotations from Hurvich and Jameson.

correlate of the achromatic aspects of the sensation, i.e., brightness and whiteness (grayness, or blackness).

A set of transformation equations that satisfies the requirements listed above are:

$$\begin{aligned} Bl_\lambda &= \quad 13.0682\bar{y}_\lambda + 0.2672\bar{z}_\lambda \\ G_\lambda &= -0.6736\bar{x}_\lambda + 14.0018\bar{y}_\lambda + 0.0040\bar{z}_\lambda \\ Y_\lambda &= -0.0039\bar{x}_\lambda + 13.4680\bar{y}_\lambda + 0.1327\bar{z}_\lambda \\ R_\lambda &= \quad 0.3329\bar{x}_\lambda + 13.0012\bar{y}_\lambda - 0.0011\bar{z}_\lambda \end{aligned} \tag{135}$$

where $\bar{x}_\lambda$, $\bar{y}_\lambda$ and $\bar{z}_\lambda$ are the CIE tristimulus values (distribution coefficients) for an equal energy spectrum. These curves are shown in Fig. [40].

The chromatic and achromatic response curves resulting from excitations of the *Bl*, *G*, *Y*, and *R* receiving substances can be expressed as:

$$\begin{aligned} y_\lambda - bl_\lambda &= k_1(Y_\lambda - Bl_\lambda) \\ r_\lambda - g_\lambda &= k_2(R_\lambda - G_\lambda) \\ w_\lambda - bk_\lambda &= k_3(0.5B_\lambda + 0.5G_\lambda + 1.0Y_\lambda + 1.0R_\lambda) - k_4(0.5B_\lambda + 0.5G_\lambda \\ &\qquad + 1.0Y_\lambda + 1.0R_\lambda) \end{aligned} \tag{136}$$

In terms of the CIE tristimulus values,

$$w_\lambda - bk_\lambda = k_5\bar{y}_\lambda \tag{137}$$ [42]

The constants k_1, k_2, k_3, and k_4 in Eqs. (136) and (136a) are assumed to be different ascending functions of the stimulus luminance and hence specify different response magnitudes in the paired $r - g$, $y - bl$, and $w - bk$ response processes at different levels.

For the reference luminance level in the present formulation (assumed to be approximately 10 mL), $k_1 = k_2 = 1.0$, $k_3 = 1.0$, and $k_4 = 0.95$. To ac-

[42] "While transformation to four receptor substances is consistent with the simplest conception for the arousal of the chromatic responses, there is no theoretical requirement that these substances be four in number. An equivalent system [and one that conserves the idea of trichromaticity and three fundamentals (C.H.G.)] that agrees as well with the phenomena to be discussed in the following development can be based on the following alternative set of transformation equations:

$$\begin{aligned} \alpha_\lambda &= \quad 6.5341\bar{y}_\lambda + 0.1336\bar{z}_\lambda \\ \beta_\lambda &= -0.3368\bar{x}_\lambda + 7.0009\bar{y}_\lambda + 0.0020\bar{z}_\lambda \\ \gamma_\lambda &= \quad 0.3329\bar{x}_\lambda + 6.4671\bar{y}_\lambda - 0.1347\bar{z}_\lambda \end{aligned} \tag{135a}$$

[77]."

The curves resulting from this transformation seem somewhat similar in appearance to Hecht's [58] $V_0G_0R_0$ curves (see Fig. 36) with γ_λ corresponding to R_0, β_λ corresponding to G_0, and α_λ corresponding to V_0. The expressions for the visual response functions in terms of α, β, and γ are

$$\begin{aligned} y_\lambda - b_\lambda &= k_1(\beta_\lambda + \gamma_\lambda - 2\alpha_\lambda) \\ r_\lambda - g_\lambda &= k_2(\alpha_\lambda + \gamma_\lambda - 2\beta_\lambda) \\ w_\lambda - bk_\lambda &= k_3(\alpha_\lambda + \beta_\lambda + \gamma_\lambda) - k_4(\alpha_\lambda + \beta_\lambda + \gamma_\lambda) \end{aligned} \tag{136a}$$

count for the fact that yellow and blue hues predominate in high luminance spectra, whereas red and green hues are more prominent in low level spectra, k_1 is assumed to be greater than k_2 for stimulus luminances higher than the standard level, and k_1 is assumed to be smaller than k_2 for luminances lower than the standard level [77].

Color mixture. Since the chromatic response functions are linear transformations of the CIE mixture curves, Hurvich and Jameson's formulation accounts for color mixture.

Spectral brightness. Since [see Eq. (137)] the $w_\lambda - bk_\lambda$ function was made equal in form to the luminosity function $\bar{y}_\lambda$ for the CIE Standard Observer the theoretical formulation accounts for spectral luminosity.

The $w - bk$ process as represented by the $\bar{y}_\lambda$ function depends conceptually on differences between photolytic breakdown (w) processes and regeneration processes (bk) in the receptor substances. This idea is not to be confused with the one applying to the chromatic $r - g$ and $y - bl$ processes. In the latter case it is assumed that all four processes r, g, y, and bl are dependent on photolytic breakdown. Achromatic and chromatic effects are considered to be relatively independent; they are presumably only slightly influenced in common by effects of chromatic adaptation.

Saturation. A previous discussion of the data of saturation centering on Fig. 7 considered Jameson and Hurvich's calculations [91] of colorimetric purity from their determinations of chromatic responses. Predicted and experimentally measured saturation functions were compared in Fig. 7. The comparison showed that the ratio of the sum of the chromatic response values to the achromatic effect for each wavelength gives a function similar to the usual curve obtained in an experiment where spectral light is added to white for a just discriminable colorimetric purity.

For present purposes,[43] the chromatic and achromatic responses for each wavelength were computed for the Standard Observer and for a constant luminance. Certain considerations (particularly, the low level of spectral light increment required for threshold saturation when the spectral color is added to white) led the experimenters to use a value of k_1 in Eqs. (136) that was much smaller than the values of k_2, k_3, or k_4; the following values were used: $k_1 = 0.5$, $k_2 = 1.0$, $k_3 = 1.0$, and $k_4 = 0.95$. The low value of k_1 was used because of the low values of yellow and blue responses, relative to red and green, encountered at low intensities.

[43] The description of the mathematical treatments of saturation and hue discrimination were contained in a letter written [September 21, 1955] by Drs. Hurvich and Jameson to the author, who wishes to express his appreciation for this great aid to clarification.

Hurvich and Jameson's analysis of saturation discrimination may be described as follows. The index of saturation discrimination, s_λ, is given by the ratio of chromatic to achromatic responses as follows:

$$s_\lambda = \frac{(|y - bl| + |r - g|)_\lambda}{(|w - bk|)_\lambda} \tag{138}$$

The terms within paired vertical lines are absolute values; it is the total chromatic response (without regard to sign) from each pair that is the important thing.

Equation (138) refers to a unit of luminance of spectral light at all wavelengths. For a luminance B_λ the equation becomes

$$s_\lambda = \frac{B_\lambda(|y - bl| + |r - g|)_\lambda}{B_\lambda(|w - bk|)_\lambda} \tag{139}$$

Figure 7 gives, among other things, the data reported by Wright and Pitt [207] compared with a theoretically predicted curve based on the following conditions. In the predicted curve, Hurvich and Jameson have computed, for a mixture of white light and spectral light, the variable amount of spectral light that must be added to a constant white light to yield a fixed minimal saturation ratio for a threshold response. The white light contributes no chromatic component to the mixture; it adds a constant achromatic component equal to $B_w(|w - bk|)_w$, where B_w is the luminance of the white light, and $(|w - bk|)_w$ is the computed achromatic response for a unit of white light luminance. The spectral light contributes to the mixture a total chromatic component $B_\lambda(|y - bl| + |r - g|)_\lambda$, and an achromatic component $B_\lambda(|w - bk|)_\lambda$. Thus for the mixture of white light and spectral light,

$$s_\lambda = \frac{B_\lambda(|y - bl| + |r - g|)_\lambda}{B_\lambda(|w - bk|)_\lambda + B_w(|w - bk|)_w} \tag{140}$$

In the type of experiment under consideration [207], where white light is constant and spectral light increments for threshold saturation are determined, the expression $B_w(|w - bk|)_w$ is known and constant; s_λ at threshold can be taken as constant and assigned some arbitrary value (say 0.1); and the terms $(|y - b| + |r - g|)_\lambda$ and $(|w - bk|)_\lambda$ are known for unit luminance. Under these circumstances, Eq. (140) can be solved for B_λ which, since it is an increment from zero, is called ΔB_λ. Once the theoretical ΔB_λ is known for each wavelength, $(B_w + \Delta B_\lambda)/\Delta B_\lambda$ can be computed and the value plotted against wavelength. The predicted curve seems to have the characteristics required to make it describe the general nature of experimental data.

Hurvich and Jameson have considered what happens when increments of white light are added to spectral colors for a first discriminable change in saturation. It is enough to say that the account describes a first discriminable change in saturation as owing to a constant increment of white light for all wavelengths at uniform luminance. This interpretation is in accord with results obtained by Wright and Pitt [206].

Manipulation of the constants k_1 and k_2 of Eqs. (136) makes it possible to describe specific changes in the form of the saturation function for different levels of stimulus luminance. On the basis of such considerations, Hurvich and Jameson have accounted for data by Purdy on colorimetric purity at different luminances of white light [150].

Spectral hue. An opponent-colors theory whose paired chromatic responses correlate with four "unitary" hues does not require that hue and spectral wavelength be invariantly correlated. Let the ratio of each separate chromatic response to the sum of both the chromatic responses at a given wavelength be called the "hue coefficient." Specifically,

$$h_\lambda = \frac{(|y - bl|)_\lambda}{(|y - bl| + |r - g|)_\lambda} \quad \text{or} \quad h_\lambda = \frac{(|r - g|)_\lambda}{(|y - bl| + |r - g|)_\lambda} \tag{141}$$

Responses bl and y, and g and r are opponent-color responses; hence, only one response of each pair can occur simultaneously for a given stimulus. Two of the values in the denominator of each hue coefficient must equal zero. For the wavelengths stimulating unitary hues, three of the chromatic responses have values of zero; at each of these wavelengths the single hue coefficient is unity.

A graph of the spectral hue coefficients is given in Fig. 41. A luminance level of 10 mL is assumed to apply to these coefficients; hence $k_1 = k_2 = 1.0$.

From the short wave spectral extreme to about 475 mμ (unitary blue) both red and blue hues are present, with the blue hue coefficient rising to a maximum of 1.0 and the red value dropping to a minimum of zero at 475 mμ. Between 475 mμ and 498 mμ, blue and green hues are present. The blue hue coefficient drops rapidly from its maximal value to a minimum of zero at 498 mμ, and the green rises from zero at 475 mμ to 1.0 at the pure green stimulus wavelength. Beyond 498 mμ, green and yellow hues are present, with the green coefficient dropping rapidly at first from its maximal value, changing more slowly in the 530–560 mμ region, and dropping rapidly again to zero at 578 mμ. The yellow coefficient values inversely image the green, rising from a minimum of zero at 498 mμ to a maximum of 1.0 at 578 mμ, the pure yellow stimulus. Beyond 578 mμ, yellow and red hues are seen, with the yellow dropping and the red rising rapidly from 578 mμ to beyond 620 mμ, and the changes beyond 620 mμ are progressively slower at the longer wavelengths [77].

Pure hues (i.e., those with hue coefficients of unity) are independent of stimulus luminance for a neutral state of adaptation, but intermediate hues are not. An orange elicited by a given wavelength becomes redder as luminance drops, whereas it becomes yellower as

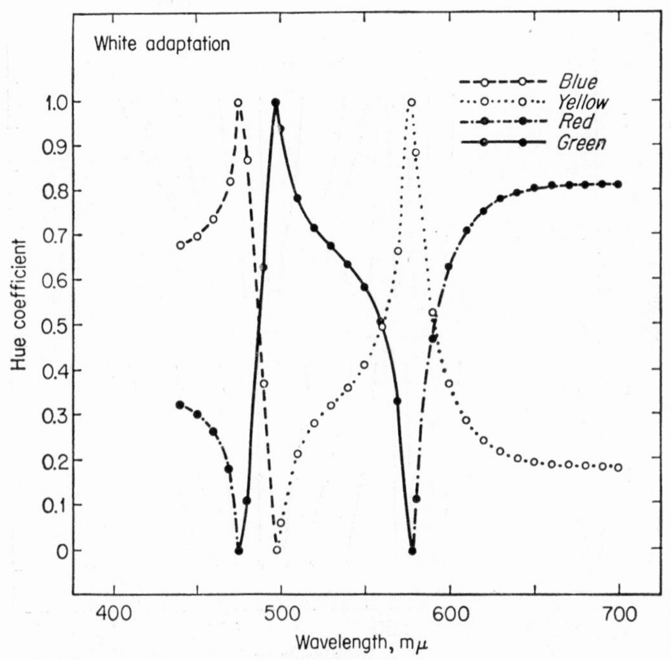

Fig. 41. Spectral hue coefficients at a standard luminance of 10 mL. *From Hurvich and Jameson* [77].

luminance increases. These and other changes can be computed by assigning different values to the constants k_1 and k_2 for the yellow-blue and red-green mechanisms.

By manipulating the constants, it is possible to draw curves representing the hue coefficients at different luminance levels.[44] Such curves have different slopes at different luminance levels. Let the wavelength required to give a constant hue coefficient for a given

[44] An interesting case occurs for luminances lower than the standard of 10 mL. At these luminances the blue and yellow chromatic responses become weaker and the red and green ones stronger, i.e., the classical Bezold-Brücke hue shift [see, for example, 183, pp. 169 ff.].

color response be ascertained at different luminances. If now the values of luminance be plotted against the corresponding critical values of wavelength, a steep, nearly vertical line called a constant hue contour, results. When several such contours have been determined, we obtain a family similar to the one shown in Fig. 42. The lower set of curves is calculated from several spectral hue coefficient curves over a range of 3.0 log units of luminance, with values of

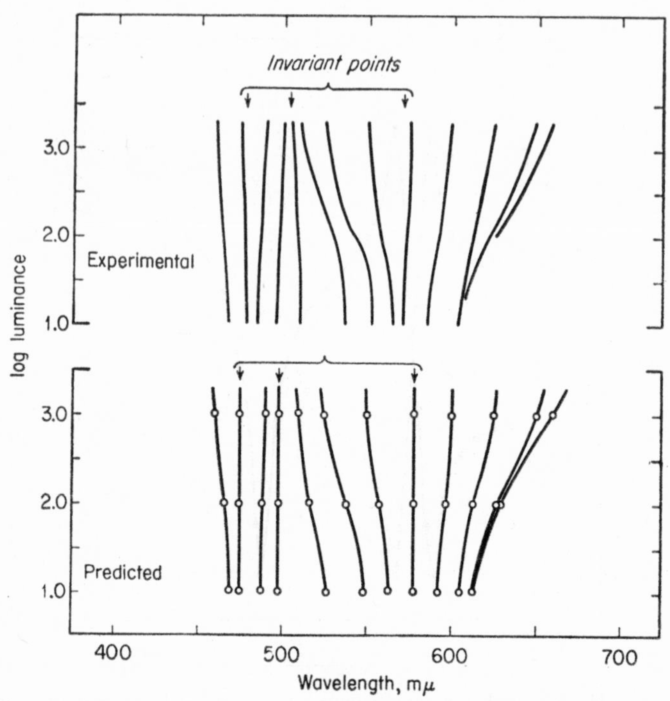

FIG. 42. The upper set of curves represents constant hue contours obtained by Purdy [150]. The lower set of curves represents computed contours as described in the text. *From Hurvich and Jameson* [77].

$k_1 = 1.0$, $k_2 = 0.8$ for the highest level; $k_1 = k_2 = 1.0$ for the standard level; and $k_1 = 0.8$, $k_2 = 1.0$ for the lowest level. The upper set of curves represents experimental data by Purdy [150]. A theoretical account of hue shift at different luminances has been made by Judd [101] on the basis of ideas that depend on an opponent-colors system but that differ in detail from those of Hurvich and Jameson.

For wavelength discrimination, it is assumed that changes in both hue and saturation with changes in wavelength determine the discrimination threshold. To predict the threshold $\Delta\lambda$ functions, Hurvich and Jameson sought the values of $\Delta\lambda$ for which a combined change in the hue and saturation coefficients would be equal to a constant, estimated minimal value K. The hue coefficient h_λ is defined in Eqs. (141). The saturation coefficient σ_λ (as differentiated from the saturation ratio s_λ) is defined as

$$\sigma_\lambda = \frac{(|y - bl| + |r - g|)_\lambda}{(|y - bl| + |r - g| + |w - bk|)_\lambda} \tag{142}$$

If $\Delta\lambda_e$ is the experimental value to be predicted, the equation to be used is

$$2\Delta\lambda_e = \Delta h_\lambda \left[\frac{\Delta\lambda}{\Delta\left(\dfrac{|y - bl|}{|y - bl| + |r - g|}\right)} \right] + \Delta\sigma_\lambda \left[\frac{\Delta\lambda}{\Delta\left(\dfrac{|y - bl| + |r - g|}{|y - bl| + |r - g| + |w - bk|}\right)} \right] \tag{143}$$

where $\Delta h_\lambda + \Delta\sigma_\lambda = K$.

As a convenient approximation, Hurvich and Jameson let $\Delta h_\lambda = \Delta\sigma_\lambda = \frac{1}{2} K$, determined the $\Delta\lambda_e$ values separately for the hue and saturation changes, and then took the average of the two values. The different luminances at which the experiments were carried out involved changes in the relative strengths of the blue-yellow and red-green response pairs. The assumption was made that the minimal value of K increases at very low luminances.

Predicted functions for the wavelength discrimination of the standard observer are plotted in the lower part of Fig. [43]. The function for the standard luminance (10 mL) shows the usual characteristics exhibited in measurements of wavelength discrimination: two rather shallow minima, one between 460 and 510 mμ, the other between 560 and 600 mμ, a mid-spectral maximum at about 530 mμ, and a rise in $\Delta\lambda$ at both ends of the spectrum indicating rapid deterioration in wavelength discrimination. The function for the low luminance shows magnified curvature; the minimum in the shortwave region is shifted toward the shorter wavelengths and is now lower than the 580 mμ minimum. The mid-spectral maximum is not only exaggerated but its locus is also shifted, occurring now at about 510 mμ rather than at 530 mμ [77].

General considerations. It is too early to make anything like a final evaluation of Hurvich and Jameson's opponent-colors theory. The relation of the theory to color blindness has not been taken up, but it may be said that Hurvich and Jameson have been able to present an account of various types of color blindness in a way that may have some advantages, although it is obvious even now that changes will be necessitated in their treatment by, for example, new data on protanopes and deuteranopes [36]. The treatment as it now exists is based on the following ideas:

For the deuteranope it is assumed that the *Bl*, *G*, *Y*, *R* receptor substances are essentially the same as for the observer with normal color sense. For the

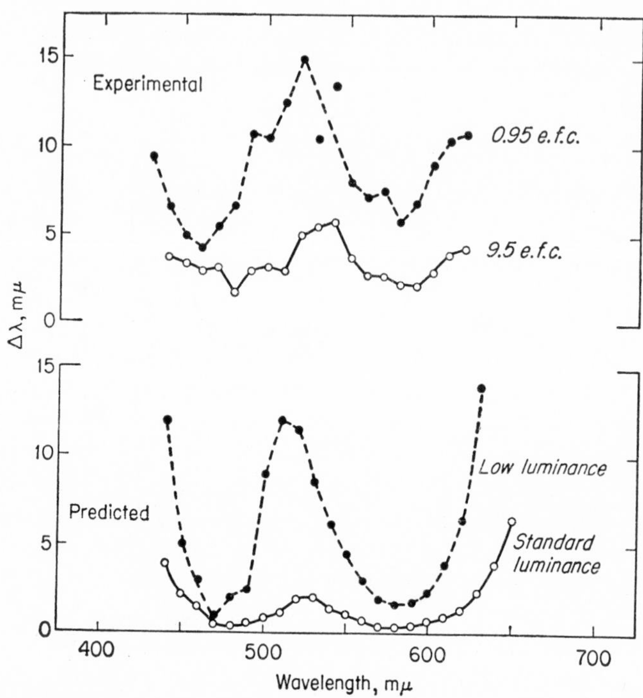

FIG. 43. Wavelength discrimination for two luminance levels. The upper curves represent (open circles) Weale's values [191] for approximately 9.5 mL and (closed circles) his values for approximately 0.95 mL. The lower curves represent predicted functions based on Eqs. (143). *From Hurvich and Jameson* [77].

protanope, on the other hand, we suggest that these four substances bear the same relation to each other as for the normal but that the whole set . . . has undergone a shift . . . toward shorter wavelengths [77].

An interesting aspect of the Hurvich-Jameson theory accounts for certain changes in hue and saturation as due to changes in the constants k_1, k_2, k_3, and k_4. Changes in these constants allow for a great increase in the degrees of freedom available to the theory for fitting data. In the eyes of certain critics, this decrease in restriction of the theory would be considered a serious defect. However, the answer to the question of a possible *need* for such parameters would seem to lie in the realm of further critical experimentation. Further analysis alone can tell us whether these factors are necessary.

To the interested student, some of the most uncertain aspects of the opponent-colors theory lie in the types of absorption substances postulated, the relations of these substances to the neural processes, the lack of precise specification of the nature of the opposed processes, and their relations to the white-black process.

METHODOLOGICAL CONSIDERATIONS

Up to now, our presentation of color vision has been of a factual and theoretical sort, informal references being made now and then, as the occasion has warranted it, to the logical status of certain concepts. The present section will attempt to fill in some of the gaps remaining in the methodological discussion. The treatment that is envisaged will not deal so extensively with methodological considerations of color theory as their importance might seem to demand. Despite this fact, it is hoped that our discussion will be useful. In what follows we shall deal with such problems as (1) the attitudes towards science and subject matter exemplified by workers in color vision; (2) the relation of color vision to the other branches of science; (3) some reference descriptive relations for color vision; (4) the data language of color vision; (5) the construct language; (6) the scope of theory and practical applications; (7) probable foci of change.

Attitudes toward science and subject matter. The literature of color vision and color theory is relatively devoid of statements concerning attitudes towards science, preferred methods of studying subject matter, and permissible (and impermissible) contexts within which the data and theories of color may be viewed. One can, nevertheless, find some informal statements on "methodology" expressed by individuals who have worked in this area.

Newton [135, 136] seems to have had strong opinions concerning appropriate methodology in science; in particular, he disliked speculative types of hypotheses. "His aim was to create a theory based directly on observation and free from all imaginings as to the hidden mechanism of things . . . 'Hypotheses,' said Newton, . . . 'are not to be regarded in experimental Philosophy' " [194]. Despite his essentially conservative view of hypotheses in science, it cannot be overlooked that he proposed, in an almost purely speculative way, a hypothetical account of color that has, extrapolative or not, turned out to be a basic formulation to the present day.

Thomas Young exhibited a more moderate attitude towards hypotheses than did Newton. Young said:

Although the invention of plausible hypotheses, independent of any connection with experimental observations, can be of very little use in the promotion of natural knowledge; yet the discovery of simple and uniform principles, by which a great number of apparently heterogeneous phenomena are reduced to coherent and universal laws, must ever be allowed to be of considerable importance towards the improvement of the human intellect; and in proportion as more and more phenomena are found to agree with any principles that are laid down, those principles must be allowed to acquire a stronger right to exchange the appellation of hypothesis for that of fundamental laws of nature [208].

The same paper that bears this statement also contains the great speculative contribution of trichromatic theory.

Helmholtz was considerably more tolerant of hypotheses than either Newton or Young. In connection with Young's theory Helmholtz says:

The . . . theory of Thomas Young is, in relation to the general theory of nerve activity as it has been developed by Johannes Müller, a special consequence of the law of *specific sensations*. In accordance with its assumptions the perceptions of red, of green, and of violet are to be regarded as determined by the specific perception energy of the corresponding three nerve apparatuses. Each arbitrary kind of excitation which can generally excite the corresponding apparatus would always be able to call forth in it only its own specific perception. The basis of the special quality of these perceptions we cannot indeed seek in the retina or the condition of its fibres, but in the activity of the central part of the brain associated with them.

I have hitherto kept the explanation of this theory relatively abstract in order to preserve it as far as possible from more far-reaching hypothetical additions. Nevertheless, for the more certain understanding of such abstraction, there is, on the other hand, great advantage in seeking to make for oneself images thereof, as concrete as possible, even if these introduce many assumptions which are not strictly necessary to the essence of the matter. In this sense I permit myself to propose the following somewhat obvious form of Young's theory. I need not indeed explain that objections to these additions do not refute the essence of Young's hypothesis.

1. In the end organs of the optic nerve fibres there are stored up three kinds of photochemically decomposable substances which have different susceptibility for different parts of the spectrum. The three colour values of the spectrum colours depend essentially on the photochemical reaction of these three substances towards light. There are present in the eyes of birds and reptiles nearly colourless spindles, in fact little rods, with red, and others with yellow-green, oil drops which can effect a favouring of single lights in the action on the posterior parts of the structure.

2. Through decomposition of each of the light perceptive substances the nerve fibres charged therewith are thrown into the state of excitation. There is only one kind of sensation exciting activity in each nerve fibre which takes place with decomposition of the organic substance and development of heat, as we know it of the muscle nerves. These antecedents are apparently of like kind throughout in the three systems of fibres. They only work differently in the brain in so far as they are connected with differently functioning parts of the brain. The nerve fibres require here, as generally, only to play the role of telegraph wires flowing through which electric currents, of like kind throughout, can set loose or call forth the most different activities in the same end apparatus connected therewith. These excitations of the three fibre systems form the above specified three *elementary excitations*, on the presumption that the intensity of excitation, for which we have yet no generally valid measure, shall be taken as proportional to the intensity of the light. This does not prevent that the intensity of the elementary excitation may be any complicated function whatsoever of the consumption of substance or of the fluctuation of current in the nerve, which latter can perhaps also occasionally be employed as a measure of the excitation.

3. In the brain the three fibre systems are in connection with three differently functioning ganglion cells, which are perhaps so placed together in space that those which correspond to the same point of the retina lie close together. This seems to result from the newer investigations on the influence of brain injuries on the field of vision. [The foregoing is a translation by Peddie, 1922, of a statement in Helmholtz; see 67, pp. 349–350.]

Clerk Maxwell's attitude toward hypotheses and theories in science is well represented by his attitude towards the work of Faraday, the implications of which he developed in his great contribution to the theory of electricity. He here set before himself the task of showing that Faraday's ideas were not inconsistent with the formulae in which Poisson and others had cast the laws of electricity. His object, he says, is to find a physical analogy which shall help the mind to grasp the results of previous investigations

> . . . without being committed to any theory founded on the physical science from which that conception is borrowed so that it is neither drawn aside from the subject in the pursuit of analytical subtleties nor carried beyond the truth by a favorite hypothesis [137].[45]

[45] It would be a relief if, in arguments that reflect different points of view such as these, we had some objective evidence of what men do with hypotheses (or, in fact, what men do) rather than what they say they do. The problem would then come down to one of finding out whether a given man (with a system of action differing from that of other men) has provided an objectively measured increment in fruitful scientific knowledge. It is obvious from what little has been said here that one cannot take a man's opinion of what that man thinks he does. For example, Newton, the despiser of hypotheses, presents us in the form of his color circle with one that is speculative in the highest degree.

Maxwell [123] seized eagerly (as did Helmholtz at about the same time) on Young's theory and combined it with the geometrical description of Newton [135, 136] to give an early mathematical dress to the study of color vision.

> The theory which I adopt assumes the existence of three elementary sensations, by the combination of which all the actual sensations of colour are produced. It will be shown that it is not necessary to specify any given colours as typical of these sensations. Young has called them red, green, and violet; but any other three colours might have been chosen, provided that white resulted from their combination in proper proportions.
>
> Before going farther I would observe, that the important part of the theory is not that three elements enter into our sensation of colour, but that there are only three. Optically, there are as many elements in the composition of a ray of light as there are different kinds of light in its spectrum; and, therefore, strictly speaking, its nature depends on an infinite number of independent variables.
>
> I now go on to the geometrical form into which the theory may be thrown. Let it be granted that the three pure sensations correspond to the colours red, green, and violet, and that we can estimate the intensity of each of these sensations numerically.
>
> Let v, r, g be the angular points of a triangle, and conceive the three sensations as having their positions at these points. If we find the numerical measure of the red, green, and violet parts of the sensation of a given colour, and then place weights proportional to these parts at r, g, and v, and find the centre of gravity of the three weights by the ordinary process, that point will be the position of the given colour, and the numerical measure of its intensity will be the sum of the three primitive sensations.
>
> In this way, every possible colour may have its position and intensity ascertained; and it is easy to see that when two compound colours are combined, their centre of gravity is the position of the new colour.

We have in the person of *Hecht* [55, 57, 58] an individual who wished the variables of color vision theory to exhibit biological reality; he implied that they should be constructs referable to and identifiable in a physiological process system. Hecht [57] was not greatly impressed by the devices of a mathematico-representational character that had played such an important role in color vision history. Concerning the color triangle, he says [57]:

> I cannot share Mr. Guild's preoccupation with the colour triangle. The *VGR* cone primaries are not for use in practice. They are designed to yield with precision, and *in terms of a mechanism* [italics by C.H.G.], the data of colour-mixture, spectrum luminosity, hue-discrimination, spectrum saturation, and complementary colours. The practical colour triangle distorts even the data of colour-mixture by ignoring luminosity considerations.

He might have added that it contains not the slightest hint of biological mechanism.

Some general considerations. Our discussion of the points of view of several investigators seems to indicate that considerable differences exist in matters of attitude to science and subject matter. Probably all of the individuals discussed would agree that poorly based hypotheses are of little or no avail. On the other hand, it would seem that Helmholtz, Maxwell, and Hecht would be more appreciative of testable hypotheses than would Young; Newton would be least appreciative. Ironically, it is the last two individuals, each regarding hypotheses with a certain skepticism, who proposed the two greatest speculations in the history of color. (A possible moral might be drawn: a compelling idea cannot be overlooked even when a disposition to do so exists. Or another: some scientists would rather extrapolate than hypothesize!)

Many individuals at present [e.g., 101], as in the past, do not favor the Hechtian sort of biological analysis: rather a positivistic account is preferred; an unadorned metric is sought. Some other workers appreciate the Hecht-type account but, for one reason or another, present their own theoretical ideas in a different context. The essential thing is that, despite the existence of considerable differences in attitude, the great run of researchers in the area of color vision do not disregard the contributions of workers with attitudes different from their own. In fact, the differences due to different biases seem small in comparison with what may be the case in other fields of psychology.

Relation of color vision to various branches of science. The topic of color theory has been of great interest to students of physics, and it has always had a place in physiology and psychology. Maxwell [128] in his appreciation of Helmholtz says:

> In no department of research is the combined and concentrated light of all the sciences more necessary than in the investigation of sensation. The purely subjective school of psychologists used to assert that for the analysis of sensation no apparatus was required except what every man carries within himself, for, since a sensation can exist nowhere except in our own consciousness, the only possible method for the study of sensations must be an unbiased contemplation of our own frame of mind. Others might study the conditions under which an impulse is propagated along a nerve, and might suppose that while doing so they were studying sensations, but though such a procedure leaves out of account the very essence of the phenomenon, and treats a fact of consciousness as if it were an electric current, the methods which it has suggested have been more fertile in results than the method of self-contemplation has ever been.
>
> But the best results are obtained when we employ all the resources of physical science so as to vary the nature and intensity of the external stimulus,

and then consult consciousness as to the variation of the resulting sensation. It was by this method that Johannes Müller established the great principle that the difference in the sensations due to different senses does not depend upon the actions which excite them, but upon the various nervous arrangements which receive them. Hence the sensation due to a particular nerve may vary in intensity, but not in quality, and therefore the analysis of the infinitely various states of sensation of which we are conscious must consist in ascertaining the number and nature of those simple sensations which, by entering into consciousness each in its own degree, constitute the actual state of feeling at any instant.

Maxwell's statement was undoubtedly agreeable to Helmholtz who was, not only in name but in fact, a physicist, physiologist, and psychologist. At any rate the subject will probably continue to be investigated by workers in these three sciences, and for psychologists in particular, much ground must be worked to coordinate the data and theories of color vision with the newly arising data from studies of conditioning and discrimination. A theory of color perception needs a theory of discrimination, but a theory of discrimination needs manifold accounts of specific stimulations in the form of "cues," including color.

At the present time the topic of color vision may be recognized as one of the most highly developed in the general province of discrimination behavior. For this reason it might be regarded as a model for theory in other areas of psychology where it is required that certain conditions of the subject (e.g., drive) must be specified in combination with effects of stimulation in order to account for response outcomes. See for example, Verplanck's discussion of "sensitivity to wavelength" as a hypothetical construct that solved problems of interaction between stimulus and conditions of the subject. Note also his consideration of how such a concept might serve as a model for the solution of the dilemma posed by "response inferred stimuli" [186].

Descriptive relations. In a series of articles, the author [29, 30, 31, 32] has taken the position that the data of perceptual experiments are specifiable in stimulus-response terms, that is, by the general relation

$$R = f(a, b, c \ldots n \ldots t \ldots x, y, z) \qquad (144)$$

This relation expresses the assumption of a behavioristic program; response is a function of certain specifiable variables. In particular, the first letters of the alphabet ($a, b, c, \ldots$) refer to properly specified aspects of stimuli; the last letters ($\ldots x, y, z$), to properly specified conditions of the subject (physiological and inferred, including the effects of instruction stimuli); R, to response; n, to number of presentations; and t to time. The terms are not always independent of each other [32].

The relation is not regarded as having any profound systematic or theoretical significance. It is, in short, a pretheoretical statement of a broad program of behavior study, within which framework one can examine certain sets of dependencies, such as those that exist in color vision.

Data language. At its most basic level, the psychophysical experiment gives rise to data that may be represented in psychophysical curves to show how some aspect R of response varies with an aspect a of stimulus according to the relation

$$R = f(a) \tag{145}$$

Other variables than R and a (including those due to instructions) are held constant. The stimulus-response relation of (145) involves basic elements of the data language[46] of color vision. For example, in finding the energy threshold for light of λ550 mμ, the monochromatic light, specifiable in terms of its wavelength and radiant flux, is presented to the eye as an area of known dimensions (e.g., diameter) illuminated for a given, probably short, duration (e.g., 5 msec). The radiation is completely specified in terms of physical theory and can be measured by operations appropriate to that theory; an unequivocal specification results. The subject's frequencies of occurrence of two mutually exclusive responses "Yes, I see it" and "No, I don't see it" are recorded. A valuable degree of quantification is made possible on the response side by this appropriate use of psychophysical methods [50].

In general, then, at the lowest level relevant to experimentation on the color vision of the human (or, in fact, lower) organism, the data language is concerned with the description of the two terms in (145): a measured response aspect R varies as a function of a stimulus aspect a.

A more highly elaborated system of data language ensues at the next level of analysis. This level may be represented by discrimination-type relations that are based on (145). In general, these functions may be represented by the equation

$$a_e = f(b, x_1, R_1) \tag{146}$$

where a_e is the threshold (or equality) setting of a stimulus; b, a stimulus variable that determines the threshold (or match) a_e; x_1, a condition of the subject determined by instructions; and R_1, a constant response frequency to which corresponds the critical value a_e of

[46] Data language—that is, the pretheoretical description and empirical terms in which are couched the observations that a theory undertakes to order [131]. See also for discussion of data language in behavior theory [106, 121, 186, 21].

stimulus. For example, the hue discrimination threshold $\Delta\lambda$ [to be taken as identical with a_e in (146)] varies as a function of λ [equivalent to b in (146)]. Such an experiment also requires a constant condition of instructions [the term x_1 in (146)]. Finally, the threshold $\Delta\lambda$ is determined by an arbitrarily designated constant value R_1, the critical value of response frequency to which the stimulus threshold corresponds.

In any case it must be emphasized that, in passing from the psychophysical functions represented by (145) to the "perceptual" functions (i.e., those involving thresholds and critical values of stimulus generally) represented by (146), we invade a new realm of data language that contains (from the point of view of behavior) much more of the nature of construct language than (145). In the case of (146) we deal with new variables that involve operations upon (145). We deal, for example, with those critical values a_e of stimulus corresponding to a critical value R_1 of R that are, in fact, thresholds or matching values of stimuli. Such new variables, compressing as they do the data from many observations into single values, are of great importance in color theory; in fact, they can be thought of as the basic data.

Finally at a higher level, data language partakes of the most elaborate complexities of the construct language. For example, the concept of chromaticity develops as a paired attribute system that represents saturation-plus-hue-without-brightness. Such a concept owes its background to the need for a term that corresponds to what is mapped in a chromaticity diagram; it even has assigned to it the psychological correlate of chromaticness [101]. Chromaticities are represented on the basis of color mixture data as given in colorimetric equations. Such equations can be shown to be special cases of Eq. (144). In particular, the more specific relation of Eq. (145)

$$d = f(a_e, b_e, c_e)$$

represents a colorimetric equation, a_e, b_e, and c_e being the critical values of the luminous fluxes of the three primaries required to match d. The critical values of a, b and c involve the subscript e. Specifically, $d = a_e + b_e + c_e$, a relation which is comparable to Eq. (12).

Construct language. We probably do not need to go into the general problem of the construct language of color theory, for it is essentially this problem that has attracted our attention in discussing color discrimination, color mixture, and theories of color vision. It is sufficient to say that, in the area of color vision, the types of theoretical concept displayed present many kinds of systematic status.

The efforts of some theorists in the development of theoretical concepts are directed toward the elucidation of representational systems or devices [135, 136] and the laws implied therein [43, 123]. To the present day a number of workers of positivistic bent [e.g., 101] have sought such systems. In general, these men seek a reliable metric for color vision and have a secondary interest in theoretical "realities."

Other theorists feel restricted in thinking about a representational system in a single plane, and so we get such accounts as those of Helmholtz [65, 66, 67] and Stiles [167], which represent the data and interrelations of color vision in an abstract color-brightness space. Advocates of such abstract theories rely on no implied similarity between data and mechanism. What is hoped for is an isomorphic relation, a point-for-point correspondence. Such treatments may imply the existence of certain substances, mechanisms, or structures, concepts that may be desirable accompaniments of the representational system but are not essential to it.

Finally, in the hands of biologists such as Hecht [55, 58] and Granit [40, 42] we find accounts of color with less formal and more "mechanical" characteristics. (Biologists are not likely to accept "explanations" of biological phenomena that have only a shadowy connection with their science! They take the point of view that, since vision is a complex of physiological processes, its theory should present biological and physiological realities. Hypothetical constructs are to be sought, not intervening variables of even the most predictive mathematical sort.)

Scope of theory. Although Helmholtz [64, 69] restricted his discussion of color theory to a narrow set of discriminations (hue discrimination, color mixture, etc.), he took a broad point of view towards psychology generally and viewed certain problems of color in the light of his own doctrine of unconscious inference. In these terms he could expand the field of color vision to cover such areas as "color constancy," "color appearances," and "modes of color perceiving." Hering [70, 71] viewed the study of vision in physiological, not psychological, terms. For him the study of color constancy was primarily the study of contrast. (In fact, even now, we still do not know to what degree constancy can be attributed to physiological mechanisms of contrast and what to past history variables.) In any case, it seems that when we now speak of color vision we usually refer to it in Hering's context rather than in Helmholtz's broad sense. A convenient line has been drawn under the basic and conventional discriminations of color vision to specify a limiting boundary.

It is true that certain allowances have been made for such topics as brightness and color contrast, and it is admitted that the topic of afterimages will, eventually if not now, require understanding. In fact, a number of theorists have considered how color vision theories might be expanded to take care of these latter phenomena [cf. 139]. But, in general, through the years and especially in the case of the adherents of trichromatic theory, the prevalent attitude seems to have been: first things first. Even advocates of the Hering theory have not been so preoccupied with these processes as one might think. Whatever may have been their status in the past, it can be foreseen that the areas of color constancy, color appearances [104, 199], contrast, and afterimages will become increasingly important areas for intensive future study.

Study of these areas, augmented by the study of "basic" problems of color vision, will provide a large arena for the research and theoretical interests of psychologists and other scientists.

Foci of change. Recent evidence indicates that the construct language of color vision may have advanced more rapidly than its data language and the empirical relations of its experiments. Many people have become interested in color vision because of practical considerations (witness the development of colorimetry!). Usable and convenient methods have been developed, possibly prematurely in certain regards, and may have outrun appropriate experimental validation. In any case, we may now be faced with the problem of changing some of our practices and seeking new experimental facts.

Two recommendations made at the Thirteenth Session of the CIE at Zurich foreshadow radical changes in photometry and colorimetry. One of these recommendations involves Abney's law; another, an appropriate size of field for the study of color-mixture functions. The resolutions are as follows:

(1) It is recommended that further studies of color-mixture functions made for the use of the C.I.E. Technical Committee on Colorimetry give chief attention to fields whose diameters subtend 10°.

(3) It is recommended that any new color-mixture functions to be adopted shall be based in principle on the results of procedures yielding in every case a complete match of the two fields being compared [103].

As concerns recommendation (1), Stiles [173, 174] has shown, in preliminary work reported at the Zurich meeting, that color matches can be made with good precision for a 10° annulus in spite of the disturbing appearance of Maxwell's spot. This work may serve to establish a system of colorimetry that conforms more to commercial practices than does the 1931 CIE Standard Observer. (It must be pointed out in this regard that such a system is probably not so appropriate for theoretical purposes as the one based on a 2° field.)

Recommendation (3) may have broad consequences. It was

pointed out in the Introduction that we may now be at a critical point in color theory. In particular, Abney's law has been open to doubt for some time (see earlier discussion under color mixture) and a basic examination of its status is recommended.

To present the implications of resolution (3), it must be recalled that prior to 1931 no direct determination of the color-mixture functions (amounts of three primaries required to match the various parts of the equal-energy spectrum) had been made. The 1931 C.I.E. standard observer was based upon a determination of the proportions of the primaries required to match the various parts of the spectrum, but because of the difficulty of measuring the radiance distribution of the spectrum observed, the absolute amounts were found by fractionating the standard luminous-efficiency (luminosity) function in accord with these proportions on the assumption (known as Abney's law and which is specifically written into the definition of luminous flux) that the luminance of an additive combination of components is equal to the arithmetical sum of the luminance of those components. Rather sizeable deviations from Abney's law (25 to 30%) have been found in the last 40 years, and Dr. H. G. Sperling at the U.S. Naval Medical Research Laboratory, New London, undertook a check of the assumption that color-mixture functions expressed in luminance terms would sum to the luminous-efficiency function of the observer. Preliminary results by Dr. Sperling, also reported at Zurich, showed for three subjects that such a sum gave a wavelength function significantly broader than the subject's luminous-efficiency function determined by equality-of-brightness settings with the spectrum at 520 mμ, both color matches and brightness matches being made with a 2° field. Although Dr. Stiles's preliminary work did not include measurements of the complete luminous-efficiency function for any of his ten observers, it nevertheless corroborated this finding because the sum of the color-mixture functions (both for 2° and 10° fields) expressed in luminance terms likewise gave a wavelength function considerably broader than the standard luminous-efficiency function. Resolution (3) expresses the view that any revision of the 1931 C.I.E. standard observer for colorimetry should result from an average of directly determined color-mixture functions uncontaminated by any adjustments to make a weighted sum of the color-mixture functions conform to any data obtained by flicker photometry of equality-of-brightness settings in the presence of a noticeable chromaticity difference [103].

Looking into the future we might believe that the consequence of resolutions (1) and (3) could be

. . . the eventual adoption of a revision of the 1931 C.I.E. standard observer defining which pairs of lights of different spectral compositions are to be taken as of identical color, that is, make a perfect, complete, visual match. If these pairs of lights be checked for luminance by the standard method of computation by means of the standard luminous-efficiency function, it will necessarily be found that although they are visually indistinguishable their luminances differ importantly. Since this situation would not be tolerable, a revision of the standard luminous-efficiency function must be expected. Adoption of any weighted sum of the color-mixture functions as the luminance-efficiency function would avoid this intolerable situation, and it is likely that the weights will be chosen so as to provide the wavelength function best suited for photometric use. The weights might be chosen, for example, to give the closest possible duplication of current luminosity data; or they might be chosen to provide the same evaluation of the lumen standards for gas-filled incandescendent lamps relative to the fundamental standard of light (platinum blackbody) as is provided by the present luminous-efficiency function. In any case, most of the data so far obtained either on color-mixture functions or on the luminous-efficiency function are likely to be rendered obsolete, and we are faced with the prospect of a radical change in the basic data both for colorimetry and for photometry [103; see also 12].

This discussion of recommended changes in the data of color and the practices of colorimetry implies that a new day may be dawning for theory. Certainly a change in something so basic as Abney's principle will have impacts on representational devices for color, and it will have reverberations in those color theories that have explicitly and implicitly accepted Abney's law.

General comment. A number of methodological considerations have been discussed in the present section and in other places. It is not easy to draw formal conclusions from all of the discussions.

In general, it may be taken as demonstrated that workers in the field of color vision have exemplified many diverse attitudes toward science in general and toward their subject matter in particular; almost all possible attitudes seem to have been encountered. Despite the diversity of attitudes that has existed and does exist from individual worker to individual worker, it seems, nevertheless, that workers in the field, in one way or another, have developed a system of acceptable data and common laws as a basis for communication in the general area of color vision.

The area of color vision exhibits many connections with psychology and other areas of science. These connections need not be discussed here. The subject itself will continue to be investigated, not only by psychologists but by many other types of scientists. From the point of view of the psychologist, it may be important in the future to relate the data of this relatively well-worked field to observations on conditioning and discrimination. The field of color should continue to be of general psychological interest, since for one thing, it represents a relatively successful analysis of some of the many possible areas of discrimination. In a sense, the analysis exemplified in color might be considered to be a reference example of "cue" analysis.

The data language of color vision consists of properly analyzed units of behavior and appropriately isolated physical energies. The data language absorbs construct language at an early stage; new construct variables in the form of, say, thresholds, are studied as functions of stimulating conditions.

The construct language of color vision is housed in its theories, and its theories are of many kinds. It may be foreseen that theories of color will, in the future, apply to broader aspects of vision than are now usually recognized as falling within that field. In particular, it may be expected that workers in the future will deal more than has been the case in the past with such "psychological" problems as the effect of past experience on color discriminations, etc. It is also to be hoped that practical applications of principles of color will be strengthened by further basic investigations of such a sort that theory and practice may be enriched at one and the same time.[47]

REFERENCES

1. Abney, W. de W. *Researches in colour vision.* London: Longmans, Green, 1913.

2. Abney, W. de W., & Festing, —. Colour photometry. *Phil. Trans. roy. Soc.,* 1886, **177,** 423–456.

3. Adams, E. Q. A theory of color vision. *Psychol. Rev.,* 1923, **30,** 56–76.

4. Auerbach, E., & Wald, G. Identification of a violet receptor in human color vision. *Science,* 1954, **120,** 401–405.

5. Barbrow, L. E. Color mixture functions to be modified. *Science,* 1955, **122,** 293.

6. Bergmann, G. Theoretical psychology. *Ann. Rev. Psychol.,* 1953, **4,** 435–458.

7. Bergmann, G., & Spence, K. W. The logic of psychological measurement. *Psychol. Rev.,* 1944, **51,** 1–24.

8. Boring, E. G. *Sensation and perception in the history of experimental psychology.* New York: Appleton-Century-Crofts, 1942.

9. Bouma, P. J. *Physical aspects of colour.* Eindhoven (The Netherlands): N. V. Philips Gloeilampenfabrieken, 1947.

10. Burnham, R. W., & Newhall, S. M. Color perception in small test fields. *J. opt. Soc. Amer.,* 1953, **43,** 899–902.

11. Chapanis, A. Spectral saturation and its relation to color vision defects. *J. exp. Psychol.,* 1944, **34,** 24–44.

12. Chapanis, A., & Halsey, R. M. Luminance of equally bright colors. *J. opt. Soc. Amer.,* 1955, **45,** 1–6.

13. Coblentz, W. W., & Emerson, W. B. Relative sensibility of the average eye to light of different colors and some practical applications to radiation problems. U.S. Bureau of Standards Bulletin, 1917, **14,** 167–236.

[47] The writer is indebted to Dr. Gerald L. Howett for the many hours that he has devoted to improving the form and content of this paper.

14. Committee on Colorimetry of the Optical Society of America. *The science of color.* New York: Crowell, 1953.

15. Crozier, W. J. On the visibility of radiation at the human fovea. *J. gen. Physiol.,* 1950, **34,** 87–136.

16. Dimmick, F. L., & Hubbard, M. R. The spectral components of psychologically unique red. *Amer. J. Psychol.,* 1939, **52,** 348–353.

17. Dimmick, F. L., & Hubbard, M. R. The spectral location of psychologically unique yellow, green, and blue. *Amer. J. Psychol.,* 1939, **52,** 242–254.

18. Donner, K. O. The spectral sensitivity of the pigeon's retinal elements. *J. Physiol.,* 1953, **122,** 524–537.

19. Dresler, A. The non-additivity of heterochromatic brightnesses. *Trans. illum. Engng. Soc.* (London), 1953, **18,** 141–165.

20. Ekman, G. Dimensions of color vision. *J. Psychol.,* 1954, **38,** 467–474.

21. Estes, W. K. Kurt Lewin. In Estes, W. K., et al. *Modern learning theory.* New York: Appleton-Century-Crofts, 1954. Pp. 317–344.

22. Fick, A. Die Lehre von der Lichtempfindung. In L. Hermann (Ed.), *Handbuch der Physiologie.* Vol. 3, pt. 1. Leipzig: Vogel, 1879. Pp. 139–234.

23. Franklin, C. L. On theories of light-sensation. *Mind,* 1893, **2,** 473–489.

24. Gibson, K. S., & Tyndall, E. P. T. Visibility of radiant energy. U.S. Bureau of Standards, Scientific Paper No. 475, 1923, **19,** 131–191.

25. Goldhammer, D. A. Die Farbenempfindlichkeit des Auges und die photometrische Helligkeit der leuchtender Körper. *Ann. Physik,* 1905, **16,** 621–652.

26. Goodeve, C. F. Vision in the ultraviolet. *Nature* (London), 1934, **134,** 416.

27. Göthlin, G. F. Polarisations-anomaloskopet, ett instrument för diagnostisk undersökning av färgsinnet. *Svenska Läkaresällskapets Handlingar,* 1916, **42,** 1665.

28. Göthlin, G. F. The fundamental colour sensations in man's colour sense. *Kungl. Svenska Vetenskapsakademiens Handlingar,* 1943, Tredje Serien, Band 20, No. 7, 1–75.

29. Graham, C. H. Psychophysics and behavior. *J. gen. Psychol.,* 1934, **10,** 299–310.

30. Graham, C. H. Behavior, perception and the psychophysical methods. *Psychol. Rev.,* 1950, **57,** 108–120.

31. Graham, C. H. Visual perception. In S. S. Stevens (Ed.), *Handbook of experimental psychology.* New York: Wiley, 1951.

32. Graham, C. H. Behavior and the psychophysical methods: an analysis of some recent experiments. *Psychol. Rev.,* 1952, **59,** 62–70.

33. Graham, C. H., & Bartlett, N. R. The relation of size of stimulus and intensity in the human eye: II. Intensity thresholds for red and violet light. *J. exp. Psychol.,* 1939, **24,** 574–587.

34. Graham, C. H., Brown, R. H., & Mote, F. A., Jr. The relation of size of stimulus and intensity in the human eye: I. Intensity thresholds for white light. *J. exp. Psychol.,* 1939, **24,** 555–573.

35. Graham, C. H., & Hsia, Y. Luminosity curves for normal and di-hromatic subjects. *Proc. 14th int. Congr. Psychol.,* 1954, 114.

36. Graham, C. H., & Hsia, Y. Luminosity curves for normal and di-hromatic subjects including a case of unilateral color blindness. *Science,* 1954, **120,** 780.

37. Graham, C. H., Hsia, Y., & Berger, E. Luminosity functions for normal and dichromatic subjects including a case of unilateral color blind-ness. *J. opt. Soc. Amer.,* 1955, **45,** 407.

38. Granit, R. The electrophysiological analysis of the fundamental prob-em of colour reception. *Proc. phys. Soc.* (London), 1945, **57,** 447–463.

39. Granit, R. The color receptors of the mammalian retina. *J. Neuro-physiol.,* 1945, **8,** 195–210.

40. Granit, R. *Sensory mechanisms of the retina.* London and New York: Oxford Univer. Press, 1947.

41. Granit, R. The effect of two wave-lengths of light upon the same retinal element. *Acta physiol. scand.,* 1949, **18,** 281–284.

42. Granit, R. *Receptors and sensory perception.* New Haven, Conn.: Yale Univer. Press, 1955.

43. Grassman, H. On the theory of compound colours. *Phil. Mag.* (4), 1854, **7,** 254–264.

44. Grether, W. F. Spectral saturation curves for chimpanzee and man. *J. exp. Psychol.,* 1941, **28,** 419–427.

45. Griffin, D. R., Hubbard, R., & Wald, G. The sensitivity of the human eye to infra-red radiation. *J. opt. Soc. Amer.,* 1947, **37,** 546–554.

46. Guild, J. The transformation of trichromatic mixture data: algebraic methods. *Trans. opt. Soc. London,* 1924–25, **26,** 95–108.

47. Guild, J. The geometrical solution of colour mixture problems. *Trans. opt. Soc. London,* 1924–25, **26,** 139–174.

48. Guild, J. A trichromatic colorimeter suitable for standardisation work. *Trans. opt. Soc. London,* 1925–26, **27,** 106–129.

49. Guild, J. The colorimetric properties of the spectrum. *Phil. Trans. roy. Soc. London,* 1931, **230A,** 149–187.

50. Guilford, J. P. *Psychometric methods.* (2d ed.) New York: McGraw-Hill, 1954.

51. Hardy, A. C. *Handbook of colorimetry.* Cambridge, Mass.: Tech-nology Press, Massachusetts Institute of Technology, 1936.

52. Hartman, L. W. The visibility of radiation in the blue end of the visible spectrum. *Astrophys. J.,* 1918, **47,** 83–95.

53. Hartridge, H. Color receptors of the human fovea. *Nature* (Lon-don), 1946, **158,** 97–98; Fixation area in the human eye, *Ibid.,* 303; Re-sponse curve of the yellow receptors of the human fovea, *Ibid.,* 946–948.

54. Hartridge, H. *Recent advances in the physiology of vision.* London: Churchill, 1950.

55. Hecht, S. The development of Thomas Young's theory of color vision. *J. opt. Soc. Amer.,* 1930, **20,** 231–270.

56. Hecht, S. The interrelations of various aspects of color vision. *J. opt. Soc. Amer.,* 1931, **21,** 615–639.

57. Hecht, S. A quantitative formulation of colour vision. In *Report of*

a joint discussion on vision held on June 3, 1932, at the Imperial College of Science by the Physical and Optical Societies. London: Phys. Soc., 1932. Pp. 126–160.

58. Hecht, S. Vision: II. The nature of the photoreceptor process. In C. Murchison (Ed.), *Handbook of general experimental psychology.* Worcester, Mass.: Clark Univer. Press, 1934. Pp. 704–828.

59. Hecht, S. Rods, cones and the chemical basis of vision. *Physiol. Rev.,* 1937, **17,** 239–290.

60. Hecht, S., & Hsia, Y. Colorblind vision. I. Luminosity losses in the spectrum for dichromats. *J. gen. Physiol.,* 1947, **31,** 141–152.

61. Hecht, S., Peskin, J. C., & Patt, M. Intensity discrimination in the human eye. *J. gen. Physiol.,* 1938, **22,** 7–19.

62. Hecht, S., Shlaer, S., & Pirenne, M. H. Energy, quanta, and vision. *J. gen. Physiol.,* 1942, **25,** 819–840.

63. Helmholtz, H. L. F. von. On the theory of compound colours. *Phil. Mag.,* 1852, **4,** 519–534.

64. Helmholtz, H. L. F. von. *Handbuch der physiologischen Optik* (1st ed.) Hamburg & Leipzig: Voss, 1866.

65. Helmholtz, H. L. F. von. Versuch einer erweiterten Anwendung des Fechnerschen Gesetzes im Farbensystem. *Z. Psychol. Physiol. Sinnesorg.* 1891, **2,** 1–30.

66. Helmholtz, H. L. F. von. Versuch, das psychophysische Gesetz auf die Farbenunterschiede trichromatischer Augen anzuwenden. *Z. Psychol. Physiol. Sinnesorg.,* 1892, **3,** 1–20.

67. Helmholtz, H. L. F. von. *Handbuch der physiologischen Optik* (2d ed.) Hamburg & Leipzig: Voss, 1896.

68. Helmholtz, H. L. F. von. *Handbuch der physiologischen Optik* (3d ed.) W. Nagel, A. Gullstrand, and J. von Kries (Eds.). Hamburg & Leipzig: Voss, 1909–11. 3 vols.

69. Helmholtz, H. L. F. von. *Treatise on physiological optics.* J. P. C. Southall. (Trans.) Rochester, N.Y.: Opt. Soc. Amer., 1924–25. 3 vols.

70. Hering, E. *Zur Lehre vom Lichtsinne.* Wien: Carl Gerold's Sohn 1878. See especially pp. 107–141.

71. Hering, E. *Grundzüge der Lehre vom Lichtsinn.* Berlin: Julius Springer, 1920.

72. Hillmann, B., Connolly, K., & Farnsworth, D. Color perception of small stimuli with central vision. *Med. Res. Lab. Report.* U.S. Naval Submarine Base, New London, Conn., 1954, **13,** No. 18 (Whole No. 257)

73. Howett, G. L., & Graham, C. H. Transformations of trichromatic coordinates in colorimetry. Research Report from the Psychological Laboratory, Columbia Univer., May 13, 1957.

74. Hsia, Y., & Graham, C. H. Spectral sensitivity of the cones in the dark adapted human eye. *Proc. nat. Acad. Sci.,* 1952, **38,** 80–85.

75. Hurvich, L. M., & Jameson, D. Spectral sensitivity of the fovea. I Neutral adaptation. *J. opt. Soc. Amer.,* 1953, **43,** 485–494.

76. Hurvich, L. M., & Jameson, D. Spectral sensitivity of the fovea

III. Heterochromatic brightness and chromatic adaptation. *J. opt. Soc. Amer.*, 1954, **44**, 213–222.

77. Hurvich, L. M., & Jameson, D. Some quantitative aspects of an opponent-colors theory. II. Brightness, saturation, and hue in normal and dichromatic vision. *J. opt. Soc. Amer.*, 1955, **45**, 602–616.

78. Hyde, E. P., Forsythe, W. E., & Cady, F. E. The visibility of radiation. *Astrophys. J.*, 1918, **48**, 65–88.

79. International Commission on Illumination, *Proc. 8th session*, 1931. Cambridge: Cambridge Univer. Press, 1932. P. 19.

80. International Commission on Illumination. Adaptation of a report by L. E. Barbrow, Secretary of the U.S. National Committee, International Commission on Illumination. *J. opt. Soc. Amer.*, 1951, **41**, 734–738.

81. Ishak, I. G. H. The photopic luminosity curve for a group of 15 Egyptian trichromats. *J. opt. Soc. Amer.*, 1952, **42**, 529–534.

82. Ives, H. E. Studies in the photometry of light of different colors. I. Spectral luminosity curves obtained by the equality of brightness photometer and the flicker photometer under similar conditions. *Phil. Mag.*, 1912, **24**, 149–188.

83. Ives, H. E. Studies in the photometry of lights of different colors. II. Spectral luminosity curves by the method of critical frequency. *Phil. Mag.*, 1912, **24**, 352–370.

84. Ives, H. E. Studies in the photometry of lights of different colors. III. Distortions in spectral luminosity curves produced by variations in the character of the comparison standard and of the surroundings of the photometric field. *Phil. Mag.*, 1912, **24**, 744–751.

85. Ives, H. E. Studies in the photometry of lights of different colors. IV. The addition of luminosities of different color. *Phil. Mag.*, 1912, **24**, 845–853.

86. Ives, H. E. Studies in the photometry of lights of different colors. V. The spectral luminosity curve of the average eye. *Phil. Mag.*, 1912, **24**, 853–863.

87. Ives, H. E. The transformation of color-mixture equations from one system to another. *J. Franklin Inst.*, 1915, **180**, 673–701.

88. Ives, H. E. The photometric scale. *J. Franklin Inst.*, 1919, **188**, 217–235.

89. Ives, H. E. The transformation of color-mixture equations from one system to another. II. Graphical aids. *J. Franklin Inst.*, 1923, **195**, 23–44.

90. Jameson, D., & Hurvich, L. M. Spectral sensitivity of the fovea. II. Dependence on chromatic adaptation. *J. opt. Soc. Amer.*, 1953, **43**, 552–559.

91. Jameson, D., & Hurvich, L. M. Some quantitative aspects of an opponent-colors theory. I. Chromatic responses and spectral saturation. *J. opt. Soc. Amer.*, 1955, **45**, 546–552.

92. Jones, L. A. The fundamental scale for pure hue and retinal sensibility to hue differences. *J. opt. Soc. Amer.*, 1917, **1**, 63–77.

93. Jones, L. A., & Lowry, E. M. Retinal sensibility to saturation differences. *J. opt. Soc. Amer.*, 1926, **13**, 25–37.

94. Judd, D. B. Reduction of data on mixture of color stimuli. *J. Res. nat. Bur. Standards,* 1930, **4,** (Research paper No. 163), 515–547.

95. Judd, D. B. Chromaticity sensibility to stimulus differences. *J. opt. Soc. Amer.,* 1932, **22,** 72–108.

96. Judd, D. B. A Maxwell triangle yielding uniform chromaticity scales. *J. opt. Soc. Amer.,* 1935, **25,** 24–35.

97. Judd, D. B. Hue, saturation and lightness of surface colors with chromatic illumination. *J. Res. nat. Bureau Standards,* 1940, **24,** 293–333.

98. Judd, D. B. Standard response functions for protanopic and deuteranopic vision. *J. opt. Soc. Amer.,* 1945, **35,** 199–221.

99. Judd, D. B. The color perceptions of deuteranopic and protanopic observers. *J. opt. Soc. Amer.,* 1949, **39,** 252–256.

100. Judd, D. B. Standard response functions for protanopic and deuteranopic vision. *J. opt. Soc. Amer.,* 1949, **39,** 505.

101. Judd, D. B. Basic correlates of the visual stimulus. In S. S. Stevens (Ed.), *Handbook of experimental psychology.* New York: Wiley, 1951.

102. Judd, D. B. *Color in business, science and industry.* New York: Wiley, 1952.

103. Judd, D. B. Radical changes in photometry and colorimetry foreshadowed by CIE actions in Zürich. *J. opt. Soc. Amer.,* 1955, **45,** 897–898.

104. Katz, D. Die Erscheinungsweisen der Farben und ihre Beeinflussung durch die individuelle Erfahrung. *Z. Psychol. Physiol. Sinnesorg.,* Ergänzbd. No. 7, 1911. Translated by R. B. MacLeod and C. W. Fox as *The world of color.* London: Routledge & Kegan Paul, Ltd., 1935.

105. Klineberg, O. *Social psychology.* (Rev. ed.) New York: Holt, 1954.

106. Koch, S. Clark L. Hull. In Estes, W. K., et al. *Modern learning theory.* New York: Appleton-Century-Crofts, 1954. Pp. 1–176.

107. König, A. Die Grundempfindungen und ihre Intensitäts-Vertheilung im Spectrum. *Sitz. Akad. Wiss.* Berlin, 1886, 805–829.
Also in: *Gesammelte Abhandlungen.* Leipzig: Barth, 1903.

108. König, A. Über den menschlichen Sehpurpur und seine Bedeutung für das Sehen. *Sitz. Akad. Wiss.* Berlin, 1894, Zweite Halfband, 577–598.
Also in *Gesammelte Abhandlungen.* Leipzig: Barth, 1903.

109. König, A. Ueber Blaublindheit. *Sitz. Akad. Wiss.* Berlin, 1897, 718–731.
Also in: *Gesammelte Abhandlungen.* Leipzig: Barth, 1903.

110. König, A., & Dieterici, C. Ueber die Empfindlichkeit des normalen Auges für Wellenlängenunterschiede des Lichtes. *Ann. Phys. Chem.,* 1884, **22,** 579–589.

111. König, A., & Dieterici, C. Die Grundempfindungen in normalen und anomalen Farben Systemen und ihre Intensitäts-Verteilung im Spectrum. *Z. Psychol. Physiol. Sinnesorg.,* 1893, **4,** 241–347.
Also in: *Gesammelte Abhandlungen.* Leipzig: Barth, 1903.

112. Kries, J. von. Die Gesichtsempfindungen. In W. Nagel (Ed.), *Handb. Physiol. Menschens.* Vol. 3. Braunschweig: Vieweg, 1905. Pp. 109–282.

113. Laurens, H., & Hamilton, W. F. The sensibility of the eye to differences in wavelength. *Amer. J. Physiol.,* 1923, **65,** 547–568.

114. Leber, T. Ueber das Vorkommen von Anomalien des Farbensinnes bei Krankheiten des Auges, nebst Bemerkungen ueber einigen Formen von Amblyopie. *Arch. Ophth.,* 1869, **15** (3), 26–107.

115. Le Grand, Y. *Optique physiologique.* Tome 2. *Lumière et couleurs.* Paris: Editions de la "Revue d' optique," 1948.

116. Le Grand, Y., & Geblewicz, E. La dualité de la vision aux brilliances élevées. *Ann. Psychol.,* 1937, **38,** 1–21.

117. Ludvigh, E., & McCarthy, E. F. Absorption of visible light by the refractive media of the human eye. *Arch. Opthal.,* 1938, **20,** 37–51.

118. MacAdam, D. L. Visual sensitivities to color differences in daylight. *J. opt. Soc. Amer.,* 1942, **32,** 247–274.

119. MacAdam, D. L. Dependence of color-mixture functions on choice of primaries. *J. opt. Soc. Amer.,* 1953, **43,** 533–538.

120. MacAdam, D. L. Orthogonal color-mixture functions. *J. opt. Soc. Amer.,* 1954, **44,** 713–724.

121. MacCorquodale, K., & Meehl, P. E. Edward C. Tolman. In Estes, W. K., et al. *Modern learning theory.* New York: Appleton-Century-Crofts, 1954. Pp. 177–266.

122. Martin, L. C., Warburton, F. L., & Morgan, W. J. The determination of the sensitiveness of the eye to differences in the saturation of colours. Great Britain Medical Research Council, *Special Report Series,* 1933, 1–42.

123. Maxwell, J. C. On the theory of colours in relation to colourblindness. *Trans. royal Scottish Soc. Arts,* 1855, **4,** Part III. In W. D. Niven (Ed.), *Scientific papers,* Vol 1. London: Cambridge Univer. Press, 1890. Pp. 119–125.

124. Maxwell, J. C. Experiments on colour, as perceived by the eye, with remarks on colour blindness. *Trans. roy. Soc. Edinburgh,* 1855, **21,** (Part 2). In W. D. Niven (Ed.), *Scientific papers.* Vol. 1. London: Cambridge Univer. Press, 1890. Pp. 126–154.

125. Maxwell, J. C. On the unequal sensibility of the foramen centrale to light of different colours. *Report. of Brit. Assoc.,* 1856. In W. D. Niven (Ed.), *Scientific papers.* Vol. 1. London: Cambridge Univer. Press, 1890. P. 242.

126. Maxwell, J. C. On the theory of compound colours and the relations of colours of the spectrum. *Phil. Trans. roy. Soc.,* 1860. In W. D. Niven (Ed.), *Scientific papers.* Vol. 1. London: Cambridge Univer. Press, 1890. Pp. 410–444.

127. Maxwell, J. C. On the theory of three primary colours. Lecture at the Royal Institution of Great Britain, May 17, 1861. In W. D. Niven (Ed.), *Scientific papers.* Vol. 1. London: Cambridge Univer. Press, 1890. Pp. 445–450.

128. Maxwell, J. C. Hermann Ludwig Ferdinand Helmholtz. *Nature,* 1877, **15.** In W. D. Niven (Ed.), *Scientific papers.* Vol. 2. London: Cambridge Univer. Press, 1890. Pp. 592–598.

129. Meehl, P. E., & MacCorquodale, K. On a distinction between hy-

pothetical constructs and intervening variables. *Psychol. Rev.*, 1948, **55,** 95–107.

130. Miles, W. R. Comparison of functional and structural areas in the human fovea. I. Method of entoptic plotting. *J. Neurophysiol.*, 1954, **17,** 22–38.

131. Mueller, C. G., & Schoenfeld, W. N. Edwin R. Guthrie. In Estes, W. K., et al. *Modern learning theory.* New York: Appleton-Century-Crofts, 1954. Pp. 345–379.

132. Müller, G. E. Ueber die Farbenempfindungen. Bd. 1 and 2. *Z. Psychol. Physiol. Sinnesorg.*, 1930, *Ergänzungsbd.* **17,** 1–430; 1930, *Ergänzungsbd.* **18,** 435–647.

133. Myers, C. S. Some observations on the development of the colour sense. *Brit. J. Psychol.*, 1908, **2,** 353–362.

134. Nelson, J. H. The colour-vision characteristics of a trichromat. *Proc. phys. Soc.* (London), 1937, **49,** 332–337.

135. Newton, I. *Opticks* (1st ed.). London: W. Innys, 1704. (2d ed., 1717; 3d ed., 1721; 4th ed., posthumous, 1730.)

136. Newton, I. *Opticks.* (Reprint from 4th ed., 1730.) London: Bell, 1931.

137. Niven, W. D. Preface to *Scientific papers of James Clerk Maxwell.* New York: Dover Publications, 1890. Pp. ix–xxix.

138. Nutting, P. G. 1919 report of standards committee on visual sensitometry. *J. opt. Soc. Amer.*, 1920, **4,** 55–79.

139. Parsons, J. H. *An introduction to the study of colour vision.* Cambridge: Cambridge Univer. Press, 1924.

140. Peddie, W. *Colour vision.* London: Edward Arnold, 1922.

141. Piéron, H. La dissociation de l'adaptation lumineuse et de l'adaptation chromatique. *Ann. Psychol.*, 1939, **40,** 1–14.

142. Pirenne, M. H. *Vision and the eye.* London: Chapman and Hall, 1948.

143. Pitt, F. H. G. Characteristics of dichromatic vision, with an appendix on anomalous trichromatic vision. Great Britain Medical Research Council, *Special Report Series,* 1935, No. 200.

144. Pitt, F. H. G. The nature of normal trichromatic and dichromatic vision. *Proc. roy. Soc.*, 1944, **132B,** 101–117.

145. Priest, I. G. A precision method for producing artificial daylight. *Phys. Rev.*, 1918, **11,** 502–505.

146. Priest, I. G. Note on the relation between the frequencies of complementary hues. *J. opt. Soc. Amer.*, 1920, **4,** 402–404.

147. Priest, I. G. Standard artificial sunlight for colorimetric purposes. *J. opt. Soc. Amer.*, 1926, **12,** 479–480.

148. Priest, I. G., & Brickwedde, F. G. The minimum perceptible colorimetric purity as a function of dominant wavelength with sunlight as a neutral standard. *J. opt. Soc. Amer.*, 1926, **13,** 306–307.

149. Priest, I. G., & Brickwedde, F. G. The minimum perceptible colorimetric purity as a function of dominant wavelength. *J. opt. Soc. Amer.*, 1938, **28,** 133–139.

150. Purdy, D. M. Chroma as a function of retinal illumination. Unpublished doctoral dissertation, Harvard Univer., 1929. [cf. Table 6.]

151. Purdy, D. M. On the saturations and chromatic thresholds of the spectral colours. *Brit. J. Psychol.,* 1931, **21,** 283–313.

152. Ray, V. F. Human color perception and behavioral response. *Trans. N.Y. Acad. Sci.,* 1953, **16,** 98–104.

153. Reeves, P. The visibility of radiation. *Trans. illum. Engng. Soc.* (U.S.), 1918, **13,** 101–109.

154. Rivers, W. H. R. Primitive color vision. *Pop. Sci. Monthly,* 1901, **59,** 44–58.

155. Rouse, R. O. Color and the intensity-time relation. *J. opt. Soc. Amer.,* 1952, **42,** 626–630.

156. Schrödinger, E. Grundlinien einer Theorie der Farbenmetrik im Tagessehen. (I Mitteilung.) *Ann. Physik.,* 1920, **63,** 397–426; (II Mitteilung.), *Ibid.,* 1920, **63,** 427–456; (III Mitteilung.), *Ibid.,* 1920, **63,** 481–520.

157. Schrödinger, E. Ueber das Verhältnis der Vierfarben- zur Dreifarbentheorie. *Sitzber. Wien. Akad. Wiss., Math.-naturwiss. Kl.,* 1925, **134,** Abt. IIa, 471–490.

158. Sinden, R. H. Studies based on spectral complementaries. *J. opt. Soc. Amer.,* 1923, **7,** 1123–1153.

159. Skinner, B. F. *The behavior of organisms.* New York: Appleton-Century-Crofts, 1938.

160. Skinner, B. F. The operational analysis of psychological terms. *Psychol. Rev.,* 1945, **52,** 270–277.

161. Sloan, Louise L. The effect of intensity of light, state of adaptation of the eye, and size of photometric field on the visibility curve. *Psychol. Monogr.,* 1928, **38,** No. 173.

162. So, M. On the visibility of radiation. *Proc. Jap. math. Phys. Soc.,* 1920, series 3, vol. 2, 177–184.

163. Southall, J. P. C. *Introduction to physiological optics.* London: Oxford University Press, 1937.

164. Sperling, H. C., & Hsia, Y. Some comparisons among spectral sensitivity data obtained in different retinal locations and with two sizes of foveal stimulus. *J. opt. Soc. Amer.,* 1957, **47,** 707–713.

165. Steindler, O. Die Farbenempfindlichkeit des normalen und farbenblinden Auges. *Sitzber. Wien. Akad. Wiss., Math-naturwiss. Kl.,* 1906, **115,** Abt. IIa, 39–62.

166. Stiles, W. S. The directional sensitivity of the retina and the spectral sensitivities of the rods and cones. *Proc. roy. Soc.* (London), 1939, **127B,** 64–105.

167. Stiles, W. S. A modified Helmholtz line-element in brightness-colour space. *Proc. phys. Soc.* (London), 1946, **58,** 41–65.

168. Stiles, W. S. Separation of the "blue" and "green" mechanisms of foveal vision by measurements of increment thresholds. *Proc. roy. Soc.* (London), 1946, **133B,** 418–434.

169. Stiles, W. S. The determination of the spectral sensitivities of the retinal mechanisms by sensory methods. *Ned. T. Natuurk,* 1949, **15,** 125–146.

170. Stiles, W. S. Investigations of the scotopic and trichromatic mechanisms of vision by the two-colour threshold technique. *Revue d'Optique* 1949, **28,** 215–237.

171. Stiles, W. S. Further studies of visual mechanisms by the two-colour threshold method. *Coloquio Sobre Problemas Opticos de la Vision I. Conferencias Generales.* Madrid: Union International de Physique Pure et Appliquée, 1953. Pp. 65–103.

172. Stiles, W. S. Personal communication. Aug. 22, 1954.

173. Stiles, W. S. The basic data of colour-matching. *Phys. Soc. Year Book.* London: Phys. Soc., 1955. Pp. 44–65.

174. Stiles, W. S. Interim report to the Commission Internationale de l'Eclairage, Zurich, 1955, on the National Physical Laboratory's investigation of colour-matching (with an appendix by W. S. Stiles and J. M Burch). *Optica Acta,* 1955, **2,** 168–181.

175. Stiles, W. S., & Crawford, B. H. The liminal brightness increment as a function of wave-length for different conditions of the foveal and parafoveal retina. *Proc. roy. Soc.,* 1934, **113B,** 496–530.

176. Thomson, L. C. Shape irregularities in the equal energy luminosity curve. *Proc. phys. Soc.* (London), 1949, **62B,** 787–792.

177. Thomson, L. C. The spectral sensitivity of the central fovea *J. Physiol.,* 1951, **112,** 114–132.

178. Thomson, L. C., & Wright, W. D. The colour sensitivity of the retina within the central fovea of man. *J. Physiol.,* 1946, **105,** 316–331.

179. Thomson, L. C., & Wright, W. D. The convergence of tritanopic confusion loci and derivations of the fundamental response functions. *J. opt Soc. Amer.,* 1953, **43,** 890–894.

180. Titchener, E. B. *Experimental psychology.* Vol. 1. *Qualitative experiments: Part I. Student's Manual.* New York: Macmillan, 1924.

181. Troland, L. T. Apparent brightness: its conditions and properties *Trans. illum. Engng. Soc.,* 1916, **11,** 947–966.

182. Troland, L. T. Report of the Colorimetry Committee of the Optical Society of America, 1920–21. *J. opt. Soc. Amer.,* 1922, **6,** 527–596.

183. Troland, L. T. *The principles of psychophysiology.* Vol. 2. *Sensation.* New York: Van Nostrand, 1930.

184. Tschermak-Seysenegg, A. von. *Einführung in die physiologische Optik.* (First edition appeared as Vol. 1 of the collection *Augenheilkund der Gegenwart.* Munich: Bergmann; Berlin and Vienna: Springer, 1942.) (2d ed.) Berlin: Springer, 1947.

185. Tschermak-Seysenegg, A. von. *Introduction to physiological optics* Paul Boeder. (Trans.) Springfield, Ill.: Charles C Thomas, 1952.

186. Verplanck, W. S. Burrhus F. Skinner. In Estes, W. K., et al. *Modern learning theory.* New York: Appleton-Century-Crofts, 1954. Pp. 267–316.

187. Wald, G. Human vision and the spectrum. *Science,* 1945, **101** 653–658.

188. Walls, G. L., & Mathews, R. W. New means of studying color blindness in normal foveal color vision: with some results and their genetical implications. *Univer. Calif. Publ. Psychol.*, 1952, **7**, pp. iv + 172.

189. Walsh, J. W. T. *Photometry*. London: Constable, 1953.

190. Walters, H. V., & Wright, W. D. The spectral sensitivity of the fovea and extra-fovea in the Purkinje range. *Proc. roy. Soc.*, 1943, **131B**, 340–361.

191. Weale, R. A. Hue-discrimination in para-central parts of the human retina measured at different luminance levels. *J. Physiol.*, 1951, **113**, 115–123.

192. Weale, R. A. The foveal and para-central spectral sensitivities in man. *J. Physiol.*, 1951, **114**, 435–446.

193. Weale, R. A. Spectral sensitivity and wave-length discrimination of the peripheral retina. *J. Physiol.*, 1953, **119**, 170–190.

194. Whittaker, E. T. Introduction. In Newton's *Opticks*. London: Bell, 1931. Pp. ix–xxv.

195. Willmer, E. N. Observations on the physiology of colour vision. *Nature*, 1943, **151**, 213–215.

196. Willmer, E. N. Colour of small objects. *Nature*, 1944, **153**, 775.

197. Willmer, E. N., & Wright, W. D. Colour sensitivity of the fovea centralis. *Nature*, 1945, **56**, 119–120.

198. Wintringham, W. T. Color television and colorimetry. *Proc. Inst. Radio Engrs.*, 1951, **39**, 1135–1172.

199. Woodworth, R. S., & Schlosberg, H. *Experimental psychology*, New York: Holt, 1954.

200. Wright, W. D. A re-determination of the trichromatic coefficients of the spectral colours. *Trans. opt. Soc. London*, 1928–29, **30**, 141–164.

201. Wright, W. D. A re-determination of the mixture curves of the spectrum. *Trans. opt. Soc. London*, 1929–30, **31**, 201–218.

202. Wright, W. D. *The measurement of colour*. London: Adam Hilger, 1944.

203. Wright, W. D. *Researches on normal and defective colour vision*. St. Louis: Mosby, 1947.

204. Wright, W. D. The characteristics of tritanopia. *J. opt. Soc. Amer.*, 1952, **42**, 509–521.

205. Wright, W. D., & Pitt, F. H. G. Hue discrimination in normal colour vision. *Proc. phys. Soc.* (London), 1934, **46**, 459–473.

206. Wright, W. D., & Pitt, F. H. G. The colour-vision characteristics of two trichromats. *Proc. phys. Soc.* (London), 1935, **47**, 207–208.

207. Wright, W. D., & Pitt, F. H. G. The saturation-discrimination of two trichromats. *Proc. phys. Soc.* (London), 1937, **49**, 329–331.

208. Young, T. On the theory of light and colors. 1807. In Vol. 2 of *Lectures in natural philosophy*. London: Printed for Joseph Johnson, St. Paul's Church Yard, by William Savage. Pp. 613–632.

209. Young, T. An account of some cases of the production of colors. 1807. In Vol. 2 of *Lectures in natural philosophy*. London: Printed for Joseph Johnson, St. Paul's Church Yard, by William Savage. Pp. 634–638.

THE QUANTUM THEORY OF LIGHT AND THE PSYCHO-PHYSIOLOGY OF VISION

M. H. PIRENNE and F. H. C. MARRIOTT[1]
University Laboratory of Physiology, Oxford

[1] Recipient of a Nuffield Foundation Biological Scholarship.

INTRODUCTION

It has long been recognized that electromagnetic radiation passing through matter without being absorbed cannot exert any chemical action upon it. Light must therefore be absorbed by the sensitive pigments contained in the photoreceptors in order to act upon the retina and to cause nervous excitation in the optic pathways. As is universally known, the quantum theory of Planck and Einstein was developed in connection with the phenomena of emission and absorption of radiation. Modern theories of retinal excitation should therefore be based upon the physical quantum theory of light, according to which light acts upon matter in elementary processes each of which involves only one quantum of energy.

Yet the physical quantum theory might not be of very great significance for the physiology of vision if the number of light quanta involved in retinal excitation were always very large. For on statistical grounds the observed effects of such large numbers of quanta would resemble the effects of light acting as a continuum, in the same way as the molecular and atomic structure of matter fails to make itself directly felt in ordinary chemical reactions.

The smallest number of light quanta required for vision however is not large. A few quanta acting upon the human retina are capable of giving a sensation of light to a human observer. By activating one molecule of visual pigment, one single quantum may cause the excitation of a dark-adapted rod cell in the retina. And one quantum is of course the smallest quantity of light which may be emitted or absorbed by matter.

Physical stimuli consisting of a small number of light quanta undergo wide uncontrollable fluctuations. This inherent instability of the light stimulus itself is of importance at the absolute threshold when the amounts of light involved in a visual act are very small.

Furthermore, on the absolute quantum scale, the amounts of light actually available for vision are often small even under conditions very different from those used for measuring the smallest amount of light necessary for seeing. Thus light intensities within the range of daylight are necessary in order to deliver just a few quanta per second to every retinal rod or cone. Accordingly quantum fluctuations may play a considerable role at intensities generally referred to as "supraliminal," as well as under absolute threshold conditions.

Whereas it seems that the effect of these physical fluctuations on the eye can sometimes be detected merely by looking at faint sources of light [6, 105], such purely subjective observations must always remain somewhat unconvincing as a proof of the existence of quantum fluctuations. For they also depend upon variations of biological or of other origin, the importance of which cannot be evaluated in the resultant phenomenon. Thus, for instance, eye movements combined with the effects of retinal adaptation and of local variations of sensitivity must account to an unknown extent for the apparent variations in intensity of a dim point source of light observed in the laboratory. (As for the scintillation of stars, it is largely explained by variations of density in the atmosphere.)

By using psychophysical methods under controlled conditions, however, it can be proved that physical quantum fluctuations play a dominant role at least in some specially designed experiments. The present paper will be largely devoted to a discussion of such experiments, particular attention being given to the relative roles played by purely physical quantum fluctuations on the one hand, and by biological and other variations on the other hand, with regard to the uncertainty of seeing which is observed experimentally. Before proceeding to this detailed discussion, a brief summary will be given of other consequences of the physical quantum theory for the psychophysiology of vision.

QUANTUM THEORY, RETINAL PHOTOCHEMISTRY, AND VISUAL EXCITATION

According to modern physical theory, the primary phase of the photochemical reaction which takes place when light acts upon visual receptors (rods and cones) must consist of a number of individual events in each of which a single light quantum is absorbed by and reacts with one molecule of the photosensitive substance (photopigment) present in the receptors (or with one chromophoric group, i.e., one of the component parts of the molecule specifically concerned with light absorption). Fractions of quanta cannot be absorbed. If the retina absorbs less than 1 quantum, therefore, it absorbs no light at all, and it remains quite unaffected by the light which may have passed through it without being absorbed. In the case of visible radiation, the energy of the quanta, which is proportional to the radiation frequency, is very small; for "blue-green" light of wavelength 0.507 μ, the energy of the quantum is 3.92×10^{-12} erg. Yet, as is well known, a few quanta of this frequency, absorbed by a human subject's retina, are sufficient under the best experimental conditions for making the subject see a small luminous test field exposed in a brief flash [54].

Summary of basic ideas. The absolute threshold of the dark-adapted human eye for a large field and long exposures, on the other hand, corresponds to a *mean* number of quanta absorbed by the retina of the order of only 1 quantum per 5,000 rods per second. In the case of a test field subtending 50° at the eye, lit with radiation of $\lambda = 0.507$ μ and viewed by the subject in exposures of 0.25 minute each, the total number of quanta entering the eye in one of these 0.25-minute exposures is about 0.5 million. The number of retinal rods covered by the image of the field is about 20 million, that is, forty times greater than the total number of quanta entering the eye. On the assumption that about 0.1 of these quanta are absorbed by the rods, the above estimate, 1 quantum absorbed per 5,000 rods per second, follows approximately from the experimental results. Although some uncertainties remain with regard to the precise value of the probability of quantum absorption by the living rods, quantitative examples such as the above leave no doubt that at the absolute threshold the number of rods which can be acted upon by light is much smaller than the total number of rods covered by the geometrical image of the field. The rods affected by the light will as a rule absorb only one quantum apiece, which reacts with one molecule or chromophoric group. Some rods may absorb more than one quantum. The other rods remain unstimulated since they have absorbed no light at all. The number of chromophoric groups contained in a rod being probably about 10^8, the fraction of these groups in the retina acted upon by light is of the order of only 10^{-12} per second at the absolute threshold for a large field.

These considerations lead to the following conclusions. The intensity required in order to produce appreciable bleaching, *assuming that* each chromophoric group which has absorbed 1 quantum is bleached, must be relatively very high. A rate of bleaching of 1 per cent per hour will require an intensity roughly 10^6 times the absolute threshold for a large field. For white light, this threshold value expressed in photometric units is about 10^{-6} candela per square meter, or 0.3×10^{-6} ml. The intensity required is, therefore, of the order of 1 cd/m^2, that is, within the range of daylight, cone, vision. As de Vries [105] and Baumgardt [7] have emphasized, therefore, photochemical theories such as Hecht's theory of the "steady state" need reconsideration. Although such theories must still apply in some form to the higher intensity range of photopic (cone) vision, they can hardly be relevant in the range of scotopic (rod) vision, since over the whole of this intensity range the concentration of photopigments must remain practically unchanged. Similarly, a considerable rise of threshold is caused by adaptation to a light which has bleached only a minute part of the pigments present in the photoreceptors; whence it follows that some simple photochemical theories of dark adaptation also need revision.

Another consequence of the high retinal sensitivity in terms of quanta is that a progressive recruiting of retinal functional units must be expected to occur as the light intensity is increased from the absolute threshold for a large field. These functional units consist of a certain number of rods and/or cones linked through dipolar cells to one ganglion cell and thus one optic nerve fibre. Their existence has been clearly established by electrophysiological and anatomical findings as well as by experiments on the living human eye. Anatomical study shows that the receptors in a given part of the retina may be connected in different ways to various ganglion cells, thus forming large functional units and smaller subunits. A remarkable example of this is shown in Fig. 8 of Polyak [85]; in the rodless central area each cone is connected to a midget ganglion cell via a midget bipolar, but a number of the same cones are connected also to one diffuse ganglion cell via various dipolar cells. There are in the periphery large units which consist of thousands of rods and which probably overlap one another. They must be concerned with the detection of large dim fields by the dark-adapted eye. At the other extreme there are in the fovea single-cone units having a private line to the brain. As the light intensity increases, the smaller units eventually receive enough light to produce a response in their nerve fibers, which explains the increase of visual acuity with intensity which is observed in many types of experiment. There are further anatomical connections in the retina (horizontal and amacrine cells) which may lead to interaction between various functional units, but such interaction may be of only secondary importance when the threshold of the relevant units is only just being reached.

Assuming for the sake of argument that the cones contain the same concentration of photopigment as the rods, and that the threshold of a cone corresponds to a few quanta absorbed during an action time of the order of 0.1 sec, it follows that intensities between 10^5 and 10^6 times the absolute threshold for a large field will be required to reach the absolute threshold of a single cone. At somewhat lower intensities the cone as a rule will absorb no light at all, that is, not even a single quantum. Functional units made up of rods, cones, or both rods and cones in varying numbers may thus be expected to be progressively recruited over the intensity range from 10^{-6} cd/m^2 to about 1 cd/m^2, the latter luminance corresponding to dim daylight. Many visual responses occurring at intensity levels which are often called "supraliminal" with reference to the threshold for large fields and long exposures, may nevertheless be dependent upon the coming into play of certain functional units whose *absolute* threshold is just reached at these "supraliminal" intensities.

These conclusions rest on two points which are universally accepted in modern photochemical theory. First, light which is not absorbed by the photopigment cannot exert any chemical action upon it. Secondly, light can be absorbed by matter only in single indivisible quanta. Accordingly, if the receptors of a functional unit have failed to absorb even one single quantum, the unit must remain entirely unaffected by the light stimulus.

Scope of the present paper. In an article published in *Biological Reviews* [81] special attention has been given to the absolute threshold for large fields in man and in animals, to the threshold for small light sources, to the functional organization of the vertebrate retina, and to the smallest number of quanta necessary for human vision. The present paper will be largely devoted to a detailed discussion from the standpoint of quantum theory of the "frequency-of-seeing" or "frequency-of-response" curves obtained at the absolute threshold under various conditions.

In view of the importance of such curves from a psychological standpoint [38, 39], it seems of value to try to demonstrate that the experimental results obtained so far are in agreement with the predictions of the physical quantum theory of light. For if it could be proved otherwise, doubt would also be thrown on the broader considerations outlined above. At a later stage in this paper, more general problems of nervous organization in the visual system will be considered.

ABSOLUTE THRESHOLD EXPERIMENTS AND THEIR GENERAL INTERPRETATION

Outline of the experiments. It may be of value to recall briefly the general conditions under which the main experiments to be discussed have been performed. These conditions were chosen with a view to stimulating the retina under reproducible conditions and to reducing biological variability. The method of fixation and flash was used.

It is universally known that when we look in daylight at some detail of an object which attracts our attention, our eyes move by a reflex action into such a position that the image of this particular detail falls on a point in the center of the fovea centralis of the retina, the region where vision of details is most accurate in daylight. Now it is clear that if the head is kept immobile, the position of the eye, and of the retina, while we look steadily at one point, will be fixed in space, since the eyeball cannot rotate round its visual axis. The image of the point of fixation is thus maintained on a point of the fovea—with an accuracy of a few minutes of arc in visual angle—and the images of all surrounding objects fall on to the retina in positions which are accurately defined in terms of the position of the objects in space. (In this connection, it must be borne in mind, however, that it is hard to keep accurate fixation for more than a second or two, for normally the eye moves in jerks from one position to another every tenth or fifth of a second.) For experiments in a darkroom the point of fixation consists of a small source of red light just bright enough to be easily seen when the subject looks straight at it. Now in the case of the experiments of Hecht et al. [54], for instance, the stimulus consisted of a circle subtending an angle of 10′ at the eye of the subject and placed laterally at an angle of 20° from the fixation point (Fig. 1). This small circular field could be illuminated in 0.001-sec flashes with radiation of wavelength 0.510 μ. The light intensity of the flash was controlled with neutral optical wedges. The subject's head was held in position by a dental impression firmly attached to the apparatus and he viewed both fixation point and test field through an aperture 2 mm in diameter, the "artificial pupil," placed in front of his eye.

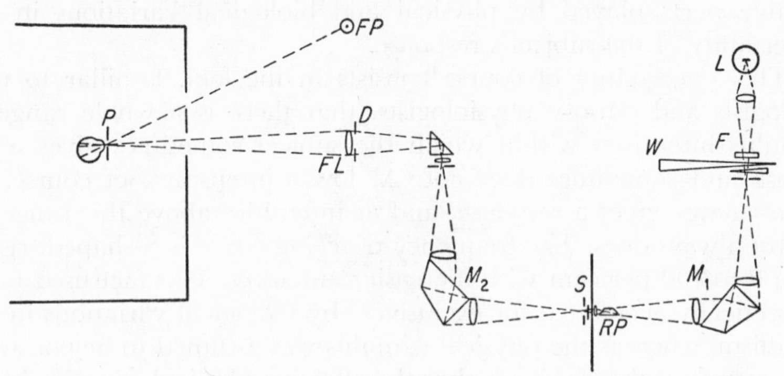

Fig. 1. Optical system for measuring minimum energies necessary for vision. The eye at the pupil *P* fixates the red point *FP* and observes the test field formed by the lens *FL* and the diaphragm *D*. The light for this field comes from the lamp *L* through the neutral filter *F* and wedge *W*, through the double monochromator M_1M_2 and is controlled by the shutter *S*. *From Hecht, Shlaer, and Pirenne* [54].

The subject, while keeping his gaze fixed on the fixation point, released the shutter when he felt ready for a trial, and signaled by pressing a key when he had seen the small lateral test field. Many such trials were repeated at different settings of the neutral wedges, which made it possible to plot the frequency with which the flashes were seen against their nominal light intensity (method of constant stimuli). The various flash intensities were presented in a random sequence unknown to the subject, mixed with "blanks," that is, with trials made as usual but with the light entirely cut off from the test field. The subject was thoroughly dark-adapted before starting the measurements.

These precautions ensured that in every trial the image of the test field was formed on the same part of the retina, within the limits of fixation accuracy. Variations in the size of the natural pupil of the eye, which is larger than the artificial pupil used, could not affect the amount of light reaching the retina.

The main variable in the experiment, therefore, was the nominal intensity of the flash (the amount of radiant energy striking the cornea of the eye) controlled by the setting of the optical wedges. The subject could only give two reports, namely, "seen" and "not seen." We shall call response a report "seen," a report "not seen" being no response. In the theory of these experiments, it is necessary to take into account the events which intervene between the stimulus—light striking the retina—and the response—pressing the signaling key. It will be seen that in spite of the complexity of these intervening events, and of our limited knowledge of them, it is possible to reach conclusions on the relative parts played by physical and biological variations in the uncertainty of the subject's response.

This uncertainty of course consists in the fact, familiar to psychologists and sensory physiologists, that there is a whole range of stimulus intensities within which the subject sometimes gives a response and sometimes does not. At lower intensities, of course, he almost never gives a response, and at intensities above this range he almost always does. The frequency-of-seeing curve is S-shaped, rising from 0 to 100 per cent with increasing intensity. This fact used to be theoretically accounted for exclusively by biological variations in the organism, whereas the physical stimulus was assumed to be constant. The quantum theory shows that the effective physical stimulus is not constant and that its fluctuations, which occur at random, must play an important role in the explanation of the observed uncertainty of response.

It may be worth emphasizing that the variability of response here referred to is that observed in any one experiment at a single sitting. From one day to another, or even in the course of one day, there may occur systematic shifts of sensitivity which are certainly not due to physical fluctuations. Thus the frequency-of-seeing curve may be moved bodily along the log intensity axis from one experiment to another. Some of these shifts might be explained, for instance, by variation in the amounts of photopigment contained in the retinal receptors. Quantum fluctuations are relevant only with regard to the range of uncertain seeing represented by curves obtained at single sittings. They do not of course explain the general change-over from one curve to another which may be observed in one subject—nor a fortiori the differences of sensitivity between one subject and another. The possibility of similar general shifts of sensitivity occurring also during the course of one single experiment cannot however be excluded; this problem will be discussed when we turn to the theory of frequency-of-seeing curves for the absolute threshold and the problem of biological variations and quantum fluctuations.

Neurophysiological formulation of the problem. The general formulation to be used here might be regarded as belonging to the realm of physiology or biophysics rather than to psychology. Experiments on human subjects in the field of special senses may always, from a certain standpoint, be considered to be psychological experiments. Yet the theoretical viewpoint here will be physiological or, more precisely, neurophysiological.

It will be assumed, as a heuristic postulate, that the light stimulus initiates in the subject's nervous system a series of reactions spreading from the photoreceptors to afferent nerve fibers, to the central nervous system, and then to effector systems—as a result of which the subject, say, presses a key to report the light seen. Thus, the experiments will be discussed on the assumption that the subject's nervous system behaves as a sort of mechanism for the detection of light stimuli [70, 72, 73, 77, 78; see also 100].

Ranson [88], in discussing the neurophysiological standpoint, wrote: "Sensory impulses from many sources reach the brain, where they pass back and forth through a multitude of association paths, augmenting or inhibiting each other before they finally break through into motor paths." The present standpoint is largely defined by this statement, to which should be added an explicit reference to the "autonomous" activity of the central nervous system [109]. A simplification of the problems involved occurs here, however, because most of the experiments were made in the very special way which has just been described. As a rule, the task of the subject consisted in signaling whether or not he had seen a certain stimulus, under strictly defined conditions. This particular method of "questioning" the organism made it possible, on the one hand, to restrict the play of factors relating to the central nervous system, and on the other hand, to draw some conclusions about the influence of these factors in the experiments under consideration.

The present systematic formulation does not rule out the existence of difficult problems relating, for instance, to the existence of the subject's "sensations" and "consciousness." The formulation is chosen a priori to avoid dealing with such problems—and therefore cannot make any contribution towards their solution [see, e.g., 72]. Nevertheless, the neurophysiological formulation might seem to be a somewhat arbitrary and artificial one. Such a criticism, however, would seem to apply with lesser strength in the case of the experiments to be discussed here than in the general study of behavior. For it might possibly be said that in these experiments the subject strives consciously to achieve something akin to reflex behavior. It might be argued that the result of the intervention of the subject's "consciousness" is precisely to set up such a state of affairs in the nervous system that it comes near to working like an automatic detector of physical stimuli [78]. If this speculation were correct, the neurophysiological formulation should be regarded as true in so far as the processes *directly* involved in the experiment are concerned, even by those who might not be prepared to accept it in wider fields of human behavior.

Historical background. In 1936 the late Selig Hecht wrote that

> . . . the process of vision as a whole involves not only the receptor processes in the rods and cones, but the nerve impulses generated by the stimulated elements and by neighbouring elements, as well as all sorts of cortical changes of which we know little or nothing. Since these are all concerned with vision, they surely influence its characteristics to some extent. The question is to what extent; and the answer can be secured only by trial.
>
> Our own viewpoint has been that, no matter what determines the nature of vision, the ultimate place of origin of the impulses passing up the optic tracts is in the action of light on the eye. Therefore, for several years we have measured various properties of vision and photoreception to ascertain whether the data owe any of their quantitative properties to the characteristics of the very first reactions which must take place between light and the sensitive elements concerned with receiving light. The advantage of dealing with this first process is that it is photochemical, and that the properties of photochemical systems have been much studied and clearly formulated.

This may still be taken as the leading idea of the present study. Thus, it will be seen that physical quantum fluctuations must always influence the response of the organism but that, on account of various biological factors, the observed uncertainty of response is not always related in a simple manner to the physical fluctuations of the stimulus.

The very emphasis which Hecht placed on the study of the more peripheral aspects of the sensory process led to the discovery of visual phenomena which are caused by the quantum nature of the light stimulus itself. Although this work has eventually made it necessary to revise some of Hecht's early theories, this is the result of the consistent application of his own method and he would have approved of it.

It may be noted here that the purely neurophysiological standpoint in the preceding subsection is not explicitly formulated in the paper by Hecht et al. [54]. Hecht, therefore, should not be held responsible for its possible shortcomings. The need for a clearly defined standpoint of this kind became particularly apparent when dealing with the binocular threshold and other problems involving "sensory integration." (See under Peripheral and Central Factors in Threshold Experiments.)

The work done by Hecht et al. in 1942 was the result of the concerted effort of a team of workers having different scientific backgrounds. One of the present writers (M.H.P.) feels he was singularly fortunate in being able to collaborate with the late Selig Hecht and with Dr. Simon Shlaer, at the time when he was changing over from the study of physics to that of biophysics. Reference to the work of other investigators will be found in the following sections of this paper; important work on the physical quantum theory of vision was undertaken independently and almost simultaneously in a number of countries.

PHYSICAL FLUCTUATIONS IN THE NUMBER AND DISTRIBUTION OF QUANTA ACTING UPON THE RETINAL RECEPTORS

General. The quantum theory asserts that transfers of radiant energy occur only as a result of discrete elementary processes in each of which 1 quantum is exchanged. Whereas the *probability* of occurrence of any one elementary process can in principle be known, it is impossible to predict in any particular instance whether or not the process will actually occur.

Consider an arrangement capable of delivering light to the retina under experimental conditions which can be kept rigorously constant. These constant conditions include the size and position of the test field, the duration of the flash or exposure, the nominal intensity of the light, and the position and physiological state of the eye and retinal receptors. When the shutter of the apparatus is opened for a "trial" (single flash or exposure), part of the radiation emitted by the light source (say, an electric bulb) passes through the apparatus and reaches the retina. Now there is only a certain probability, in general very small, that any one atom, or electron, or other elementary system constituent of the light source will during one trial emit a light quantum which will become absorbed by one of the molecules of photosensitive substance contained in a given receptor among those corresponding to the retinal image of the field (Fig. 2). In any particular trial, therefore, it is impossible to predict whether or not this or any other atom, among the large number forming the filament of the electric bulb, will deliver a quantum to the retinal receptor. It may by chance happen that none of the atoms constituting the filament delivers a quantum; or it may happen that one atom delivers a quantum, or that many atoms deliver each a quantum, to this particular receptor.

Since the same reasoning is applicable to the other receptors covered by the image of the field, fluctuations are bound to occur both in the total number and in the spatial distribution of the quanta delivered to the retina.

Thus, if an experimental arrangement delivers in each trial the same constant *mean* total number a of light quanta to the photoreceptors of the retina, the actual number x acting upon the receptors will vary from trial to trial. There will be a finite probability of the actual number x assuming any integral value—the probability for values of x

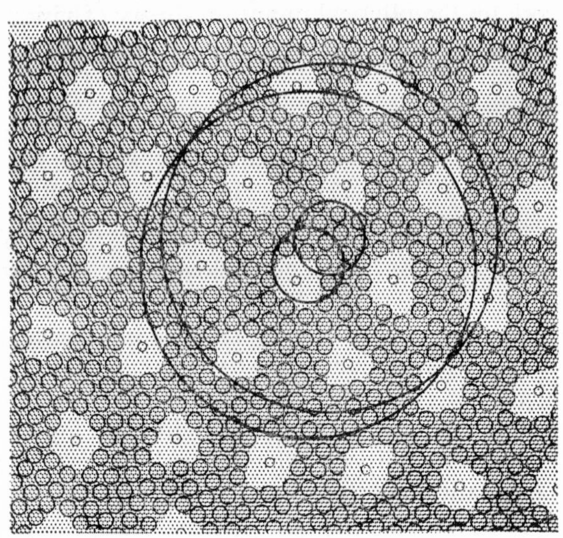

FIG. 2. The mosaic of rods and cones in the periphery of the human eye a few millimeters from the fovea. The smallest circles, seen in the centers of empty spaces, are the tips of cones. The numerous, slightly larger, circles are rods. Original magnification 500 times, increased to 700 times on reproduction. *After Schultze* [95].

The two large circles superimposed on the drawing give the *geometrical* images of two circular test fields subtending 10′ at the eye. The two smaller circles correspond to fields subtending 2′. In each instance the centers of the two fields are separated by an angular distance of 1′. The actual optical images of such fields are considerably greater than the geometrical images owing to light diffraction and diffusion. *From J. A. V. Butler & J. T. Randall (Eds.), Progress in Biophysics, vol. 2, London, Pergamon Press,* 1951. [75]

much higher than a, however, becomes negligibly small in practice. For instance, it is impossible to control experimental conditions in such a way that, say, 6 quanta are delivered to the retina in each trial. Only the mean number per trial can be kept constant. If this mean is 6, the actual number will assume the values 0,1,2,3,4,5,6,7,8,-9,10, etc., with different probabilities, the most probable values being

5 and 6. The distribution of the quanta among the receptors covered by the retinal image of the test field will also vary from trial to trial, even if in two trials the total number happens to be the same (Fig. 3).

A similar reasoning applied to time intervals within the total duration of a trial shows that fluctuations are also bound to occur in the temporal distribution of the quanta. They will be absorbed at random times during the flash or exposure.

According to the quantum theory of electromagnetic radiation, therefore, both the actual number and the distribution of absorbed quanta in space and time must undergo considerable variations from one trial to another even when all physical and physiological conditions are rigorously constant. These quantum fluctuations occur at random. It is only when large numbers of quanta are *directly* involved that the importance of these physical variations may sometimes become relatively insignificant. The fact that the number of quanta emitted by the lamp, or entering the eye, may be much greater than the *number absorbed* by the receptors has no direct bearing on the fluctuations occurring in the latter number.

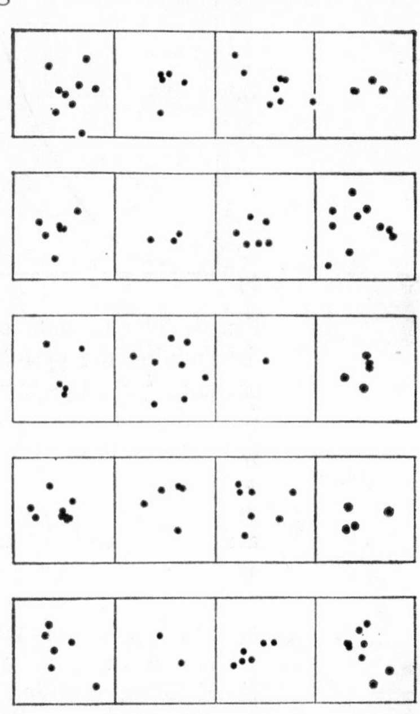

FIG. 3. Diagrams illustrating the variations in the numbers and spatial distribution of acting quanta. The figure shows the variations which might occur between 20 flashes of the same nominal intensity corresponding to a mean of 6 acting quanta. Each black dot represents 1 acting quantum; each of the 20 separate squares contains the result of one flash. The actual number of quanta varies according to the Poisson distribution, in this instance between 1 and 10. About 1 flash out of 400 at this intensity would contain no acting quanta. The spatial distribution of the acting quanta has been determined by random sampling from a bivariate normal distribution (see Fig. 4).

Although it is widely held that the prediction of actual quantum events is theoretically impossible, the practical conclusion would here remain the same even if this impossibility were the result of our ignorance of the hidden parameters of a "deterministic substratum" of the quantum events. In physics the existence of quantum fluctuations is as generally accepted as that of Brownian movement, and fluctuation phenomena play an important role in wide fields.

It may be pointed out that it would be erroneous to conclude from the above considerations that light quanta behave like ordinary "particles" traveling between the source and the retina. Such a view would lead to entirely false conclusions with regard to diffraction and

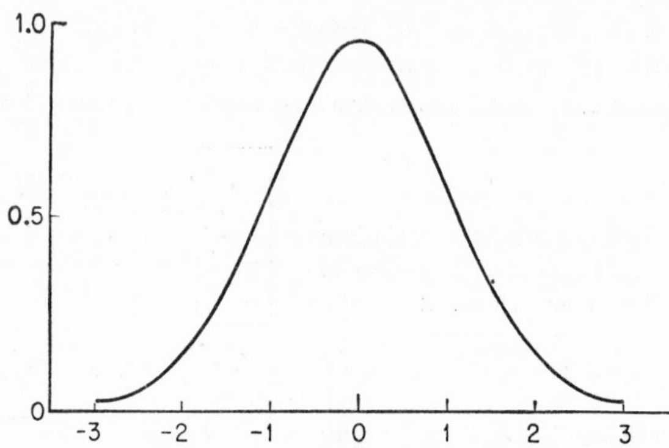

FIG. 4. The normal, or gaussian, distribution used in determining the positions of the points in Fig. 3. The ordinate gives the mean intensity at a given distance from the center of the flash. The image is thus supposed to be most intense at the center, falling away to low values near the edge of the square corresponding to each flash. The abscissa units are equal to the standard deviation of the normal distribution, and the side of each square in Fig. 3 is equal to 6 such units. The ordinate gives the mean number of quanta per unit area in Fig. 3. The maximum value is 0.95.

The work of Flamant [36] shows that, for small visual fields, diffusion scatters the light over an area considerably greater than the theoretical Airy disc. The form of the imaginary distribution illustrated here is roughly similar to the curves obtained by Flamant.

interference phenomena. Quantum phenomena are in evidence only when radiation is emitted or absorbed by matter. Radiation in transit, on the other hand, can be regarded as obeying the laws of classical wave theory. It is possible, therefore, to calculate the general distribution of light in the retinal image on the basis of the wave theory, and then to apply quantum considerations in order to obtain information about the actual retinal stimulus, which always consists of an integral number of absorbed quanta. The light intensities in the different parts of the retinal image are here replaced by a probability distribution of quanta at each point of the image (see, e.g., Fig. 4).

Light waves and diffraction effects. It may be of value to examine briefly some examples of test stimuli in concrete situations. Consider experiments made using an "artificial pupil" 2 mm in diameter. This is a circular aperture in a piece of metal placed close to the eye in front of the natural pupil. The subject views the test stimulus (and the fixation point, if any) through this artificial pupil. As a test stimulus we first consider a "point" source emitting light of 0.51 μ in wavelength. This source will be taken to have angular dimensions similar to those of a star; that is, it will subtend less than 1″ of arc at the eye.

Owing to the wave properties of light, the optical image of this source on the retina will not be a very small spot corresponding to the geometrical image of the source (0.08 μ for 1″ of arc) but a diffraction pattern of much larger dimensions. The greater part of the light (84 per cent) will be concentrated within the "Airy disc," the diameter of which here will be about 9.3 μ; and this Airy disc will be surrounded by faint luminous rings of increasing diameters and decreasing intensities [see, e.g., 46]. This assumes that the dioptric system of the human eye functions as a perfect optical instrument. On this assumption the diameter of the Airy disc will be smaller for a larger pupil; for an 8-mm natural pupil, it will be 2.3 μ. But the eye suffers from various defects so that a larger pupil will not in fact lead to the degree of sharpening of the retinal image which might be expected theoretically.

Now the distance between the centres of two adjacent cones in the "bouquet central" of the fovea, the most accurate region of the retina for form vision in daylight, has in general a value between 2 and 2.5 μ. Again, in the periphery the diameter of the human rods is about 2 μ (Fig. 2); these rods are interspersed with a smaller number of cones which have a thick inner segment [see, e.g., 72]. It is practically impossible, therefore, to make the "optical image" of a small source, or even merely the Airy disc, fall entirely within a single foveal cone or a single rod. In the case of a 2-mm artificial pupil, diffraction alone will spread the light over roughly 15 rods or foveal cones. This unavoidable blurring of the image is in practice increased by diffusion of light in the eye and the retina itself, by various optical defects of the eye, and by fluctuations of accommodation [2, 3, 36; see general discussion in 58]. In the case of the periphery, image formation will generally be less good than in the fovea.

There are also inaccuracies of fixation which are probably greater than 1′ of arc, an angle which may be taken to correspond to a distance of 4.85 μ on the retina. Thus in the case of a steady light source, the retinal image will be unsteady to an extent corresponding to several times the diameter of a foveal cone or of a rod. In the case of brief flashes of light, using a fixation point, it is likely that the image will suffer similar displacements from one flash to another.

Quantum absorption in the image of a point source. At sufficiently low intensities, the quantum properties of light will in some cases restore a more sharply localized stimulation, in spite of the fact that the wave properties of light and the optical defects of the eye tend to spread out the region of excitation over the retina. For the intensity distribution in the optical image, calculated on the basis of the wave theory of light, does in fact represent the probability of quantum absorption, this probability being of course highest where the intensity distribution is maximal. If only a few quanta are absorbed, therefore, the outer parts of the image, where the intensity distribution is a small fraction of the maximal value, will as a rule receive no light at all. Thus, the actual quantum distribution is different from the intensity distribution which would be expected from a continuum theory of light based on the wave theory only. Sometimes, for instance, all the quanta may be absorbed in the same receptor. In the extreme case of one single quantum absorption, the actual distribution retains only a remote connection with the probability distribution (Figs. 3 and 4).

On the other hand, as has been shown, it is theoretically impossible for the retinal stimulation to be exactly reproducible. In the course of time for a steady light, or in successive trials if flashes are used, the total number of absorbed quanta will fluctuate, and the quanta will be distributed differently among the receptors covered by the optical image of the source—quite apart from the effect of inaccuracies of fixation (Fig. 3). If one single quantum is absorbed by the retina, only one of the receptors covered by the optical image can be stimulated. If the experiment is repeated and one single quantum is again absorbed, it will be either in the same receptor as before, or in another. Supposing now that 2 quanta are absorbed in an experiment, they may be absorbed in the same receptor or in two different ones. If in several experiments 2 quanta each time are absorbed, their distribution among the receptors will, therefore, vary in many different ways. In the case of 3 quanta or more, the number of possible arrangements will become increasingly large—there being still a finite probability that all the quanta be absorbed in the same receptor.

A 10′ test field. Hecht et al. [54] used a circular test field the diameter of which subtended 10′ of arc at the eye; this was placed at an angle of 20° from the fixation point and viewed through a 2-mm artificial pupil. The geometrical image of this test stimulus on the retina would be an area 48.5 μ in diameter. Since according to Østerberg [65] the number of rods is about 150,000 per mm^2, at an eccentricity of 20° such an area covers on the average 280 rods (and also about 10 peripheral cones). The actual optical image must be larger than the geometrical image [20, 36]. If the main, central part of the optical image has a diameter of 48.5 + 9.3 = 58 μ, it will cover 400 rods (9.3μ is the diameter of the Airy disc). A round value of 500 rods was taken by Hecht et al. [54].

Larger test fields. Image formation may be poor at an eccentricity of 20°. For a 2-mm pupil, the image of a point source may spread far beyond the Airy disc at least in certain eyes, and there may be little difference between, say, a 1′ and a 10′ field. But in the case of larger test fields, for instance, 1° in diameter, the relative importance of the spread of light beyond the geometrical image will, of course, decrease with increasing field size. If the number of quanta absorbed is small, inaccuracies of fixation also will tend to lose their importance; the quantum distribution in the image of a 1° field with fixation inaccuracies of a few minutes will then be hardly distinguishable from the distribution which would correspond to a slightly larger field with perfect fixation.

Conclusion. This suggests that threshold experiments will be easier to interpret for a moderately large test stimulus than for a "point" source. For a given small number of quanta absorbed, multiple quantum absorptions in rods will occur much less frequently for 500 rods than for, say, 15 rods [81]. The use of a field 10′ or larger in diameter, therefore, helps to eliminate theoretical uncertainties in the interpretation of threshold experiments, for it is not known in what manner the result of a multiple quantum absorption in a rod differs from that of a single absorption. According to Graham and Margaria [40], the minimum amount of light necessary for vision in a very brief flash, at an eccentricity of 15°, varies but little for field diameter up to 1°, so that from the point of view of sensitivity there is no particular advantage in using very small fields.

Under conditions where multiple absorptions are of negligible importance, both the total number of quanta and the distribution of the quanta in space in the retina and in time within the duration of the exposure must still vary from one trial to the next even under constant experimental conditions.

As will be seen, the simplest hypothesis that can be made here is that the outcome of each trial is determined by the total number of quanta involved, independently of their distribution in space and time. This hypothesis in most cases must be an oversimplification.

The general condition for a threshold response in any given trial is that one of a number of favorable spatio-temporal distributions of quanta "acting" upon the retina be realized, all other possible distributions leading to no response. The phrase "acting quanta" refers to the fact, to be discussed in the next section, that all quanta absorbed may not be effective in stimulating the receptors. Quantitative predictions can be made with regard to this general condition in spite of its wide scope.

THEORY OF FREQUENCY-OF-SEEING CURVES FOR THE ABSOLUTE THRESHOLD

The Poisson equation. We shall first consider fluctuations in the total numbers of light quanta acting as visual stimuli, disregarding fluctuations in the distribution of these quanta.

A detailed discussion [75] based on the consideration of fluctuations in the quanta acting upon the retinal receptors shows that the probability Π_x that the actual number of quanta acting upon the receptors has a particular value x depends only upon the mean a and is given by the Poisson equation

$$\Pi_x = \frac{e^{-a}a^x}{x!} \qquad (1)$$

where x is, of course, an integer whereas a, being a mean value, can be fractional (see p. 300).

The phrase "quanta acting upon the receptors" here means quanta absorbed by the photosensitive substance of the photoreceptors *and* able to take part effectively in the visual excitation process. It has often been assumed that all quanta absorbed by the photosensitive substance were effective in this way. The number of effective quanta might, however, be smaller than the number of absorbed quanta; for instance, a quantum absorbed by a rod might have only one chance in two of stimulating the rod [45, 81]. Here, therefore, a and x represent numbers of quanta which *act effectively* on the retina. (Equation (1), of course, applies also to the numbers of *absorbed* quanta, when a and x refer to absorbed quanta. The number of absorbed quanta is greater than or equal to the number of acting quanta.)

Equation (1) is valid provided that the retinal receptors under consideration contain a large number of photosensitive molecules in comparison with the number of acting quanta. This assumption will generally be fulfilled, at any rate in experiments on the dark-adapted retina. If it were not fulfilled Eq. (1) might no longer be exact, but there would still be fluctuations obeying a different law. The occurrence of quantum fluctuations cannot be prevented by using any particular experimental arrangement.

The existence of irregularities in the retina and in the intensity distribution of the retinal image does not affect the validity of Eq. (1). The equation holds even when there are gaps in between the retinal receptors, when different receptors contain different amounts of sensitive pigments, and when some of them are partly shaded by preretinal or retinal structures. Needless to say, however, if experimental conditions did change in such a way that the mean number a of quanta acting upon the retina were altered, the probability Π_x would be altered correspondingly.

Equation (1) refers only to the number of the quanta acting upon the receptors, not to their distribution in space among the receptors or in time within the duration of the exposure. It applies equally to a small and to a large test field, or even to a field divided into several distinct parts, provided the relevant number a be used in each case.

The validity of Eq. (1), within the conditions stated, rests upon basic principles of quantum theory. But the equation relates only to the *numbers* of quanta acting upon the retina. Further assumptions are required on the relationship between the conditions for a response of the visual mechanisms and the number and distribution of acting quanta. Therein lies the main difficulty in interpreting the experimental frequency-of-seeing curves.

A simple biological hypothesis. The simplest hypothesis which can be made is the following: the organism always gives a response when the number of quanta acting upon the retina is equal to or greater than n; it never gives a response when this number is less than n. (As will be explained later, this hypothesis is only at all reasonable for small fields and short exposures.) The probability of the organism giving a response is then

$$p_n = \sum_{x=n}^{\infty} \Pi_x = 1 - \sum_{x=0}^{n-1} \Pi_x \tag{2}$$

where Π_x is given by Eq. (1).

If by "response" we mean the fact that the subject signals that he has seen the illuminated test field, the frequency-of-seeing curve will be a Poisson probability sum p_n, the shape of which is determined by the single parameter n (Fig. 5). For an abscissa a equal to n, the value of p_n depends upon n; for $n = 1$ it is 0.63 and for higher values it decreases, tending to 0.50. The value of a which corresponds to a 55 per cent frequency of seeing may therefore be taken as a rough approximation to n.

The mathematical function p_n here represents the probability of the eye's receiving a light stimulus just sufficient for vision. It may be worth stating explicitly that although, as shown by Fig. 5, this probability decreases with decreasing values of the mean nominal intensity a—that is, of the intensity read on the scale of the instrument—the just sufficient stimulus, which consists of n acting quanta, is of course the same at all intensities a. At lower values of a, the subject will see the test light less and less frequently, but when he sees it he

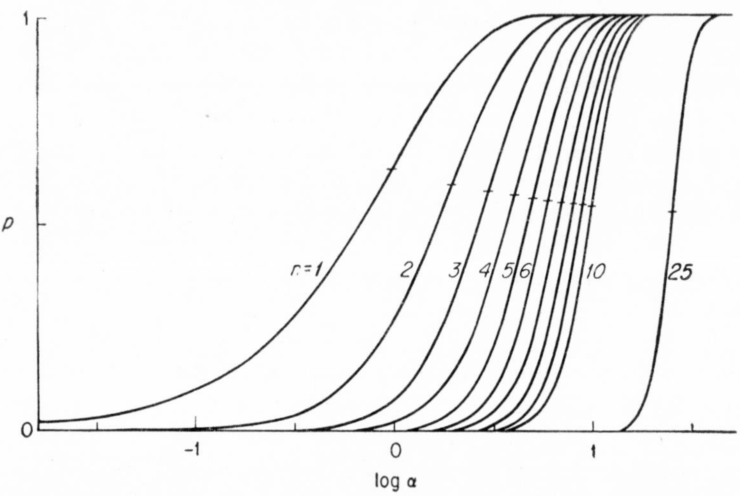

FIG. 5. The Poisson sum curves p_n for $n = 1$–10 and $n = 25$ plotted against $\log_{10} a$, a being the mean number of quanta acting upon the retina. When the condition of equivalence applies, the frequency-of-seeing curve is of this form, and a comparison of the experimental curve with these theoretical curves makes it possible to deduce the value of n. In the more general case a comparison of the slope of the experimental curve near the 55 per cent point with those of the Poisson sum curves gives a lower limit for the mean number of quanta acting upon the retina at this frequency.

The points corresponding to $a = n$ are marked on the curves. The corresponding probability, taken as approximately 55 per cent, falls from 63.2 per cent at $n = 1$ to 52.7 per cent at $n = 25$, and for values of n often suggested by practical curves, $n = 5$–10, it is very close to 55 per cent.

will be unable to distinguish it from a test light of higher nominal intensity a which would have delivered to his retina the same actual number x of quanta. Furthermore, test lights of lower nominal intensity a will sometimes be seen (or look brighter) while lights of higher a values will sometimes remain unseen (or look dimmer). As a is progressively decreased, the subject will less and less often receive stimuli the actual intensity of which is liminal or supraliminal. The relative proportion of supraliminal (x greater than n) to liminal

($x = n$) stimuli will also decrease. But stimuli of liminal intensity will not, needless to say, become fainter. Actual stimuli of liminal and supraliminal strength will merely become very rare when the nominal intensity a is made very small. There is no theoretical positive value of a below which such stimuli entirely cease to occur and the test light is never seen.

In the experiments of Hecht, Schlaer, and Pirenne [54], the number of quanta which must be absorbed by the retinal rods to make a small test field just visible in a short flash was estimated on the basis of energy measurement at the cornea to be 5 to 14 quanta, as an upper limit. (The present estimate based on more direct determinations of light absorption by the living rods is not very different: 6 to 17 quanta. See under Comparison of Experimental Frequency-of-Seeing Curves with the Theory.) On the other hand, the shape of the frequency-of-seeing curves in those experiments which were considered to be the most reliable was found to correspond approximately to Poisson sums p_n having parameters n which varied between 5 and 8 quanta, depending on the subject. As it was thought in 1942 that all absorbed quanta were also acting quanta, it was concluded that the above very simple hypothesis was not incompatible with these experimental results. It was also fully realized, however, that the accuracy of calculations and experiments was not sufficient to prove that this hypothesis was exactly true. Calculations were made—as will be explained in the next subsection—to find out how the curve would be affected if n did not remain constant during the course of the experiment. The calculations showed that n could vary to a fairly large extent without greatly affecting the shape of the frequency-of-seeing curve. This result is due to the very considerable magnitude of the purely quantum fluctuations which must be expected to occur for small values of n such as, say, 6 quanta. It was finally concluded that, even if there is a marked amount of biological variation of sensitivity, the purely physical fluctuations of the stimulus itself must play a dominant part in the uncertainty of seeing observed in these particular experiments.

At a later stage it was realized that the simple hypothesis might have to be modified on account of further physiological complications. Yet, as will be seen in the next section, the comparison just mentioned still forms the general critical test for the theory of quantum fluctuations at the absolute threshold.

It had been recognized by earlier investigators [6, 97, 18] that quantum fluctuations must play a role in the uncertainty of seeing which occurs at the absolute threshold. The fluctuations in the number of quanta entering the eye were taken into consideration but, as this number is of the order of 50 or 100, it was thought [97] that quantum fluctuations were too small to explain more than a minor part of the observed range of uncertain seeing. This discrepancy largely disappeared once it was realised that the number to be taken into consideration is not the number of quanta entering the eye—any more than, say, the number leaving the light source—but the number of quanta which are directly involved in stimulating the receptors taking part in the visual response [54, 99]. Essentially the same conclusion was reached by Brumberg, Vavilov, and Sverdlov [19] and Vavilov and Timofeeva [102, 103], and by van der Velden [104].

The above "simple biological hypothesis," while very useful as a basis for theoretical discussion, constitutes an extremely simplified, ideal form of the physical quantum theory of the absolute threshold. It is not known whether it is ever strictly valid, even in the most favorable cases. Before studying the complications which, in the case of large test fields, for instance, do certainly render it invalid, the influence of biological variations of sensitivity will be discussed.

Biological variations: variations of the retinal threshold *n*. In order to take theoretically into account the biological variations of visual sensitivity which may occur during the course of an experiment, we now assume that the simple hypothesis holds *for any single trial* but that the value of the threshold n may vary from one trial to the next. (There may be other complications, arising, for instance, when the retinal image of the test field covers several functional units; these are not considered in the present theoretical model, which implies that the "condition of equivalence" discussed in a later subsection is fulfilled.)

We assume that experimental errors and variations are negligible. The geometrical image of the test field falls on the same part of the retina in each trial. The properties of the subject's eye do not change during the experiment, there being no variations in the value of the *mean* proportion of light absorbed, because of variations in the optical density of the eye media or of the photosensitive substance contained in the receptors. Again, the subject never signals "seen" when no light has been delivered to his retinal receptors.

The modified hypothesis then states that, at any given instant of the experiment, for a given subject, the visual threshold n has a definite value. It is assumed that under any given set of experimental conditions there must be a stimulus of such intensity that it is just sufficient to elicit a response, while weaker stimuli are unable to do so; and here all stimuli, of course, consist of integral numbers of quanta.

As already stated, this considers only total numbers of quanta and disregards fluctuations in the distribution of the quanta among the rods. It can be justified by the fact that for small peripheral test fields the value of the absolute threshold is little affected by the actual area of the field, which suggests that the spatial distribution of the quanta is not very critical. It can be demonstrated that the condition for a response is not the absorption of 2 or more acting quanta in 1 rod [81]. If the distribution of the quanta among the rods affects the results, this can be formally treated in the same way as the biological variations of n here considered. A similar argument applies to temporal distribution, the threshold energy reaching a constant low value for brief flashes.

In the course of the experiment, n may thus assume different values n_1, n_2, etc. The probability p of the organism giving a response for a given value of a is then the mean of the values p_n, Eq. (2), for $n = n_1, n_2, \ldots$, etc. This mean must be taken in such a way that the values p_{n_1}, p_{n_2}, . . . are given statistical weights w_1, w_2, . . . $(\Sigma w_i = 1)$ which correspond to the proportion of trials in which n is equal to $n_1, n_2, \ldots$, etc.

$$p = w_1 p_{n_1} + w_2 p_{n_2} + w_3 p_{n_3} + \cdots \tag{3}$$

To be useful in practice, this equation requires the use of special methods of stimulus presentation, that is, that the different intensity levels should be presented in random order. Theoretically, however, it is generally applicable.

An example. Suppose that the various flashes are presented in order of decreasing (mean, nominal) intensity. First, say, 50 flashes are presented at the highest intensity used in the experiment; then 50 flashes at the next lower intensity, and so on. It is likely that the subject of the experiment will then to some extent become aware of the manner in which the stimuli are presented to him, and this will tend to affect his response. At a late stage in the experiment, the subject knows that the flashes have decreased in nominal intensity and that his chance of seeing them must also have decreased. As a result of this knowledge, he may relax his attention and respond "not seen" to a flash which delivers to his retina the same actual amount of light as a flash of higher mean intensity to which he responded "seen" at an earlier stage of the experiment. This means that the subject's retinal threshold n has become higher in this than in the earlier trial. The coefficients w relating to this subject would therefore undergo progressive changes during the course of the experiment. The mean value of n, defined as

$$\bar{n} = w_1 n_1 + w_2 n_2 + w_3 n_3 + \cdots \tag{4}$$

would accordingly increase as the experiment progresses, and would be lower for high than for low nominal intensities. Now, if the time course of the coefficients w were exactly known, it would be possible to calculate on the basis of Eq. (3) a curve which could legitimately be compared to the experimental results. In fact, it seems hardly possible to obtain independent information on the changing values of these coefficients, so that the calculation is in general impracticable. But it is interesting to consider a theoretical, imaginary, example.

Suppose that the mean intensity a is made to decrease systematically during the experiment, in steps of 0.1 $\log_{10}$ unit, and that n increases by 1 quantum each time the mean intensity goes down by one step. When the experiment starts, at the highest value $a = 10$, the threshold n is equal to 4 quanta and the flash is almost always

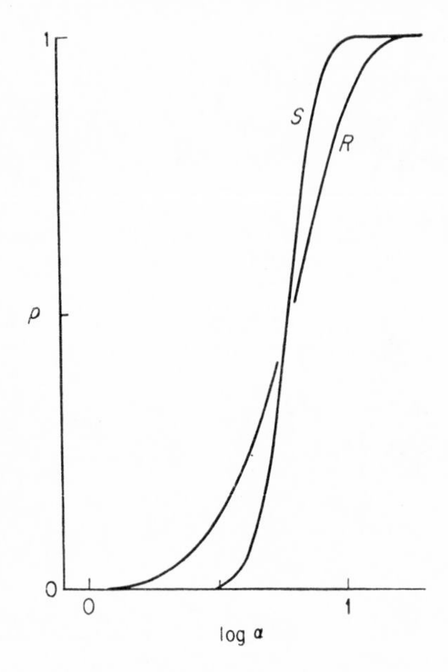

FIG. 6. Curves showing the effect of biological variations in n. Curve R is the theoretical curve when n takes the values 4–9 with equal frequency and stimuli are presented at random. The shape is rather similar to a Poisson sum, the slope being intermediate between that of the Poisson sums for $n = 4$ and $n = 5$ (apparent value $n' = 4$).

Curve S illustrates what may happen when stimuli are presented in systematic order. Groups of stimuli are presented at levels 0.1 $\log_{10}$ unit apart, in a decreasing sequence starting with $a = 10$. It is supposed that the threshold n is 4 when $a = 10$, and rises by 1 for each reduction in a, reaching $n = 9$ when $\log a = 0.5$. The mean value of n is the same as for R, but the curve is about as steep as the Poisson sum $n = 25$.

seen. Then the intensity is decreased by 0.1 $\log_{10}$ unit and n becomes 5. For the next intensity step, n becomes 6; and so on up to $n = 9$ for the lowest value of a, when the flash is almost never seen. According to Eq. (3), for the highest intensity step all the coefficients w except one are zero so that $p = p_4$; for the next step, $p = p_5$, and so forth.

Figure 6 shows the resulting curve S. It resembles the simple Poisson sum p_n [Eq. (2)] for $n = 25$; it is much steeper even than the Poisson sum for $n = 9$ (Fig. 5.) The curve R which would correspond to the same variations of n, but with randomization as will be explained presently, is also shown in Fig. 6. It is quite different from the former and resembles a Poisson sum $n = 4$.

Randomization of stimuli. Equation (3) is of practical value when the coefficients w have the same values for every point of the intensity scale at which the frequency of seeing is measured. This is so if the various flash intensities are presented at random in a sequence unknown to the subject.

The subject must not be told the values of the nominal intensities which are being presented to him. Otherwise, he may be influenced by this knowledge and there may be a systematic variation of the coefficients w with varying nominal intensity. And to prevent the subject from guessing the order of presentation, the intensities must be presented at random.

Randomization is also required to obviate the effects of drifts of sensitivity, of whatever origin, during the course of the experiment.

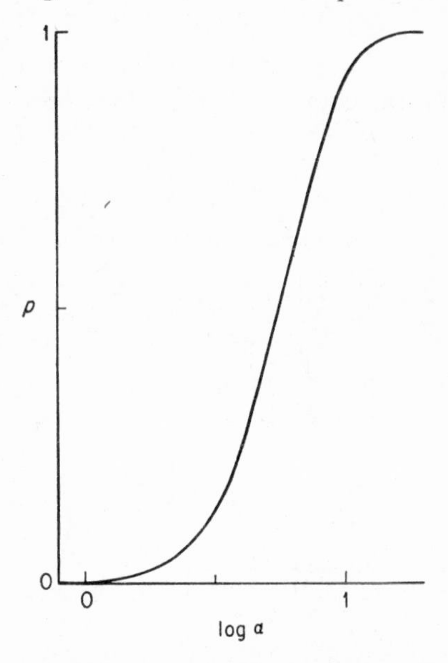

FIG. 7. A typical curve illustrating the sort of biological variations in n which are likely to arise in practice. The retinal threshold n takes the values 4,5,6,7, and 8 with relative frequencies 1,2,4,2, and 1. Stimuli are randomized. The curve is very similar to the Poisson sum for $n =$ 5, but is slightly less steep. (Apparent value $n' = 4$.)

Changes in the value of n may, for instance, be the consequence of the complex influence which a given trial may exert on later trials in the experiment; after seeing a bright flash, the subject may be "encouraged" to respond "seen" to following flashes; that is, his average threshold n may be lower after flashes reported "seen" than after those reported "not seen." Regular or irregular variations in sensitivity may also occur as the result of many other causes. If the various intensities succeed each other in random order, however, all such variations must affect with approximately the same frequency the trials made at all flash intensities. This means that the w's in Eq. (4) are independent of a.

By assuming certain plausible values, the effect of variations of n on the shape of the curve can be studied theoretically. For instance, suppose n takes the values 4, 5, 6, 7, and 8 with the statistical weights

$w_4 = 0.1$, $w_5 = 0.2$, $w_6 = 0.4$, $w_7 = 0.2$, and $w_8 = 0.1$. The resultant curve p, Eq. (3), is shown in Fig. 7. In shape it resembles the Poisson sum p_5 but it is a little less steep, being in fact intermediate between p_4 and p_5. In such cases the lower of the two values will be taken as the "apparent value n'" corresponding to the curve under consideration. Thus, the effect of the biological variations assumed here is to decrease the slope of the curve. The apparent value $n' = 4$, derived from the slope of the curve by comparison with Poisson sums of varying parameter, is lower than the weighted mean $\bar{n} = 6$ of the values assumed by n during the experiments, but it will be noted that *in this example* n' is included among the true values of n. That is, the false hypothesis n = constant would still lead to one of the true values assumed by n. (In the example of Fig. 6 where $w_4 = w_5 = \cdots = w_9$, the apparent value n' is equal to 4.) It is on the basis of such considerations that Hecht et al. [54] concluded that the greater part of the variability observed in their experiments must be ascribed to quantum fluctuations in the light stimulus itself, rather than to biological variations of sensitivity.

Figure 7 shows that, although the shape of the mean curve p is fairly similar to that of p_5, the curve as a whole is displaced relative to p_5 by about 0.09 $\log_{10}$ unit towards higher values of a.

"Conditions of equivalence" implied in the preceding theory. All the preceding discussion is based upon the hypothesis that, in any one trial, the organism will give a response, provided the retina has received n quanta or more, and will give no response if fewer than n quanta have been absorbed. While this hypothesis is not an implausible one in the case of a brief flash (e.g., 0.001 sec) and a small test field (e.g., 10′ of arc in diameter), it is certainly wrong for long exposures (e.g., 15 sec) and large test fields (e.g., 50° in diameter). The well-known facts of temporal and spatial summation show that if similar quantities of light are "concentrated" within a short time and a small retinal area they are more effective in causing visual stimulation than if they are widely spread out in time and space. Now if *nominally* a quantity of light is evenly spread out in space or time, the *actual* distribution of the absorbed quanta will not be even. Certain "concentrations" of light will occur by chance at certain times of the exposure and in certain parts of the retinal area. Whether or not the threshold of stimulation is reached, therefore, will generally depend not on the actual number x only, but also on when and where the x quanta are acting upon the retina.

Thus the use of Eqs. (2) and (3) is legitimate only when the following "condition of equivalence" is fulfilled, namely: the response produced by a given number of acting quanta is the same whatever the distribution of these quanta within the duration of the trial and within the optical image of the test field on the retina.

The case of several independent functional units. The value of the absolute threshold reaches a constant low value for exposure times below a certain value (about 0.1 sec for a 10′ field in the periphery); further concentration of the quanta in time ceases to influence the threshold value. Accordingly, it is likely that the condition of equivalence with regard to time is fulfilled when a sufficiently brief flash is used. With regard to area, on the other hand, there is no certainty that the use of a small test field leads to a similar result, even if the fluctuations in the spatial distribution of the quanta which were mentioned above are of negligible importance. For, however small the test field, we must expect more than one retinal receptor to be covered by the retinal image of the field (see Physical Fluctuations in the Number and Distribution of Quanta), and the possibility cannot be ruled out that the various receptors belong to the receptive fields of separate optic nerve fibres. The existence of overlapping receptive fields has been demonstrated by electrophysiological experiments in the vertebrate eye. What is known of the microscopic structure of the primate retina leads one to expect that the same situation may exist in the human eye [81].

The image of even a small test field may, therefore, fall upon the receptive fields of more than one functional unit.

Now for each of these units taken separately the preceding hypothesis, including the possibility of variations of n, may be expected to apply. We now assume that if the threshold of at least one of the units is reached, the subject gives a response. The probability of the subject giving a response may then be easily calculated, provided the probabilities of response for the various units be statistically independent.

For a certain nominal quantity of light reaching the retina the probability of unit A responding is p_A, that of unit B responding is p_B, that of unit C is p_C, etc. The probability p_A, for instance, will be given by an equation of the type (3), itself based on the Poisson equation (1), but here the variable a must be replaced by a_A, the mean number of quanta acting upon those receptors which belong to unit A. The probability of unit A not responding is $(1 - p_A)$, the probability of B not responding is $(1 - p_B)$, etc. Now the probabilities p_A, p_B, etc., being independent, the probability of *none* of the units A, B, C, . . . responding is $(1 - p_A)(1 - p_B)(1 - p_C) \ldots$ and the probability P of at least one of them responding, that is the probability of the organism giving a response is

$$P = 1 - (1 - p_A)(1 - p_B)(1 - p_C) \ldots \quad (5)$$

It is found experimentally that two separate retinal areas chosen sufficiently far apart will respond independently in the manner assumed above (see under Physiological Independence of Retinal Units). The situation with regard to the units contained in a single retinal area may, however, be more complex.

The above line of reasoning was used by Meetham and Lambert

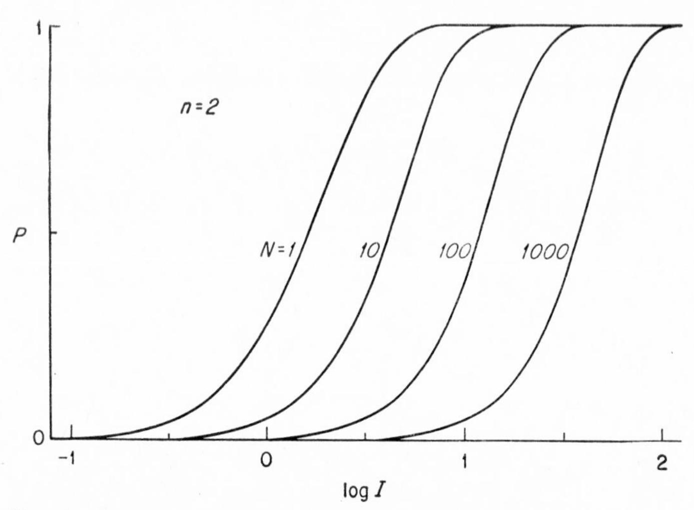

Fig. 8. Curves P arising when the condition of equivalence does not apply. N units are involved, and there is a response when any unit receives 2 quanta or more. The curves grow steeper as N increases, but reach a limiting slope for large values of N; here, the shape is almost exactly the same for $N = 100$ and $N = 1,000$, and the slope at $P = 0.55$ corresponds roughly to the Poisson sum for $n = 4$.

The abscissa scale gives $\log_{10} I = \log_{10} Na$, a being the mean number of quanta acting for each independent retinal unit and I, therefore, the mean total quantity of light acting upon the retina.

[62] and by van der Velden [104]. The related case of the binocular threshold (see the section cited above) was discussed by Pirenne [67].

Independent units all similar. The simplest case in theory is that in which $p_A = p_B = p_C = \cdots$ when Eq. (5) becomes

$$P = 1 - (1 - p_A)^N \tag{6}$$

N being the number of independent units involved. Figure 8 gives the values of P calculated on the basis $p_A = p_2$ (Poisson sum for $n = 2$) for various values of N plotted against log I, where $I = Na$, the total number of quanta required. It is seen that when N increases, the slope of the curve P plotted against log I increases, and the curve as a whole is displaced towards larger values of log I. However, the value of a, the mean number of quanta *per unit*, for a given probability, decreases with increasing N. The shape of the curve differs more and more markedly from that of a Poisson sum as N increases, and seems to be tending to a limiting shape (see below).

The above example is probably greatly oversimplified in compari-

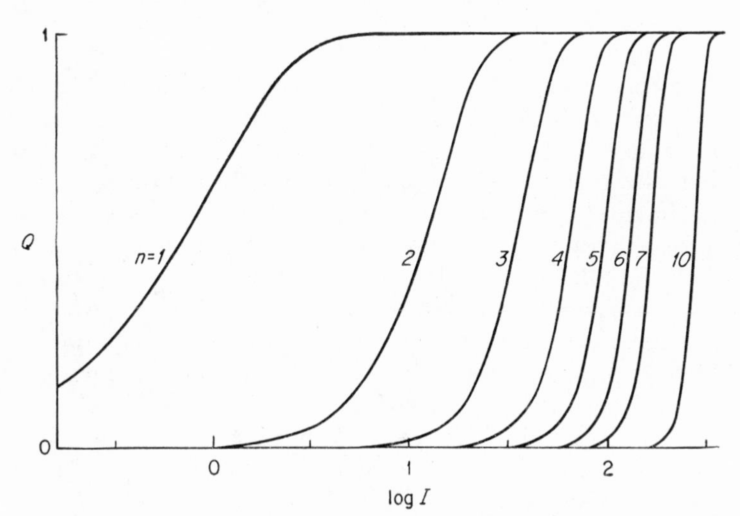

FIG. 9. Limiting curves Q for a large number N of units if there is a response whenever any one unit receives n quanta or more.

To determine the abscissa scale, $\log_{10} I\ (= Na)$, it is necessary to take some definite value of N, and here the curves are plotted for $N = 100$. It should not be assumed, however, that the limiting shape, which is shown here, is necessarily closely approximated for $N = 100$; for the larger values of n the limit is approached rather slowly.

For $n = 1$, of course, the division into units has no effect because the condition of equivalence always applies, and the curve is the same as the Poisson sum for $n = 1$ whatever the value of N.

son with reality and must be taken only as a theoretical illustration of the principles involved.

Limiting slope. Brindley [16] has demonstrated that there is a limiting value to the slope of the curve P, Eq. (6), when N increases indefinitely. His reasoning applies to time as well as to area, provided a long exposure can be considered as equivalent to a number of independent flashes of duration equal to the summation time of the retinal units.

The frequency-of-seeing curve should, for a large number of functional units or a long exposure time, tend to a limiting slope dependent on the number of quanta n (acting during the summation time) required to stimulate an individual unit. If n quanta are required to stimulate each unit, the limiting curve is

$$Q = 1 - e^{-Na^n/n!} \tag{7}$$

where Q is the probability of seeing, a the mean number of quanta absorbed per unit per summation time, and $I = Na$ the mean total number of quanta absorbed during an exposure. Examples for various values of n are given in Fig. 9.

If the conditions under which an experimental curve has been obtained were such that it must be represented by Eq. (6) in which $p_A = p_n$, n and N being unknown, it would, therefore, be possible to derive a lower value of the parameter n by comparing the shape of the experimental curve with that of the theoretical limiting curve.

Whereas the special conditions assumed above are very unlikely to be exactly fulfilled in actual experiments, Brindley [16] has shown that, at least in certain cases, the preceding argument remains valid under more realistic conditions which allow for variations in the physiological properties of the functional units and for lack of independence between them.

Other cases in which there is no equivalence. According to a different hypothesis put forward by Baumgardt [8, 9], the necessary condition for a response would be that a certain number of functional units have each been acted upon by at least 2 quanta. A numerical example is given in Fig. 10, curve B.[2]

Here, as in the case of independent units, it is necessary for a response that the acting quanta be distributed in a particular manner among the photoreceptors. The condition of equivalence is not fulfilled. Now whereas it may be difficult to decide between such theories and to ascertain what the conditions for a response actually are, there is a simple theorem which is applicable in all cases and which may serve as a general test of the physical quantum theory.

General limit set by quantum fluctuations. This theorem relates to the slope of the curve and to the *total* mean number of quanta, I (55 per cent), acting upon the retina for a frequency of seeing equal to about 55 per cent; this number will be called the "mean threshold intensity." Assume for the sake of argument that the simple biological hypothesis discussed at the beginning of this section is valid. The frequency-of-seeing curve is then the Poisson sum p_n for $n \doteq I$ (55 per cent). It can be shown [83] that the theoretical curve so calculated

[2] Baumgardt's hypothesis is in fact somewhat more complicated (private communication).

must always be as steep as or steeper than the actual curve, this actual curve in general being the resultant of quantum fluctuations, complicated physiological mechanisms, biological variations, and possibly, experimental variations. This theorem is valid only when the experimental curve has been obtained under suitable conditions, including randomization of stimuli.

Thus the slope of experimental curves obtained under suitable conditions must be smaller than or equal to the slope of a simple

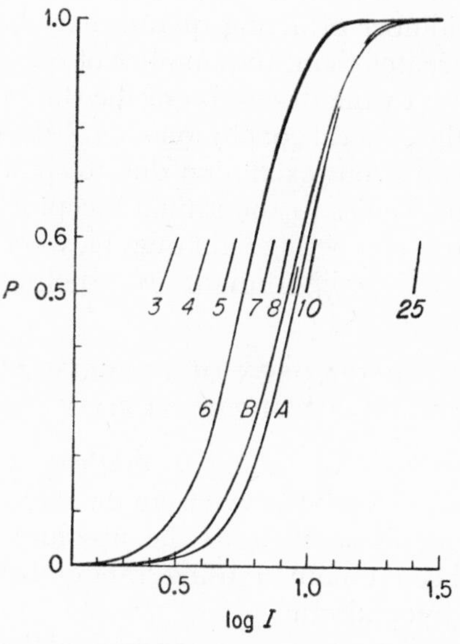

FIG. 10. Curve A represents the probability of response for the case of two independent functional units of similar characteristics for each of which $n = 6$. The total mean amount of light to be delivered to the retina for a 55 per cent probability of response is then 9.4 quanta, whereas it would be about 6 in the case of a single unit. The curve is less steep than the single Poisson sum of parameter $n = 10$ which is next above it, the slope corresponding to $n' = 7$.

Parts of the Poisson sums for values of n between 3 and 25 are shown near a probability of seeing, $P = 0.55$; the relevant value of n is indicated below each segment, except for $n = 9$, and the curve for $n = 6$ is drawn in full.

Curve B corresponds to the case where there are four similar units, the condition for a response being that three, at least, have been acted upon by 2 quanta. This curve has a 55 per cent intensity value of 8.8, whereas the minimum number of quanta required is 6. The curve is shallower than the Poisson sum for $n = 9$, which is next above it, the slope corresponding to $n' = 5$. *From Pirenne and Marriott* [83].

Poisson sum the parameter of which is approximately equal to the "mean threshold intensity." Quantum fluctuations set a limit below which the uncertainty of seeing cannot be reduced. If the simple biological hypothesis were fulfilled and there were no experimental errors or variations, the slope of the actual curve should reach this limit; in other cases it must be expected to be less steep (Fig. 10, curves A and B).

The main test of the physical quantum theory of the absolute threshold must, therefore, consist in comparing the apparent value n', that is, the parameter n of the Poisson sum having approximately the same slope as the actual curve, with the mean threshold intensity I

(55 per cent). The apparent value n' must be smaller than or equal to I (55 per cent).

Conversely, taking the quantum theory as correct, it is possible to derive from the slopes of the experimental curves a lower value of the mean threshold intensity I (55 per cent). In this connection it must always be borne in mind that the latter quantity refers not, for instance, to the quanta acting upon a particular functional unit, but to all the quanta acting upon the retina, including those which may be "wasted" with regard to causing a response. And, of course, the number of acting quanta may be smaller than or equal to, but not greater than, the number of quanta absorbed by the receptors.

In the discussion of the differential threshold, it will be seen that the general conclusion $n' \leqslant I$ (55 per cent) remains valid even if there is nervous excitation due to spontaneous activation of photopigment molecules in the retinal receptors. The quantity I (55 per cent) still refers to acting light quanta, whereas the excitation is now determined by these light quanta *plus* spontaneous activations.

COMPARISON OF EXPERIMENTAL FREQUENCY-OF-SEEING CURVES WITH THE THEORY

The preceding theoretical discussion shows that certain conclusions can be drawn from the shape of experimental frequency-of-seeing curves relating to the absolute threshold *provided* the curves have been obtained using randomization of stimuli and other suitable precautions.

In an extensive methodological investigation, Blackwell [10] showed that frequency-of-seeing curves often vary in shape and in other characteristics when the method of presenting stimuli to the subject is changed. This investigation refers to the differential threshold, but it seems likely that the main conclusions will also be applicable to the absolute threshold. Blackwell used 18 different methods of stimulus presentation; one of these ("YNR" [10], p. 18) fulfilled the main conditions of randomization, etc., which are required for comparing the experimental results with the present theory. The fact that different methods give different results shows that it is essential to select a method suited to the present purpose. However, contrary to a view sometimes put forward, it cannot invalidate the use of frequency-of-seeing curves when they are obtained by methods appropriate to the theory. Even though the use of appropriate methods will not always remove variations in shape from one curve to another, it makes it possible, for instance, to check that the value of n' never exceeds that of I (55 per cent). The aim here is not, say, to select the most convenient method for some practical purpose, but to make the experiments under the precise conditions assumed in the theoretical calculations.

Shape of the curves. It is nevertheless true that the shape of the experimental curve, considered in itself without reference to other information, is of no great value for testing the physical quantum theory. This is so for two reasons. First, large numbers of observations are needed to discriminate between a Poisson sum and, say, a log normal ogive or a normal ogive. For most experimental frequency-of-seeing curves such discrimination will therefore be very difficult. This justifies Blackwell's statement [11] that "Any theory which predicts the form of threshold data would do well to depend upon other predictions for verification." The second reason is that the physical quantum theory does not predict that the frequency-of-seeing curve must always be exactly a Poisson sum. When the condition of equivalence is not fulfilled, the theoretical curves differ from simple Poisson sums. When this condition is fulfilled but there are biological variations in the value of the retinal threshold n, the resultant curve is not exactly the same as a Poisson sum although it may be very similar to it.

Thus if it could be demonstrated that frequency-of-seeing curves relating to the absolute threshold for a small field and a brief flash were different in shape from a Poisson sum, this would merely prove that the "simple biological hypothesis" assuming both perfect "equivalence" and threshold constancy is invalid. But this hypothesis is an extreme form of the theory which has hardly ever been held by anyone to be strictly valid. For large fields and long exposures, on the other hand, the curve must theoretically be expected to differ in shape from a simple Poisson sum but for the same reason as above, it would probably be difficult to demonstrate that it is so.

The physiological mechanism of the differential threshold is much less clearly understood than that of the absolute threshold; the frequency-of-seeing curve is the result of a more complicated situation and is more likely to differ from a simple Poisson sum than in the case of the absolute threshold (see under Biological Variations and Quantum Fluctuations). Blackwell [10, p. 91] states, with regard to his investigations of the differential threshold, "As far as the present data are concerned, we may expect that suitably chosen Poisson sums *could* have been adequately fitted to the individual sets of data."

Shape and position of the curves. The crucial test of the theory consists in the comparison of the observed slope of the curve with the quantum fluctuations of the small number of quanta which must act upon the retinal photoreceptors for a threshold response, *this number being independently estimated* [54, 99]. That is, the parameter n' must be compared with the absolute value of the "mean threshold intensity," I (55 per cent), estimated by an independent method.

Test of the theory. In experiments using large fields and long exposures, to be discussed in the next section, I (55 per cent) is often much larger than n'. This is a result to be expected since, owing to the limited range of spatial and temporal summation, a great many of the quanta acting upon the retina must then be wasted. The real test of the theory is given by experiments made with small fields and brief flashes, in the retinal periphery.

The steeper curves obtained in experiments of the latter kind by Hecht et al. [54] correspond to $n' = 5$ to 8 (Fig. 11), those obtained

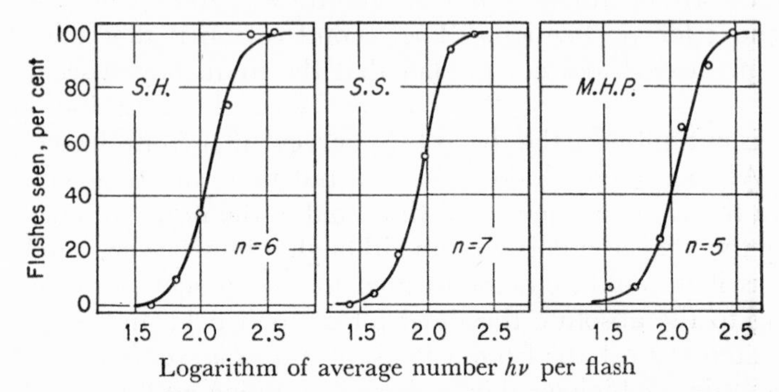

FIG. 11. Relation between the average energy content of a flash of light (in number of light quanta) and the frequency with which it is seen by three observers. Each point represents 50 flashes except for *S.H.* where it represents 35 flashes. The curves are the Poisson sums for n values of 5, 6, and 7. The abscissa scale gives the logarithm of the mean number of incident quanta measured at the cornea. *From Hecht, Shlaer, and Pirenne* [54].

by Baumgardt [7] to $n' = 4$ to 10. Rushton [93] has estimated by an ophthalmoscopic method the proportion of the light incident on the retina which becomes absorbed by the dark-adapted rods in the living human eye; this estimate is 20 per cent for $\lambda = 0.507\ \mu$ at an eccentricity of 20°. On the basis of 54 to 148 quanta for a 60 per cent frequency of seeing at the cornea [54], and assuming 50 per cent absorption by the preretinal media for the same wavelength [60], we find 5 to 14 quanta absorbed by the rods for a 55 per cent frequency of seeing. (The estimate,[3] 1 to 3 quanta [28], is based on extracted human rhodopsin and there are several reasons to think that this method leads to an underestimation of the proportion of light absorbed by the rods.) If we assume that all the quanta absorbed are effectively acting upon the rods, we have therefore I (55 per cent) $= 5$ to 14

[3] By Crescitelli and Dartnall.

quanta, which is larger than $n' = 4$ to 10. Various uncertainties in the estimation of I (55 per cent) make it hardly possible to compare this quantity exactly with the parameter n' but the order of magnitude seems undoubtedly the same for both parameters. In the hypothesis [81] that a quantum absorbed has only one chance in two to cause stimulation—a possibility suggested by the work of Hagins [45]—the quantity I (55 per cent) would become 2.5 to 7 quanta, that is, rather less than n', but the difference could hardly be taken as significant in view of the difficulty of the measurements. Thus, the available evidence, which is further discussed in [81],[4] is in agreement with the theory, and indicates that quantum fluctuations play a dominant role in these experiments. There is no evidence that the inequality considered at the end of the discussion of Theory of Frequency-of-Seeing Curves for the Absolute Threshold is not satisfied.

In the experiments made by Hecht et al. [54] the various flash intensities were presented at random, mixed with "blanks" also at random. This was known to the subject but otherwise he was given no information on the actual course to be taken by the experiment. The main condition for comparing experimental and theoretical curves was thus fulfilled. The subject operated the shutter himself when he felt ready for a flash, thus being able to select the conditions which subjectively appeared the best to him; for instance, he could as a rule avoid the moments when brighter phosphenes appeared in the part of the visual field where the actual light stimulus was expected. Assuming that a subject may go through periods of heightened and lowered sensitivity during an experiment, such a method may help to eliminate the influence of the periods of lower sensitivity and thus lead to more constant results than when the stimulus is presented to the subject at intervals chosen by the experimenter.

The curves published by Hecht et al. were all "good" curves, that is, they were (relatively) steep curves obtained under the most reliable conditions.

They were given by subjects who never answered "seen" in response to "blanks." Steeper curves than these could not be obtained, but "bad" curves having a greater range of uncertain seeing were obtained by Hecht et al. in certain cases. Two subjects at first gave extremely shallow curves—some of which were even shallower than the Poisson sum for $n = 1$. The curves gradually became steeper as the subjects repeated the measurements, finally corresponding to $n = 5$ to 7, but they never became smooth enough to be included in

[4] In this review article, a slightly larger estimate, namely, 24 per cent instead of 20 per cent, was used for the proportion of light absorbed by the rods, but this does not affect the argument.

the publication. In the case of more reliable subjects, occasional "bad" curves are generally associated with fatigue or other conditions which seem likely to conduce to high biological variations. Large biological or experimental variations of course become combined with the purely physical fluctuations and can thus lead to very wide ranges of uncertain seeing.

Other experiments made using small fields and brief flashes. Van der Velden [104] and Bouman obtained shallower curves than Hecht et al. [54]. The slope corresponds approximately to $n' = 2$ according to the authors, although judging from van der Velden's [104] diagrams, the value $n' = 3$ would seem to give a better fit. In this connection Bouman [13] referring to the remark—published by Denton and Pirenne [30]—that experienced subjects tend to give steeper curves than inexperienced ones, writes: "Actually, our findings are essentially the reverse. Perhaps—because of the very large number of frequency of seeing curves measured by each of our subjects under various conditions—the experience obtained by each observer in our investigation is larger." In the absence of further details on the experimental methods used, it would seem difficult to form an exact opinion on this observation but it seems strange at first sight that experienced subjects gave a greater experimental scatter than inexperienced ones, the magnitude of this scatter apparently reaching a stabilized value after suitable training.

Peyrou and Piatier [66] worked with flashes of randomized intensity, mixed with blanks, and presented in a sequence unknown to the subject. Using a field subtending 2′ at the eye and placed about 25° from the fixation point, they obtained for three subjects frequency-of-seeing curves having parameters n' equal to 2, 3, and 5. The first subject, for whom $n' = 2$, answered "seen" to some of the blanks. Using a 4′ field, the authors found $n' = 5$ and $n' = 6$ for the two latter subjects.[5] These results are therefore in general agreement with those of Hecht et al. [54].

Brumberg, Vavilov, and Sverdlov [19], on the other hand, obtained steeper curves than Hecht et al. [54]. The parameters n' defining the slope of the curves for four subjects were 18, 23, 29, and 32 quanta; in another series of experiments made in 1936 the parameters were found to be 30 and 8 for two subjects. In earlier experiments, Brumberg and Vavilov [18] had found $n' = 47$ for the subject who gave $n' = 30$ in 1936. All these values except $n' = 8$ are markedly higher than those obtained by Hecht et al. It seems that this rather puzzling difference between the results of two groups of authors who

[5] The time of exposure in these experiments was 0.02 sec. We are indebted for this and other details quoted above to a personal communication from Monsieur C. Peyrou.

performed similar experiments independently of one another may be explained by the fact that Brumberg et al. did not randomize the stimulus intensities. Many flashes were presented together at each chosen intensity, and it seems that the intensity was decreased in a regular series, or that the subject altered it himself. Now the first method of stimulus presentation, according to the experiments of Blackwell [10], can lead to a considerable increase of the slope of the curve. Again, the theoretical example relating to Fig. 6 shows that a systematic variation of retinal threshold n during the course of a non-randomized experiment may lead to a curve much steeper than that calculated for the same variations of n but with randomization. It seems likely, therefore, that the higher values of n' obtained by Brumberg et al. may largely be ascribed to the particular method of presentation used by these authors. In any case, on account of the lack of randomization, it would not be legitimate to compare these n' values with independent estimates of I (55 per cent) with a view to obtaining a critical test of the theory.

Crozier [29], experimenting with a small field in the fovea, found in some experiments that the slope of the frequency-of-seeing curve (corresponding to n') changed when the subject breathed oxygen instead of air, while on the other hand the position of the 55 per cent point on the scale of intensity, measured at the cornea, was hardly affected. From this and other related results on the use of oxygen, Crozier concludes that his experimental curves cannot be represented by the simple Poisson sums of Eq. (2), for in these Poisson sums $n' = n \doteq I$ (55 per cent) so that the slope could not vary without change in position. This conclusion seems inescapable, but it only implies that the ideal conditions of "equivalence" and threshold constancy do not hold in the corresponding experiments. Suppose the condition of equivalence is fulfilled, but there are variations of the retinal threshold n; if these variations are smaller when oxygen is breathed instead of air, the curve may become steeper without being displaced on the intensity axis. Again, if the condition of equivalence does not hold, breathing oxygen might change some of the functional nervous connections in the fovea, which in turn might lead to independent variations of n' and of I (55 per cent). Crozier's experiments can therefore be explained in various ways without abandoning the physical quantum theory; his experiments only disprove the extreme form of this theory, corresponding to the "simple biological hypothesis" presented earlier. (The experiments under discussion were made using a "very small red fixation dot appearing just above the test field as a threshold red." It would seem that such an arrangement might introduce certain complications in the experiment.)

Crozier does not make the critical comparison of n' with I (55 per cent), but in cone vision the latter quantity would be harder to estimate than in the case of rod vision [see 81]. It would appear that Crozier rejects the notion of physical fluctuations in the number of quanta absorbed by the retina, explaining the variability of response entirely on the basis of biological variations of sensitivity occurring in the nervous system, but he does not put forward a direct refutation of the existence of these quantum fluctuations.

Conclusion. Application of the critical test in which the values of n' and I (55 per cent) are compared reveals no contradiction between experiments and theory. There is no evidence to prove that fluctuations can be reduced below the minimum predicted by the quantum theory.

In some experiments, the magnitude of the observed fluctuation comes close to the value of the theoretical minimum. This indicates that the quantum fluctuations in these cases must dominate the situation. It does not, however, rule out the existence of a certain amount of biological variability and of various complications in the nervous mechanisms involved.

On the basis of the quantum theory, the existence of considerable fluctuations of purely physical origin seems to be established beyond all doubt. If a critic were to argue that the observed uncertainty of response is entirely of biological origin, he would also have to prove that the physical fluctuations predicted by the quantum theory do not take place in these experiments on the living eye.

BIOLOGICAL VARIATIONS AND QUANTUM FLUCTUATIONS

In order to study biological variations in relative isolation, it is necessary to design experiments in which a large number of quanta are involved, but this may not be sufficient. A large proportion of the quanta may be wasted, the outcome of the experiment being determined by a small fraction only of the light entering the eye.

Large fields and long exposures. In absolute threshold measurements made with a 45° field and 5-sec exposures [33], the number of quanta acting upon the retina in each exposure is of the order of 20,000. If complete spatial and temporal integration took place in the visual system, the quantum fluctuations would be reduced to their theoretical lower limit. This corresponds approximately to a range of uncertain seeing (defined on the theoretical curve as from 0.14 to 99.86 per cent seen) of $20{,}000 \pm 3 \times \sqrt{20{,}000} = 20{,}000 \pm 424$, that is, a range of 0.018 $\log_{10}$ units. Thus here the threshold might theoretically be very sharply defined, but of course, integration of the light stimulus falls far short of the ideal assumed above. It is probable that the test field is seen when at least one, or a few, of the larger functional units of the retina (which have a diameter of about 1° or more) have by chance absorbed a threshold number of quanta, of the order of 10 or less, within their action time (which is equal to about 0.1 sec).

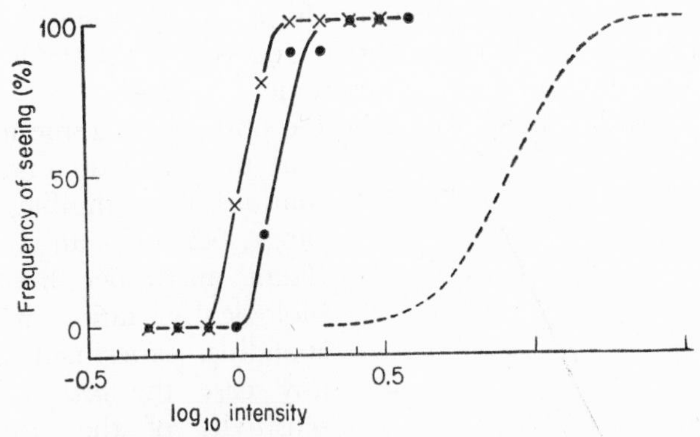

FIG. 12. Curves (full lines) giving the frequency with which a 45° field, presented binocularly without fixation in 5-sec exposures, was seen at different light intensities by two subjects. Crosses (×) refer to subject M.H.P., black circles (•) to E.J.D. Each experimental point refers to 10 exposures at one given intensity. On the abscissa scale, log intensity = 0 corresponds to an intensity of 7.52×10^{-7} erg/sec × steradian × cm^2 (field) for light of wavelength $\lambda = 0.51\mu$. For purposes of comparison, the curve (dotted line) on the right of the figure gives the shape of the Poisson sum for $n = 5$. This curve is positioned arbitrarily on the log intensity scale. Frequency-of-seeing curves of similar shape to this theoretical curve were obtained [54] for subject M.H.P. using a 10′ test field presented uniocularly 20° from a fixation point in 1 msec flashes (Fig. 11). In terms of the total amount of energy entering the eye during one single exposure, the curves representing the latter experiments should be placed on the log. intensity scale about 3 $\log_{10}$ units below the steeper curves (full lines) obtained under the present conditions. *From Denton and Pirenne* [33].

The experimental range of uncertain seeing was about 0.3 and 0.4 $\log_{10}$ unit in two subjects in "good" experiments (Fig. 12). In a subject who was tired ("bad" experiment) the range was greater, namely 0.6 $\log_{10}$ unit (Fig. 13). This increase in the range of uncertain seeing is clearly due to an increase in magnitude of the biological variations. It may also be surmised that the greater range of one of the two subjects in the "good" experiments was due to greater biological instability. The smaller range observed, 0.3, must stem from a combination of biological and physical variations, but their respective shares cannot readily be calculated because detailed quantitative information on the mechanisms involved is not available.

Although Brindley's limiting curves (Fig. 9, discussed earlier under Limiting slope), for $n = 2$ or 3 are certainly shallower than the good experimental curves, the curve for $n = 5$ quanta gives a reasonable fit. This shows that the "good" curves might theoretically be explained by quantum fluctuations alone.

If on the other hand we make the opposite extreme assumption that the effect of quantum fluctuations is negligible, the total range, 0.3 $\log_{10}$ units, must represent an upper limit for the biological variations in the corresponding experiments. Thus in any case the *average* biological sensitivity of the visual system taken as a whole—eye, brain, and motor mechanisms—cannot have varied from one 5-sec trial to another by more than a factor of 1 to 2. It may have varied by much less than this.

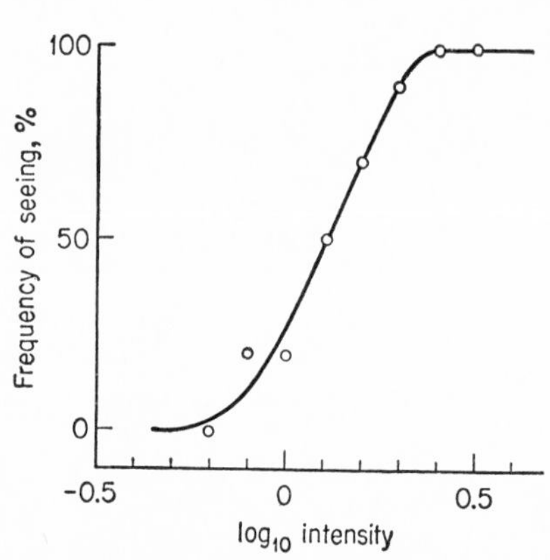

FIG. 13. Frequency-of-seeing curve, obtained under the same conditions as the full-line curves of Fig. 12 but for a subject (M.H.P.) who fell ill with influenza the day after the experiment. *From Denton and Pirenne* [33].

In these experiments the various intensities were presented at random, mixed with "blanks." The subject was free to choose his own time for each trial. It may perhaps be emphasized that the above reasoning refers exclusively to the average biological sensitivity during the individual 5-sec trials and gives no information about the sensitivity during the intervals of rest between trials. Again, larger biological variations may possibly have occurred during the course of each 5-sec trial, but this does not affect the present conclusion which is concerned only with the average over 5 sec.

Detection of dark targets. In more complicated experiments on the detection of dark targets against a low intensity background (representing ships on the horizon seen against a night sky) smaller ranges of uncertain seeing, about 0.1 $\log_{10}$ unit or less (Fig. 14), were obtained in a number of subjects [27]. This shows that in certain visual experiments the upper limit of the biological variations can be reduced to less than 0.1 $\log_{10}$ unit.

The detailed interpretation of the experiments is not straightforward, but it seems likely that the detection of the dark targets is due to the coming into play of "off-fibers" [47; see also 81]. These presumably summate the action of light for a much longer period than the retinal action time (about 0.1 sec) which applies to vision of bright targets,

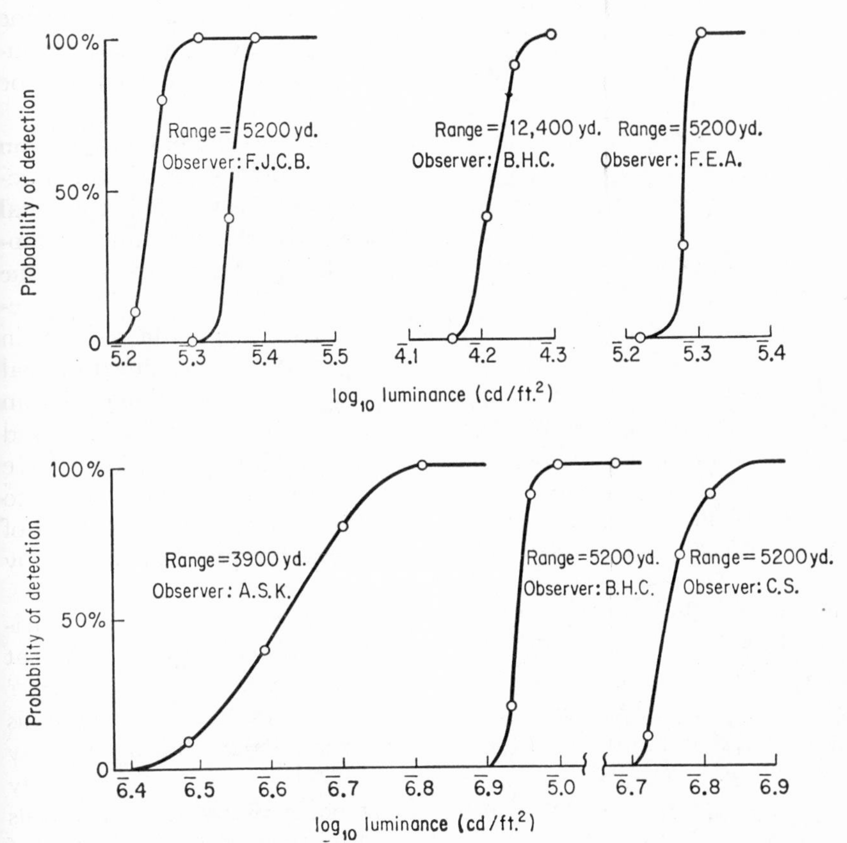

FIG. 14. Relation between probability of detection and field luminance using 7 × 50 bloomed binoculars for various subjects and various simulated ranges, the target being an armed trawler of assumed size 100 by 10 ft. *From Crawford and Pirenne* [27].

and they respond when the dark image of the target falls upon their receptive field as a result of a movement of the eye. In 10 sec the number of quanta absorbed in the receptive field would be of the order of 2,000, which corresponds to a minimum range of uncertain seeing, defined as above, of 0.06 $\log_{10}$ unit. The narrow range observed might therefore be explained on such a basis.

Experiments on the detection of a black target under conditions which should not involve off-mechanisms gave much shallower curves [27], a fact which gives support to the hypothesis that, in the above experiments, the detection of the dark target depended on the action of off-mechanisms capable of long-range temporal summation.

Quantum fluctuations at high intensities. The shallowness of most experimental frequency-of-seeing curves, for instance those relating to intensity discrimination [64], may be due to the fact that even when a large total number of quanta enters the eye in each trial, the subject's response may be determined by much smaller numbers of quanta acting on particular retinal units such as single foveal cones. Whereas the absolute threshold for large fields is of the order of 10^{-6} cd/m^2, an intensity of the order of 1 cd/m^2 is probably required to deliver a few quanta to a single cone during the action time. Quantum fluctuations must therefore be expected at the beginning of the cone vision range of intensities.

At higher intensities, the number of quanta reaching the retina will be increased. Because of the bleaching of pigment [94, 17], the number of quanta absorbed by the retina will not increase proportionately, but it may nevertheless become very high. Yet the changes which take place in the retina in such a state of light adaptation are not well understood, and it is possible that the chance of an absorbed quantum becoming an "acting" quantum may decrease under such conditions. Wald [108] has suggested a mechanism which would lead to such a decrease in quantum efficiency for the case of the rods; Wald's hypothesis however cannot account for the effects of light adaptation on the *Limulus* preparation studied by Hartline, Milne, and Wagman [49]. Indeed little is known for certain concerning the mechanism of the visual process at high intensity levels, so that it would be unsafe to assume that quantum fluctuations must then necessarily become negligible.

Experiments without randomization of stimuli. Bornschein [12] determined the absolute threshold by a different method, as follows: while the dark-adapted subject fixed his gaze on a fixation point, white light was flashed for 0.5 sec every 1.5 sec on to a 5° field placed 15° from the fixation point. The first intensity level presented was too low for the subject to see the test field; its value was chosen at random by the experimenter and was unknown to the subject. The intensity was then increased progressively in steps, the size of which was chosen to suit each experiment. Two flashes were presented at each intensity level. The threshold value was defined as that intensity at which the subject first reported a flash as seen. No blanks were used. One threshold determination required 30 sec. Using this method, Bornschein observed in a number of subjects marked cyclical variations in the threshold value, having periods of between 6 and 10 min and amplitudes of about 0.5 or 0.6 $\log_{10}$ unit. Other subjects gave a much smaller range of variation, roughly 0.1 $\log_{10}$ unit with little evidence of cyclical variations in time.

It will be noted that the light stimuli here succeeded each other rather quickly, every 1.5 sec, whereas in the experiments of Hecht et al. [54] the interval between them was much longer, of the order of 15 sec, and the subject was free to operate the shutter when he felt conditions were best. As a result of this the disturbing effect of phosphenes which Bornschein noticed in some experiments must have been lessened in the experiments of Hecht et al.

Even apart from these considerations, Bornschein's method in fact differs considerably from the ordinary frequency-of-seeing method. The possibility cannot be ruled out that in Bornschein's experiments the subject, consciously or unconsciously, estimates the threshold—as defined in these experiments—by a method which makes use of the whole information available to him, including his knowledge of the fact that the nominal intensities of the flashes increase in a definite manner. That is, the fact that a subject reports the first flash as seen, thus determining the threshold value, may not be merely the outcome of the subject's response to this flash taken in isolation, but may also be based on the subjective appearance of all the flashes presented to him, even though he does not report them as seen.

The number of quanta acting upon the retina at threshold for a 5° field and a 0.5-sec exposure is of the order of 100. This leads to a range of uncertain seeing, defined as above, of about 0.3 $\log_{10}$ unit. This is less than the amplitude of the cyclical variations observed in some of Bornschein's subjects, but it is greater than the narrower range of (apparently random) variations, about 0.1 $\log_{10}$ unit, which was observed in some subjects. The above estimate, 0.3 $\log_{10}$ unit, is approximate only, yet there is prima facie evidence that in some subjects the observed range is narrower than would be theoretically possible if the subjects responded to each flash in complete isolation. This supports the above interpretation.

The wide cyclical variations observed in some subjects must be largely biological in origin, for purely quantum fluctuations should of course be completely random. Of course, the fact that large biological variations are observed in some experiments is no proof that similar variations will occur in all experiments. Indeed the results just discussed would suggest that for some of Bornschein's subjects a high degree of biological stability was achieved.

Using somewhat different methods, Lee, Finch, and Pounds [57] had earlier reported threshold variations similar to Bornschein's

[12]. These variations occurred only in about one-third of the subjects examined by these authors. The higher visual stability of the other two-thirds seems susceptible of the same general explanation as that observed in a proportion of Bornschein's subjects. In some of the experiments of Lee et al., however, the subject himself controlled the stimulus intensity by turning a knob, a fact which may have introduced nonvisual factors in the experiments. Apparently neither Lee et al. nor Bornschein used "blanks" in their investigations.

Bornschein, as well as Lee et al., suggests that the results of Hecht et al. might largely be due, not to quantum fluctuations, but to biological variations. There is no evidence to support this suggestion. In both sets of experiments, some of the subjects give a range of uncertain seeing of the order predicted by quantum theory for the relevant experimental conditions, while other subjects give a wider range which is readily explained by the coming into play of other factors, including biological variations, in addition to the purely physical quantum fluctuations.

In this connection, it has perhaps not always been realized that if it could be demonstrated that the fluctuations expected on the basis of the quantum theory of light did in fact fail to occur this would be a discovery of fundamental importance for physical theory. The experiments of Hecht et al. might logically be considered as an unsuccessful attempt at such a demonstration.

Nonindependence of successive responses. Verplanck, Collier, and Cotton [106] have made experiments in which they found that a subject's successive responses "seen" or "not seen" to a series of flashes were not independent. In these experiments for the most part a single light intensity level was used with continuous fixation and flashes were either presented at regular intervals or controlled by the subject who operated the shutter. Under these conditions Verplanck et al. found two systematic effects: (1) slow fluctuations in sensitivity without any marked trend or regular cycle; (2) a tendency—apart from (1)—to respond more readily "seen" after a flash also reported "seen."

These effects, however, were much reduced when fixation was relaxed between flashes. When several levels were presented in randomized order, (2) was absent though (1) was still present. Later work showed that effect (1) can be minimized by long intertrial intervals, 10-sec intervals being sufficient for this purpose.

While designing practical methods of threshold measurements, other workers were led to suspect the existence of effects of the type here systematically studied by Verplanck et al. For instance, although on a priori statistical grounds it might seem that measurements at a single intensity level should be very efficient, in practice they are often found to be unreliable (see remarks in [84] on [48]). No doubt this is one of the reasons which led Stiles and Crawford [101] and independently Hartline and McDonald [48] to develop a practical method in which observations are made at a number of intensity levels ranging from "never seen" to "always seen."

As far as their effect on frequency-of-seeing curves is concerned, effects (1) and (2) may be treated as biological variations in the mathematical calculations, as explained under Theory of Frequency-of-Seeing Curves for the Absolute Threshold. It does not seem possible from the main data given by Verplanck et al. [106] to determine the effects in experiments of the type performed by Hecht et al. [54], because the conditions were different. Collier, Cotton, and Verplanck, however, conducted a number of other investigations on the problem of nonindependence of successive responses [24, 25, 26, 107]. According to a personal communication from Dr. Verplanck, later work confirmed that randomization of stimulus intensities here can eliminate serial dependencies of type (2). Variations of type (1) were observed in the second as in the first series of investigations, but, as stated above, their importance can be greatly reduced by intertrial intervals of 10 sec or more—as used by Hecht et al. [54].

If quantum fluctuations were the only cause of variations, the responses "seen" and "not seen" for a given nominal flash intensity would occur at random throughout the experiment and be independent of the intensities of and responses to preceding flashes. The systematic trends observed by Verplanck et al., therefore, prove that there are other sources of variations. Since these variations can hardly be ascribed to the apparatus, they must be largely biological in origin.

The extent of these biological variations may be expected to vary from one experiment to another. It would have been interesting to analyze from the present standpoint the results of the experiments of Hecht et al. [54] but unfortunately the records are no longer available. The results of Verplanck et al. suggest that in such experiments biological variations are small in extent.

This kind of analysis may make it possible to estimate the extent of the biological fluctuations in experiments of the type made by Hecht et al. [54]. Assuming that the condition of equivalence is fulfilled, the problem would be to derive information about the various values assumed by the retinal threshold n with their respective statistical weights w (see under Theory of Frequency-of-Seeing Curves for the Absolute Threshold). Such a derivation must perforce be based on the assumption that the physical quantum theory is correct. By the nature of the case, purely physical fluctuations may occur and be studied in isolation, but biological variations can only be observed in combination with a certain amount of physical fluctuations. The problem here is to disentangle the two.

Experiments made by Riezler, Esper, and Meurers [89] are of interest in the present connection. These authors found that the frequency-of-seeing curves obtained in short sittings were steeper than the average curve obtained by combining the results of several of these short sittings. Biological variations occurred for one subject from one short sitting to another, causing changes in both position and shape of the frequency-of-seeing curve. This of course led to a flattening of the average curve. It must be pointed out however that the frequency-of-seeing curves obtained for a number of subjects by Hecht et al. [54] in long single sittings (300 flashes) were as steep as the curves obtained in short sittings by Riezler et al. Thus the subjects used by the latter authors must have been less "stable" than those used by Hecht et al. The question whether a certain amount of biological variations did or did not occur in the case of the *steepest* curves obtained by either group of workers remains unsettled.

To summarize, biological variations can take three forms:

1. Slow variations in sensitivity. These should show up in the record as differences in threshold in different parts of the experiment. Obvious cases of this form of variation would occur if insufficient time were allowed for dark adaptation, so that the threshold was higher at the beginning of the experiment, or if the subject became fatigued, so that the threshold rose at the end of the experiment.

2. A relationship between successive responses. This could be due to some sort of physiological or psychological facilitation by a flash which was in fact seen, or if sufficiently bright flashes were used, an opposite effect might be caused by dazzle. This would appear as a difference in the proportion of responses to a particular level according to whether the previous flash was seen—but such an effect might also be produced by variations of type 1.

3. Purely random biological variations from flash to flash. These cannot be distinguished from random physical variations by mere examination of the records; they may be inferred if, for example, a subject sometimes produces much shallower curves than usual without a large change of threshold and without any evidence of nonrandomness in his responses.

The estimation from experimental records of the parts played by random and nonrandom variations is a difficult statistical problem. It is clear, however, that if there are marked effects of types 1 and 2, these must, provided proper precautions are taken to insure the stability of the apparatus, arise from biological causes, and must lead to a flattening of the response curve and to a value of n' considerably less han I (55 per cent). If on the other hand there is no evidence of nonrandomness, then biological variations only of type 3 can be nvolved. If n' is nearly equal to I (55 per cent), it may be concluded hat the biological variations are not a major factor, and, further, that he condition of equivalence provides a good approximation to the actual state of affairs—the "simple biological hypothesis" of the ection on Theory of Frequency-of-Seeing Curves for the Absolute Threshold thus being a good approximation.

Electrophysiological experiments. On the subject of quantum luctuations of the visual threshold, Granit [42] wrote in a review article: "Flamant and Stiles [37] point out that there are biological variations also to be taken into account. This, of course, is true as all the work on the fluctuating 'brain waves' shows." Yet there seems to be ittle evidence available on the relationship between "brain waves" and the subject's response at the absolute threshold of vision, particuarly from a quantitative standpoint, so that the existing information hardly throws any light on the magnitude of the biological variations which may occur in threshold experiments.

On the other hand Granit [41], in recording electrically the impulse in single fibers of the retina, found at the threshold a "fluctuation of excitability," or rather a fluctuation of response, to which he did not ascribe a definite origin. It would seem that this observation might also be explained in part by physical fluctuations of the light stimulus itself.

Strong evidence for such fluctuations was found by Hartline, Milne, and Wagman [49] in a study of the single optic nerve fiber preparation of the king crab. This has not yet been published in full; because of the importance of this work, the authors' own preliminary communication is reproduced here.

The uncertainty of response of single visual sense cells to repeated flashes of light of "constant" intensity has been studied by recording the action potentials of single fibers dissected from the optic nerve of *Limulus*. A series of short flashes delivered to the eye at a given intensity near threshold elicits occasional responses of one or more nerve impulses, interspersed among failures to respond. Occurrence of responses in any given series is random, according to statistical tests. The frequency of occurrence of responses increases with increasing intensity of the flashes. In most dark adapted preparations, the intensity range within which frequency of responses is greater than zero and less than 100% covers approximately one logarithmic unit. This range is not measurably affected by a temperature change of 10°C. A similar uncertainty has been found for eliciting responses equal to or exceeding some fixed number of impulses greater than one; the greater this number, the narrower is the range of uncertainty.

Light adaptation raises the threshold of the sense cell; at the same time the range of uncertainty is narrowed, on a logarithmic scale of intensity. This effect is reversed by dark adaptation.

The uncertainty of response might be explained by statistical fluctuations in the number of quanta absorbed from the "constant" flash, following the explanation that has been suggested for the uncertainty of seeing by human observers. Possibility of fluctuations in sensitivity of the receptor cell and its axone, analogous to those reported for axones stimulated electrically, must also be considered.

THE DIFFERENTIAL THRESHOLD AND "DARK NOISE"

The differential threshold. In experiments to determine the differential threshold, or contrast threshold, a flash may be superposed on a small "test area" of a luminous background. The subject is required to say whether he can distinguish the flash against the background.

For low background intensities, the quantum nature of light will lead to fluctuations in the actual numbers of quanta from the test area acting on the retina and hence to frequency-of-seeing curves similar to those found in measurements of the absolute threshold. The theory underlying these curves, however, is complicated by the presence of the luminous background. Mueller [63] has discussed the theory of these curves and made experiments for foveal vision [64]. We shall outline here some considerations relating mostly to the simpler case of rod vision.

Suppose that x quanta from the flash act on the retina, and that, in a period equal to the retinal action time and including the flash, y quanta from the test area arising from the background illumination act on the retina. (It is assumed here that the appropriate summation time and area are known.) The quantities x and y may be supposed to follow independent Poisson distributions with means m_x and m_y, and, by a well-known theorem, $x + y$ also follows a Poisson distribution with mean $m_x + m_y$.

Now it is reasonable to suppose that the observer reports the flash as "seen" whenever $x + y$ is sufficiently greater than m_y, the mean number of background quanta from the test area. Consequently, the frequency-of-seeing curve will correspond to a Poisson sum in which $x + y$ (and not x) is the variable [63]. Further, it may be plausibly postulated that the level at which the flash is reported seen will correspond to a constant low probability (independent of m_y) of seeing blanks; that is, the subject will respond "seen" whenever the probability of getting so many quanta from the test area, if it were illuminated only by the background illumination, falls below a certain level.

Unless m_y is very small, y may be regarded, to a first approximation, as normally distributed with mean m_y and standard deviation $\sqrt{m_y}$. Then the last paragraph implies that, roughly speaking, the subject responds "seen" whenever

$$x + y > m_y + r\sqrt{m_y} \tag{8}$$

where r is a constant independent of m_y. The conclusions of this paragraph were obtained by Rose [90, 91] who reasoned from a comparison of the retina, regarded as an optical instrument, with the photographic film and the television pick-up. Similar square-root relationships were independently suggested by de Vries [105] and Pirenne [68].

Equation (8) is based on a number of approximations, and can be expected to give a reasonable approximation to the differential threshold over only a limited range of values of m_y. Both at the lower end of the scale, near the absolute threshold, and for higher intensities, where the cones may begin to play a part, other considerations may outweigh the arguments of this section. It would seem to be a fairly simple matter to test the validity of Eq. (8); a plot of the 55 per cent value of the *additional* light m_x against the square root of the background intensity should give a straight line with a slope depending on r, or a plot of log m_x against log m_y should give a straight line with slope ½. In practice Stiles [98] using a 1° field in the parafovea obtained results in good agreement with this theory, but later, using a large (9°) test field [1] found a slope of about 1. The practical problem is complicated by the question of light adaptation, which may affect the experimental results. The changes brought about in the retina and visual nervous system by the action of a continuous luminous background are not clearly understood. There is a further theoretical complication which may upset this model; this is considered in the next section.

Possibility of spontaneous excitation in the visual system ("dark noise"). Visual purple in vitro bleaches slowly even in the complete absence of light, and in electrophysiological preparations a considerable background of spontaneous excitation is often observed. It seems probable that the molecules of visual pigment in the intact eye may also occasionally react spontaneously. These spontaneous excitations may or may not produce the same effect as excitations caused by light. Thus it may possibly be that all vision can be regarded as the detection of light stimuli against a continuous faint background of random spontaneous action in the retina. (This does not, of course, imply that a subject in complete darkness would necessarily be aware of a luminosity arising from spontaneous action in his retina. It is well

known that a subject whose eye is exposed to a uniform faint illumina
tion ceases to be conscious of it and cannot detect changes of intensit
if these are made sufficiently slowly.)

If this view is correct, Eq. (8) must be modified. If z molecules ar
spontaneously excited in the test area during the retinal action time
and z follows a Poisson distribution with mean m_z, then the conditio
for seeing becomes

$$x + y + z > m_y + m_z + r\sqrt{m_y + m_z} \qquad (9$$

The rate of spontaneous excitation in the living eye is not known
If it is of very low intensity, the interpretation of experiments such a
those of Hecht et al. [54] is hardly affected [33]. If, however, it is o
considerable magnitude in comparison with the stimuli involved, i
may modify the conclusions to be drawn from absolute threshol
experiments.

The estimation of the parameters in Eq. (9) is not an easy matter
because the range of validity of the equation is not known. The param
eter m_z may vary from subject to subject, and may undergo variatio
with time in one and the same subject. The parameter r define
quantitatively the criterion of "seeing" adopted by the subject: i
may undergo similar variations, and may even be consciously varie
by the subject—that is, the subject may, by responding "seen" in al
cases in which he has any sensation of a flash, respond to a highe
proportion of flashes at the expense of responding to a higher (thoug
still small) proportion of blanks. Rose [90] suggested the value $r = 5$
but Barlow [5] considers that smaller values may be appropriate i
some circumstances.

Dark noise and the absolute threshold. As long ago as 1945
Hecht [52] suggested that the reason why a single light quantum wa
not sufficient for vision was that its effect would be confused with a
spontaneous excitation occurring in a single rod, whereas the chanc
of, say, six such spontaneous excitations occurring together in such a
way that they would be confused with a genuine 6-quantum signa
would be much smaller. Yet, provided the dark noise level is no
quite nil, the probability of confusions of the latter type must retai
a finite value.

It is tempting to wonder whether Eq. (9) might apply for values o
m_y down to $m_y = 0$, that is, down to the absolute threshold [33, 5]. I
is, of course, by no means certain that the spontaneous excitations are
the limiting factor in vision at the absolute threshold; other considerations may become important, and raise the value of r for very low
values of m_y. The consequences arising from this view of the absolute
threshold experiments are, however, of interest.

1. The absolute threshold, defined above, depends on the two parameters m_z and r. The frequency of "false positives"—blanks reported seen—is also directly related to r. This leads to the conclusion that there must exist some interrelation among the following factors: the minimum number of quanta required for seeing a light source, the level of dark noise in the visual system, the criterion of stimulus visibility adopted by the subject in the experiment, and the frequency of false positives—even though this may, in practice, be very low. A more explicit consideration of the frequency of false positives, therefore, may lead to a more complete understanding of visual experiments [5].

2. The frequency-of-seeing curves no longer correspond exactly in shape to Poisson sums. For m_x, and not $m_x + m_z$, is used as abscissa, and a logarithmic abscissa scale is used. If the curves could be plotted on a linear scale, they would merely be shifted to the left by an amount m_z, but as a logarithmic scale is used this shift is accompanied by slight distortion.

3. The conclusion of the section on Theory of Frequency-of-Seeing Curves and the Absolute Threshold that the slope of the curve gives a lower limit to the total number of quanta required for vision still holds; the curves must be less steep than those corresponding to the mean number of additional quanta required [61].

4. If the effective area of the flash is multiplied by a constant k, m_z is also multiplied by k, and hence, from Eq. (9), the amount of light required for vision is multiplied by $\sqrt{k}$. Thus, in a uniform part of the retina, the threshold luminance is inversely proportional to the square root of the area stimulated (Piper's law), and this holds for any values of m_z and r. This result is of theoretical importance, since it has been held that the validity of this law would be proof of the hypothesis that 2 quanta are sufficient for vision [104, 14, 13]. However, variations in retinal sensitivity make it extremely difficult to establish the law relating threshold and area [82]. (Cf. Physiological Independence of Retinal Units.)

In conclusion, it should be emphasized that the idea of dark noise as a fundamental limiting factor in vision near the absolute threshold, although it may prove an important contribution to the understanding of visual function, is based, at present, upon very little evidence. Spontaneous excitations have never been directly measured in an intact organism, and the theory is largely based upon an analogy with optical instruments. Again, assuming that noise is the limiting factor for a retinal unit of large area and that subunits do summate both noise and light signal over markedly smaller areas, the noise may no longer be the limiting factor in the case of a subunit working in isolation [33]. Much experimental work is needed before the theory can be regarded as proved or disproved.[6]

Thermal radiation in the eye. In 1879, the physiologist Fick wrote that the spectrum visible to the human eye was limited towards the infrared on account of the presence of the thermal radiation always filling the eye [35]. The eye may be regarded as a "black body" at blood temperature. Experimental and theoretical studies of the spectral energy distribution in black bodies were undertaken after the date of Fick's suggestion, culminating in the well-known Planck equation [92]. On this quantitative basis it can easily be shown [74] that if, instead of being a very selective detector of radiation, the human retina were completely nonselective—that is, if it were uniformly sensitive to radiations of all wavelengths, including the infrared—then the thermal radiation in the eye would cause such an intense permanent background of excitation that the radiations coming from external objects and superimposed on this background would generally remain undetected. In the brightest conditions of sunshine on the earth, it is unlikely that an eye similar to the human eye but with a nonselective retina could distinguish external objects other than the sun itself.

Further quantitative considerations based on Planck's black-body equation, however, show that the thermal radiation in the eye must be of negligible importance at wavelengths *smaller* than about 1 μ, and thus in the range of the "visible" spectrum. It is, therefore, the high wavelength selectivity of the actual human eye which makes its high absolute sensitivity possible. In accordance with Fick's view there is a fundamental objection to the eye having a high sensitivity range extending into the infrared much beyond the actual human range.

Thus it seems safe to say that the retina possesses properties such that it is unaffected by *the greater part* of the thermal radiation which is always present in the eye. The problem of "noise" raised in the preceding paragraph, however, is of a different order, and remains to be solved.

PHYSIOLOGICAL INDEPENDENCE OF RETINAL UNITS

Change of threshold luminance with area. Leaving aside the obvious case of test fields so small in angular dimensions that the size of their retinal images is determined by diffraction, optical defects, and light diffusion rather than by the actual field dimensions (see Physical

[6] Recent evidence shows that the observed increase of the increment threshold with increasing background luminance may be due to inhibitory effects exerted by the background, even at very low luminances (M. H. Pirenne, *Ann. N.Y. Acad. Sci.*, 1959, **74**, 377–384).

Fluctuations in the Number and Distribution of Quanta Acting upon he Retinal Receptors), it is often observed that the threshold lumi-iance of a test field, expressed in terms of the intensity per unit area, lecreases when the area of the field is increased. Now, although it is rue that physiological summation or facilitation occurring between he various parts of the retina which receive the image of the test ield must of course lead to a decrease in threshold luminance, such a lecrease does not by itself constitute evidence of the existence of physiological summation or facilitation.

Suppose the smaller area A′ forms in the eye an image covering a etinal area A, while the larger test field A′ + B′ corresponds to a arger retinal area A + B. Generally the threshold luminance for A′ + B′ is lower than that for A′; for this there are several possible explanations which will be considered in turn.

The added area has a lower threshold than the original area. This very obvious point has often been overlooked in practice. When the retinal area B is much more sensitive than A, the threshold luminance for A + B is much lower than that for A, but practically the same as that or the additional area B. The retina, even when the fovea and para-ovea are excluded, is far from uniform in its light sensitivity, and this act invalidates many of the conclusions drawn from experiments to letermine the relationship between area and threshold luminance.

For the dark-adapted eye, in white light, a centrally fixated field 20° in diameter has a lower luminance threshold than a similar field of smaller diameter. Hecht, Haig, and Wald [53] showed that a periph-eral field composed of 1° circles situated on the circumference of a circle 20° in diameter has almost as low a threshold as the full circular ield of 20° diameter. The authors concluded that "in centrally fixated ields of different size [up to 20° in diameter] the general character of he dark adaptation and the value of the final threshold are deter-mined essentially not by the area as area, but by the fact that as the areas increase in size their edges reach into regions of increasingly greater sensibility of the retina." The nonuniformity of the retina, even in its peripheral parts, makes it almost impossible to draw valid conclusions from threshold experiments made with concentric circular ields of different sizes [82].

Probability summation. Suppose that, for a certain luminance, the probability of response is P_A for the field A′ and P_B for B′. Suppose, urther, that the retinal areas A and B respond independently, and he subject responds to A′ + B′ whenever *either A or B* is stimulated sufficiently to elicit a response. Then the probability of response to A′ + B′, P_{A+B}, is given by:

$$P_{A+B} = 1 - (1 - P_A)(1 - P_B) \tag{10}$$

For example, if $P_A = P_B = 0.5$,

$$P_{A+B} = 1 - (1 - 0.5)(1 - 0.5) = 0.75$$

Similarly, at every luminance level, P_{A+B} is greater than P_A and P_B, s that the whole frequency-of-seeing curve for A′ + B′ is to the left (the curves for A′ and B′, and, although there is no physiological sun mation or facilitation, the threshold is lower for the total area than fc either of its constituent parts. (The general case of probability sun mation for several independent units has been discussed unde Theory of Frequency-of-Seeing Curves for the Absolute Threshold.)

This effect is most marked when A′ and B′ have similar luminanc thresholds, so that P_A and P_B are roughly equal. When (as in th preceding subsection) one has a much lower threshold than th other, probability summation has less practical importance, althoug theoretically it should still operate. The effect of probability summa tion on the threshold value is also most marked when the frequency of-seeing curves have a large range; for very steep curves, the threshol is little affected.

The assumptions underlying Eq. (10), that the probabilities c response for A and B are statistically independent and that the subjec responds to A + B whenever he would respond to A or B, requir justification, and may not always apply. There is evidence, howeve that they are valid in many important practical applications. Fo example, if A′ and B′ are small fields separated by an angular distanc greater than about 3.5°, Eq. (10) is found to fit the data satisfactoril [31]. Again, Pirenne [71] has described experiments in which A′ + E was a 20° circular field having two semicircular parts A′ and B The results obtained fitted Eq. (10), and, as would be expected, th subject often mistook the whole field A′ + B′ for one of its constituen parts.

It is easy to imagine situations in which these assumptions woul not apply. Suppose, for example, the uncertainty of seeing were en tirely due to biological variations affecting the whole retina, so tha when A + B is illuminated, whenever A responds B also responds an whenever A fails to respond B also fails to respond. In this case P_A, P_B and P_{A+B} are all equal. Another case of the possible breakdown of th assumptions is described in the following section on the binocula threshold.

Physiological summation. Whenever true physiological summation o facilitation occurs

$$P_{A+B} > 1 - (1 - P_A)(1 - P_B) \quad (11$$

A simple example (which may never occur in practice) is when A an B lie within a single retinal unit and affect no other units. Suppose, i this case, A and B each receives a mean of 4 quanta, and the unit re-quires 6 quanta to respond. Then $P_A = P_B = 0.21$, $P_{A+B} = 0.81$.

This is an extreme example of physiological summation, in which P_{A+B} is far greater than the value (0.38) predicted by Eq. (10). How-ever, physiological summation will occur, and the inequality (11) apply, whenever there are retinal units, playing a considerable part in he experiment, which lie in both A and B. (In the experiment with emicircular fields, described above, the fields used were compara-ively large, and the marginal units probably played only an insig-iificant role.)

In general, the fact that (11) holds implies the existence of physio-ogical summation between A and B. Theoretically, (11) might be explained by biological variations of a peculiar kind in which A would iave a greater sensitivity when B's sensitivity is lower, and vice versa, out true physiological summation or facilitation through nervous convergence, for which there is independent electrophysiological and anatomical evidence, will clearly be the correct interpretation. There nay be, also, exceptional cases—especially when the subject is not vorking at the physiological limit—in which the statistical inequality (11) may not necessarily imply a simple physiological relationship. One such case is discussed in the section on binocular vision.

Applications of physiological and probability summation. *The size of retinal units.* The size of the summating units in the retina has oeen the subject of considerable controversy, and the experiments of lifferent workers have seemed to give conflicting results. Experiments nade with concentric circular fields of varying sizes are difficult to nterpret, and seem to be less direct in their application to the problem han experiments using small fields at varying distances apart. If uch experiments are to give general results, they must be carried out n several positions in a particular part of the retina, and the conclu-ions can only apply to that part of the retina. It cannot be assumed hat the sensitivity of the retina is uniform, even in the peripheral oarts, and further, there is strong evidence that the size of units is different in different parts of the retina.

If two small fields A′ and B′ an angular distance *d* apart are used, hen the following conclusions can be drawn:

1. If inequality (11) applies, then there are at least some units of angular diameter *d* or greater in the retinal area being investigated.
2. If Eq. (10) applies for all pairs of fields *d* or more apart, then here are no units in the area much greater than *d* in angular diameter. There may be units about *d* in diameter, since the chance of two fields *d* apart falling within such a unit would be very small.

Using this technique, Denton and Pirenne [31] found no physio-

logical summation with 10′ fields 3.5° apart at an eccentricity of 20° in
the retinal periphery, but there was evidence of physiological summa
tion when the intercenter distance was reduced to 0.5°. Qualitativel
similar results were obtained by Bouman and van den Brink [15].

Most workers are agreed that small fields sufficiently far apar
behave independently, and Eq. (10) holds, whereas for small fields clos
together, (11) applies, showing that there is physiological summation
However, there is no general agreement about the size of the larges
retinal units in the periphery [81].

The area-threshold relationship. The investigation of the theoretica
area-threshold relationship is a difficult problem which will requir
further experimentation. No part of the retina can be assumed to b
uniform without thorough testing. Apart from the general variation o
sensitivity with eccentricity, accurate measurements in the peripher
reveal short-range variations of threshold, perhaps due to blood ves
sels, when the retina is explored with a small test field a few minutes in
diameter. The gradual variation of sensitivity with eccentricity itsel
also seems to present peculiar features; for instance, in the peripher
the threshold is lowest at an eccentricity of the order of 10° when
small test field is used, whereas the highest sensitivity is found a
greater distances from the fovea for test fields some degrees in diamete

Experiments by Bouman and van der Velden [14] gave values fo
the threshold for concentric circular fields of different areas whic
were in good agreement with Piper's law (total threshold energy pro
portional to the square root of the area). However, the retinal area
they used were so very far from uniform (even including the fovea in
some cases) that it has been argued [82] that their results prove tha
some different law, with the threshold depending on a lower power o
the area, must be the true theoretical relationship.

The binocular threshold: independence and level of response. In the case o
the binocular threshold, the areas A and B fall one in the right eye
the other in the left eye, of the subject. It was found in experiment
made by Pirenne [67] that areas in separate eyes do respond inde
pendently (Fig. 15). Similar conclusions for the case of binocula
acuity in daylight were reached independently by Bárány [4].

In contradistinction to these results, however, Collier [23] ha
reported experiments in which he found that the frequency of seein
for two eyes was significantly greater than that computed from th
uniocular frequencies on the basis of probability summation. In th
experiments made by Pirenne [67], many of the conditions were simila
to those chosen by Hecht et al. [54] in their study of the uniocula
threshold. In Collier's experiments, the conditions were different
The subject had no cue as to when the shutter was being opened

he was instructed to maintain fixation and to signal "seen" whenever he saw the flash. Collier's subjects, therefore, could not relax between presentations of stimuli and they were not able to concentrate their attention at the particular moment when the stimulus was supposed to appear. It seems possible, therefore, that the subjects' criteria of visibility may have been different in these experiments, and that the

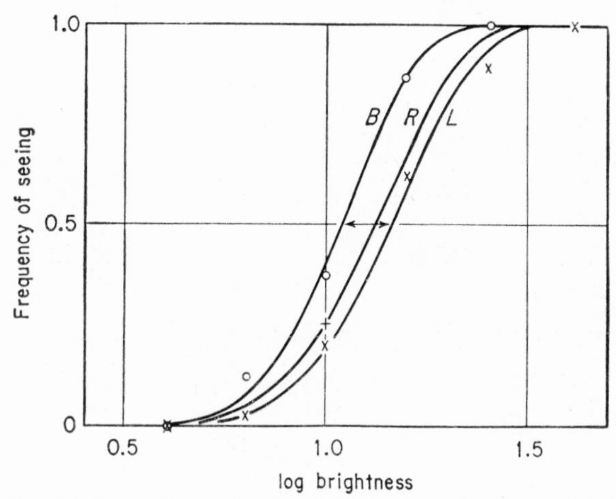

FIG. 15. Binocular and uniocular absolute threshold. *L* left eye alone, *R* right eye alone, *B* both eyes together. *From Pirenne* [67].

threshold values may have been higher. This might account for Collier's finding, as shown by the following considerations:

(α) Assume for the sake of argument that the absolute threshold is reached and the flash is reported seen by the subject when at least one nerve impulse is discharged in one optic nerve fibre. If two retinal areas A and B, responding independently, are involved in the experiment, the above detailed discussion of probability summation must then be valid. The subject will see the flash when at least one impulse, either from A or from B, reaches his brain.
(β) Now make a different assumption, namely that there is a response only when at least two impulses have reached the subject's brain. Here there are two possibilities:
(β1) If it is necessary for a response that these two impulses both originate from one and the same fibre, or from one and the same area, the conclusion is the same as for (α).
(β2) But if no such restriction applies, the frequency of response will

increase above that predicted by probability summation. One impulse may now come from A and one impulse from B, or two impulses may come from A, or two from B. The chance of a response here is greater than the chance of having at least two impulses either from A or from B.

It would be idle to go into further details since we lack knowledge concerning the exact neurophysiological events which take place at the threshold of human vision—the above numbers of impulses are instances given purely for the sake of illustration—but the results so far obtained suggest that a situation similar to (α) or to (β1) applied in Pirenne's [67] experiments whereas the state of affairs in Collier's experiments was similar to (β2). If the visibility criterion was in fact higher in the case of Collier's subjects, this would readily explain the different results obtained. In Collier's experiments, the subjects would have responded only when there was a "supraliminal" excitation in one eye or when there was "liminal" or "supraliminal" excitation from both eyes, "liminal" excitation here referring to a visibility criterion lower than that actually used by Collier's subjects. This interpretation is confirmed by the fact that in three cases Collier obtained significant summation even when the flash was never seen monocularly by one of the subject's eyes.

Thus it would seem possible that true liminal responses, leading to mere probability summation, are obtained in some experiments only. If so, simple probability summation should be evidence that the subject is responding very near his physiological limit.

PERIPHERAL AND CENTRAL FACTORS IN THRESHOLD EXPERIMENTS

Functional units as trigger mechanisms. For the sake of simplicity consider an experiment which would involve only one retinal functional unit and in which the condition of equivalence would be fulfilled. The theory assumes that the only relevant biological variations in this case are variations in the retinal threshold n. The outcome of any trial—that is, the subject signaling either "seen" or "not seen" —is determined by the number of quanta which have in this trial acted upon the receptors of the functional unit. Now at first sight, this might be taken as a rigid assumption implying that no event taking place more centrally than the level of the receptors can influence the subject's response, but such an interpretation would be mistaken. First, it must be noted that it is the design of the experiment itself which eliminates all but two mutually exclusive modes of response by the subject. Secondly, the threshold value expressed as a number n of quanta acting upon the retinal receptors is dependent upon extra-retinal factors, for these peripheral receptors constitute only the first link in a chain of nervous events.

Excitation must be transmitted from the receptors to the central nervous system and to the effector mechanisms, and in order to do so, the excitation has to pass a number of barriers. One of these barriers must be a critical one, such that if the excitation has passed it it will proceed unchecked to the effectors. Now the magnitude of the retinal threshold n will depend on the size of this critical barrier, even though the barrier may be not in the retina but in the brain or at the effector end. For if the critical barrier, which we may call A, becomes higher, the excitation necessary at the level of A will be stronger; and in order to produce this stronger excitation at A, the excitation at the level preceding A will also have to be stronger, and so forth. This reasoning eventually leads one back to the level of the receptors themselves. For these the strength of excitation, under the present assumptions, only depends upon the value of n. Thus psychological and physiological factors, of whatever origin, which may influence the subject in such an experiment, can only make themselves felt through a change in the value of the retinal threshold n.

Actual experiments probably correspond to more complicated situations, involving, for instance, several functional units which may be independent or not. With suitable modification, however, a similar conclusion still applies in the general case. In a given trial, the subject will respond "seen" if the light stimulus has acted upon his retinal receptors in one of a certain number of definite ways, all of which could theoretically be specified with regard to the number and distribution of the acting quanta in space and in time. He will respond "not seen" when the actual retinal stimulus does not fulfil any of these conditions. The conditions corresponding to a response "seen" may change from one trial to the next; such changes may be large and occur irregularly in time, which explains the results obtained in some "bad" experiments. Thus although the design of the experiments under discussion is admittedly rigidly controlled, the theory itself is no more rigid than the deterministic concepts universally accepted in physiological studies of nervous excitation and conduction.

The possibility must be mentioned here of central influences being brought to bear on the retina through the action of centrifugal optic nerve fibers. The sensitivity of electrophysiological preparations is often lower than that of the intact animal [81]. It is, therefore, not impossible that the high sensitivity of the human eye is, in part, due to such central influences. Again these central influences, if they exist, might reduce [80, 43] in the intact organism the considerable background of spontaneous excitation which is often observed in electrophysiological preparations of the retina [81].

In any case, "simple" threshold experiments involve much more than the peripheral receptors alone. They certainly involve a chain of events propagated through the whole nervous system to the effectors and possibly complex central influences acting upon the receptors. Again the criterion of visibility used by the subject may depend on the level of "dark noise" and this implies that a "comparison" must somehow be made between the excitation in the retinal region receiving the stimulus and the excitation which may occur spontaneously in other regions. Finally there are also "illusions" which sometimes take place in experiments, the subject seeing something resembling the actual test field when the shutter is worked with the light entirely cut off ("blank" reported as seen). These illusions may be related to the dark noise. They may also be related to the intriguing observations of "conditioned afterimages" described by Popov [86] and by Popov and Popov [87].

In spite of complications, however, the section on Theory of Frequency-of-seeing Curves for the Absolute Threshold remains applicable. (This theory as stated assumes that the subject answers "seen" only to a negligible number of blanks, but if this were not so it should be possible to make suitable modifications on the basis of the considerations contained in the section on The Differential Threshold and "Dark Noise.") The physical quantum theory of the absolute threshold, therefore, does not suffer from the defect of rigidity which has sometimes been ascribed to it—in particular, it implies neither exact constancy in the sensitivity of the visual system nor perfect independence of the subject's responses. It will be remembered that the test of the theory consisted in verifying, not an ordinary equation, but an inequality, $n' \leq I$ (55 per cent), as explained earlier under Physical Fluctuations in the Number and Distribution of Quanta Acting upon the Retinal Receptors.

Evaluation of peripheral and central factors. A priori, the present general considerations leave open the question of the relative parts played in the uncertainty of response by the physical quantum fluctuations, which of course occur at the extreme periphery, and by biological variations which may occur in more central parts of the nervous system. It was only on the basis of further considerations—relating to the extreme smallness of the light stimulus at the absolute threshold—that it was concluded that the physical fluctuations dominate the situation in specially designed experiments. Thus there seems to be but little conflict in principle between the present considerations and a theory such as Crozier's [29] which draws particular attention to the possible play of biological factors in the central nervous system, *provided* the latter theory does not axiomatically rule out the existence of physical variations of the stimulus. In visual experiments in general, the determination of the relative importance of quantum fluctuations and of biological factors must be considered as a problem to be solved experimentally for each particular case. Once this is accomplished, further steps will be necessary to determine at which nervous levels the biological factors themselves are operative.

Number of light quanta and other parameters. In the physical theory of quantum fluctuations, only numbers of radiational quanta are used as parameters. Thus, assuming the simple biological hypothesis to be valid, the shape of the frequency-of-response curve would define the value of the retinal threshold n, but it would give no information whatever on other parameters such as the number k of impulses which must be elicited in the optic nerve for a threshold response. This number k does not appear in the equations of the physical quantum theory.

Accordingly it seems impossible to accept an opinion put forward in 1944 by Wright [110] who, on the grounds that nerve currents have the same quantum character as has light radiation, suggested that the same uncertainty of seeing "might be anticipated if, say, six nerve impulses were, on the average, necessary to arouse a threshold sensation, as if six light quanta were on the average necessary to cause some given photochemical decomposition." The knowledge that at least six nerve impulses are required for a response would be insufficient as a basis for calculating the statistics of the response, for the relationship between the physical stimulus and the number of nerve impulses elicited is not necessarily the same in all cases and is not generally known. Hartline, Milne, and Wagman [49] observed in the *Limulus* preparation a range of uncertain response of about 1 $\log_{10}$ unit in physical light intensity for a response consisting of at least one nerve impulse. The observed range of uncertainty corresponds to a parameter of about five or six. This parameter probably corresponds to a threshold number of light quanta, but is clearly not the number of nerve impulses, namely one.

The preceding argument incidentally shows that the physical quantum theory cannot be readily adapted to nonvisual sensory mechanisms. Lifschitz [59] determined frequency-of-response curves for the absolute thresholds of human hearing and touch. These curves are fairly similar to the curves obtained in the case of vision, their shapes resembling that of a Poisson sum of parameter $n = 8$. Yet Lifschitz's conclusion, namely that eight independent "elements," probably nerve impulses, are involved at the threshold, seems to lack a sufficient theoretical basis.

Independent functional units. It has been seen that under certain conditions separate retinal regions, belonging either to one eye or to the two eyes of a human subject, respond to light stimuli independently of one another. To these retinal regions must, therefore, correspond separate functional units, and these must also respond independently of one another. This independence refers only to the probability of response. In other respects the various units or mechanisms of course depend on common factors affecting the whole organism, such as the oxygenation of the blood. Again the various mechanisms in threshold experiments may be considered as possessing a final common path, since the same effectors are brought into action by the subject's response no matter which of the mechanisms has been supraliminally stimulated—but this particular type of nervous convergence entails neither summation nor facilitation.

It follows that if a large retinal area is stimulated near threshold, only a few, or a single one, of the independent mechanisms must be expected to respond. Subjectively, the field appears to be continuous, with vague outlines, but introspective observations of this kind may be misleading. If the theory is true, however, confusion must be expected to occur sometimes between the whole field and parts of the field presented alone, since in many cases presentation of the whole field must in fact lead to a few discrete stimulations, or to one stimulation only. Experiments in which a circle 20° in diameter and half circles of the same diameter were used gave results in agreement with this prediction [71]. However, even at threshold, a test field a few minutes of arc in diameter often looks very different from these large fields; in this case the difference is probably genuine and due to the fact that the small field may stimulate small retinal units, or subunits, whereas at threshold the large field only stimulates large units with great powers of summation.

In the case of a large field presented at an intensity a few times the absolute threshold level the shape of the field, if it is fairly simple, can easily be distinguished by the subject—at an intensity three times threshold the subject can distinguish the fingers of his hand spread out in front of the illuminated screen [33]. Here a fair number of the larger functional units must be responding. The fact that the shape of the field is then clearly seen seems to imply that some interaction must take place between the elementary stimulations. Yet from the standpoint of the simple threshold experiments the various units presumably respond independently of one another. The point is related to the problem of "sensory integration" which was raised in 1906 by Sherrington [96]. The matter cannot be pursued further here, but it may be emphasized that such perception of form takes place even when the field is presented in a single brief flash at a barely supraliminal intensity, eye movements playing no part in the experiment. Similar problems of sensory integration arise in the case of binocular vision [96, 72].

Another problem relating to "independent" units has been briefly mentioned in connection with "dark noise" in the visual system; it referred to the "comparison" which must be made by the nervous system between various parts of the test field. A similar problem arises in some specially designed experiments on visual acuity in the neighborhood of the absolute threshold. Those functional units which remain unstimulated by the light from the background must be expected to form by chance groups or clusters, the average size of which is related to that of the smallest black disc which can be detected on the luminous background [69, 76, 27]. Detection of the black target must, therefore, depend on the CNS receiving "information" on the clusters of unstimulated functional units which occur naturally over the whole field even in the absence of any black target—but which are not readily perceived as such. Little is known about the neurological basis of the mechanisms by which such "comparisons" can be made between different parts of the visual field. The words "comparison" and "information" in other contexts refer to processes in the human mind, but here we are concerned exclusively with mechanistic nervous processes as explained under Absolute Threshold Experiments and their General Interpretation; these words are used as a convenient abbreviation.

Attention may finally be drawn here to a study of visual perception at low light intensities in which a significant positive correlation was found between absolute threshold and the efficiency of form perception [84]. This investigation would seem to suggest that the physical quantum theory is also of value in the investigation of visual psychological problems of greater complexity than those discussed in the present paper.

NOTES ON THE HISTORY OF THE APPLICATION OF THE PHYSICAL QUANTUM THEORY TO THE STUDY OF VISUAL PROCESSES

Newton leaned toward a corpuscular theory of light and until the advent of the wave theory, the corpuscular doctrine remained largely unchallenged. Yet, as far as the present writers are aware, the possible implications of a corpuscular theory with regard to the processes of visual excitation were hardly discussed until the advent of the modern quantum theory of Planck and Einstein, in which both "corpuscular" and wave properties of radiation are taken into consideration (see [92] for a history of the early development of the quantum theory).

The calculations independently made by Henri and Wurmser [55] and by Chalmers [22] showed that the number of light quanta necessary for vision must be very small—even though, contrary to these authors' suggestions, it is in fact more than one single quantum. The smallness of the number of quanta acting upon the retina per unit area when an extended source is just visible to the dark-adapted eye was demonstrated by Dufay and Schwégler in 1930 [34]. In 1923, Lasareff [56] had developed some theoretical considerations based on the discrete nature of light absorption, according to which some of the receptors would be excited by the absorption of quanta while others would remain entirely unaffected by the light stimulus. Lasareff pointed out that the number of receptors excited must increase with increasing intensity, but he did not discuss the purely physical fluctuations which must occur in such weak radiational stimuli. This point attracted the attention of Stiles [97], Barnes and Czerny [6], and Brumberg and Vavilov [18]. As explained in the discussion on pages 309 and 310, satisfactory theoretical accounts of these fluctuations, based on the consideration, not of the quanta entering the eye, but of those, fewer in number, which act effectively upon the retinal receptors, were published independently about ten years later by Hecht, Shlaer, and Pirenne [54], Brumberg, Vavilov, and Sverdlov [19], Vavilov and Timofeeva [102, 103], and by van der Velden [104] whose work was continued and extended by Bouman and his collaborators. De Vries in 1943 [105] dealt with various visual functions from the standpoint of the quantum theory, but did not study the particular problem of the quantum fluctuations at the absolute threshold. Baumgardt's monograph [7] focused attention on the fact that in terms of quanta the amounts of light acting upon the eye are in many cases so small that some hitherto widely accepted photochemical theories of the visual process required revision. Dartnall and Goodeve had introduced the quantum interpretation of spectral sensitivity in 1937 (see [81]). Many other papers were published from 1942 onward.

In the earliest phase of the study of vision and light quanta, ideas and suggestions were put forward independently by various authors, but for some time they failed to lead to further developments. Since 1942, however, the field has expanded in more regular fashion, so that the historical account becomes largely coincident with the scientific account of the theory as given in the present paper or, say, in the review article by Pirenne [81].

SUMMARY

The present article is not subdivided into the topics for discussion usual in this series because it can be considered as belonging to biophysics as much as to psychology. The basis of the argument resides in the fact that the physical properties of light itself, considered as electromagnetic radiation, affect very deeply the manner in which the light stimulus acts upon the visual receptors in the eye. Accordingly, a great deal of attention is devoted to peripheral mechanisms, even though events occurring in the whole organism are taken into consideration when the visual response is examined as a whole. The physical quantum theory, as against the "continuum" theory of light which in the past has in general been implicitly assumed to be valid in discussing such problems, presents novel and seemingly paradoxical features which are discussed in detail in so far as they relate to the excitation of the retina by light.

1. In the latter part of the nineteenth century it was discovered that the rod receptor cells of the retina of vertebrates, including man, contain pigments sensitive to light. Thus the greater number of the rods of the frog contain a pink pigment, the color of which can be observed in dim light. This is called rhodopsin, or "visual purple," and is very similar to the pigment contained in the human rods. When the retina is brought into bright daylight, the rods lose their pink color, turn yellowish, and eventually become colorless. The pigment is, therefore, bleached by the light it has absorbed. A considerable amount of research has been devoted to the properties of such pigments, in particular to their absorption spectra. In the case of rhodopsin a very close parallelism has been demonstrated between the absorption spectrum of this substance and the spectral sensitivity of the eye under such conditions that the rod visual system alone is functioning, the light being too dim to stimulate the cones. The eye is then maximally sensitive to light of the wavelength which is maximally absorbed, while it is very insensitive to lights a very small fraction of which is absorbed by rhodopsin. This quantitative parallelism suggests very strongly that the first step in the initiation of the response to light in the visual system is a photochemical one, rhodopsin being the pigment acted upon by light in the case of the rod system. This theory is now generally accepted. Recent measurements in the living human eye have shown that the cones also must contain pigments sensitive to light.

2. The mechanism by which light absorbed by the pigment contained in a visual cell causes excitation of the nervous ending of the cell, however, remains largely unknown. Furthermore, some plausible

theoretical expectations have been disproved by experiment. Thus when part of the rod pigment has been bleached by exposure to strong light, no *simple* parallelism is found to exist between the amount of pigment remaining in the retina and the sensitivity of the eye. Bleaching of a minute fraction of the pigment can cause a large increase in absolute threshold. Thus while the basis of the photochemical theory remains perfectly solid, the details of the photochemical reaction taking place in visual receptors are not clearly known. In any case photochemistry cannot provide a complete theory of vision, since structural and physiological properties of the receptors themselves, of the second- and third-order neurons to which receptors are connected, and of more central nervous mechanisms must be taken into account in a complete explanation of the visual process. Nevertheless, it is on the periphery of the nervous system that the light stimulus acts, and some of the characteristics of this initial photochemical reaction must influence the response at all other levels.

3. Some of the physical properties of light itself, namely its quantum properties, must affect the visual response. According to modern physical theory, light acts upon matter in elementary processes in each of which only 1 quantum of energy is involved. The visual pigment in the receptor therefore cannot absorb less than 1 quantum if it is to absorb any light at all. Measurements, made at the cornea of the eye, of the energy required for the absolute threshold of vision, show that this energy is extremely small, corresponding to a number of the order of 100 quanta only. Further measurements show that the number of quanta absorbed by the rhodopsin of the rods is only of the order of 10. These quanta are absorbed among several hundred rods, but not more than 10 rods can be affected by the light stimulus, since quanta cannot be "split" or "shared" between rods, or pigment molecules. Moreover, physical stimuli consisting of such small numbers of quanta are not exactly reproducible; they undergo wide uncontrolled fluctuations. This inherent instability of the light stimulus itself can be theoretically calculated and compared with the uncertainty of response always observed at threshold and expressed by the sigmoid frequency-of-response curve. The agreement obtained in the best experiments is satisfactory. Thus it appears that part at least of the variations in the response must be due to physical variations in the stimulus.

4. Comparison of experimental frequency-of-response curves with the probability of seeing calculated on the basis of the number of light quanta directly involved in the stimulation process, *this number being independently estimated*, provides a crucial test of the theory. The theory predicts that under suitably chosen experimental conditions, the un-

certainty of response can only be increased, not decreased, by biological and other variations which add their effect to the purely physical quantum fluctuations. A review of the existing evidence shows that this theoretical expectation is fulfilled. Indeed, quantum fluctuations are observed in many physical systems, and there is no more reason to doubt their existence in the case of biological systems than to doubt the existence of Brownian movement.

5. A number of interesting consequences follow from the physical quantum theory. From what has been said, one rod cell can be excited by one single light quantum. This quantum is absorbed by and acts upon one pigment molecule only. The rod cell considered as a light detector thus reaches the theoretical limit set by the nature of light. On the other hand, various considerations show that one excited rod is not sufficient to cause a sensation of light. But a few rods, each excited by one quantum, are sufficient. In night vision, the number of light quanta absorbed by the receptors per second may be much smaller than the total number of receptors corresponding to the geometrical retinal image. Many receptors therefore remain completely unaffected by light. Spatial summation makes it possible for several excited rods, by pooling their responses, to determine the excitation of a ganglion cell and thus of a fiber of the optic nerve. Under the same conditions, single cones absorb quanta only at very infrequent intervals, and spatial summation is much less important in the cone than in the rod system. Thus the cone mechanism is largly inactive—the fovea is blind in scotopic vision—not because individual cones receive light stimuli which are too weak to reach their threshold, but because most of these cones receive no light at all.

6. In the case of the absolute threshold, physical quantum fluctuations set a limit to the sharpness of the threshold on the intensity scale; the range of uncertain seeing may be increased but not decreased by the coming into play of other factors. In the case of a differential threshold, similar fluctuations must occur in the background intensity I and these must set a limit to the mean intensity increment ΔI which can be detected by the eye over the background. For if the background undergoes physical fluctuations of the same order as ΔI, an actual increment equal to ΔI will be hardly distinguishable from a naturally occurring fluctuation. Discussion of the problem requires a knowledge of the extent of spatial and temporal summation under the conditions of the experiment. In some cases it would appear that the value of ΔI is markedly greater than the theoretical limit. It has been suggested also that, for similar reasons, the spontaneous excitation which occurs in the dark sets a limit to the absolute sensitivity of the eye. If so, absolute and differential thresholds would both be limited

by the presence of a background of excitation. These problems are still being investigated.

None of the existing evidence relating to vision provides a disproof of the physical quantum theory. There is no reason to doubt that, where they are relevant, the quantum properties of light affect the functioning of the eye, any more than that the wave properties limit the sharpness of the retinal image. When the quantum theory is being applied to complex visual problems, however, difficulties arise from the psycho-physiological side because, strictly speaking, the quantum theory relates only to the light stimulus and to the pigment molecules which absorb this stimulus. To go further it is necessary to have information about the functioning of the receptors and visual system. Yet it is probable that such physiological information could not be acquired on the basis of a continuum theory of light, even if such a theory were considered as a mere working hypothesis, because of the very large extent to which the quantum properties of light affect the nature of the response at the level of the visual receptors.

REFERENCES

1. Aguilar, M., & Stiles, W. S. Saturation of the rod mechanism of the retina at high levels of stimulation. *Optica Acta,* 1954, **1,** 59–65.

2. Arnulf, A., Dupuy, Odette, & Flamant, Françoise. Contributions à l'étude des limites de perception. Effet des ombres entoptiques et des micro-fluctuations d'accommodation de l'oeil. *Optica Acta,* special issue, May, 1951, 13–19.

3. Arnulf, A., Dupuy, Odette, & Flamant, Françoise. Répartition de la lumière dans l'image d'un point lumineux sur la rétine. *C. R. Acad. Sci., Paris,* 1951, **233,** 974–976.

4. Bárány, E. A theory of binocular visual acuity and an analysis of the variability of visual acuity. *Acta. Ophthal., Kbh.* 1946, **24,** 63–92.

5. Barlow, H. B. Retinal noise and absolute threshold. *J. opt. Soc. Amer.,* 1956, **46,** 634–639.

6. Barnes, R. B., & Czerny, M. Lässt sich ein Schroteneffekt der Photonen mit dem Auge beobachten? *Z. Phys.,* 1932, **79,** 436.

7. Baumgardt, E. *Les théories photochimiques classiques et quantiques de la vision et l'inhibition nerveuse en vision liminaire.* Paris: Éditions de la Revue d'Optique, 1950.

8. Baumgardt, E. Sehmechanismus und Quantenstruktur des Lichtes. *Naturwissenschaften,* 1952, **17,** 388–393.

9. Baumgardt, E. Seuils visuels et quanta de lumière. Précisions. *Année psychol.,* 1953, **53,** 431–441.

10. Blackwell, H. R. Psychophysical thresholds: experimental studies of methods of measurement. *Bull. Dep. Engng. Res. Univer. Mich.,* 1953, No. **36.**

11. Blackwell, H. R. Studies in the form of visual threshold data. *J. opt. Soc. Amer.*, 1953, **43**, 456–463.

12. Bornschein, H. Die absolute Lichtschwelle des menschlichen Auges. Eine experimentelle-varianzanalytisches Kritik ihres subjektiven Bestimmungsmethoden. *v. Graefes Arch. Ophthal.*, 1951, **151**, 446–475.

13. Bouman, M. A. Absolute threshold conditions for visual perception. *J. opt. Soc. Amer.*, 1955, **45**, 36–43.

14. Bouman, M. A., & van der Velden, H. A. The two-quanta explanation of the dependence of the threshold values and visual acuity on the visual angle and the time of observation. *J. opt. Soc. Amer.*, 1947, **37**, 908–919.

15. Bouman, M. A., & van den Brink, G. On the integrate capacity in time and space of the human peripheral retina. *J. opt. Soc. Amer.*, 1952, **42**, 617–620.

16. Brindley, G. S. The order of coincidence required for visual threshold. *Proc. phys. Soc. Lond.*, B, 1954, **67**, 673–676.

17. Brindley, G. S. A photochemical reaction in the human retina. *Proc. phys. Soc. Lond.*, B, 1955, **68**, 862–870.

18. Brumberg, E. M., & Vavilov, S. I. Visuelle Messungen der statistischen Photonenschwankungen. *Bull. Acad. Sci. U. R. S. S.*, 1933, 919–941.

19. Brumberg, E. M., Vavilov, S. I., & Sverdlov, Z. M. Visual measurements of quantum fluctuations. I. The threshold of vision as compared with the results of fluctuation measurements. *J. Phys. Moscow*, 1943, **7**, 1–7. (In English.)

20. Byram, G. M. The physical and photochemical basis of visual resolving power. Part I. The distribution of illumination in retinal images. *J. opt. Soc. Amer.*, 1944, **34**, 571–591.

21. Byram, G. M. The physical and photochemical basis of visual resolving power. Part II. Visual acuity and the photochemistry of the retina. *J. opt. Soc. Amer.*, 1944, **34**, 718–738.

22. Chalmers, S. D. In discussion following Paterson, C. F., & Dudding, B. P., Visibility: Notes on some practical aspects of the question. *Illum. Engr, Lond.*, 1915, **8**, 218–220.

23. Collier, G. Probability of response and intertrial association as functions of monocular and binocular stimulation. *J. exp. Psychol.*, 1954, **47**, 75–83.

24. Collier, G. Intertrial association at the visual threshold as a function of intertrial interval. *J. exp. Psychol.*, 1954, **48**, 330–334.

25. Cotton, J. W., & Verplanck, W. S. The dependence of frequencies of seeing on procedural variables: II. Procedure of terminating series of intensity-ordered stimuli. *J. gen. Psychol.*, 1955, **53**, 49–57.

26. Cotton, J. W., & Verplanck, W. S. The dependence of frequencies of seeing on procedural variables: III. The time-interval between successive stimuli. *J. gen. Psychol.*, 1955, **53**, 59–66.

27. Crawford, B. H., & Pirenne, M. H. Steep frequency-of-seeing curves. *J. Physiol.*, 1954, **126**, 404–411.

28. Crescitelli, F., & Dartnall, H. J. A. Human visual purple. *Nature, Lond.*, 1953, **172**, 195–197.

29. Crozier, W. J. On the visibility of radiation at the human fovea. *J. gen. Physiol.*, 1950, **34**, 87–136.

30. Denton, E. J., & Pirenne, M. H. The minimum number of quanta necessary for vision. *J. Physiol.*, 1951, **115**, 68P.

31. Denton, E. J., & Pirenne, M. H. Spatial summation at the absolute threshold of peripheral vision. *J. Physiol.*, 1952, **116**, 32P.

32. Denton, E. J., & Pirenne, M. H. On the functional stability of the retina. *J. Physiol.*, 1952, **117**, 55P.

33. Denton, E. J., & Pirenne, M. H. The absolute sensitivity and functional stability of the human eye. *J. Physiol.*, 1954, **123**, 417–442.

34. Dufay, J., & Schwégler, R. Mesure visuelle des brillances très faibles. *Rev. Opt. (théor. instrum.)*, 1930, **9**, 263.

35. Fick, A. *Hermann's Handbuch der Physiologie*. Vol. 3, Pt. 1. Leipzig: Verlag von F. C. W. Vogel, 1879. P. 182.

36. Flamant, Françoise. Étude de la répartition de lumière dans l'image rétinienne d'une fente. *Rev. Opt. (théor. instrum.)*, 1955, **34**, 433–459.

37. Flamant, Françoise, & Stiles, W. S. The directional and spectral sensitivities of the retinal rods to adapting fields of different wave-lengths. *J. Physiol.*, 1948, **107**, 187–202.

38. Graham, C. H. Behavior, perception and the psychophysical methods. *Psychol. Rev.*, 1950, **57**, 108–120.

39. Graham, C. H. Behavior and the psychophysical methods: an analysis of some recent experiments. *Psychol. Rev.*, 1952, **59**, 62–70.

40. Graham, C. H., & Margaria, R. Area and the intensity-time relation in the peripheral retina. *Amer. J. Physiol.*, 1935, **113**, 299–305.

41. Granit, R. Rotation of activity and spontaneous rhythms in the retina. *Acta physiol. scand.*, 1941, **1**, 370–379.

42. Granit, R. Physiology of vision. *Ann. Rev. Physiol.*, 1950, **12**, 485–502.

43. Granit, R. *Receptors and sensory perception. The aims, means and results of electrophysiological research on the process of reception.* New Haven, Conn.: Yale Univer. Press, and London: Oxford Univer. Press, 1955.

44. Guild, J. Contribution to the discussion following the paper by Stiles. *Proc. phys. Soc. Lond.*, 1944, **56**, 352.

45. Hagins, W. A. The quantum efficiency of bleaching of rhodopsin *in situ*. *J. Physiol.*, 1955, **129**, 22–23P.

46. Hardy, A. C., & Perrin, F. H. *The principles of optics.* New York and London: McGraw-Hill, 1932.

47. Hartline, H. K. The response of single optic nerve fibers of the vertebrate eye to illumination of the retina. *Amer. J. Physiol.*, 1938, **121**, 400–415.

48. Hartline, H. K., & McDonald, R. *The frequency of seeing at low illuminations.* Published with a report by Pirenne, Marriott, and O'Doherty in Great Britain, Medical Research Council *Special Report Series,* No. 294, 1957.

49. Hartline, H. K., Milne, L. J., & Wagman, L. H. Fluctuation of response of single visual sense cells. *Fed. Proc.*, 1947, **6**, 124.

50. Hecht, S. Intensity discrimination and its relation to the adaptation of the eye. *J. Physiol.*, 1936, **86**, 15–21.

51. Hecht, S. Rods, cones, and the chemical basis of vision. *Physiol. Rev.*, 1937, **17**, 239–290.

52. Hecht, S. Energy and Vision. *Science in Progress,* Series IV, 75–97, New Haven, Conn.: Yale Univer. Press, 1945.

53. Hecht, S., Haig, C., & Wald, G. The dark adaptation of retinal fields of different size and location. *J. gen. Physiol.,* 1935, **19**, 321–337.

54. Hecht, S., Shlaer, S., & Pirenne, M. H. Energy, quanta, and vision. *J. gen. Physiol.,* 1942, **25**, 819–840.

55. Henri, V., & Wurmser, R. Energie absorbée dans les réactions photochimiques. *C. R. Acad. Sci., Paris,* 1913, **156**, 1012–1015.

56. Lasareff, P. Untersuchungen über die Ionentheorie der Reizung. VI. Über die Empfindung der Lichtintensität beim peripheren Sehen auf Grund der Ionentheorie. *Pflüg. Arch. ges. Physiol.,* 1923, **199**, 290–291.

57. Lee, R. H., Finch, E. M., & Pounds, G. A. Periodic fluctuations in the dark adapted threshold. *Amer. J. Physiol.,* 1945, **143**, 6–10.

58. Le Grand, Y. *Optique physiologique.* Vol. 3. *L'Espace visuel.* Paris: Éditions de la Revue d'Optique, 1956.

59. Lifschitz, S. J. Sensation elements for hearing and touch. *C. R. Acad. Sci. U. R. S. S.,* 1945, **48**, 479–481. (In English.)

60. Ludvigh, E., & McCarthy, E. F. Absorption of visible light by the refractive media of the human eye. *Arch. Ophthal. N. Y.,* 1938, **20**, 37–51.

61. Marriott, F. H. C. Frequency-of-seeing curves and spontaneous excitation. *J. opt. Soc. Amer.,* 1956, **41**, 661.

62. Meetham, A. R., & Lambert, G. E. V. Report to the Ministry of Home Security. Unpublished, quoted by Stiles, *Proc. phys. Soc. Lond.,* 1944, **56**, 329–356.

63. Mueller, C. G. Quantum concepts in visual intensity-discrimination. *Amer. J. Psychol.,* 1950, **63**, 92–100.

64. Mueller, C. G. Frequency of seeing functions for intensity discrimination at various levels of adapting intensity. *J. gen. Physiol.,* 1951, **34**, 463–474.

65. Østerberg, G. Topography of the layer of rods and cones in the human retina. *Acta. Ophthal., Kbh.* 1935, Suppl. 6.

66. Peyrou, C., & Piatier, H. Emploi de méthodes statistiques dans l'étude de la sensibilité de l'oeil. *C. R. Acad. Sci., Paris,* 1946, **223**, 589–591.

67. Pirenne, M. H. Binocular and uniocular thresholds of vision. *Nature, Lond.,* 1943, **152**, 698–699.

68. Pirenne, M. H. Contribution to the discussion of the paper by Stiles. *Proc. phys. Soc. Lond.,* 1944, **56**, 354–355.

69. Pirenne, M. H. On the variation of visual acuity with light intensity. *Proc. Camb. phil. Soc.,* 1946, **42**, 78–82.

70. Pirenne, M. H. On physiology and consciousness. *Brit. J. Psychol.,* 1947, **37**, 82–86.

71. Pirenne, M. H. Independent light-detectors in the peripheral retina. *J. Physiol.,* 1948, **107**, 47P.

72. Pirenne, M. H. *Vision and the Eye.* London: Chapman & Hall, 1948.

73. Pirenne, M. H. Descartes and the body-mind problem in physiology. *Brit. J. Phil. Sci.,* 1950, **1**, 43–54.

74. Pirenne, M. H. Limits of the visual spectrum. *Research, Lond.,* 1951, **4,** 508–515.

75. Pirenne, M. H. Quantum physics of vision. Theoretical discussion. In J. A. V. Butler & J. T. Randall (Eds.), *Progress in Biophysics.* Vol. 2. London: Pergamon Press, 1951. Pp. 192–223.

76. Pirenne, M. H. The absolute sensitivity of the eye and the variation of visual acuity with intensity. *Brit. med. Bull.,* 1953, **9,** 61–67.

77. Pirenne, M. H. Physiological mechanisms in the perception of distance by sight and Berkeley's theory of vision. *Brit. J. Phil. Sci.,* 1953, **4,** 13–21.

78. Pirenne, M. H. The mind-brain problem (Review-essay on *The neurophysiological basis of mind: the principles of neurology* by J. C. Eccles). *Brit. J. Phil. Sci.,* 1954, **5,** 153–159.

79. Pirenne, M. H. Human visual purple and absolute threshold. *Nature, Lond.,* 1954, **173,** 215–216.

80. Pirenne, M. H. Absolute visual thresholds. *J. Physiol.,* 1954, **123,** 40–41P.

81. Pirenne, M. H. Physiological mechanisms of vision and the quantum nature of light. *Biol. Rev.,* 1956, **31,** 194–241.

82. Pirenne, M. H., & Marriott, F. H. C. Quantum theories of the absolute threshold: the influence of retinal position and area. *Optica Acta,* 1954, **1,** 151–155.

83. Pirenne, M. H., & Marriott, F. H. C. Absolute threshold and frequency-of-seeing curves. *J. opt. Soc. Amer.,* 1955, **45,** 909–912.

84. Pirenne, M. H., Marriott, F. H. C., & O'Doherty, E. F. *Individual differences in night-vision efficiency.* Published with a report by Hartline & McDonald in Great Britain, Medical Research Council *Special Report Series,* No. 294, 1957.

85. Polyak, S. L. Retinal structure and colour vision. *Docum. ophthal.,* 1949, **3,** 24–46.

86. Popov, N. A. Le conditionnement dans l'écorce cérébrale chez l'homme étudié par la méthode électroencéphalographique. III. La différentiation des réflexes conditionnés électrocorticaux et le conditionnement des images consécutives. *C. R. Acad. Sci., Paris,* 1953, **236,** 744–746.

87. Popov, N. A., & Popov, Catherine. Contribution à l'étude des fonctions corticales chez l'homme. IV. Action du café sur les images consécutives et les images consécutives conditionées. *C. R. Acad. Sci., Paris,* 1954, **238,** 2026–2028.

88. Ranson, S. W. *The anatomy of the nervous system from the standpoint of development and function.* (7th ed.) Philadelphia and London: Saunders, 1943.

89. Riezler, W., Esper, F., & Meurers, H. Die Abhängigkeit der Reizschwelle des menschlichen Auges von der Dauer der Lichtimpulse und der Wellenlänge des Lichtes. *Z. Phys.,* 1954, **137,** 238–255.

90. Rose, A. The relative sensitivities of television pickup tubes, photographic films, and the human eye. *Proc. Inst. Radio Engrs, N. Y.,* 1942, **30,** 295–300.

91. Rose, A. The sensitivity performance of the human eye on an absolute scale. *J. opt. Soc. Amer.,* 1948, **38,** 196–208.

92. Rosenfeld, L. La première phase de l'evolution de la Théorie des Quanta. *Osiris,* 1936, **2,** 149–196.

93. Rushton, W. A. H. The rhodopsin density in the human rods. *J. Physiol.,* 1956, **134,** 30–46.

94. Rushton, W. A. H., Campbell, F. W., Hagins, W. A., & Brindley, G. S. The bleaching and regeneration of rhodopsin in the living eye of the albino rabbit and of man. *Optica Acta,* 1955, **1,** 183–190.

95. Schultze, M. Zur Anatomie und Physiologie der Retina, *Arch. mikr. Anat.,* 1866, **2,** 175–286.

96. Sherrington, C. *The integrative action of the nervous system.* (New ed.) Cambridge: Cambridge Univer. Press, 1947.

97. Stiles, W. S. Oral remarks. In *Report of a Joint Discussion on Vision.* London: The Physical Society, 1932. Pp. 326–327.

98. Stiles, W. S. The directional sensitivity of the retina and the spectral sensitivities of the rods and cones. *Proc. Roy Soc.,* B, 1939, **127,** 64–105.

99. Stiles, W. S. Current problems of visual research (with a report on a discussion). *Proc. phys. Soc. Lond.,* 1944, **56,** 329–356.

100. Stiles, W. S. Visual properties studied by subjective measurements on the colour-adapted eye. *Brit. med. Bull.,* 1953, **9,** 41–49.

101. Stiles, W. S., & Crawford, B. H. The effect of a glaring light source on extrafoveal vision. *Proc. Roy. Soc.,* B, 1937, **122,** 255–280.

102. Vavilov, S. I., & Timofeeva, T. V. Visual measurements of quantum fluctuations. II. Fluctuations when the eye is light-adapted. *J. Phys. Moscow,* 1943, **7,** 9–11. (In English.)

103. Vavilov, S. I., & Timofeeva, T. V. Visual measurements of quantum fluctuations. III. The dependence of the visual fluctuations on the wavelength. *J. Phys. Moscow,* 1943, **7,** 12–17. (In English.)

104. van der Velden, H. A. Over het aantal lichtquanta dat nodig is voor een lichtprikkel bij het menselijk oog. *Physica, 's Grav.,* 1944, **11,** 179–189.

105. de Vries, Hl. The quantum character of light and its bearing upon the threshold of vision, the differential sensitivity and visual acuity of the eye. *Physica, 's Grav.,* 1943, **10,** 553–564.

106. Verplanck, W. S., Collier, G. H., & Cotton, J. W. Nonindependence of successive responses in measurements of the visual threshold. *J. exp. Psychol.,* 1952, **44,** 273–282.

107. Verplanck, W. S., & Cotton, J. W. The dependence of frequencies of seeing on procedural variables: I. Direction and length of series of intensity-ordered stimuli. *J. gen. Psychol.,* 1955, **53,** 37–47.

108. Wald, G. On the mechanism of the visual threshold and visual adaptation. *Science,* 1954, **119,** 887–892.

109. Weiss, P. A. Autonomous versus reflexogenous activity of the central nervous system. *Proc. Amer. phil. Soc.,* 1941, **84,** 53–64.

110. Wright, W. D. Contribution to the discussion following the paper by Stiles. *Proc. phys. Soc. Lond.,* 1944, **53,** 354.

THEORY OF STEREOSCOPIC VISION

KENNETH N. OGLE
Section of Biophysics and Biophysical Research,
Mayo Clinic and Mayo Foundation

INTRODUCTION

Stereoscopic depth perception is the single outstanding function of vision with the two eyes. In the primates, the position of eyes in the front of the head has provided the most favorable situation for the development of stereoscopic depth perception. This gain in depth perception phylogenetically has been accompanied by a loss of panoramic vision and, in addition, has greatly complicated the processes of vision, because a highly complex and intricate motor coordination of the two eyes is required to preserve bifoveal fixation and single vision. In no other respect is binocular vision more concerned than in the role it plays in spatial localization. The sensation of brightness in binocular observation is only slightly, if at all, greater than that in monocular observation. Nor is visual acuity of both eyes together greatly superior to visual acuity of one of the eyes. In spatial localization, however, there emerges in binocular observation an entirely new sensation, *stereoscopic* depth perception, not even suggested by vision with one eye alone. Stereoscopic depth is relative depth—the apparent difference in "farness" or in "nearness" between two objects in space—and is especially related to the visual distance of the point of fixation and the "*Kernfläche*" of Hering [14]. It is a sensation in its own right and is exemplified by the vividness of depth between objects—the sense of space between them in depth.

An analysis of the bases and concomitant concepts of stereoscopic vision will be discussed here, so far as feasible, within the general outline set for the series of essays in this volume. In this discussion we shall not be concerned with the theoretical problems associated with a general theory of space perception, especially whether or not visual space has a certain given structure or whether it can be described by a metric at all [19]. Nor shall we be concerned with the problem of egocentric distance localization (absolute distance), although stereoscopic depth is undoubtedly one of the powerful components in such localization for the individual with normal vision. The greater part of any discussion of stereoscopic vision must be based on statements of experimental findings, and in a theory of stereoscopic vision there are relatively fewer hypothetical notions needed to explain or relate these findings. Thus the discussion, by the very nature of the subject matter, cannot rigorously adhere to the same set of rubrics which apply to a subject composed for the greater part of hypotheses.

BACKGROUND FACTORS AND ORIENTING ATTITUDES

The systematic approach to the subject matter in this manuscript cannot fail to reflect the writer's training in physics and mathematics, nor can it fail to bear an imprint of the influence of years of research in visual problems within the atmosphere of medical research, and in the association with men actively engaged in the clinical practice of ophthalmology. The underlying philosophy is probably an eclectic one, for it cannot be said to adhere closely to any particular psychological "school." Although it has been influenced by the critical experiments of Hering [14], and perhaps accordingly a somewhat phenomenological point of view is expressed, emphasis has been placed on the types of experimentation and of analysis with which Helmholtz [27] made his great contributions to physiological optics. Similarly, the writings of Hofmann [16], Hillebrand [15], and Tschermak [29] have provided constant guides. However, the contact for so many years with the late Professor Ames—who on the whole was an intuitive worker, and who was occasionally mystical in his philosophic outlook—has left its effect. In a sense the resulting orienting attitude might be said to approach scientific empiricism.

So far as consistently possible, the substitution of physicophysiological mechanisms in explanation of experimental findings for vague descriptive words or notions seems highly desirable. Consequently a wholly gestalt approach to visual problems seems to the writer to lead nowhere, perhaps because the writer does not fully understand that approach. However, one must be aware of the experimental findings of gestalt workers, and perhaps the differences in approach may lie in the problem of what constitutes an explanation. Actual differences in explanatory theories may be settled by experiment. However, such notions as "good gestalt," "closure," and so forth, seem to have actually little explanatory power. Although there may be something gained in a study of vision from the point of view of a "total perception," this may be so complicated as to be virtually impossible. One must study the simple components before more general explanatory formulations are possible, at the same time guarding against oversimplification. To a marked degree, at least in respect to stereoscopic depth perception, this view brings us closer to the physiological and neuroanatomical facts of the visual processes of the living organism.

So far as possible, statements of quantitative relationships are desirable, if not imperative. The more precise the experimental facts, the more satisfying is the general theory for their explanation. Although we are basically concerned in this study with a type of stimulus-response relationship, we cannot ignore but, on the contrary, must be vitally concerned with, the many concomitant exogenous psychic or experimental influences and variables which may enhance, inhibit, or modify the simple experience of depth which we might otherwise obtain if the stimulus were "pure," that is, acting alone. We are concerned mainly with the stability of those relationships between the experience of stereoscopic depth and the characteristics of the stimuli.

Thus, the subject matter here will be discussed with emphasis on the optics and sensory physiology involved, rather than from the usual point of view of perception in general. The theory outlined and analyzed here rests basically on existent empirical data, stemming from the fundamental experiments of Wheatstone and including the most recent data obtained under modern optimal conditions. In experimental situations where secondary or empirical motives to spatial localization have been maximally reduced, the stereoscopic perceptual response will be assumed to be related directly to the stimulus field. Hence, stereoscopic depth will be considered less of a construct or a result of a contemplation, for, if present, disparity as the stimulus gives an all-or-none type of information both immediate and compelling in nature. Consequently the orienting attitude here implies a process dependent in large part on an innate structure. So closely also have the facts of stereopsis been dependent on those empirical variables and systems involved in resolving power (visual acuity) of the eye (eyes), that empirically determined data existing in this area provide additional framework and concepts for stereoscopic systematic theory.

Models. If we were to consider the role of a model important in a theory of stereopsis, that model conceivably would be an anatomical-physiological one, linked to consciousness by a receptor-sensationlike mechanism. That is to say, the basis of our model would be the anatomical facts, consisting of (1) the mosaic structure of the receptor elements of the retinas of the two eyes, (2) the pathways of the nerve fibers from these retinas along the optic nerves, (3) the decussation of those fibers so that fibers from homonomous halves of the retinas of the two eyes would pass to the same occipital lobe, (4) the demonstrated close juxtaposition of the fibers from "corresponding" parts of the retinas of the two eyes even at the level of the lateral geniculate body [7, 8], (5) the passage of these juxtaposed radiation fibers to the area about the calcarine fissures of the occipital cortex (area 17), (6) the probable dendritic termination of radiations in the *area striata* of the cortex, and finally (7) the multiplication and overlapping of these terminating fibers in those areas. Stimulation of the retinas, then, would result in disparate excitations in those cortical areas, excitations which would affect the surrounding associated areas of the cortex, where one would assume the beginning of the psychic experience to originate.

UNDERLYING STRUCTURE IN SYSTEM OF STEREOSCOPIC DEPTH PERCEPTION

On the basis of the behavioristic assumption [12] that the subjective depth response can be described as a function of certain specifiable variables, the data obtained in experiments delineating stereoscopic depth perception can be expressed by:

$$D = f(\eta \cdot \cdot \cdot Q) \quad (1)$$

in which η, the identifiable chief empirical independent variable, is the disparity between the ocular images of the two eyes of any two stimulus objects in space. The symbol, Q, will, for the moment, be used to denote a complex of structural variables related to the general perceptual behavior of the subject and to nonstereoscopic depth clues, and depending, perhaps, on the past visual experience, and so forth, of the individual. Under controlled experimental conditions of reduction, the parameter complex Q may be nearly eliminated, except so far as the fundamental quality of any visual experience implies an innate three-dimensional attribute, or it may be made constant.

The empirical independent variable disparity, η, (construct language), is itself a function also of specifiable or theoretically calculable independent variables:

$$\eta = f(E_R, E_L, P_1, P_2, \ldots, H, M) \quad (2)$$

In this, the system E_R, E_L, P_1, P_2 consists of geometrically measurable parameters specifying the coordinates of the eye positions (E_R and E_L) and the coordinates of any two positions of object stimuli points (P_1 and P_2) in the visual plane. The parameters H and M pertain to the topologic organization of the optical imagery (including effect of spectacles) within the two eyes in relation to corresponding retinal elements. The latter, in turn, are a part of the neuroanatomical structure of the visual processes. The importance of the parameters H and M lies in the fact that the "physiological" true disparity stimulus η generally differs from the "geometric" disparity η_g, which can be calculated from the geometric relationships of eye positions and object stimuli point positions in space [22]. In practical situations where the stimulus object point positions are near the mean direction of pointing of the eyes, the parameters H and M play little part and $\eta \simeq \eta_g$.

It is probable that the subjective depth experience D does not represent a segment of a subjective mensurational scale. The depth D, in the absolute sense of indicating so many feet or inches, demands the participation of the complex Q in Eq. (1). With more than two points in the visual plane, the various D's related to the disparity of the images of any two stimulus points may provide only a rank-order scheme [2].

In a large variety of experiments in which attempts are made to determine the structure of stereopsis, we are concerned with the rate of change of D with η, and in particular with the value of $(\Delta\eta)$ corresponding to the least perceptible (ΔD). Then we have $(\Delta\eta)$ as another function of identifiable systematic independent variables:

$$\Delta\eta_{(\Delta D\ \mathrm{min})} = f(V, A, C, t, p, n, J, \ldots) \tag{3}$$

In this, V specifies the visual acuity pattern of the two eyes, which involves the dimensions of the constituent parts of the retinal mosaics as well as the perfection of the optical imagery of the eyes; A, the level of adaptation of the eyes; C, the contrast between the stimulus objects and the adapting illumination; t, the time of exposure of test stimulus objects; p, certain physiological states of the retinal function; n, the degree to which the physiological nystagmoid oscillatory movements of the two eyes lack synchronization; and J, the characteristic of the test stimulus object (line, point, and so forth). The series of . . . may also imply such variables as age, discriminatory training, and so on, which probably would be included in the Q factor. It is possible also through unknown processes that $\Delta\eta_{(\Delta D\ \mathrm{min})}$ varies with observation distance.

It is not an easy matter to place these different variables into the categories thought to be necessary for the systematization of the theory. Perhaps it is easiest in the case of the dependent variable, for this is the subjective experience of depth, and if one point in space can be designated the reference point (for example, fixation point), the basic dependent variable is the experience of the other "test" point as being "farther" or "nearer." This experience of "nearer" or "farther," although representing a subjective quality of visual experience, does not represent a mensurational quantity. It is, on the other hand, definite with respect to sign. This sign of direction, "nearer" (+) or "farther" (−), is specifically determined by the sign of the disparity—crossed disparity being correlated in respect to sign with "nearer," and uncrossed disparity being correlated with subjective "farther." In this respect we have an aspect of strict psychophysical parallelism.

Whereas disparity, the actual stimulus giving rise to the experience of stereopsis, constitutes the primary independent variable in the strict meaning of the word, as shown earlier in this discussion, it is not itself a completely independent empirical variable, but in the laboratory especially it is manipulated as if it were. At least it can always be identified as the stimulus. To repeat, it is determined by the geometric relationships between given objects and the station points of the eyes. Furthermore, the disparity relates to a difference in separation between the images of *any* two given objects falling on the retinas of the two eyes, and is essentially independent of eye positions. In turn, the optical stimuli must result in specific physiological stimuli, in that two pairs of specific retinal elements in the two eyes are activated. Thus the disparity is dependent on certain neuroanatomical structures and on optical and physiological properties of the visual processes themselves. This statement means that one cannot specify precisely the angle of disparity between the images of two objects in space from the geometric relationships alone.

It is possible, however, that in certain experimental procedures the empirical independent and dependent variables, as defined previously, may seem to be interchanged. That is to say, if we "set" a subjective depth criterion, we then manipulate the empirical variable until it satisfies that criterion. We then have the relationship

$$\eta = \phi(D,Q) \tag{4}$$

which is basically inverted from (1). However, in most of the everyday functioning of the two eyes, relationship (1) must be considered the more usual, and the following discussion proceeds on this basis.

We may categorize the several independent variables, then, in the following manner:

The *systematic independent variables* which serve as the operationally identifiable and manipulatable and, in most cases, measurable variables that make up the antecedent conditions for the theory of stereopsis are as follows:

1. Peripheral angle in the visual field.
2. Magnitude of the resolving power of the two eyes.
3. Light adaptation level of the two eyes.
4. (related to 2.) Contrast of the observable test stimulus objects against the background.
5. Time of the exposure of the stereoscopic stimulus objects.
6. Type of configuration used as stimulus objects.
7. Degree of synchronization of the physiological oscillatory micronystagmoid movements of the two eyes.
8. Physiological state of retinal function, such as that of photopic or scotopic vision.
9. Inherent difference in the relative magnification of the ocular images of the two eyes.
10. Degree to which existent empirical clues to space perception and the subject's basic orientation enter into the act of binocular vision [11].

The systematic independent variables 1 to 5 are easily identifiable and measurable. The remaining variables are less amenable to measurement but under certain experimental conditions are certainly identifiable. Only in the case of the last item might this prove more difficult.

The *empirical independent variables*, namely, those that are not only identifiable and measurable, but that are actually used operationally to effect changes or responses of the dependent variable, are simply:

1. Disparity between the images determined geometrically by the sagittal distances between the stimulus objects in space.
2. Lateral visual angle subtended by these objects to one eye.
3. Introduction of optical means to modify the magnifications of the total images in the two eyes.

The "*mathematical*" *independent variables*, in the sense that these variables are identifiable and measurable, which enter into the specifications or equations describing the response in terms of mathematical parameters would be:

1. Interpupillary distance.
2. Distance to the fixation point.
3. Degree of symmetrical or asymmetrical convergence.
4. Inherent differential magnifications between the two eyes—as defined by H in Eq. (2).

The majority of the variables listed are held constant in critical experiments, and for the most part, changes in them affect stereopsis only in terms of the discrimination of small differences in depth, that is, in terms of stereoscopic acuity.

INITIAL EVIDENTIAL GROUNDS FOR ASSUMPTIONS OF SYSTEM

The invention by Wheatstone [32] in 1833 of the stereoscope, by means of which different pictures would be presented to each eye separately, made possible the clear demonstration of the *fundamental* difference between binocular stereoscopic depth perception and the monocular conception of depth and distance (by empirical clues or motives). Suppose each of the two eyes is presented with targets on which a pair of vertical parallel lines has been drawn, differing, however, in separation. If the difference in separation is not too great, the images of the two patterns are fused and there is an almost immediate and certainly a striking spatial experience that one of the lines is more distant than the other, an appearance as though two line objects at different distances in space were actually being observed. Such figures drawn for the stereoscope are essentially free from most ordinary empirical depth clues, and the obvious, striking, and impelling sensation of depth differences constitutes a unique phenomenon of binocular vision, not even hinted by either target when observed alone.

It will be clear, if we diagram the geometric spatial relationships, that the difference in separation of the two pairs of line images seen by the two eyes corresponds to the images of two actual line objects in space at different distances observed by each of the two eyes from the two different "station points." Thus the difference in separation of the images formed in the two eyes is directly a function of the difference in distance. Concomitantly, the difference in separation of the images specifies the chief empirical independent variable, the disparity—in this case, the geometric disparity η_g. Since no other variables which could account for the phenomenon are present, it is this and only this stimulus that gives rise to the sensory experience of visual depth—the dependent variable. In this experiment we have isolated the chief empirical independent variable in terms of immediate language, namely, the difference in separation of images in the two eyes gives rise to a sense of stereoscopic depth.

This fundamental experiment of Wheatstone was a crucial and strategic one, for it ended, or brought into disrepute, those theories that binocular spatial localization was the result of some kind of position sense of the two eyes from the tensions in the extraocular muscles, and thus that distance and depth were somehow the result of a triangulation process. Following this discovery, it has developed that stereoscopic depth is now considered the *primary* factor to spatial localization, and all other conceptions of depth from empirical or learned clues are considered *secondary* factors [30].

The present status of the theory of binocular vision has been based to a marked extent on the early experiments stemming from Wheatstone's time, followed by the impact of the work and writings of Hering, Helmholtz, and their pupils. The contributions in recent years have been to reduce the range of uncertainty and to investigate some of the more basic problems of stereoscopic vision as made possible by modern laboratory procedures.

Stereopsis appears to be a unique experiential response, a sensation in its own right, and not subservient to some other visual process. Its basis seems to be innate and stable. However, spatial judgments probably rest on learned associations, as is true of the interpretations from other sense modalities. Being automatic in nature, stereopsis can be dominated by those empirical clues which are made meaningful by experience [10].

CONSTRUCTION OF FUNCTION FORMS

There is no clearer way of demonstrating the construction of the function forms of a theory of stereoscopic vision or the development of its rationale than by describing the following fundamental experiment.

Let the two eyes fixate steadily an object point F. Upon a track, the center of the near end of which lies directly beneath the entrance

upil of the left eye, a slender knitting needle or drill rod is mounted
ertically on a rider which can be slid easily along the track. By this
rrangement the image of the needle seen by the left eye always falls
n the same retinal elements of that eye, and the separation of the
etinal images of F and of the needle in that eye remains the same.
The position of the image of the needle in the right eye varies with
he position of the needle along the track. Hence the separation of the
etinal images of F and of the needle in the right eye is variable, some-
imes being greater than the corresponding separation of the images in
he left eye, sometimes smaller. A horizontal slit aperture is placed be-
ore the eyes so that the ends of the needle cannot be seen, regardless of
ts position on the track.

Now the needle is slid along the track so that at one time it appears
tereoscopically nearer, at another time farther, than the fixation
oint. The stereoscopic difference in the distance of the needle and
ixation point is easily seen. It will be noticed, however, that as the
eedle is placed farther and farther beyond the fixation point, one
uddenly observes that the needle appears double, that is, the image
f the needle in each of the two eyes is seen in *two* different subjective
irections. The separation of the two "half-images" appears to in-
rease the farther the needle is moved away from the fixation point.
Moreover, if the needle is brought closer and closer, nearer than the
ixation point, the images will again be seen "double." Once more
he separation of the two half-images appears to increase the greater
he distance of the needle in front of the fixation point. However, the
loubling when the needle is farther than the fixation point differs
rom that when the needle is nearer in that, while the images are
een double if the right eye is suddenly closed, the right image of the
wo vanishes in the former case, and the left image vanishes in the
atter.

When the images of the needle are seen double, the two half-
mages are said to be physiologically and patently "disparate." They
re double, we say, because they fall on retinal elements of the two
yes which are "disparate," and thus are seen in different subjective
lirections. When the needle is beyond the fixation point, the half-
mages are said to be *uncrossed* disparate, because when the right eye is
losed the right half-image vanishes (the half-image on the right is
een by the right eye). When the needle is nearer than the fixation
oint, the reverse holds true, and the images are said to be *crossed*
lisparate, because when the right eye is closed the left half-image
anishes (the half-image on the left is seen by the right eye). Obviously
f the double images are uncrossed, the subjective directional separa-
ion of the images of F and of the needle in the right eye is greater than

the subjective directional separation in the left eye. For crossed double images, the inequality is reversed.

Obviously, for disparities to exist there must be at least two objects in the binocular field of view. When there are a large number of objects at different distances in the field of view, one can speak of the disparity between the images in the two eyes for any two of these objects.

Now it is clear that, if the two half-images are uncrossed disparate when the needle is beyond the fixation point, and the apparent directional separation increases the farther away the needle is, and if the two half-images are crossed disparate when the needle is nearer than the fixation point, and the apparent directional separation of these crossed half-images increases as the needle comes closer to the eyes, then somewhere between these two situations the half-images must be neither crossed nor uncrossed disparate. This special position is of particular interest in binocular vision, for it is said that the needle at that position lies on the horopter. There is a certain spatial region nearer and farther than this position within which the uncrossed and crossed disparate images will not be seen double, but in spite of this there is only one position of the needle in this region at which its images are neither crossed nor uncrossed. This region in which doubling is not experienced, but in which the images must, save for the one point, be logically disparate, is said to determine the horizontal dimension of Panum's areas of fusion, as measured by a visual angle but corresponding to retinal distances, for that lateral position of the needle. Within these functional areas the appearance of doubling of all disparate images is masked [31].

Implicit in the foregoing description of the interrelations of the empirical independent-dependent variables in stereoscopic depth is that theory, so fundamental to binocular vision, known as the theory of "corresponding retinal points." We state that images falling on corresponding points are not disparate. In fact, we say that images in the two eyes from the same object in space which do not fall on corresponding points are disparate. This "theory" is not to be regarded entirely as a pure hypothesis, for it has its basis in fact, not only phenomenologically but also neuroanatomically. Phenomenologically, retinal elements in the two eyes when stimulated give rise to the same *primary* subjective sense of "height" and "breadth" referred to the principal visual direction associated with the fixation point of either eye, according to the Hering law of identical visual direction [14]. Neuroanatomically, neural fiber tracts which have their origin in homonomous parts of the retinas of the two eyes can be traced and are found to come into close juxtaposition as they approach the occipital cortex. The important problem regarding corresponding retinal elements is not whether they exist—they exist as defined earlier in this paragraph—but rather, whether their organization is a distinct, stable one.

Thus, although we see that disparity, the stimulus for stereoscopic depth, exists by virtue of the corresponding point organization of the retinas of the two eyes, this notion itself does not account for the emergence of the sensation or visual experience of depth when transversely disparate retinal elements in the two eyes are stimulated by images falling on those elements. The subjective *directions* associated with retinal elements constitute only a two-dimensional elaboration of the world of objects. Perhaps at this point we should be satisfied simply with the statement: disparity is the stimulus; subjective depth experience is the response. However, as in color vision, insight into causal relationships in terms of anatomical structure or physiological events would lead to a more satisfying explanation. Failing that specifically, hypothetical constructs or intervening variables based on antecedent knowns are desirable, providing they are in accord with the facts and, still better, are testable. Only two theories to account for the emergence of stereopsis need be considered: the Hering theory of local depth signs and the theory based on the compulsion to fusion reflex. Actually these two theories have a common theoretical basis, in that retinal local signs are predicated, and yet there are problems involved in both.

Hering proposed that the binocular perception of depth, just as the localization of relative direction, depends on a type of local sign associated with the receptive elements of the retinas. Each retinal element situated transversely from the principal vertical meridian through the fovea, in addition to having a breadth directional value, has also a definite *depth value* in relation to that of the fovea. Elements on the nasal parts of each retina have "far" values, which are relatively greater the farther they are nasally. Similarly, retinal elements on the temporal parts of each retina have "near" values, which increase the more temporal the elements are from the fovea. Hering assumed that these depth values provided an innate capacity for depth localization, although he considered this aspect of the theory to be of minor importance. The observer localizes similar disparate images falling on the retinas of the two eyes as "nearer" or "farther" than the apparent distance of the fixation point, depending on the dominance (in the sense of an algebraic addition) of the "far" and "near" values from the two retinas. These local signs must be thought of as functional qualities of a special kind, in that *binocular simultaneity* is necessary and, furthermore, the disparity cannot be too great. In a way, one can speak then of an antagonistic effect of these depth values. Attempts to find a depth experience from nasally or temporally stimulated elements of one eye *alone* have failed, and this fact has been cited to discredit the theory.

This theory provides a useful description of binocular depth perception, in agreement with actual facts for *symmetrical convergence*. That there is a parallelism or relationship between the "depth values" and "breadth values" associated with retinal elements is indicated by those studies that correlate the Hering-Hillebrand horopter deviation and uniocular partition experiments.

The Hering theory of retinal depth values (a theory which Hering did not actually stress) is at present, as it has been in the past, not without opposition: first, because of a certain artificiality (ex post facto), second, because of an implication of innate spatial qualities to be associated with neuroanatomical structures, and third, because stereoscopic depth as a sensory experience can be suppressed in surroundings where contrary empirical clues predominate.

The view has been generally held that stereoscopic depth is somehow related to the fusion processes of binocular vision. In fact, ophthalmologists do call the presence of stereopsis a proof of "third-degree fusion." The fact that stereoscopic depth can be shown to exist with disparate images which are seen double has been taken by some as evidence that fusion is not associated with the emergence of stereopsis. This may be evidence, but it is, of course, not proof.

The theory that stereoscopic depth emerges through the fusion compulsion processes comes from the well-known fact that disparate images of themselves alone can and do cause fusional movements of the eyes, movements that direct the eyes in such a way that those images are brought as near as possible to fall on corresponding retinal elements, neutralizing the disparity and preventing the appearance of double images. This is true whether the disparate images are formed in the central or in the peripheral parts of the binocular visual field. In the normal use of the eyes, where there may be a pattern of different sets of transversely disparate images, these fusional movements cannot take place because *attention* is maintained at a point of fixation, the images of which are not normally disparate. Therefore, in the horizontal meridian we tend to think of the fusional movements of the eyes that occur to avoid double images as being the result of *psycho-optical* reflexes [16]. That is, once the attention is directed from one object whose images are not disparate to one whose images are disparate, the eye movements act as reflex movements. Thus, with the eyes directed to one object in space, the images of other objects in space which are horizontally disparate nevertheless provide constant innervations for fusional movements—movements which do not take ace because of the attention to the one fixation object. It would be e "unsatisfied" innervations for the fusional movement which would ovide the basis for the stereoscopic sensation, in that all innervations : eye movements would have sensory components. This theory obvi- ısly rests on a notion of "local signs," of breadth motor values, which ay or may not be identical with the local sign of relative directional eadth. Such a theory permits stereoscopic response from disparate ıages which are also seen double.

Evidence against such a theory is the fact that the motor behavior ıtterns of the eyes in binocular vision are subject to reeducation, as evident from those patients who wear unequal ophthalmic correc- ɔns in the two eyes and who "learn" to compensate for the prismatic fect of the glasses, so that compensation becomes automatic with tended fixation eye movement. Stereoscopic depth perception is ɔt affected by such corrections unless the image magnifications on .e retinas are at the same time affected unequally. Those who are mpathetic to the theory that all sensory processes arise originally ɔm the innervations for motor responses to stimuli look with favor on .e compulsion to fusion theory of stereopsis.

However, both the theories just discussed fail to explain ade- ıately the binocular stereoscopic perception of normal subjective ·ientation of objects when the eyes are converged to a point in asym- .etric convergence, unless other hypotheses are also made. If the .me pairs of corresponding points (or pattern of disparate points) ıat give rise to the "normal" surface for symmetrical convergence he *Kernfläche*) are used when the eyes are asymmetrically converged, ıe resulting surface perceived stereoscopically cannot be "normal" the subjective direction of the fixation point. This follows because ıe point of fixation is now at different distances from the two eyes, ıd there is, accordingly, an effective difference in magnification of ıe images of the two eyes. This is to say, a given angular disparity etween the images of the fixation point and any other point in the isual plane would result in a different subjective depth judged from ıe "normal" perceptual plane when the eyes are converged asym- ıetrically than when converged symmetrically. Experimental data ıow that the longitudinal horopter, as determined by the criterion of ןuating the subjective directions, is in fact not "normal" to the sub- :ctive direction of the point of fixation, but tends to agree with the ıngent to the Vieth-Müller circle at the fixation point. Only on the ypothesis that a kind of compensatory change occurs in the entire :ereoscopic field, in the sense of a rotation of a fixed amount about a ertical axis at the fixation point, can we account for the setting of the normal" plane when the eyes are in asymmetric convergence. This rotation would be the equivalent result of magnifying the image of the eye farther from the fixation point in the horizontal meridian. Such a hypothesis means a reevaluation of the transverse disparities across the binocular visual field. Nevertheless, this does damage to any theory which assumes a stable stereoscopic depth from algebraic summation of innate "depth" or "motor" values.

Experiment has shown that a stereoscopic compensatory process of the kind just discussed indeed actually does occur and can be initiated by the introduction of a change of magnification of the image of one of the two eyes in the vertical meridian, when the eyes are in symmetric convergence. This is the so-called induced effect.

MENSURATIONAL AND QUANTIFICATIONAL PROCEDURES

Much of the theory of stereoscopic vision rests on the fact that rather precise mensurational procedures are possible. Basically, we are dealing with a stimulus-response system in which the empirical independent stimulus can be accurately controlled by manipulation of geometrically placed stimulus objects and quantified by the laws of geometric optics. At the same time, the systematic independent variables are under precise control. Using psychophysical methods, one can determine the positions of the manifold of operationally controlled stimulus objects which will correspond to certain criteria (that is, equality in depth, inequality as in fractionation, or judgment by a subjective "meter stick," and so forth) for a stabilized subjective visual experience.

Quantitative experiments in stereopsis have been concerned with four types of relationship between the empirical independent variable, *disparity*, and the dependent variable, *subjective depth experience*, namely:

1. The determination of stereoscopic sensitivity (thresholds) in terms of limens, just noticeable differences, standard deviations, mean errors in adjustment, and so forth.

2. The determination of the locus of points in space which satisfy the criterion of apparent equal distance of the fixation point—the apparent frontoparallel plane; the effort to determine the spatial counterparts to those image relationships for which the disparity is "zero," or for which there is a constant disparity, if a fixation disparity is present.

3. The determination of the locus of points in space which subjectively satisfy fractionation criteria such as "same" distance, "farther" depth equals "nearer" depth, and so forth ("alley" experiments).

4. The determination of the subjective stereoscopic vertical—a determination depending on the declination of the images in the

vo eyes, and certainly involving cyclotorsional movements of the two yes.

The operational procedures available in any given instance would ıclude (1) method of constant stimuli, (2) method of limits, (3) ıethod of adjustment, etc. These are all well-known psychometric ıethods, some more useful or applicable in certain experiments than thers. So far as possible, the two-category method of constant stimuli ith forced choice is the method believed to be most reliable when recise quantitative data are desired. For systematic analysis of ereoscopic data, the objective depth measurements are always calcu- ıted in angular disparity, expressed in minutes or seconds of arc.

Within the limitations set by the systematic independent variables, ıe experimental procedures satisfy the mathematical requirements ɔr an accurate description of the phenomenon. The stereoscopic ıreshold (η_t) is a statistical quantity determinable by psychometric ıethods, and in the results of mathematical formulations involving ıis quantity it must be understood as a parameter similar to a fre- uency-of-seeing function. Furthermore, (η_t) will depend on the ex- erimental situation, being different if points of light in the dark are sed as the test stimulus objects, or if long vertical line stimulus ob- :cts, whose images will then affect a larger number of retinal ele- ıents in the two eyes, are used. It will also depend on those other ystematic independent variables already stated.

The following illustration is cited as an example of the mathe- ıatical quantificational procedures:

1. Obviously there is a limitation in the ability to perceive depths :ereoscopically beyond a certain critical distance b, namely, when $= 2a/\eta_t$, where $2a$ is the interocular separation and η_t is the angular ıreshold stereoscopic depth (expressed here in radians). Thus if η_t is aken as 20″ (0.00010 radians), with an average interpupillary separa- on of 6.3 cm, b, the critical distance, would be 630 m. A recent field tudy shows in a particular experimental situation a critical distance f about 1,900 ft, which corresponds to a value of η_t of the same order s that assumed [28].

2. On the basis of the same limiting angular disparity threshold of tereopsis one can determine the least spatial difference (Δb) in dis- ance between two objects which just can be discriminated, for $b = b^2/(2a\eta_t)$. Thus, the actual least difference in distance between wo objects which can be discriminated stereoscopically increases as he square of the distance of one of the objects. This formula pertains nly to objects near the median plane; it is approximate for more eripherally located objects.

3. If we assume that the locus of points in the visual plane cor-

responding to horopter settings (determined by any criterion) is d
scribed by a portion of a conic section—and experiments have show
that such a description is quite adequate—then that locus can
defined by certain parameters H and M (in addition to the usu
mathematical independent variables, the observation distance b ar
interpupillary separation $2a$) [21]. The parameters H and M speci
the functional asymmetric distortion between images (in an inclusi
sense) of the two eyes, and the relative magnification of the image
one eye compared to that of the other, respectively. The parameter
also describes the "curvature" of the horopter determinations at tl
fixation point, and M the degree to which the curve representing tl
horopter data is rotated about the point of fixation in the visual plan
We have the following relations:

$$\frac{1}{M \tan \alpha_1} - \frac{1}{\tan \alpha_2} = H \qquad (5$$

in which α_1 and α_2 are the visual angles subtended at the left and rig
eyes, respectively, by the fixation point and any other given point c
the determined locus. The parameters H and M are readily determi
able from the data. The parameter H is especially useful in studies
the apparent stability of the corresponding point organization.

4. These quantification procedures have also been useful to d
scribe the false stereoscopic spatial localization which results when tl
magnifications of the images of the two eyes are made unequal. F
example, suppose one magnifies the image in the right eye only in tl
horizontal meridian by inserting a meridional afocal lens of magn
fication M before the right eye. If x, y, z are the coordinates of ar
given point in binocular visual space, then the coordinates x', y', z
the spatial coordinates of that point in space which corresponded t
the altered horizontal disparities, would be given parametrically b

$$\left.\begin{aligned} x' &= -a\,\frac{(M+1)x - (M-1)a}{(M-1)x - (M+1)a} \\ y' &= \frac{-2ay}{(M-1)x - (M+1)a} \\ \text{and} \qquad z' &= \frac{-2az}{(M-1)x - (M+1)a} \end{aligned}\right\} \qquad (6$$

Here $2a$ is the interpupillary separation [22]. The origin of the c
ordinate system coincides with the midpoint between the entran
pupils of the eyes; the xz plane coincides with the frontal plane; tl
xy plane coincides with the visual plane; and the yz plane coincid
with the median plane. Thus, x measures distances right or left of tl

nedian plane, y the sagittal distances from the frontal plane, and z the listance above or below the visual plane. The manifold of points in he x', y', z' coordinate system would correspond to the visual space een by the observer wearing the lens.

5. The study of stereoscopic depth and stereoscopic spatial orienta-ion about the fixation point when observed in asymmetric conver-gence necessitates a careful analytic approach. Errors in interpretation of data can be found in the literature because of failure in this regard.

For the fixation point given by coordinates (Θ, b) and the left and ight eye points at $(-a \cos \beta, -a \sin \beta)$ and $(a \cos \beta, a \sin \beta)$, respec-ively, where $2a$ is the interpupillary separation and β the amount which the head is rotated about the midpupillary point, the tangent o the Vieth-Müller circle would be given by

$$\tan \chi = -\left(\frac{b^2 - a^2}{b^2 + a^2}\right) \tan \beta \qquad (7)$$

This tangent is not normal to the mean direction of fixation. A com-pensatory rotation of the entire visual field of angle $-\chi$ is necessary o make this surface normal to the direction of fixation. However, mages of points on this normal surface (line) in the two eyes now do not fall on those pairs of retinal elements which gave rise to the sub-ective apparent frontoparallel plane when the eyes were in sym-metrical convergence. The theory of the induced effect is based on his compensatory phenomenon.

6. The analysis shows further that equal differences in depth be-ond and nearer than the fixation point demand different magnitudes f uncrossed and crossed disparities. Or stated in another way, equal ncrements of disparity do not correspond to equal increments of epth. Thus, validity of stereoscopic judgments requires some addi-ional knowledge, and in particular that of the egocentric distance of he point of fixation. The presence of empirical clues may be necessary or this [26].

FORMAL ORGANIZATION OF THE SYSTEM

The theory of stereoscopic vision lends itself to a rather explicit tep-by-step formulation. In a certain respect this formal organization ests on notions and data to be found in the older literature [6], but is certainly made more explicit by the results of subsequent and more efined critical experiments. The aim of such a formulation would be o arrive at a theory of stereopsis which would require as few inter-ening or antecedent hypotheses as possible.

To emphasize the explicitness of this organization, the following table is presented, which relates the axioms and successive theoretical notions to the subjective experience and to the psycho-physiological geometrical experimental procedures. The underlying hypothesis for this arrangement is that a type of stable relationship exists between events in objective space (the surroundings) and the subjective experience of those events, and that for vision those events are mediated through the optical and visual processes of the two eyes. How else could the seeing organism be competent in its environment [13]? The table has been arranged to present, so far as binocular vision is concerned, the various elements, from the more fundamental to the complex, involved in this relationship. The table is more or less self-explanatory.

The following specific considerations are necessary if one is to round out the formal organization of the system and clarify the particulars briefly tabulated in the foregoing itemization.

Retinal correspondence. For stereopsis to occur, there must be a normal correspondence between the retinas of the two eyes and there must also be essentially bifoveal fixation [4]. There is clinical evidence that either stereopsis is present or it is not present. Strabismic patients whose eyes themselves are normal (no deep-seated suppression or amblyopia) frequently report stereopsis immediately after operation which eliminates the strabismus. On the other hand, there are individuals with normal eyes—normal visual acuity, fusion, prism vergences, and no suppression—who give no evidence of obligatory stereopsis. These individuals may, however, have a qualitative sense of depth. No amount of training seems to affect their gaining stereopsis. This is not to imply, however, that the accuracy or discriminatory ability of an individual with stereopsis for depth cannot be improved with training. That stereopsis rests on normal correspondence is evident, because those strabismic patients who have developed a harmonious abnormal correspondence never experience stereoscopic depth, even though the positions of the eyes are corrected surgically.

Stereopsis has been shown to exist for those temporal and corresponding portions of the two retinas which have never been used binocularly, because of the screening of that part of the binocular visual field by the nose.

Contours. We must stress the importance of contours, those lines of demarcation between the "figure" and the "background." In every case stereoscopic depth depends on the disparity between the images of identifiable contours. Stereoscopic depth can be obtained with dark or light figures of different colors, as used in anaglyphs, or with pictures presented in the stereoscope, one positive (dark lines on white background) and the other negative (light lines on black background)

TABLE 1. RELATION OF THEORETICAL TO EXPERIMENTAL ELEMENTS

Axioms and theoretical notions	Experimental	
	Subjective experience	Geometric-physiological bases
	Basic structure	
I. Hypothesis of retinal local signs	Relative subjective visual direction of ordinal "breadth" and "height"	Peripheral angle 1. Transverse 2. Vertical Resolving power
II. Corresponding retinal points, equal local signs	Identical visual directions	Hering experiment Nonius experiments
III. Noncorresponding retinal points	Physiologically double images 1. Transverse (crossed and uncrossed) 2. Vertical 3. Cyclotorsional	Determination of certain spatial coordinates of objects in space and station points of the two eyes
IV. Fusion of noncorresponding points, Panum's areas	Singleness of known disparate images	Region of single binocular vision
V. Transverse disparity of images in the two eyes	Stereoscopic depth 1. Obligatory 2. Qualitative	Difference in distance of objects from eyes Apparent frontoparallel plane
VI. Stability of corresponding retinal points	Equalities of subjective depth	Validity experiments False stereoscopic spatial localization Artificial and natural aniseikonia
	Associated structure	
I. Myosensory factors	"Feel" of eye position and therefore clue for convergence (?) and distance (?)	Validity data (?) Normal plane in asymmetric convergence
II. Functional asymmetry of spatial counterparts of corresponding retinal elements	Equal subjective directions on either side of fixation point in frontoparallel plane	Correlation of partition experiments with Hering-Hillebrand horopter deviation
III. Compensatory orientation phenomenon Asymmetric convergence Induced effect	Apparent "normal" plane	Normal plane in asymmetric convergence Vertical image magnification differences
IV. Presystematic influence of knowledge (empirical factors)	Empirical depth conception	Validity experiments Depth interval vs. disparity
V. Horopter	Equating depth, equating direction, limits of singleness, and so forth	Five criteria

Fusion and double images. Fusion of the disparate images is n
a prerequisite for the existence of stereoscopic depth [23]. Experime
has shown that this depth can be seen after the disparity has becom
so large that the images are seen double and consequently fall outsi
Panum's fusional areas. Both half-images participate in the dept
experience. However, this disparity cannot be too large, for there a
limits beyond which stereopsis fails and the two half-images are the
indefinitely localized as to depth. These limiting disparities amount
about 20′ near the fovea, and they increase rapidly toward the perip
ery, so that at a peripheral angle of 8° these limiting disparities ma
be several arc degrees. The absolute magnitude of these limiting di
parities is not sharply defined, and varies somewhat with the cond
tions under which the measurements are made.

Obligatory and qualitative stereopsis. The character of stere
scopic depth perception, however, changes as the disparity betwee
the images, which are already seen double, is increased. When th
doubling is relatively small, the stereoscopic depth is patent and vali
in the sense that the subjective magnitude of depth bears a defini
relationship to the disparity. For disparities still larger, the stere
scopic depth becomes less definite, in the sense that while there
never confusion as to whether the images are farther or nearer tha
the fixation point, it becomes difficult to tell how much farther or ho
much nearer. That is, the subjective stereoscopic depth no long
increases with increased disparity. One speaks of these two aspects
stereopsis as obligatory depth, which is patent and valid, and qualit
tive depth, which is only qualitatively "farther" or "nearer." F
still larger disparities all sense of depth vanishes.

Role of vertical disparity. It has been shown that vertical di
parities between the images in the two eyes of an object stimulus poi
do not give rise to a subjective depth, as do transverse disparities [26
There are, however, limits in the magnitude of vertical dispariti
(often the images are seen vertically double) for which transverse di
parity components can no longer give rise to stereoscopic experienc
The magnitude of these limiting vertical disparities is amazingly larg
even at the maculae, where one never experiences vertical dispariti
except in individuals with a vertical muscle imbalance—and the
not exceeding about 6′. Furthermore, these limiting vertical dispar
ties apparently, on the basis of data so far available, do not increas
and may even decrease with peripheral angle.

This negative role of vertical disparities for images of particul
stimulus points in the visual field must not be confused with the pos
tive role played by a general pattern of vertical disparities in absolu
spatial *orientation* which one finds in the compensatory phenome

vith the eyes in asymmetrical convergence, or in the laboratory when
he image of one eye is magnified in the vertical meridian only, by
focal meridional magnifying lenses (the induced effect).

Problem of simultaneity. For stereopsis to be perceived the disparate images in the two eyes must exist "simultaneously." By simul-
aneous we understand, however, that the disparate retinal elements
nvolved in given stimuli must be in an excited state at the same time.
This follows because stereoscopic depth may be experienced from disparate images presented successively first to one eye and then to the
other. Under such conditions we are probably dealing with after-
mages or a persistence of the excitations. It has been often reported
hat stereoscopic depth can be experienced from afterimages induced
n each eye separately. The stereoscopic effect from such images
apparently lasts only as long as the afterimages themselves persist.
On the other hand, stereoscopic depth can be experienced for test
timuli exposed for durations as short as 0.0001 sec.

Visual acuity. Stereoscopic acuity is correlated with the visual
acuity of the eyes themselves, and it has been stated that it can be no
better than the visual acuity of the poorer eye. It is true that no strong
orrelation has been found in the range of the higher visual acuities,
but no comparative study has been reported in which identical test
details were used for the test of visual acuity and of stereoacuity.
There is evidence that the vernier (nonius) acuity for one eye, or both
f both eyes view the test, is superior to stereoacuity. This might be
accounted for, however, by the small fluctuations of eye positions in
tereoscopic vision, where the stimulus is different in vision with two
eyes from that in vision with one eye. Stereoscopic acuity is, in general, influenced by those same factors which influence visual acuity,
uch as variation in illumination, contrast, and so forth. Stereopsis
xists in low scotopic levels of illumination, although, as would be
xpected, with much reduced sensitivity. It also exists over the whole
binocular field of view and is not restricted to regions near the point
of fixation, although it is in the latter region that stereoscopic acuity
s maximal because there visual acuity is maximal. Stereoscopic acuity
s correlated with the visual acuity of the peripheral parts of the
etinas.

Stability of retinal correspondence. The relationship between
tereoscopic depth perception and the organization of retinal elements
of the two eyes with the brain (the basis of corresponding retinal
points) appears generally to be a stable one. In no other aspect of
binocular vision is this stability more evident than in the results of
measurement of aniseikonia by the use of stereoscopic test procedures.
The unequal magnification of the images in the two eyes (aniseikonia)

that results from the correction of unequal refractive errors in the two eyes would cause a change in the otherwise normal disparities between the images of the two eyes, with a concomitant emergence of a false stereoscopic spatial localization. While the conflict between the stereoscopic localization and the perception of space from empirical motives or clues may be resolved in ordinary and familiar surroundings, the fact remains that the basis for the false stereoscopic localization persists. Actually the aniseikonia is measured, in tests where the empirical clues are eliminated, by the degree of the false stereoscopic localization present. Such a phenomenon could only be interpreted to mean that the organization of corresponding retinal points is stable. Absolute stability of these processes, that is, stability over very long periods of time, is yet to be proved, but the fact is that the aniseikonia (measured by stereoscopic tests as well as by other tests) remains the same over years, and in many instances the magnitude and character of the results can be predicted from the anisometropic refractive correction. These facts suggest the innateness of the structure on which stereoscopic vision rests.

Validity of stereoscopic depth. For a given observation distance it has been shown that there is a remarkable validity between stereoscopic depth as related to the disparity, and the corresponding objective depth. One cannot ask, however, whether the subjective sense of depth is identical with the objective depth. A valid stereoscopic depth would imply only a proportionality to objective depth, the constant of proportionality being, of course, indeterminable [25]. Two stereoscopic depths produced by two different sets of disparities can be readily compared, but if an estimate of a given depth in terms of a learned scale is to be made, other and probably central factors must enter into the perceptual act. The validity of stereoscopic depth refers, then, to the relative correctness of ordinal values of stereoscopic depth. Even in the comparison of different stereoscopic depths, the data show that some central factor is operating, because equal apparent depth intervals are not identical to equal intervals of disparity, and in some manner the subject must know the observation distance [24].

The problem of the horopter. Since the primary empirical independent variable in the theory of stereoscopic vision is a "disparity" between the images of the two eyes produced by two object points in space, since disparity implies a departure from corresponding retinal points, and since the objective counterpart of corresponding retinal points for a given distance of fixation is the horopter, the theory of stereopsis is bound in part to the problem of the horopter.

If "farther" is associated with uncrossed disparity and "nearer" with crossed disparity, and if one assumes that the images of the fixation point fall on corresponding retinal points, then it should follow logically that if the disparity were zero the two stimulus object points would be seen at the same distance as the fixation point from the observer. While this may be substantially true for stimulus points near the fixation point, there is some ambiguity in what constitutes "same" distance for more widely separated objects. Furthermore, two object points can be seen at the same distance if the disparities relative to a fixation point are equal, that is, when the point of fixation or point of convergence of the eyes differs from either of the two given object points. Thus, in experiments where one attempts to find some aspect of the horopter by setting a series of vertical needles so that they all appear to be at the same distance as a needle being fixated, the images of the fixation point itself may be disparate when a horizontal muscular imbalance exists between the eyes. Then the series of needles would be judged so that the image of each would have equal disparity.

The criterion that the images in the two eyes of a peripheral point which appears to be at the same distance as does the fixation point will fall on corresponding retinal elements is fraught with difficulties—difficulties which necessitate expansion of some general concepts. By definition, images that fall on corresponding retinal elements have zero disparity. That is to say, they would give rise to the same "primary" subjective direction, if exposed to one or the other eye alone. Again by definition, those points in space (if they can be found) the images of which fall on corresponding retinal elements lie on the horopter. Although, strictly speaking, this criterion would imply that under those circumstances subjective "breadth" and "height" of elements were being equated, it is easy to see, however, that for near vision any point in space that lies above or below the visual plane and to the right or to the left of the median plane has images which are geometrically vertically disparate. The magnitude of the vertical disparity varies with the distance of the fixation point from the observer and with the distance of the test stimulus point from the median plane. Thus, for the same lateral visual angle, whether the images of the test point are disparate or not, there can be different degrees of vertical disparity depending on the circumstances.

Now two facts seem to be borne out by experiment: (1) a vertical disparity from a given object point in space *in itself* does not give rise to any subjective depth experience pertaining to that point (Hering and others); (2) recent experimental results show that considerable vertical disparity may be introduced between the images of transversely disparate images without materially affecting the stereoscopic sense of depth [26]. Consequently in stereoscopic depth we are concerned only with the *transverse* or *longitudinal* component of a general

disparity between the images in the two eyes. Thus, it has come abou
that attempts to determine the horopter for a given observation di
tance have utilized plumb line threads or narrow vertical wires fc
test objects—and the resultant locus of positions determined by th
specified criterion has been called the "longitudinal horopter."

There are five criteria for the determination of the empirical long
tudinal horopter:

First, the apparent frontoparallel plane (Hering) is a criterio
based on the logical notion that when the threads of the apparatu
(in the absence of empirical or secondary factors of spatial localiza
tion) all appear at the same distance as the fixation point, then th
transverse disparity of the images of each thread is "zero," and there
fore the images fall on corresponding retinal elements. Logically thi
criterion is unassailable, but the difficulty arises in (1) the assumptio
that the images of the fixation point fall on corresponding retina
points, and (2) the ambiguity between apparent frontoparallel plan
and "same distance" surface. The latter two are not synonymou
The objective frontal plane is that theoretical geometric construct of
plane that passes through the centers of rotation of the two eyes and i
perpendicular to both the median plane and the visual plane when th
latter is horizontal. A frontoparallel plane through the fixation poin
will be parallel to the objective frontal plane. On the other hand, th
locus of "apparently same distance" cylindrical surface could imply
circle in the visual plane about the "egocentric center" of the subjec

This criterion, the apparent frontoparallel plane, is usually used
and in a sense it might be considered the "standard." Most of th
discussion of the "horopter" in the literature is based on data ob
tained by this criterion. However, it would be preferable that we d
not call the result "the longitudinal horopter" unless preceded by th
terms "apparent frontoparallel plane." Actually the criterion has now
come to be used in two ways: (1) as a measure of the organization c
the binocular visual processes for analyzing space localization in th
broad sense, as, for example, in Luneburg's theory, and (2) in th
Hering sense, as a means of determining the spatial counterparts o
corresponding retinal elements. Because of the afore-mentioned am
biguity there is an unsolved problem here. Nevertheless, the criterio
of the apparent frontoparallel plane has been used to answer th
question: Are corresponding retinal points stable? This problem i
beyond the scope of this discussion, yet the fact that the locus of th
threads of the apparatus changes with distance of the fixation poin
is actually a point in fact, which, however, does not imply an insta
bility of the organization of corresponding points.

In experiments of this type, the presence of some empirical factor spatial localization cannot be avoided—just the spacing of the ıreads themselves in the experiment adds an empirical factor. Ex-eriment has also suggested that if only one thread of the series be set t a time, all others being excluded, the final locus of all the threads eviates in the direction of the Vieth-Müller circle from that obtained hen all are exposed. The chromatic difference in magnification as ıtroduced by chromatic aberrations in the optical systems of the eyes ill change the locus, although the criterion remains the same. Simi-ırly, short periods of exposure of the test threads, or such devices as a falling bead," result also in a change—all these changes being toward ıe Vieth-Müller circle.

The second criterion, described as the "equating of primary visual irections," is the ideal criterion of the five, since it conforms more losely to the basic definition of corresponding points, namely, that a test object is seen by each of the two eyes in the same primary isual direction, the images of the object fall on corresponding retinal lements. Experimentally this criterion is used when, with a constant xation, certain screens are placed before the eyes, so that the images f a given test-stimulus vertical thread are seen as a nonius or vernier ask, the upper half of the thread being seen by one eye, the lower alf by the other. Only when the position of the thread is so adjusted hat the two halves appear aligned—therefore seen in the same visual irection by each eye separately—would the images be said to fall on orresponding retinal elements. Unfortunately for the ideality of this riterion, the accuracy of adjustment of the threads is much poorer han that for the apparent frontoparallel plane by stereoscopic vision. Nevertheless, for a given fixation point the locus of the threads when onforming to this criterion is nearer the Vieth-Müller circle than is hat of the apparent frontoparallel plane.

The third criterion is the determination of the middle of the re-gion of single binocular vision. With a given fixation point, each test hread of the apparatus is moved farther (or nearer) until double mages (uncrossed or crossed) occur. The area between the loci of the stimated positions across the binocular visual field where doubling ust occurs, on the far and on the near side of the fixation point, de-ines a spatial region within which even disparate images are seen ingle (fused). The center of this region is *assumed* to be the locus where he images of the threads would fall on nondisparate or corresponding etinal elements. Again, lack of accuracy, the influence of training, etc., prevent this from being a highly precise criterion.

The fourth criterion is based on the notion of Tschermak [29] that stereoscopic sensitivity is maximal in the vicinity of the horopter. This s a difficult criterion to use.

The fifth criterion is based on the experimental fact that disparity between the images in the two eyes also constitutes a stimulus for a fusional movement of the eyes, a movement initiated in an effort to reduce that disparity. Thus, the longitudinal horopter would be the locus of the threads such that there would be no stimulus for fusional movements. There is no satisfactory way of testing this criterion.

From this discussion, it is clear that we have as yet no precise method of determining the spatial counterparts of corresponding retinal points. The criterion used most frequently, the apparent frontoparallel plane, is actually unreliable, first, when a fixation disparity [22] exists (that is, the eyes are actually overconverged or underconverged for the point of fixation when a lateral heterophoria exists). The second criterion, using the nonius method for equating primary subjective visual directions, shows strikingly the influence of this disparity, for the locus of the threads when adjusted according to this criterion actually lies in front of, or behind, the thread used for fixation. The locus of the threads for the apparent frontoparallel plane will (almost always) pass through the position of the thread being fixated, although a fixation disparity may be present. One would presume in this case that equal stereoscopic depths are utilized across the binocular visual field corresponding to the disparity of the images of the fixation point.

The criterion of the apparent frontoparallel plane is also unreliable, second, when the eyes fixate a thread at near vision in an asymmetric convergent position. Actual experiment has shown that an over-all compensation of the binocular stereoscopic field must occur in the sense of a rotation of that field from the tangent to the Vieth-Müller circle at the fixation point to the apparently normal position. The nonius criterion provides data closely associated with the Vieth-Müller circle; therefore, the threads adjusted for the apparently normal position (or apparent frontoparallel plane) must be seen with disparate retinal images—uncrossed on one side of the fixation point and crossed on the other. Further pursuit of these complicated problems lies outside the scope of this discussion.

Fortunately the subjective experience of stereoscopic depth does not depend on our specific knowledge of the location of the longitudinal horopter. A stereoscopic depth difference will be experienced for every difference of disparity between the images in the two eyes.

Role of empirical factors in spatial localization. No adequate discussion of stereoscopic depth perception today can fail to consider the role played by the empirical or experiential clues and factors for space perception as they are related to stereoscopic depth. In fact, in almost no experimental situation can they be entirely eliminated [1].

This does not imply, on the other hand, that these clues are an integral part of or a prerequisite for stereoscopic perception. An apparent difference in distance of two points of light in total darkness can be judged, with or without eye movements, with considerable precision. In the usual surroundings encountered in ordinary life, the stereoscopic and empirical aspects of depth perception agree and aid each other.

By implication the various familiar so-called empirical clues to depth perception have been learned as a result of experience in association with retinal images of objects and configurations of familiar objects in space. Throughout the learning period this association was a meaningful one, for in every instance the perceptual content of localization was important in one's dealing with the environment [10]. In contrast to these clues, the stereoscopic responses are to be considered more automatic and thus have no such perceptual content or meaning. As a result, it is to be expected that in those surroundings that have been artificially produced to provide a conflict between stereoscopic stimuli and empirical factors, the meaningless stimuli may be suppressed by the meaningful, that is, by the perceptions from the empirical motives for depth. On the range finder the stereoscopic image of the reticles cannot be made to appear to recede through a building with details in spite of the uncrossed disparity introduced by the instrument. Similarly, the forceful empirical clues incorporated in the Ames trapezoidal window [1], set up in a closed space where few other stimuli are present, greatly modify or completely mask stereoscopic depth from disparate stimuli.

On the other hand, in artificially arranged surroundings where the empirical motives for depth are ambiguous or susceptible to many interpretations, the stereoscopic depth from disparate images may determine the perception of the surroundings. Such is the case of the leaf-room. In monocular vision the interior of the room appears as an indefinitely localized hollow cavity which, however, when seen binocularly appears cubical—its true shape. Under the influence of meridional afocal magnifying lenses placed before the eyes, the room will become apparently distorted in a manner which can be predicted from the geometry involved and the relationships between the disparities of the images in the two eyes as modified by the lenses. Even here some empirical motives are present, for with a certain meridional magnification of the image in one eye, one wall of the room should appear very far away (infinite), but the apparent distance never seems to exceed a certain maximum.

In other situations, as when figures of a cross with unequal crosslines for the two eyes are observed in the stereoscope, the interior parts of the unequal horizontal lines are indefinitely localized, but the disparities between the images of the ends of the lines serve as anchors causing the entire line to appear stereoscopically rotated about th vertical line. This is especially evident when the horizontal lines ar not centered with respect to the vertical lines. The horizontal line are seen stereoscopically as a single rotated horizontal line in front of or behind, a vertical line. The stereopsis can provide a means whereb indefinitely localized configurations are given specificity of localiza tion. In most of our ordinary surroundings involving spatial localiza tion, the empirical factors probably play a dominant role. Stereopsi adds an accuracy of depth discrimination to the totality of perceptio not attainable in any other way. One also must not forget the role c binocular empirical factors at near vision.

In all quantification procedures for studying stereoscopic depth i as nearly pure a form as possible, namely, reduced to the elementa structure of binocular vision, a great difficulty is the elimination of th secondary clues to spatial localization. Even in those experimenta setups where these clues are virtually eliminated, the question the arises as to whether the very absence of some empirical clues does no constitute a negative type of empirical factor. That is to say, the farthe of two similar or known objects should subtend a smaller visual angl to the eyes than the nearer object. When it does not in a reduce experimental situation, could there not be an inhibiting effect on th depth experienced by stereopsis? Generally, however, the existence o such "negative" clues is believed to be negligible, and the greater th reduction in the empirical clues, the more it is possible to stud stereoscopic depth in an elemental sense.

Convergence. Convergence plays a role in stereoscopic vision onl to the extent that convergence movements of the eyes are necessary t provide bifoveal fixation on the object point of attention. A role fo convergence as a myosensory activity or a muscle sense to provide a clue to distance, both in the absolute sense and in the relative (stereo scopic) sense, is frequently postulated. The existence of a type of muscl spindle in the extraocular muscles of man might suggest such a pro prioceptive sense. That change in the convergence of the eyes per se i not a necessary requirement in the emergence of stereoscopic dept was proved by experiments in which extremely short periods o illumination were used—durations of exposure so short that there wa no opportunity for eye movements to occur. The afterimage in suc tests would provide a longer persistence of the stimulus. All othe critical experiments tend to deny the existence of such a muscl sense [9]. This is not to say that fixation eye movements do not enhanc stereoscopic depth, but they do so by virtue of the fact that with suc movements retinal areas of higher visual acuity come into play. Th physiological micronystagmoid movements of the eyes in another wa may intensify this perception. Stereoscopic acuity is, however, uninfluenced by heterophorias.

Accommodation. Just as for the role of convergence, experiments have shown that changes in accommodation in distance localization are most unreliable as guides to distance perception.

Physiological basis of stereopsis. Of the topics discussed previously, the following as a group are said to speak strongly for the position that stereopsis from disparity between the images, together with its accompanying processes, is basically physiological in nature:

1. The immediacy or automatic features of the response to the disparity stimulus.
2. The correlation between stereoacuity and visual acuity.
3. The existence of functional limitations in transverse and vertical disparities.
4. The stability of stereoscopic localization as related to retinal correspondence.
5. The demonstrable existence of stereopsis in portions of retinas never used binocularly because of the screening effect of the nose.
6. The necessity for normal retinal correspondence.
7. The aftereffects in the third dimension [17].
8. The all-or-none aspect of the existence of stereopsis in a given individual.

Against this general notion is the fact that in certain surroundings the stereoscopic depth sometimes seems to develop slowly. These situations are usually those in which the stereoscopic depth and the empirical factors to depth are at variance. This time lag in appearance of stereoscopic depth varies with individuals and may be related to the proneness of the individual to rely more on the empirical clues to depth perception.

RANGE OF APPLICATION OF SYSTEM

The systematic theory of stereoscopic vision as presented in this chapter applies to a relatively narrow range of visual phenomena; yet there are certain interrelations to several subsets of such phenomena. Specifically we can cite the general problem of apparent size of visual objects and the problem of size constancy in situations in which binocular vision plays a dominant role [3]. Similarly, recent discussions on the metric character of visual space and its relation to objective space are vitally concerned with the system under discussion here. It would seem that the building of the superstructure of such a metric from purely mathematical hypothetical constructs without considering the fundamental nature of binocular vision can lead only to a metric system beset with exceptions [19]. Again, the phenomenon of stereoscopic depth perception provides a tool for the study of such binocular functions as cyclotorsional and cyclofusional eye movements, as well as of vertical motor imbalances between the eyes, and also for the determination of aniseikonia. Mention has already been made of the role of stereoscopic vision in the problem of the stability of, or, conversely, the compensatory processes of, the organization of corresponding points and, therefore, of the retinas to the brain.

CONCLUDING REMARKS

The concepts and empirical data discussed leading up to the Hering theory of "depth local signs" of the retinas and to the theory of the compulsion to fusion as explanations for the emergence of stereoscopic depth still require much further experimental and theoretical elucidation. The former theory implies a certain innate quality in the character of the visual processes, and a stability independent of environmental changes, but without the hypothesis of compensatory visual field orientation it fails to predict the "normal" surface in asymmetric convergence for near vision. Similarly, the theory of the compulsion to fusion from disparate images falls short in this same regard; furthermore, it is faced with the possibility of compensated (relearned) motor coordination of the eyes to meet changed conditions in the optical environment.

The horopter problem is far from being solved. There are discrepancies between the determination of the spatial counterparts of corresponding retinal points found by the equating of directional values and their determination as found by the functional stereoscopic depth. Then, too, there is the influence of unavoidable empirical factors. The difficulty of achieving adequate precision of measurements in these experiments is in some respects what makes the problem unresolvable.

The extent to which a stability of the organization of corresponding retinal points actually exists still remains a most important problem [5]. The false stereoscopic localization of objects in space, when the optical images in the two eyes are altered by the magnification properties of ophthalmologic lenses, so far as transverse disparities are concerned, has been successfully predicted—if not exactly quantitatively under all circumstances, it has certainly been predicted qualitatively. Furthermore, our ability to determine existent differences in the magnifications of the images of the two eyes on the basis of the false stereoscopic perception of selected test contours speaks in favor of a continuing stable organization of corresponding retinal elements in the two eyes. The possible existence of such a stable organization has pertinent implications for the neuroanatomical structure of the visual system. Certainly such an organization is involved in those problems encountered in clinical ophthalmology in which possible imperfections in it may be the cause of suppression, strabismus, and false retinal correspondence [18].

On the other hand, there is the school of thought that would explain stereoscopic depth as a result of the "working up of gestalt forms" from each of the two eyes [33]. These enthusiasts would deny any importance to disparity—and even claim that the disparity is a result or by-product of the perception and certainly is not the stimulus. In almost all instances, the evidence is obtained from introspection of particularly selected drawings observed in a stereoscope. There would be reasons to believe that the "working up of forms" would occur after the basic physiological stimulus has already arrived in consciousness. The factors which are utilized in the creation of form must be inherent in the fundamental stimuli.

In conclusion it is clear that the systematic analysis of the theory of stereoscopic vision as presented in this essay must not be considered *the* definitive and final theory. It is a progress analysis.

REFERENCES

1. Ames, Adelbert, Jr. *The nature of our perceptions, prehensions and behavior.* Princeton, N.J.: Princeton Univer. Press, 1955.

2. Bergmann, Gustav, & Spence, K. W. The logic of psychophysical measurement. *Psychol. Rev.,* 1944, **51,** 1–24.

3. Boring, E. G. *Sensation and perception in the history of experimental psychology.* New York: Appleton-Century-Crofts, 1942.

4. Burian, H. M. Stereopsis. *Docum. ophth.,* 1951, **5,** 169–183.

5. Charnwood, J. R. B. *An essay on binocular vision.* London: The Hatton Press, Ltd., 1951.

6. Chavasse, Bernard. Ocular muscles: The nature and antiquity of stereopsis. *Tr. ophth. Soc. U. K.,* 1931, **51,** 268–286.

7. Clark, W. E. L. The visual centres of the brain and their connexions. *Physiol. Rev.,* 1942, **22,** 205–232.

8. Clark, W. E. L. *Anatomical pattern as the essential basis of sensory discrimination.* Springfield, Ill.: Charles C Thomas, 1948.

9. Cogan, D. G. *Neurology of the ocular muscles.* Springfield, Ill.: Charles C Thomas, 1948.

10. Fleischer, E. Die Querdisparation als physiologische Grundlage des binokularen Tiefensehens. *Ztschr. Psychol.,* 1939, **147,** 65–132.

11. Gibson, J. J. *The perception of the visual world.* Boston: Houghton Mifflin, 1950.

12. Graham, C. H. Behavior and the psychophysical methods: An analysis of some recent experiments. *Psychol. Rev.,* 1952, **59,** 62–70.

13. Hebb, D. O. *The organization of behavior: A neuropsychological theory.* New York: Wiley, 1949.

14. Hering, Ewald. *Spatial sense and movements of the eye.* C. A. Radde (Trans.) Baltimore: The American Academy of Optometry, 1942.

15. Hillebrand, F. *Lehre von den Gesichtsempfindungen.* Berlin: Julius Springer, 1929.

16. Hofmann, F. B. Physiologische Optik (Raumsinn). In Graefe, A., & Saemisch, T., *Handbuch der gesamten Augenheilkunde.* Vol. 3, Pt. 2. Berlin: Julius Springer, 1925.

17. Köhler, Wolfgang, & Emery, D. A. Figural after-effects in the third dimension of visual space. *Am. J. Psychol.,* 1947, **60,** 159–201.

18. Kretzschmar, Serge. La fausse correspondance rétinienne. *Docum. ophth.,* 1955, **9,** 46–208.

19. Le Grand, Y. Etudes binoculaires. II. La théorie de l'espace visuel de Luneburg. *Att. d. Fond. Giorg. Ronchi,* 1954, **9,** 44–51.

20. Linksz, A. *Physiology of the eye.* Vol. 2. *Vision.* New York: Grune & Stratton, 1952.

21. Ogle, K. N. Die mathematische Analyse des Längshoropters. *Arch. ges. Physiol.,* 1938, **239,** 748–766.

22. Ogle, K. N. *Researches in binocular vision.* Philadelphia: Saunders, 1950.

23. Ogle, K. N. On the limits of stereoscopic vision. *J. exper. Psychol.,* 1952, **44,** 253–259.

24. Ogle, K. N. Precision and validity of stereoscopic depth perception from double images. *J. optical Soc. Am.,* 1953, **43,** 906–913.

25. Ogle, K. N. On stereoscopic depth perception. *J. exp. Psychol.,* 1954, **48,** 225–233.

26. Ogle, K. N. Stereopsis and vertical disparity. *A.M.A. Arch. Ophth.,* 1955, **53,** 495–504.

27. Southall, J. P. C. *Helmholtz's treatise on physiological optics.* Vol. 3. *The perceptions of vision.* Opt. Soc. Amer., 1925.

28. Teichner, W. H., Kobrick, J. L., & Wehrkamp, R. F. The effects of terrain and observation distance on relative depth discrimination. *Am. J. Psychol.,* 1955, **68,** 193–208.

29. Tschermak, A. Optischer Raumsinn. In Bethe, A., Bergmann, G. V., Embden, G., & Ellinger, A. *Handbuch der normalen und pathologischen Physiologie mit Berücksichtigung der Experimentellen Pharmakologie.* Vol. 12(2). Berlin: Julius Springer, 1931.

30. Vernon, M. D. *A further study of visual perception.* Cambridge: Cambridge Univer. Press, 1952.

31. Walls, G. L. The problem of visual direction. Part I. The history to 1900; Part II. The tangible basis for nativism; Part III. Experimental attacks and their results. *Amer. J. Optometry,* 1951, **28,** 55–83; 115–146; 173–212.

32. Wheatstone, Charles. Contributions to the physiology of vision.—Part the First. On some remarkable, and hitherto unobserved, phenomena of binocular vision. *Phil. Tr. roy. Soc.* London: 1838, 371–394.

33. Wilde, Kurt. Der Punktreiheneffekt und die Rolle der binocularen Querdisparation beim Tiefensehen. *Psych. Forschung.,* 1950, **23,** 223–262.

THE LUNEBURG THEORY OF BINOCULAR SPACE PERCEPTION[1]

ALBERT A. BLANK
Institute of Mathematical Sciences, New York University, and Department of Mathematics, University of Tennessee

[1] It is the wish of Luneburg's colleagues that his name be permanently affixed to the theory.

INTRODUCTION

This paper is intended as an analysis of the methods and concepts of Luneburg and the author in accordance with the suggested topic outline of the APA Study of Psychological Science, Project A.

The Luneburg theory is a rarity of sorts among theories of perception. The contribution of mathematicians, it possessed from its inception some of that definitive quality which is ordinarily associated only with the theories of physical science. Perhaps this theory will have no other value for further studies in perception or psychology in general, but its existence demonstrates that it is not vain to look for a theory of classical type in these fields.

The development of the theory proceeded quite rapidly from the time in 1945 when, while visiting the Dartmouth Eye Institute, Luneburg was shown certain puzzling data which seemed to contradict some of the commonly held preconceptions about visual space perception. To the mathematician these data indicated that the phenomena of vision could not be described in purely euclidean terms. His first publication on the subject [10] appeared two years later. Subsequent refinements appeared in 1948 [11], and posthumously in 1950 [12]. In his last paper Luneburg recognized that many of the experimental observations made by Hardy, Rand, and Rittler in the Knapp Memorial Laboratories at Columbia University were not in accord with the theory of [10]. Luneburg's untimely death in 1949 interrupted theoretical progress. The experimental program at the Knapp Laboratory continued but ran into difficulties which could not be resolved in the framework of the existent theory. Toward the end of 1950 the author joined the staff at the Knapp Laboratory to continue the theoretical investigations. In the summer of 1952, the experimental and theoretical investigations at the Knapp Laboratory were concluded with the feeling that a considerable measure of success had been achieved. An exposition by the author of a modified and simplified theory appeared in 1953 [1] and again shortly afterward in a joint publication of the staff at the Knapp Laboratory [8]. It is essentially the theory and experimental results of the last two works which are under discussion here. The author is also drawing on a special theory concerning the physiological aspects of vision [2].

The author would like to apologize beforehand for any lack of clarity in this analysis. It was his original intention to include a goodly amount of expository material, but much was mathematically technical and almost all, though little known, could be found in the literature. He would like also to ask the reader's indulgence for any misuse or abuse of the psychologist's conventional language for which ignorance may be responsible.

METATHEORY

Luneburg and the author were not committed to any school of philosophical or psychological doctrine. If pushed to take sides, most likely they would feel least alien in the camp of the logical positivists and the behaviorists, although no great effort has been made to conform to those tenets. The use of dualistic terminology in their writings, for example, is not evidence of a philosophical position but is purely a matter of linguistic convenience. As indicated in the introduction to [8], it would have been possible to phrase everything in monistic operational language.[2] The theorists have simply been

[2] The section on the operational definition of theoretical terms below shows, in effect, how to construct a glossary for the purpose of converting the dualistic terminology of the published theory into operational language. Two systems which have the same structure and differ only in the language in which they are presented are said to be isomorphic. To the mathematician, the language of presentation is inessential, hence the seeming indifference here to the philosophical point of view.

makers of mathematical models. As mathematicians, they prefer to leave to specialists the large questions as to the significance of the theory for philosophy and psychology in general. The metatheoretical considerations which guided them were not thought of in connection with any larger domain than the immediate concern of the theory.

From the beginning, it seemed evident that a mathematical theory of binocular visual phenomena was feasible. Vision is clearly a highly organized and strongly patterned function. Furthermore, in metric geometry there appeared to be a domain of mathematics ideally suited to a description of visual phenomena. The construction of the theory was based upon the assumption that there are measurable invariable constituents of binocular visual perception. Luneburg stated in [12]:

> Visual sensations are not merely the chance result of coincidental psychological conditions but are governed by certain constant factors which, though not determining the sensations completely, play an integral part in their formation. These factors must be related to the external physical situation as well as to certain elements in the personality of the observer.[3] The denial of the existence of such constant elements in the relationship of a living organism to external nature would be tantamount to denying all objectivity in visual sensations and therefore would be absurd.

Empirically, these constants were sought by rigorously deleting from the environment factors which are not essential to the binocular perception of space. The study of the phenomena due to the superimposition of the binocularly inessential elements, though certainly of interest in the theory of learning, did not concern the theorists.

The attractiveness of a mathematical model is surely centered in the use of deductive methods. In a completely inductive science, the best of inferences is only somebody's guess. There are, almost invariably, broad areas of disagreement among the workers in such a field. Where available, a mathematical model is useful in contracting the area of dispute. For a properly formulated mathematical system the inductive elements are restricted to the formulation of the postulates. For this reason Luneburg and the author have sought as explicit a statement of the postulates as possible.

There is something more to be said for an apt mathematical model. So elegant was Luneburg's theoretical development that it was not abandoned despite the initial failure of experimental results to conform to the theory. The faith of the experimenters was eventually justified by the construction of a modified system which

[3] The word observer, in the Knapp Laboratory parlance, signifies human experimental subject.

remedied the discrepancies and led to conclusions which were empirically validated. As Dirac [5] wrote of another theory, "The moral of the story is that one should have faith in a theory that is beautiful. If the theory fails to agree with experiment, its basic principles may still be correct and the discrepancy may be due merely to some detail that will get cleared up in the future."

For present purposes, it will be best not to give undue emphasis to the predictive aspects of theory. In the initial stages of a theoretical construction there is rarely any concern with unexplored domains of factual knowledge. A theory usually begins as an attempt at explanation of known phenomena. Should it also serve the purposes of prediction, the prospects for its acceptance are markedly increased and the theorist is immensely gratified.

If it is granted that a given theory is created not for the purpose of prediction but to explain, then it may well be asked, just what is such an explanation to consist of? For the author, an explanation consists of a statement of the variables and fundamental relations of a system. The words variable and system are used here in a precise technical sense and no attempt has been made to place them in the "independent-intervening-dependent variable" schema. A system consists of certain classes or categories. A variable is simply a generic symbol denoting a member of a specific class. A value of a variable is a particular member of its associated class. A relation is a propositional function on the variables. In other words, a relation is a sentence with certain unspecified nouns. The nouns may be filled in by choosing values of the variables. For each choice the relation has a truth value, either true or false.

In geometry, for example, the variables would be points, lines, surfaces, etc. As an example of a typical geometrical relation consider $R(P,L,L)$ defined on the class P of points and the class L of lines.[4] For a specific point P_0 and lines L_1, L_2 the relation $R(P_1,L_1,L_2)$ states that P_1 lies on both the lines L_1 and L_2. In projective geometry, given any point and any pair of lines, the truth or falsity of this relation can be decided. Hereafter, the writing of a relation for specific values will mean that it is true. To indicate falsity, a bar will be drawn through the relation symbol, as $\not{R}$.

For a given relation, it sometimes happens that whenever all the variables but a certain one are assigned specific values, there exists precisely one value of the remaining variable for which the relation is true. In that case the mathematical convention is to refer to the variable which has its value determined in this fashion as the depend-

[4] In writing relations the convention employed will be to use unmodified symbols for classes, subscripted symbols for members of the classes.

ent variable and to say that it is a function of the others, the independent variables. In the example given above, if the restriction be made that L_1 and L_2 are not the same then the point is a function of the pair of lines.

A mathematical system is determined abstractly by the classes of symbols employed and the stated relations. Two systems are mathematically identical (isomorphic) if the objects of the systems, classes, elements, relations, may be paired off one-to-one in such a way that truth values in the two systems match in the correspondence. A scientific theory, in one special sense, may be considered as a mathematical system in which the abstract symbols correspond to experiential data. Prediction amounts to deduction by means of the relational calculus.

THE STRUCTURE OF THE LUNEBERG THEORY

A. The variables and their fundamental interrelations. The Luneburg theory is geometrical. Its variables are the class of points and certain of its subclasses such as curves and surfaces. A point may be thought of as an entity defined by physical mensuration, an ordered triple of real numbers, its coordinates, which specify its position in a frame fixed with respect to the observer [8, p. 4]. For the purposes of this study, the physical space as determined by physical mensuration is assumed to be euclidean.

Binocular observation orders the points of space. One point is seen to be higher or lower, more to the right or left, nearer or farther than another. Lengths are ordered also. The distance between one pair of points is seen to be larger or smaller than that between another pair. The topology of physical space is preserved. Nothing more is required for a geometry of vision except that the observer be empirically consistent in these matters, that his observations be repeatable in some class of environmental situations.

For linguistic convenience, space as ordered by binocular observation will be called visual space in contradistinction to physical space, space ordered by physical measurements.

It would be possible to utilize primitive observations of the kind cited above to erect a complete formal set of fundamental postulates. The author will not attempt here to exhibit an exhaustive list of the primitive relations of Luneburg theory, but will present the mathematical details in a technical publication.[4a] Nevertheless, a sketchy presentation of some of the primitive relations may prove illuminating.

[4a] A. A. Blank, Axiomatics of binocular vision, *J. opt. Soc. Am.* (will appear May, 1958).

The most interesting ones for this purpose are the visual ordering of lengths and visual alignment.

1. *The length-ordering relation.*

There exists a nontrivial ordering of point pairs (lengths) in visual space.

This relation will be denoted by $O[(P,P),(P,P)]$. Nontriviality amounts to an assertion that the relation is neither always true nor always false. The symbol $O[(P_1,P_2),(P_3,P_4)]$ is to be understood as a statement that the length between P_1 and P_2 is seen to be less than the length between P_3 and P_4. An ordering relation $O[A,A]$ is defined in general by:

a. $\emptyset[A_0,A_0]$.

b. If A_1 is distinct from A_2 then either $\emptyset[A_1,A_2]$ or $\emptyset[A_2,A_1]$. If both $\emptyset[A_1,A_2]$ and $\emptyset[A_2,A_1]$, then A_1 is said to be equal to A_2.

c. $\emptyset[A_1,A_2]$ and $\emptyset[A_2,A_3]$ imply $\emptyset[A_1,A_3]$.

In addition, a length ordering must satisfy a requirement of symmetry:

d. Length ordering is independent of the order of the points in each pair,

$$O[(P_1,P_2),(P_3,P_4)] \equiv O[(P_2,P_1),(P_3,P_4] \equiv O[(P_1,P_2),(P_4,P_3)],$$ [5]

and a requirement of regularity:

e. If P_2 and P_3 are distinct points, then

$$O[(P_1,P_1),(P_2,P_3)] \text{ and } \emptyset[(P_1,P_1),(P_2,P_2)].$$

If the reader places point pairs as the elements in the definition of an order relation he will have little difficulty in lending meaning to the formal statements above, nor will he have trouble deriving such deductive consequences as the proposition, "Not both $O[(P_1,P_2),(P_3,P_4)]$ and $O[(P_3,P_4),(P_1,P_2)]$." In fact, so intuitively evident is the content of these postulates that the author has had difficulty on occasion in preventing a feeling of impatience in his audience at the erection of such an elaborate scaffolding for so little. The necessity for such explicitness is made clear by the fact that the visual ordering of lengths does not coincide with the physical ordering. It is a simple matter empirically to find two pairs of points for which the visual length ordering is the reverse of the physical length ordering.

2. *The alignment relation.*

The sense of straightness is one of the signal characteristics of visual perception. Binocular alignments are made readily in all localizations and orientations in the binocular visual field. This property is summarized in the postulate:

There exists an alignment relation in visual space.

[5] The symbol $\equiv$ is read as, "is equivalent to."

The alignment relation $L(P_1,P_2,P_3)$ is to be understood as a statement that the points P_1, P_2, P_3 are aligned visually with P_2 between P_1 and P_3. An alignment relation is characterized by properties *a*—*f* following:

a. $L(P_1,P_2,P_3) \equiv L(P_3,P_2,P_1)$.
b. $L(P_1,P_2,P_3)$ implies $O[(P_1,P_2),(P_1,P_3)]$.

From these properties it follows that the alignment of three points implies their distinctness. It also follows that $L(P_1,P_2,P_3)$ implies $\not{L}(P_1,P_2,P_3)$:

c. $L(P_1,P_2,P_3)$ and $L(P_1,P_3,P_4)$ imply $L(P_1,P_2,P_4)$ and $L(P_2,P_3,P_4)$.
$L(P_1,P_2,P_3)$ and $L(P_2,P_3,P_4)$ imply $L(P_1,P_2,P_4)$ and $L(P_1,P_3,P_4)$.
d. $L(P_1,P_2,P_3)$ and $L(P_1,P_2,P_4)$, with P_3 distinct from P_4, imply either $L(P_1,P_4,P_3)$ or $L(P_1,P_3,P_4)$.
$L(P_1,P_2,P_3)$ and $L(P_1,P_4,P_3)$, with P_2 distinct from P_4, imply either $L(P_1,P_2,P_4)$ or $L(P_1,P_4,P_2)$.

A line is defined as the class of all points which are in any of the three possible alignment relations with two of its given points. The properties *c*, *d* assure that a line is determined by any pair of its points.

e. Let P_1 be distinct from P_2, P_3 from P_4. There exists a point P_0 such that $L(P_1,P_0,P_2)$ and $O[(P_1,P_0),(P_3,P_4)]$.
f. Let P_1 and P_2 be any pair of distinct points. The segment S joining the two points is defined as the class of all points P_s with $L(P_1,P_s,P_2)$ plus the end points P_1 and P_2. For every subdivision of S into two disjoint nonempty classes A and B such that, for all P_a in A and P_b in B, $O[(P_1,P_a),(P_1,P_b)]$, there exists a point P^* in S with the property that $O[(P_1,P'),(P_1,P^*)]$ implies that P' is in A and $O[(P_1,P^*),(P_1,P')]$ implies that P' is in B.

The last two postulates assure such consequences as the possibility of dividing a segment into a given number of equal parts, or the possibility for a given segment of finding a subsegment which is equal in length to any given shorter segment.

Again, the visual relations and physical relations do not coincide. Physical alignments are generally not visually straight and a binocular visual alignment is, in general, not physically straight.

The primary purpose of the foregoing has been to show that the postulated relations of visual space have an uncomplicated primitive character which leads to a ready intuitive understanding and direct empirical tests. It would be fruitless to continue to write a sufficient set of such primitive postulates to characterize Luneburg theory, since the principal purpose in such a listing is to show that all the deductions of geometry derive from certain elementary considerations. It is sufficient to mention the possibility here rather than present a complete statement. Instead, the author will present a shorter postulate set for the sake of conciseness. The one set is completely equivalent to the other in the sense that the postulates of the one are deductive consequences of the postulates of the other.

A postulate set for Luneburg theory. The postulate set above could be extended to show the existence of a visual metric or real-valued function measuring visual distance relations. For the present, let this be the point of beginning.

The psychometric of binocular visual space. A metric is a function which assigns a real value to each pair of points. It is to be understood as a kind of measure of distance between two points. Let such a metric be denoted by D. As a distance-measuring function, D must conform to certain laws:

a. $D(P_1,P_1) = 0$. $P_1 \neq P_2$ implies $D(P_1,P_2) > 0$.

In words, a point is at zero distance from itself. Distinct points have positive distance.

b. $D(P_1,P_2) = D(P_2,P_1)$.

The distance between two points is independent of their order.

c. $D(P_1,P_2) + D(P_2,P_3) \geq D(P_1,P_3)$.

The distance between two points is as short or shorter than the sum of the distances going by way of a third point. If equality holds, P_2 is said to be aligned between P_1 and P_3.

Metrics are conceivable in infinite variety. The most familiar is the euclidean metric,

$$D(P_1,P_2) = [(x_1 - x_2)^2 + (y_1 - y_2)^2 + (z_1 - z_2)^2]^{1/2},$$

where P_1 and P_2 are specified by their three real coordinates, $P_1 = (x_1,y_1,z_1)$ and $P_2 = (x_2,y_2,z_2)$. In order for a metric to be a psychometric for binocular vision it must describe the visual relations of length-ordering and alignment. Formally, it is required that

d. $O[(P_1,P_2),(P_3,P_4)]$ if and only if $D(P_1,P_2) < D(P_3,P_4)$.

The distance between one pair of points is seen as less than that between another if and only if the corresponding values of the metric stand in the same relation.

e. $L(P_1,P_2,P_3)$ if and only if

$$D(P_1,P_2) + D(P_2,P_3) = D(P_1,P_3).$$

The points P_1, P_2, P_3 are seen aligned in that order if and only if the metric distance from P_1 to P_3 is the sum of the metric distances going by way of P_2.

The properties, *a—e*, are summarized in the postulate:

(A1) *There exists a psychometric distance function for binocular vision.*

It is possible to change the scale simply by multiplying the metric by a positive constant. Such a change of scale would not affect the truth of the properties *a—e*. In other words, any pair of distinct points may freely be chosen to define the unit of length. As a consequence of two further postulates it can be proved [10] that the metric of binocular vision is uniquely determined except only for the freedom of choice of unit or scale:

(A2) *The visual space is convex.*

This postulate asserts the possibility of finding between each pair of distinct points a third point aligned with them. Formally, if $P_1 \neq P_3$ then there exists at least one additional point with

$$D(P_1,P_2) + D(P_2,P_3) = D(P_1,P_3).$$

(A3) *The visual space is finitely compact.*

Every bounded infinite set of points has at least one cluster point. Intuitively, this means that the restriction of an infinite set of points to a bounded region forces them to bunch together somewhere. These concepts are given precise definition in terms of the metric. A set is said to be bounded if there exists a point P_0, a positive real number M such that for all points P_i of the set, $D(P_i,P_0) < M$. A point P' is said to be a cluster point of a set if for every real positive number ϵ, there exists at least one point P_ϵ of the set such that $0 < D(P_\epsilon,P') < \epsilon$.

The reader will be quick to note that the postulates A2 and A3 have a special quality. They are too fine-structured for our visual experience in requiring infinitely many discriminations. In A2, for example, if points are thought of as dots of light, it is clear that if two lights are sufficiently close physically, say on the verge of the limit of ocular resolution, the insertion of a light between them will result in an impression in which the identity of the individual lights is lost. These postulates are to be taken as an idealization of the actual visual phenomena, and it must be kept in mind that conclusions drawn from them may fail if they are applied to phenomena which are too fine-grained. It should not be expected, therefore, that threshold space perceptions may be explained on the basis of the theory or, conversely, that the macroscopic visual spatial organization will be explained by an analysis of threshold perceptions.

A space which satisfies the three postulates A is called a metric space. In summary, it is asserted that the visual space is metric.

Characterization of the psychometric. In principle, it would be possible to determine empirically which of the infinity of possible metrics best describes the visual spatial relationships. The characterization of the visual metric is simplified by the introduction of further postulates. These lack the direct intuitive character of the primitive postulates of a metric space, but are also susceptible of direct empirical test.

(B) *The visual space is locally euclidean.*

The locally euclidean property means that euclidean relations hold in the small. In other words, within a sufficiently small neighborhood it may be assumed for all practical purposes that the metric relationships are euclidean. On the earth, for example, this statement represents common practice. The survey of a small patch of earth such as a real estate development is conducted under the assumptions of euclidean plane trigonometry. The mapping of large areas or navigation over large distances requires spherical trigonometry in which the metric methods of elliptic geometry are used; the failure to allow for the curvature of the earth in such applications would produce anomalous results.

One way of thinking of the locally euclidean property is that it implies the possibility of constructing a local cartesian coordinate frame at any point. In other words, the visual metric would agree with the euclidean metric defined on this frame in the neighborhood of the point. More precisely, let P_0 be any point. It is possible to find a euclidean metric $D_0(P_1,P_2)$ so that

$$\lim_{\substack{P_1 \to P_0 \\ P_2 \to P_0}} \frac{D(P_1,P_2)}{D_0(P_1,P_2)} = 1.$$

It is important to realize that the locally euclidean property has nothing whatever to do with the euclidean character of physical space. It means simply that sufficiently small visual configurations may be described adequately in a euclidean frame. It is not possible, for example, to construct a large configuration which is visually a rectangle, that is, a quadrilateral with equal and parallel opposite sides and right-angled corners. However, by making the configuration sufficiently small this ideal may be approximated visually as closely as desired. Even with the restriction on size, it is not true that such a configuration would satisfy the physical metric properties of a rectangle. The sides would not necessarily be physically straight nor would opposite sides have equal length nor would the angles at the corners necessarily be right angles. As with other properties, visual and physical rectangularity cannot be inferred from one another.

Postulate B is equivalent to another statement which may be more familiar to students of differential geometry, namely,

(B′) *The geometry of visual space is riemannian.*

The latter statement of the postulate means that the metric may be specified in differential terms as a positive definite quadratic form. While B′ is the more familiar form of the postulate, it is certainly farther removed from immediate sense data.

The last postulate is simple enough in its meaning, but it has far-reaching consequences.

(C) *Every unaligned triple of points in the visual space is contained in precisely one visual plane.*

A plane is a proper convex subspace which contains at least one triple of unaligned points. In other words, a plane is more than a line and less than the full space and if a plane contains two points, it contains the line segment consisting of all points aligned between them. A geometry having this property is called desarguesian.

The concept of plane is so familiar that it may come as something of a surprise to the nonmathematical reader that postulate C is a very uncommon property. Among the infinity of riemannian geometries there are only three which satisfy the postulate, the so-called homogeneous geometries or geometries of constant gaussian curvature. The homogeneity of these spaces refers to the property that it is possible to construct at any position and orientation in the space a configuration which is metrically congruent to any given configuration. The geometry of zero curvature is euclidean. The geometry of constant positive curvature is called elliptic and the geometry of constant negative curvature, hyperbolic. In two space dimensions the metric relations of elliptic geometry are the distance relations on a spherical surface imbedded in euclidean space. The hyperbolic geometry may be familiar to the reader as the geometry of Lobachevsky and Bolyai. In two space dimensions its metric also describes the distance relationships on a surface imbedded in euclidean space, a sort of trumpet-shaped affair.

The empirical problem of determining the metric of visual space is now greatly reduced. There are only three possible visual metrics; one suitably designed experiment would enable us to decide among them. Actually a deciding experiment had already been performed by Blumenfeld [3] and the only possible conclusion for his observers is that visual space is hyperbolic.

There is a simple analytic formula for the hyperbolic metric in a number of possible coordinate systems. It would almost seem that there is no further problem to solve. There remains the problem which proved in actuality to be the most resistant of all, the problem of associating visual coordinates to physical points. The analytic formula for the hyperbolic metric describes distance relationships among the points of an abstract space. It is necessary to find the coordination between the points of physical space and the points

' this abstract space to attach a physical meaning to the concept, ›int of visual space. The treatment of this problem will be part our next concern.

At this point progress in the development of the theory was inter- ›pted by Luneburg's tragic death. Although he had many signifi- ınt suggestions as to the solution of the final problem, the key lay nong hypotheses he had discarded. It was more than two years 'ter his death before the final difficulties were resolved. This, then, a good point to pause and review the content of this section and uneburg's achievement.

Luneburg emphasized that the spatial relations obtained through ıysical mensuration do not in fact coincide with binocular visual ›atial relations. Visual space must, therefore, be treated as of un- ıown character and the question of describing the space arises. isual spatial relations may be idealized and explored by means of a athematical model. The abstract mathematical model which is ited to the explanation of visual geometric relations is that of a etric space. From certain experimental evidence [11, pp. 228f.], it ay be inferred that the visual space is one of the locally euclidean, ›mogeneous spaces. This conclusion retains its force although the iginal empirical basis for it is now interpreted otherwise [8, pp. 15]. he problem of selection among the only three possibilities had ready been settled by experiment [10, pp. 74ff.].

THE EMPIRICAL BASIS OF THE LUNEBURG THEORY

There are many factors which may influence the perception of ›atial relations. Spatial connotations are attached to perspective, otion parallax, variations of hue and brightness, the presence of miliar objects of known size, the dioptric accommodation of the 'es, manual explorations, and perhaps even the state of digestion. he Luneburg theory is concerned with only one factor, binocularity. is not that the theorists are unmindful of the effects of extrabinocular ctors, or that they are felt to be unimportant, but simply that the udy of the binocular visual apparatus, nature's most conspicuous strument for the divining of three-dimensional spatial relations, is ›nsidered to be a worthwhile object in itself. It is felt also that nocular visual space perception is to a large extent governed by the ›ural and anatomic structure of the organism so that ordinarily it ›comes stable in infancy or childhood and is not greatly affected by rther maturation or learning. The binocular space sense is therefore ıought of as a constant substratum upon which visual spatial judg- ıents are based.

An experimental technique devoted to the exploration of tl
single factor of binocularity in isolation from all other effective agen
must possess a certain stringent purity. A statement of the expe
mental conditions in the Knapp Laboratory experiments is as esse
tial to the theory as the mathematical analysis. The observer's hea
was fixed in a headrest in a comfortable upright position. A cartesia
reference system, rigidly fixed with respect to the observer's hea
served as the frame for physical measurements [8, p. 4]. The expe
ments were conducted in a darkroom, the only visible objects bei
tiny isolated electric lights, in appearance much like stars. The ligh
were adjusted to give an impression of equal brightness to the ol
server. The intensity of the lights was sufficiently low that there w
no perceptible surrounding illumination. The observer was n
allowed to manipulate the lights in making experimental settin
(these were made by means of vocal instructions to the experimente
nor was he allowed to see his settings under room illumination. A
lights were restricted to the binocular field, within sight of both eye
and care was taken that no light be occluded by another for eith
eye. Ocular motility was not restricted. The observer was asked
survey carefully the entire configuration[6] of lights until he was satisfie
with his setting. The settings are static. Motion is not as yet with
the scope of the theory. The observers were either free of aniseikon
and optical disorders or else fully corrected by glasses.

Operational definition of theoretical terms. The primitive co
cept of the system, that of point, has two different operational mea
ings. Each point has two names, a physical name and a visual nam
The physical name may be thought of most simply as the thr
measured coordinates which locate the light source in a cartesia
frame of reference. The visual name is taken to refer to the san
material light source but its definition is given in terms of visu
metric relations. The problem of assigning an operational meanir
to the concept of point of visual space is the problem of coordinatir
a visual name with the physical name.

The points of physical space are to be matched with the poin
of an abstract metric space. It may not be possible to accomplis
this in one-to-one fashion. Consider, for example, a configuratio
consisting of three lights in visual alignment. Operationally th
means that the observer has set the lights in obedience to the instru
tion that the lights be placed to appear in alignment. Suppose th
some fourth light is introduced into this self-contained situation. It
not at all clear that, in the presence of the fourth light, the origin

[6] The word configuration will be used henceforth to denote the entire configurati
of lights presented to the observer.

hree retain their appearance of alignment. There is no reason to uppose that the introduction or[7] removal of lights in a physical coniguration will leave visual metric relations unchanged among the emaining points. Such a hypothesis may be entertained as an a priori udgment subject to possible experimental refutation. This hypothesis s tacit in Luneburg wherever he has proposed a coordination between isual points and physical points. In the revised theory, this hypothesis nas had to be given up. The weight of experimental evidence indiates that the visual metric relations do depend upon the particular hysical configuration of points. As a necessary adjunct to the Luneurg theory, the laws of this dependence require exploration. It is ecessary to develop a theory within a theory.

The horizontal plane. The following discussion will be restricted to hysical configurations which lie in the horizontal plane through the cular rotation centers.[8] The primary reason for this restriction is hat the Knapp Laboratory experiments were conducted primarily n the horizontal plane. Although certain considerations of plausiility lead to an extension of the theory to the full three-dimensional pace the author feels that it would be well at this time to let the xtension of the theory await further experiment. Configurations in he horizontal plane have the property of visual planeness. The horiontal plane corresponds to a plane in visual space.

The egocenter. It is a rather curious empirical observation that the bserver is rarely conscious of the two-eyed origin of his visual pereptions but acts as though they could be referred to a point center. To the observer there is no incongruity in such statements as, "Point A ppears to lie in the same direction from me as point B," or, "Point C ppears to be nearer to me than point D." The observer utilizes an gocentric frame of reference. This phenomenon is acknowledged in he theory by taking this center of reference as the origin or egocenter f visual space. Operationally, the egocenter is to be thought of as lefined by remarks concerning positions relative to the observer ither in the instructions or in the observer's statements. The egoenter, by its very definition, cannot be made to correspond to any hysical point. It is odd that the first point of visual space to be lefined in the attempt to coordinate the points of that space to those f physical space can not be so coordinated.

The horopters. The egocentered nature of visual perception sug-

[7] The word or, in mathematical parlance, has the significance of the legal term, nd/or. Changes in position of points of the configuration are included in the above tatement since placing a point in a new position is equivalent to removing it from he configuration and introducing it at another site.

[8] Referred to hereafter simply as the horizontal plane.

gests that the appropriate coordinates to use in writing the visual metric are polar coordinates. These will be written (r,φ). The radial coordinate r represents visual distance from the egocenter. The radial coordinate is not to be thought of as describing the absolute sensation of distance but as giving distances in their correct proportion. The observer's sense of absolute scale seems to be highly variable and arbitrary. At one time he will report a sense of vastness, at another time, speaking of the same configuration, he will say that it is quite small and close. His sense of relative scale, proportion, or shape seems to be invariable. The radial coordinates of points merely give their sensed distances in the correct proportion. The equation $r = r_0$, where r_0 denotes a constant, describes a circle centered at the visual origin; it is a set of points of constant visual distance from the egocenter. The angular coordinate φ describes the sensed angular deviation from the sensed sagittal forward direction. The equation $\varphi = \varphi_0$, where φ_0 is a constant, describes a visual line of points lying along a ray through the egocenter; it is a set of points of constant direction from the egocenter.

The physical curves corresponding to the visual circles $r = r_0$ and the visual radii $\varphi = \varphi_0$ of the visual polar coordinate mesh are called horopters.[9] A circumhoropter consists of the physical points which are sensed all at the same distance from the egocenter. A radial horopter consists of the physical points which are sensed all in the same direction from the egocenter. Operationally these are defined by the responses of the observer to directions such as, "with the light A fixed, adjust the position of lights B, C, D, . . . so that they appear to be at the same distance from you as A," and, "With light A fixed, adjust B, C, D, . . . so that they appear in the same line with you as A." The empirical circumhoropters are well approximated by physical circles which pass through the ocular centers, the so-called Vieth-Müller circles. A circle of visual space centered at the visual origin corresponds to a physical circle which, if large, is such that the observer is on the circumference rather than anywhere near the center. The empirical radial horopters are well approximated by certain rectangular hyperbolas which pass through the ocular centers and have asymptotes passing through a point midway between the ocular centers. These are the so-called Hillebrand hyperbolas.

The hypotheses of physico-visual coordination. Luneburg assumed that the physiological determiner for localization in visual space is the attitude of the eyes in fixation. In his scheme the circumhoropter corresponds to the locus of points of constant convergence angle, the

[9] This usage is special and does not coincide with any of the various definitions of horopter used in other works on binocular vision.

adial horopter to the locus of constant mean angular deviation of the yes from the position in which the visual axes are directed sagittally orward. This author believes that visual localization is determined y the manner in which the optical images shift on the retina as the yes look from point to point. Two points are sensed at the same istance from the egocenter if the optical images suffer homologous etinal displacements in looking from one point to the other. Two oints are sensed as lying in the same direction from the egocenter the displacements are homonymous (equal in amount) and oppote [2]. The two ideas yield approximately the same theoretical oropter curves. The latter point of view leads to conclusions which re in accord with the experimental evidence.[10] As a first hypothesis e have:

(H1) *The localization, relative to each other, of points in visual space epends only upon the shifts of the optical images on the retinas in looking from oint to point and is independent of the attitude of the eyes in fixation.*

The hypothesis indicates that localizations are relative rather than bsolute. This leaves room for the possibility that absolute orientation, sense of horizontal, vertical, right-and-left, is attained through other han visual means, certainly through labyrinthine influences and robably partly through proprioception with respect to the ocular nd other muscles. It must be concluded from the hypothesis that, iven one physical configuration, if it is possible to construct another o that the images on the retinas are displaced in the same way in hifting fixation from point to point, then the visual metric relations re the same for the two configurations. Such configurations are said o be binocularly equivalent. It is not difficult to demonstrate in the orizontal plane, the existence of a two-parameter infinity of configurations which are equivalent to any specified configuration. It is hen possible to exhibit physical configurations which have widely iffering physical metric properties yet possess identical visual metric elations. The analysis of binocularly equivalent configurations xplains an observation made by Helmholtz and others [9, vol. 3, p. 318], that configurations consisting of three points seen in alignment nay be physically convex toward the observer, concave toward him, or traight, depending upon their physical localization.

A second hypothesis which experiments support is that of horopter onstancy:

(H2) *The appearance of equidistance or sameness of direction given by ny two points on the same horopter is not altered by introducing or removing ny other points in the horizontal plane.*

[10] This is not the only possible physiological model which will serve to explain the xperimental results.

If the hypothesis concerning the physiological basis for the empiri cal settings of the horopters is correct, this result is to be expected nonetheless, it requires explicit statement.

The hypothesis H2 does not preclude the alteration of visua metric relations by the introduction or removal of points; it mean only that horopters pass into horopters under the transformation The hypotheses H1 and H2 are insufficient to specify connection between configurations which are not binocularly equivalent. Thi deficiency is remedied by two new hypotheses.

(H3) *Visual radial distance from the egocenter of a point in a configuratio is a function of transverse retinal displacement disparity as measured in shiftin the fixation of the eyes between the horizon and the point in question. The visua radial distance of a point is otherwise independent of the physical characteristic of the configuration.*

The horizon or outermost circumhoropter associated with a con figuration is selected from the set of circumhoropters passing througl points of the configuration as that which has the greatest dista extension. It contains the points of the configuration which are seer at the greatest distance from the observer. The displacement disparity may be measured from any point on the horizon.

The hypothesis H3 has a number of surprising consequences There is an upper bound to the visual radial coordinate r, and thi bound is reached in every configuration on the horizon. This resul agrees with the observation that there is nothing in visual experience to correspond with the concepts of infinitely large or infinitely distant Points introduced within the horizon do not affect the extant visua metric relations; points introduced outside, do. This hypothesis was not altogether anticipated but arose in part from the unforeseer results of experiment. The author has only the most tenuous con- jectures concerning the physiological origin of the sensory role of the horizon.

The hypothesis H3 characterizes the nature of the correspondence between the visual radial coordinate and physical points. To obtain a complete coordination some statement about the visual angular coordinate is needed.

(H4) *The visual central angle between two points is equal to the mean of the transverse retinal displacements in shifting the eyes from one point to the other.*

The visual central angle is the visual angle subtended by the two points at the egocenter.

The two hypotheses H3 and H4 contain the hypotheses H1 and H2 and serve as the basis for the coordination of points of visual space to those of physical space. The problem of coordination may ıen be solved for a given observer by an experimental determination f the function in H3.

Outline of the definition of theoretical terms. A point of the physical pace of the horizontal plane is determined by its coordinates in a artesian frame. Secondary coordinates are assigned to physical oints in a way dependent on the configuration containing them. 'hese coordinates Γ, Φ may be expressed in terms of the cartesian oordinates by means of analytic formulas and they may be conidered to be defined operationally in terms of those formulas. The oordinates Γ, Φ may be thought of as the transverse retinal displaceıent disparity measured with respect to the horizon and as the mean ransverse retinal displacement measured with respect to any point ensed as lying in the frontal direction. The visual angular coordiate φ is set equal to Φ. The visual radial coordinate r is a function f Γ which is determined empirically by trigonometric methods haracteristic of the noneuclidean visual geometry.

Chief classes of empirical evidence. Empirical results connected vith the Luneburg theory may be considered in their relation to the ollowing statements: (1) the visual space is metric; (2) it is locally uclidean and homogeneous; (3) it is hyperbolic; (4) it is coordinated o physical space by the rules of H3 and H4.

The visual space is metric. The postulates pertaining to the relations f length-ordering and alignment which may be used to prove that he visual space is metric are, in themselves, of such intuitive character hat the reader may wonder that empirical evidence need be cited t all. In fact, in the course of the experimental history of the subject hese visual relational properties seem to have remained unquestioned y experimenter and observer. That, in itself, is some evidence that o glaring inconsistency arose from assuming the properties. The bservers at the Knapp Laboratory, in particular, made visual size natches and alignments consistent with the assumption.

The visual space is locally euclidean and homogeneous. The locally uclidean character of visual space does not seem to have received ny attention in the previously extant literature except, perhaps, nder the condition, inapplicable here, of constant ocular fixation. The Knapp Laboratory made some informal observations of the kind ited under the postulate. The same sort of nonquantitative observaion was made in connection with postulate C. The properties of isual planes seem to have been accepted without question in the iterature. It is simplest to test postulate C through an equivalent as ollows: Suppose $L(X,Y,Z)$, then, if $L(X,U,Y)$ and $L(X,V,Z)$, there xists a point W with $L(Z,W,U)$ and $L(Y,W,V)$. Luneburg exhibited ther evidence for a homogeneous metric in the two-dimensional case of the horizontal plane [12, p. 638], but the experimental procedu makes the result dependent upon the physico-visual coordination.

The visual space is hyperbolic. This conclusion follows directly fro an empirical result of Blumenfeld's [3]. In a classic experimen Blumenfeld compared the visual parallelism of lines with the visu criterion of equidistance. If the visual geometry had been euclidea the two criteria should have yielded the same settings. The directio of the discrepancy in the settings for most observers is characteristi of the hyperbolic geometry. The experiment was checked by Hard Rand, and Rittler [7], with much the same results. The princip empirical difficulty appears to be that some observers are unable t make any distinction between sensory parallelism and the visu impression given by physically parallel lines, which most agree is n one of parallelism. Other experiments have been devised which di pense with the visual judgment of parallelism and these are unifor in yielding hyperbolic results.

The physico-visual coordination accords with H3 and H4. There is a extensive and somewhat confused empirical literature on the horopte problem. Horopters have been defined by many different criteria an the empirical criteria employed have often not been related to th definitions [13, p. 18ff.]. The author is not aware of any previou definition of horopters which does not require the condition of co stant ocular fixation. The theoretical horopters defined by H3 and H on the basis of a very simple ocular model [2] agree sufficiently we with the empirical horopters determined in the Knapp Laborator experiments to justify their use in a first approximation. For mor precise work, the circumhoropters, at the least, ought to be dete mined empirically or based on a more adequate model.

The hypotheses H1, H2, H3, H4 were attacked by experimen at the Knapp Laboratory. The first and fourth hypotheses, on th basis of the simplified ocular model, led to a theoretical set of mathe matical transformations, so-called iseikonic transformations, unde which binocular metric relations are invariant [2]. A number o empirical tests yield results in accord with the transformation law [8, p. 39ff.].

The four hypotheses are in accord with a number of independen empirical determinations, based on the simplified ocular model, of th functional dependency of the visual radial coordinate r upon Γ. I these hypotheses did not correctly describe the physico-visual corre spondence, different experimental techniques would result in differin estimates of the function. The consistency of independent experi mental designs in yielding similar estimates of $r(\Gamma)$ is a strong indi cation of their validity.

The function $r(\Gamma)$ was determined empirically by means of several .yperbolic trigonometric techniques [8, pp. 48ff.]. In contrast to ,uneburg, no a priori assumption as to the form of $r(\Gamma)$ was made.

RELATIONS BETWEEN THE VARIABLES

Construction of geometrical relations. In a metric geometry all he fundamental geometrical relations may be derived from the netric distance function. In order to obtain a complete specification f the visual geometry it is sufficient to determine the visual psycho-netric. The psychometric of binocular vision, it has been noted, is lefined for any given pair of points within a specified configurational iorizon. The circumhoropters form a one-parameter family of curves nd the horizon is therefore specified by a single real number. Since ach point of the horizontal plane is defined by two real coordinates, he visual psychometric in the horizontal plane may be considered .s a function of five real variables. In the full three-dimensional space he psychometric would be a function of seven real variables. Once he visual psychometric is obtained it may be used to characterize 'isual straightness, length, angle, area, volume, congruence, and the ike. The simple analytic form of the metric provides a complete lescription of the visual geometry within a small compass. All the elations in the visual geometry may be referred back to the metric.

Signal among the achievements of the theory is the reduction f the problem of specifying the psychometric function to the problem f determining empirically a single function of one real variable, the unction $r(\Gamma)$. The values of this function for a given observer com-pletely characterize his binocular visual perception in an environment levoid of extrabinocular clues. In other words, once the empirical letermination of the function $r(\Gamma)$ is complete, it is possible to precalculate on a deductive basis the future experimental settings f the observer in the darkroom experiments. In the Knapp Labora-ory precalculation was not employed because the roles of experi-nenter and observer were frequently interchanged and it was con-idered important to avoid the influence of prejudgement as to the performance of any observer. The close agreement of the values of the unction $r(\Gamma)$ derived separately from three different kinds of experi-nent has quite the same force as agreement with precalculation.

Grounds for confidence in the constructed relationships. Since ll the stated relationships of the theory are deductively derived from he postulates and hypotheses it is necessary only to give grounds for confidence with respect to these fundamental assumptions of the heory. Every one of the postulates has an empirical basis. It is possible

to frame a primitive postulate set so that empirical test is direct an
nonquantitative; in particular, the existence of a visual psychometri
may be reduced to such a primitive set of postulates. The hypothese
are supported by indirect evidence in that their deductive conse
quences agree closely with experimental phenomena. The particula
ocular model used to describe the physico-visual coordination is nc
essential to the theory. The author believes that the physiologica
determiner for visual localization is retinal image displacemen
Reference to the model could be omitted and the psychical phenomen
explained in terms of the mathematical transformation formula be
tween physical and visual coordinates. It is evident on the basis of th
empirical results that future developments may result in some quanti
tative refinements, but will not affect the theoretical correspondenc
between physical and visual space in any of its basic characteristics.

The whole postulational structure is given further support by th
close agreement of the various experiments in yielding values of th
function $r(\Gamma)$. Had there been any greatly erroneous assumption a
the basis of the system it is to be expected that it would have bee
made manifest at this level. In point of fact, the inadequacy c
Luneburg's hypothesis concerning the physico-visual coordination wa
revealed by attempts at measuring the visual radial coordinate r.

Extensions of the mathematical model. *Extension to three spac dimensions.* As has already been mentioned, the hypotheses of physico
visual coordination are strictly applicable only to the two-dimensiona
case of the horizontal plane. It is anticipated that this coordinatio
extends in simple fashion to the full three-dimensional space. Bot
Luneburg and the author have proposed hypotheses to cover the thir
dimension. These extensions are based upon certain references in th
literature concerning the role of vertical disparities in visual localiza
tion. Since authorities seem to differ in their treatment of vertical dis
parities, the empirical evidence at this time is not deemed sufficien
to warrant a formal extension of the hypotheses. If the author were t
resume work on the geometry of vision his first step would be a
attack on the problem of extension of the hypotheses to three-space.

Extension to space-time. The problem of treating motion in the visua
field requires further postulation concerning the metric characteristic
of visual space-time. There is little extant experimental evidence t
indicate how to proceed. For example, there exists no evidence in th
literature of a counterpart to the postulate on visual planeness. It i
anticipated that the space-time metric will be akin to the relativisti
metrics since an effect similar to that of the Lorentz-Fitzgerald con
traction of physics has been observed. Again, the author prefers t
defer the formulation of a definite postulate until more evidence i
forthcoming.

MENSURATIONAL PROCEDURES IN VISUAL SPACE

The visual mensuration problem. The fundamental problem of visual mensuration is to determine the localization in visual space of a point within a configuration in the binocular field. The problem is considered solved when visual coordinates are assigned to the point. The most convenient coordinates for this purpose are the visual polar coordinates which signify visual distance and direction with respect to the egocenter. The problem is not altogether unlike that of localization in physical space where objects are assigned position in a physical coordinate frame. Mensuration in visual space is accomplished by means of hyperbolic trigonometry. It is more complicated than ordinary physical measurement, not so much because of the slightly increased complexity of the mathematical formulas as for the empirical impracticability of basing visual measurement on anything but the primitive sensations such as alignment, equality of distance, and orthogonality. Once the function $r(\Gamma)$ is determined for a given individual, however, the problem of visual mensuration is reduced to that of physical mensuration.

Quantitative adequacy of the theory. Since all geometrical relations may be defined metrically, the theory is placed upon a completely quantitative basis. The coordination of theoretical constructs to quantitative empirical data is immediate and precise. In particular, the points of visual space have operational definitions in terms of the language of the instructions to the observer and the corresponding mathematical operations on the physical coordinates.

Asked what limitations there are in principle to the degree of quantitative specificity of systematic efforts in psychological science generally, this author is inclined rather to devote his remarks to related but more specific questions. In general, it is not to be expected that every theory has a quantitative basis. A relational calculus need not always be expressed in terms of number. Much mathematics, for example, is not concerned with number. Whether or not to seek numerical analytical methods is a question which must depend on the kind of data and relations under investigation. Metric methods, in particular, will apply when there exist both relations of betweenness (alignment) and ordering of contrasts (length ordering).

FORMAL ORGANIZATION OF THE THEORY

The assumptions. The theory of binocular space perception is based upon two classes of formal mathematical assumption: first, the postulates, concerned with the intrinsic characteristics of the space; second, the hypotheses, concerned with the coordination of physical to visual localizations. Conclusions concerning the binocular visual perception of a given individual are derived by deduction from the theoretical assumptions and from the results, qualitative and quantitative, of experimental procedures. Among conclusions of this character are the result that the visual space is hyperbolic and the result which gives the individual's psychometric in terms of physical coordinates.

The system reached its present mode of organization through an attempt to place each postulate upon an empirical base. The assumptions were reduced to postulates which referred to simple visual properties and were subject to direct test on a qualitative basis. In particular, the postulates A1–3 were reduced to a set of elementary assertions concerning the relations of length ordering and alignment. The two postulate sets are equivalent in the sense that one can be deduced from the other.[11] All that is required of the observer is consistency in making assertions as to the truth or falsity of the fundamental relations.

The hypotheses of physico-visual coordination are essentially quantitative in character. For the sake of convenience in formulation they have been based upon a simplified model of ocular optics and neuroanatomy. A more straightforward procedure would have been to base the hypotheses directly upon the empirical horopters. Since the horopters calculated from the model are in fair agreement with the empirical horopters, it was felt advantageous to have simple theoretical parameters for the purposes of immediate testing rather than refinements which could well be postponed until the need for greater quantitative precision made itself felt.

Definition of theoretical concepts. In the formal theory, the fundamental concept is that of point and all other concepts are defined in terms of points and the relations among them. Attention will therefore be concentrated primarily on the definition of the concept of point. In the abstract mathematical system, point is an undefined term except in so far as it is given definition implicitly through the relations imposed by the postulates. In application, the concept also acquires an operational significance.

A point may be considered to have two operationally defined names, a physical name and a visual name. The physical name consists of an ordered triple of real coordinates which assign a physical position to the point, and these coordinates may be considered to be

[11] Actually, this is not strictly true. Postulates Al–3 must be supplemented by a postulate concerned with the uniqueness of visual geodesics. This is not done here since the requisite uniqueness property follows upon the inclusion of postulate B. In other words, slightly more than the postulates Al–3 may be deduced from the elementary postulates.

efined operationally by the method of physical mensuration em-
loyed. Operationally, the visual name is defined by calculation from
he physical name and the configurational horizon parameter.

The method of calculating the visual name is itself operationally
etermined for the individual observer by the outcome of measure-
nents made in the light of the theory. The objective content of the
heory lies in statements relating the binocular visual instrument to
he physical world. The characteristics of the sensory frame of refer-
nce are made known to the experimenter through the physical
napping of sensory entities. The property of visual straightness, for
xample, is studied by constructing configurations which have the
ensory attribute of straightness. The method is entirely analogous to
hat of relating the geometry of earth to the properties of a map in one
f the flat projections.

Views on formality and explicitness. None would gainsay the
esirability of an explicit formal system. The advantage of establish-
ng a relational calculus with explicit reference to a precisely specified
lass of data is that conclusions may be derived by formal deduction
ather than inspired guesswork. The only rational controversy must
onsist of questions concerning experimental data and their interpre-
ation at the empirical level, and questions concerning the accepta-
ility of the postulates at the theoretical level. Failure of the theory
esults in concentration at the crucial points. The value of such a
ystem is plain.

On the other hand, attempts at formalization may fail for lack
f empirical or mathematical development or both. The author
elieves that even the failures are useful in suggesting areas for
mpirical or theoretical exploration. It is certainly worthwhile to
ttempt a completely formal explicit system in any area.

Range of application of the system. The Luneburg theory, as at
resent constituted, is a theory of binocular space perception. It may
e thought of as dealing with the factor of stereopsis in normal space
erception. In a way, it is an attempt to measure the native space
ense unaffected by learning factors. It is meant to describe the
rimitive geometrical information relayed to higher centers through
he optico-neural apparatus.

The range of the theory ought to be extended to allow motion
with respect to the observer and so to bring visual space-time within
ts purview. Although it is possible to do so by the introduction of
nore or less arbitrary presuppositions concerning the character of
visual space-time and the psycho-visual coordination of velocities, it is
felt that, without an adequate empirical basis, such a postulational
procedure is not warranted.

It was surprising to the author that the Luneburg theory o binocular vision does not have very extensive connections with th classical theoretical work in vision. The primary reason for this stat of affairs is that most of the prior research was conducted under th restriction of constant ocular fixation and a great deal of work wa concerned with acuities and thresholds. The Luneburg theory pre- supposes complete ocular freedom and is concerned with macroscopi visual geometric relations.

The author is sanguine about the possibility of relating the theor to a theory of learning above and a neuro-physiological theory below He hopes to see answers to questions such as, "How is informatior from the sense receptors utilized in learning to draw inferences con- cerning physical metric relations?" and, "What feature of neura organization leads to a visual geometry characterized by a homo- geneous metric?"

NEW RESEARCH STIMULATED BY THE THEORY

Chief empirical studies. These remarks will be confined to th work at the Knapp Laboratory since it was stimulated directly b the theory and had in return the most direct impact upon furthe theoretical development. The new experimental program had it inception in the failure of the original program to yield consisten values of the hypothetical parameters proposed by Luneburg. There were three categories of experimental investigation, the first con- cerned with tests of the postulates, the second with tests of the hy- potheses, the third with empirical verification of the deductive conse- quences of the theory. The categories overlap with certain experi- ments shedding light on all three.

Tests of the postulates. Suspicion was directed primarily at the "free movability" postulate of Luneburg which asserts the existence of a complete rigid transport group. This assumption is equivalent to the postulates B and C together. The empirical evidence adduced by Luneburg for the existence of the full rigid transport group was not conclusive and, in fact, the empirical material was found to be relevant rather to the hypotheses of physico-visual coordination. As a result of the rejection of the evidence for this postulate, the entire axiomatic foundation of the theory was reexamined with the conse- quent replacement of the assumptions by more primitive and directly verifiable assertions. The result was an alternative postulate structure, completely equivalent to that of Luneburg's, but tied directly to empirical evidence with little apparent room for ambiguity. Attention was then turned to the problem of physico-visual coordination.

Revision of the hypotheses. The hypotheses of physico-visual coordina-
ion are part of the theoretical superstructure. In principle, the
roblem they solve may be reduced completely to an empirical one.
t is doubtful, however, that simple empiricism would have led so
uickly to a practical solution of the problem.

The only hypothesis which retains some of the substance of
uneburg's original conjectures concerning the relation between the
hysical and visual spaces is H4, which had already been given some
upport by certain rudimentary observations in the old experimental
rogram.

The first step in examining the hypotheses was to dismiss any
resuppositions as to the relation of visual radial distance to physical
ata. An experiment, the equipartitioned parallel alleys, was devised
o measure the visual radial coordinate while using only an assump-
ion similar to H4. The data from the initial run of this experiment
n a single observer led to hypothesis H1. An immediate corrobora-
ion of the new hypothesis was found in the data of old experiments,
he three- and four-point Vieth-Müller circles, which had hitherto
een considered inexplicable [8, pp. 43ff.]. Since it was felt that the
oropter properties had a constant anatomical and physiological
asis, hypothesis H2 was entertained with the full realization that it
vas sensitive to the results of experiments measuring the visual radial
oordinate and might later have to be rejected.

Hypothesis H3 concerning the role of the horizon was intimately
onnected with the problem of the empirical verification of the
deductive consequences of the theory and will be discussed under the
next heading.

The hypotheses of physico-visual coordination are stated in terms
of anatomical features and this is the way in which they were originally
conceived by the author. In the published work, however, the hypotheses are formulated in terms of mathematical parameters. These
parameters are derived from the statement of the hypotheses presented in this analysis on the basis of a simplified ocular model [2].
The several calculations based upon these parameters are in good
quantitative agreement with experiment and each other. It is not
necessary, therefore, to base the hypotheses on an anatomical model
and in [1] and [8] reference to the model is slight. The presentation
of the hypotheses in the form given in this analysis arises from the
author's feeling that empirically based refinement will yield worthwhile improvements in the quantitative results of the theory.

Tests of the deductive consequences. From the postulates and hypotheses, it is theoretically possible, by a kind of visual triangulation, to
assign a value of the visual radial coordinate to every point in a

configuration consisting of two or more points.[12] From such triangu
lations it might then be possible to infer in what way the visual radia
coordinate depends on the configuration. Whereas the method c
calculation from the data was a deductive consequence of the theory
the assignment of numerical values of the radial coordinate was not
The calculated values give no test of the deductive implications of th
theory but serve as the material for an inference which would hav
deductive consequences testable by independent techniques. Th
initial run of the equipartitioned parallel alleys experiment was th
somewhat equivocal basis for the inference of hypothesis H3 whic
indicates that the visual radial coordinate depends on only the on
configurational parameter defined by the horizon. The equiparti
tioned parallel alleys were then utilized in a systematic test progran
to calculate the function $r(\Gamma)$ and simultaneously to test the hy
potheses. In addition they substantiated the earlier inference tha
among homogeneous geometrics, only the hyperbolic geometry coul
possibly fit the experimental data.

It remained a possibility that the calculated functional dependenc
of the visual radial coordinate r upon the disparity Γ was an artifac
of the experimental technique. In theory, all possible techniques o
calculating the visual radial coordinate should yield the same results
A check by means of other experimental techniques would therefor
have value as a test of the entire deductive structure of the theory
The first check came through reexamination of the five-year-old
Knapp Laboratory data on the Blumenfeld alleys. The second chec
was obtained through an experiment, the double Vieth-Müller circle
which had been proposed by Luneburg to avoid the empirical diffi
culties of interpretation encountered in setting the parallel alleys
The results were gratifyingly concordant [8, Fig. 28, p. 61].

Other empirical studies. A related study on size constancy was con
ducted at the Knapp Laboratory by C. J. Campbell [4]. The result
were not analyzed in terms of the visual metric of the observers, bu
Dr. Campbell reported that they seemed to be in accord with th
hypotheses of physico-visual coordination. Dr. Campbell's researche
also led to useful technical improvements in laboratory methods.

In connection with the matter of experimental technique, th

[12] It is not possible, except by fiat, to do this for configurations consisting of on
point since there would then be only one length, the distance from the egocenter, an
hence, no comparison of lengths is possible. The values of the metric and the visua
radial coordinate, in particular, do not give a measure of the absolute sensation o
length but measure only the proportions of sensed lengths. Furthermore, darkroon
observation shows that it is impossible to obtain an absolute sensory scale since an
observer may report about one and the same configuration at one time that it is ver
small and at another, very large.

work of L. H. Hardy, Gertrude Rand, and M. C. Rittler deserves explicit separate mention. The development of an experimental machinery adequate to cope with all the many complicating details amounts to a research study in itself. The theory could hardly have progressed in such expeditious fashion without their ability to anticipate sources of trouble and their meticulous attention to the development of precise, straightforward, and economical technical methods for carrying out the most complex theoretical designs.

Factors stimulating research effort. The factors leading to the development of the theory were (1) the existence of patently noneuclidean data, and (2) the availability of an adequate mathematical system.

The factors stimulating the empirical development were (1) the existence of an elegant theory, and, not least, (2) the initial failure of that theory.

EVIDENCE PERTAINING TO THE SYSTEM

Pro and con. The empirical evidence in favor of the theory is reviewed in considerable detail with only minor omissions in [8, Part Two]. Since Luneburg's initial publication a certain amount of empirical material has been published which, in the view of those writing, has seemed to be incompatible with the theory. In everything of the kind seen to date (August 1955) by this author, the material has failed of cogency to the Luneburg theory for either of two reasons: the experiments were conducted under the condition of constant ocular fixation; the experiments were not conducted with due care in eliminating extrabinocular factors.

The theory has also been criticized by implication and directly for not explaining such matters as (1) human ability to utilize the noneuclidean visual perception in getting about in a physical world which is practically euclidean, and (2) the superior ability (presumptive) in learning and apprehending euclidean relations as contrasted with hyperbolic relations. The problems are genuine and the author does not wish to minimize them. Nonetheless, it is perfectly plain that these are questions in the theory of learning and not in the theory of perception. Although the author has some ideas about the answers to questions of this kind, he prefers not to place the burden of some ill-integrated ideas about learning upon a theory which is not framed to provide such answers.

On "critical" experiments. It is in the nature of a deductive theory that every relevant experiment appears to be crucial. There is cause for investigation should it seem that an experiment goes counter to the theory. If the experiment proves to be properly conducted and properly interpreted and yet in conflict with a correctly deduced conclusion of the theory, it is evidently the theory which must give. Yet it has proved profitable in the past to retain an elegant theory in the face of a certain amount of conflicting evidence. This course has had its justification in the development of unforeseen refinements which removed the apparent discrepancies [5]. For this reason, the author is prepared to place only due weight and no more upon "critical" experiments. For a theory to be retained, the preponderant weight of empirical evidence should lie in its favor. Unexplained discrepancies, if few, should provide a cause for study, not for junking the theory.

The extensive systematic constructions, frequent in psychology, which are so soon destroyed cataclysmically, are not so much prey to the *experimentum crucis* as to their own internal deficiencies in matters such as the inelegant proliferation of hypotheses and the lack of explicit operational definitions of terms adequate to provide an empirical basis for the construction of a relational calculus.[13]

Since all experiments relevant to the Luneburg theory may, in a sense, be considered crucial, there is no great value in submitting experimental designs. Should anyone wish to test or extend the theory, the author suggests only that the future experimenter look at the Knapp Laboratory work and the experiments of A. Ames for models of procedure.

Alternate formulations. The Luneburg theory is a study of visual space perception and is appropriate to data obtained under the conditions of binocularity, unrestricted ocular motility, elimination of extrabinocular clues. The author is aware of no alternate formulation which systematically treats the same class of data. In particular, there exists no alternate account which handles simultaneously the data of (1) the Blumenfeld alleys, (2) the Ames equivalent rooms, (3) binocular "size constancy," (4) the Helmholtz frontal geodesics. Since a good deal of the Knapp Laboratory data is new to the literature, the author has not included it in his enumeration.

CONCEPTS AND PRINCIPLES OF POTENTIAL APPLICATION TO OTHER DOMAINS

A sensory order need not reflect in any obvious way the organization of the physical environment. The sensory intermediacy of violet between blue and red, for example, is in no obvious relation to the

[13] Thorough scholarly analyses of several systems in psychology are treated in W. K. Estes, et al., *Modern Learning Theory* [6].

ordering of light vibrations according to wavelength. Although a sensory order need not be structured in the same way as the physical environment, there must be some sort of consistent relationship between the two, else learning and knowledge would be impossible. The principle utilized in the development of the Luneburg theory is that the physical and sensory orders may be treated as abstract mathematical systems connected by a transformation or mapping function. The specification of the sensory order and its relation to the physical order is the fundamental problem in any theory of perception.

STATUS OF THE SYSTEMATIC PROGRAM AND STRATEGY FOR FURTHER DEVELOPMENT

The system provides at this date a complete description of binocular space perception in the horizontal plane.

In any continuation of the systematic program, the first evident step would be to extend the hypotheses to three spatial dimensions by means of suitably designed experimentation. After that, it would be appropriate to include motion and extend the theory to visual space-time. Ultimately, it would be desirable to treat the coordination of the visual geometric sense with other geometric senses such as auditory localization and labyrinthine orientation.

The problem of extension to three spatial dimensions appears to be related to the problem of determining the role, if any, of vertical disparities in visual localization. The extant literature is not decisive on this point, containing evidence varying from the negative statement, "Vertical disparities have no effect on depth localization" [14, p. 179], to empirical indications that vertical disparities may, indeed, have definite visual significance [13, chaps. 15–17]. Extension to space-time appears to be a more difficult undertaking. There is much less material in the literature devoted to the study of kineoscopy than to that of visual localization. It would seem that a theorist working on this problem has little to build a theory upon. The final problem of establishing linkages with other sensory systems is beyond the sphere of professional competence of the author.

REFERENCES

1. Blank, A. A. The Luneburg theory of binocular visual space. *J. opt. Soc. Amer.*, 1953, 43, 717.

2. Blank, A. A. The geometry of vision. *Brit. J. physiol. Optics* (3), 1957, 14, 154, 222.

3. Blumenfeld, W. Untersuchungen über die scheinbare Grösse in Sehraume. *Z. Psychol. Physiol. Sinnesorgane*, 1913, 65, 241.

4. Campbell, C. J. An experimental investigation of the size constancy phenomenon. Unpublished thesis (doctoral dissertation), Columbia Univer., 1952.

5. Dirac, P. A. M. Letter. *Sci. Monthly,* 1954, **79,** No. 4.

6. Estes, W. K., et al. *Modern learning theory.* New York: Appleton-Century-Crofts, 1954.

7. Hardy, L. H., Rand, G., & Rittler, M. C. Investigation of visual space. *Arch. Ophthal.* (Chicago), 1951, **45,** 53.

8. Hardy, L. H., Rand, G., Rittler, M. C., & Blank, A. A., Boeder, P. *The geometry of binocular space perception.* New York: Knapp Memorial Laboratories, Inst. Ophthalmol., Columbia Univer., Coll. Physic. Surg. 1953.

9. Helmholtz, H. L. F. *Physiological optics.* J. P. C. Southall (Trans.) Rochester, N.Y.: Opt. Soc. Amer., 1924–25.

10. Luneburg, R. K. *Mathematical analysis of binocular vision.* Princeton, N.J.: Princeton Univer. Press, 1947.

11. Luneburg, R. K. Metric methods in binocular visual perception. In *Studies and essays, Courant anniversary volume.* New York: Interscience, 1948.

12. Luneburg, R. K. The metric of binocular visual space. *J. opt. Soc. Amer.,* 1950, **40,** 627.

13. Ogle, K. N. *Binocular vision.* Philadelphia: Saunders, 1950.

14. Tschermak-Seysenegg, A. V. *Physiological optics.* P. Boeder (Trans.) Springfield, Ill.: Charles C Thomas, 1952.

THE SYSTEMATIC PSYCHOLOGY OF WOLFGANG KÖHLER

W. C. H. PRENTICE
Swarthmore College

INTRODUCTION

Two facts make it hard to epitomize and analyze Köhler's views for this series. First, it must be done from outside; the author of the "System" is not himself dissecting it for public observation and discussion. The second difficulty is as great because, in the rather special sense of the present volume, the "System" is probably not a system at all. The many theoretical views, hypotheses, and concepts that Köhler has proposed over the forty years of his association with a particular point of view are often only loosely related. Certainly he has never made any attempt to derive large numbers of facts in psychology from a limited number of postulates, nor even to state in any precisely formulated way just what the postulates and presuppositions of his particular theory might be. We must deal instead with a viewpoint and with certain basic and recurring attitudes toward science and toward nature.

Still, that viewpoint is a consistent and an important one, and it is necessary to see whether we can understand its backgrounds, its conflicts with other points of view, its contributions to psychology, and its promise for the future.

BACKGROUNDS

The philosophical atmosphere in which gestalt psychology was born has been discussed by a number of authors[1] and it is not necessary here to rehearse all of their agreements and disagreements. The spirit of the time in which the theory was born was marked by an increasing concern among a minority of philosophers, biologists, and psychologists with problems of unity and wholeness. Some years before analytic and atomistic views of life and behavior reached their maximum influence, numerous critics had already begun to point out logical and empirical difficulties created by assuming that the elemental phenomena of the life sciences are discrete and independent parts of the living wholes that we observe. It is easy to find writers between 1880 and 1910 voicing one or another kind of concern about the problem of understanding how unity could result from all this diversity. It seems inevitable (to amateur historical hindsight) that sooner or later someone should decide that this issue must be settled before other problems can legitimately arise. The gestalt psychologists and some of their predecessors rejected the widespread view that experience and behavior are made up of summated neutral and constant units—the mosaic or bundle hypothesis, as it has variously been called. They proposed to consider these units (stimuli, responses, sensations, ideas, et al.) as deriving their properties and often their very existence from relational conditions of the field in which they appeared. There have always been misunderstandings about gestalt views on the permissibility of analysis in psychology, and both sides have spent too much time attacking caricatures of their opponents' positions, but the issue is a real one, and it had been debated in various forms during the decades immediately preceding the development of gestalt theory.

The role of phenomenology as an approach to experimental problems in perception deserves separate comment. This too can be considered as part of the *Zeitgeist*. One of the things that too much ana-

[1] Too many to list here. Among the more important are Mildred Focht, *What Is Gestalt-Theory?* [1]; and George Hartmann, *Gestalt Psychology*, [5]. The bibliographies in these two references cover most of the others.

lytic sophistication invariably produces in any field is inattention to molar phenomena; in perception, presuppositions about the nature of elemental sensory data had for some time precluded an unbiased examination of perceptual experience as such. But a few pioneers had begun to study certain modes of visual perception in this way, and the techniques and discoveries of Katz [7] and of Rubin [24] surely belong to the intellectual substrate from which gestalt psychology arose.

Another aspect of the "spirit of the times," behaviorism was embarking on its most radical phase. In these days when we are all "behaviorists," it is easy to forget what behaviorism meant thirty-odd years ago. Its extreme antiphenomenal bias, its persistent effort to explain all phenomena in terms of adding and subtracting reflex elements, and its radical environmentalism were all attacked at one time or another by the gestalt psychologists. It is fair to guess that gestalt theory itself might have developed more slowly or more diffusely if it had not been confronted at just this time with such an opponent.

It would be easy to exaggerate the influence of specific scientists and philosophers. There is no doubt that the concept of gestalt quality, discussed as early as 1899 by Ehrenfels, made a direct contribution to the thinking of Wertheimer and of Köhler (although Wertheimer tended to minimize the Ehrenfels influence); the writings of Ernst Mach also seem to have contributed both in general and in rather specific ways to the development of the gestalt viewpoint—though some almost antithetical points of view also trace themselves to that same writer. It is my own guess that the works of Dilthey, Husserl, and others who are often mentioned in this connection did not in fact influence the growth of gestalt theory in any essential way.

Köhler's own biography is another matter. Several events and people played undoubtedly constructive parts. First, he had extensive training in physical science; concepts derived from those studies have never been far from the center of his psychological theory. Physical and chemical phenomena, mathematical relationships and modes of representation of those phenomena, and the general conception of the organism as a physical system—all these contribute continually to Köhler's writings, generally in the role of analogies but always with the implication that these analogies are getting us close to the truth even if they are not yet truth itself.

Köhler studied sensory psychology under Carl Stumpf. Stumpf's interest in the persistent philosophical problems attending psychological investigation and theory may have had some influence on Köhler's thinking, but it is not possible to find anything like gestalt theory in Stumpf's own views. He was interested in phenomenology, and he was at one time greatly concerned with the "structure" of thought. Perhaps in these senses he may be considered a minor contributor to the evolution of gestalt thinking.

The influence of Max Wertheimer is well known. His experiments on visually perceived movement provided, along with early work by Rubin and Katz, the first empirical bases for the gestalt-theoretical approach to visual perception. Köhler's association with Wertheimer's views and experiments must be included as a "background factor" *par excellence.*

An "orienting attitude" that must be recorded is Köhler's broad concern with psychology as the science of human behavior and experience. Psychology is important in understanding human life as we know it; a psychology that does not contribute to that understanding is not succeeding in its main task; it is always useful to return to ordinary experience to see whether those phenomena of daily living that are normally taken for granted may be capable of suggesting new categories of scientific analysis—instead of whether they may be forced into the molds of already created categories. These are implicit attitudes coloring much of Köhler's research and theory construction. They seem to me to be in the forefront of his criticisms of systems of "scientific method" that appear proscriptive, stultifying, and negativistic instead of liberating and productive.

Historical backgrounds, most of them intangible and difficult to assess objectively, may perhaps be considered the materials out of which grow attitudes and inclinations that are in principle fundamental. In the present case, these might be classified as three, the organism as a physical system, the role of phenomenology in science, and the concept of organization.

1. We know the animal organism as we know other natural objects; its properties are discovered by the same processes of observation and inference as the properties of other systems. So far as we can judge, it is subject to all the same natural laws as other systems. One of the things we discover by careful and unbiased investigation is the intimate relationship between the organism and phenomenal facts. So intimate is this connection that we often have trouble distinguishing what we mean by our experienced bodies from what we mean by the inferred (Köhler uses the adjective *transphenomenal*) organism of the biologist. Nevertheless, organism as a biological construct has laws that must be a part of more generally understood laws of physics and chemistry. Ultimate explanatory sentences in psychology must relate phenomena to organismic laws of this sort. The concept of isomorphism, about which we shall have to speak shortly, is one hypothesis about the relations between phenomenal or experienced fact and organism.

2. The role of phenomenology is closely related to these views. Scien-

tists inevitably begin with their own sensory experiences. All science starts as a systematic exploration of a human observer's experiences and their interrelationships, an exploration in which discoveries are made about events that are not themselves experiences. One need not become involved in epistemological or ontological arguments about the status of the discoveries: whether they are "real," whether they are "fictions," whether there is a finite number of nonexperienced events that could "explain" the experienced correlations, etc. The simple fact is that science consists of making statements about events that are known indirectly through the medium of sensory experience, but are not themselves experiences or sequences of experiences. In psychology, we are primarily concerned with those aspects of experience that show themselves to be especially dependent on the properties of the experiencing organism. If we are to understand these facts in all their richness, it is essential that we examine the totality and the details of the experience itself—something we do not do when using, for example, a meter-reading as a scientific datum. When studying thermal phenomena, we must know what the experimenter saw when he looked at a thermometer under certain conditions, but nothing is important that does not change the one datum with which we are concerned, the coincidence of the end of a column of fluid and a scale marking. If we are trying to discover the laws of visual organization, however, we must explore all potentially connected aspects of visual experience; we may not ignore conditions of brightness, field clarity, obtrusiveness of figure-ground relationships, experiences of hue, afterimages, etc., etc. And here only the experiencing observer can give us the observations and descriptions that we need to get us started. All properties of the experience qua experience must have some counterpart in physical events in the organism. We should start our search for the laws of such events by studying experience in all its richness. Anatomy, contemporary neurophysiology, or special brands of logic sometimes seem to provide preconceptions that threaten to displace the sensory phenomena themselves as a starting point for psycho-physiology.

The temptation to write about vision as it "must be" instead of as it is should be resisted. Size constancy provides a good example of an important problem that tends to be explained away by too sophisticated a physicalistic approach. The "apparent size" of the physicist is not the phenomenal size at all, but it is called "apparent" because students accepted their knowledge of geometric optics as an account of visual facts instead of studying experience as such.

3. The concept of organization plays a central role in gestalt theory. Following what seemed to be the logic of the physical sciences during their classical period, psychological theories have tended to seek for

elements that are independent of one another and that interact only according to laws of combination extrinsic to the elements themselves. Experience and behavior are originally chaotic according to such views. It is only when special influences producing combinations are impressed on behavior and experience that combinations begin to take shape and to become orderly, stable, and predictable. The concept of "association" in its various historical guises has been made such a combinatorial influence. "Attention" has sometimes played a similar role, as have "set," "determining tendency," and related concepts.

The general point of view of gestalt psychologists has been one in which a certain measure of order is instead taken as a basic property of experience; they have held that order must be included among the primary phenomena to be described and investigated. The gestalt psychologist would urge that we investigate all kinds of experienced orderliness impartially and do not presuppose without proof that all order is a secondary effect of other influences. Certain kinds of segregation, certain kinds of part-whole relationships, certain kinds of boundary phenomena, certain kinds of dominance of one part of an experience over another tend to recur in a way that suggests lawfulness. The figure-ground distinctions are among these primitive kinds of order; so also are the facts of grouping described by Wertheimer [28]; contrast phenomena and certain aspects of perceived movement provide still other examples. Should we not try to write useful laws about the experienced phenomena of order instead of trying to explain them away as instances of "judgment," "learning," or other secondary events? In some cases these kinds of order are suggestive of known and equally orderly relationships in the physical world. Perhaps we can find here direct clues for the understanding of organic processes. If so, it is legitimate to doubt that all experienced order is produced indirectly by the action of association and reward and need—and hence to doubt the extreme forms of environmentalist or empiristic theory.

This is not the place to discuss the alleged "nativism" of gestalt theory in any detail, but the theory's genuinely antiempiristic attitude stems undoubtedly from the much more basic conception of order as a primary property of experience and of nature. Recognition of the importance of order derives from phenomenological observations. The frequently supposed chaotic sensory world of early infancy has never been directly observed, and every attempt to produce something comparable by experimental procedures, or to find it in adults newly recovered from blindness, has always turned up considerable segregation and order.

The existence of orderly structure in no way prevents analysis of the nature of that structure. A common misunderstanding of the gestalt-theoretical position has been the interpretation that it is antianalytic, whereas it merely insists that the type of analysis chosen should reflect the realities of the phenomena investigated. To attempt to study the potential differences between some two points in an electrical network without consideration of the entire network would be tedious and unfruitful. To start out with the assumption that the network could be best understood as a summation of all possible point-to-point potential differences would simply be mistaken. In the same way, Köhler and his colleagues have protested against arbitrary analysis of psychological phenomena into presumptively independent "sensations" or other such units. There is too much evidence to indicate that they are not independent at all.

The general protest against the "constancy hypothesis" and the "bundle theory" in psychology forms a common thread running through all gestalt writings. The "constancy hypothesis," as Köhler uses the term, is the notion implicit in much psychological writing that a given physical stimulus has one and only one characteristic effect on the organism. If a light of a given intensity falls on a particular spot in the retina, according to this view, it can give rise to only one sort of experience. If on one occasion that experience is called white and in another gray, we must seek the explanation in "learning," "judgment," or some other extrinsic influence. The term "bundle theory" refers to the view seemingly held by some writers that experienced units are summations of small elements of experience, that, for example, a tune is made up of the serial addition of the individual notes. This view has had important consequences for the study of sensory psychology, because it has directed research in many cases toward isolation of parts of a complex stimulus, thus losing the very integration and interdependence that gave the original experience its peculiar properties.

But which aspects of experience are significantly interdependent, and which are not? That is an empirical question. We must still analyze relationally determined phenomena into their particular significant relationships, and no one will be disturbed if the discovery of significant relationships happens to involve a good deal of arbitrary analysis into nonfunctional parts before the proper ones are discovered. All the everyday tools of the scientist are available to the gestalt psychologist. He merely cautions against prejudging the structure of experience and against ignoring relational dependency in psychological events.

These then are the "background factors and orienting attitudes" that have gone into the creation of the point of view known as gestalt psychology. What are the actual properties of that point of view when analyzed into the conventional categories of scientific logic? What are the independent variables? What are the dependent variables? What are the intervening variables? What are the major structural aspects of the psychological model that results?

STRUCTURE

In so far as the gestalt point of view may be said to have a logical structure comparable to more systematic theory constructions, that structure inheres in the physicochemical model that is both implicitly and explicitly involved in discussions of psychological facts. In 1920 Köhler [9] expounded his views on certain kinds of steady physical states and the organizational principles that they involved. Ever since that time physicochemical models have recurred in his writings [cf. 11, 13, 15, 20]. It is not always easy for the reader to know what logical status these models may have. In some instances they are clearly little more than analogies. For example, perception or memory may be said to behave in some cases much as certain known physical systems do, and it is apparent that the physical model is used merely to emphasize important relationships in the psychological phenomena that might otherwise be overlooked. One case would be that in which Köhler compares certain aspects of recall to bipolar situations in physics. In other cases, the model is more directly applicable, as in cases where brain fields are under discussion and principles of current distributions are invoked as hypothetical explanations of brain activity coordinate with the psychological facts under discussion. Even then, the model was sometimes loosely meant: "Perhaps something like this will ultimately be discovered; perhaps it would satisfy our needs for explanatory principles." In still other cases, the physical model is clearly a genuine hypothesis meant to be subject to empirical test either now or in the future.

In all three of these kinds of circumstance, however, it is clear what the general features of an ultimate explanatory device will be. The viewpoint clearly anticipates the ultimate discovery of electrical and chemical information about the animal brain, information that will clarify our understanding of articulated fields of physical activity having properties coordinate with the structural properties of experience or behavior. It is probably unnecessary to emphasize the word "field." Every reader undoubtedly knows that, in Köhler's physical models, anatomical arrangements are not the only important facts. The phenomena of perception have many aspects (contour-formation, adaptation and contrast, and relational determination of many kinds) that suggest a field interpretation and seem to fit such a model much more readily and more elegantly than they do an interpretation based on a mosaic of elements.

An aspect of gestalt theory almost indistinguishable from the above is the much debated, often misunderstood, concept of psychoneural isomorphism. The main outlines of this working proposal have been foreshadowed in the preceding pages. Let me say once for all that the concept of isomorphism is not an attempt to solve the mind-body problem in its usual metaphysical form. It takes no stand whatsoever on the question of whether "mind" is more or less "real" than "matter." Questions of reality and existence are not raised at all. Mind and body are dealt with as two natural phenomena whose interrelations we are trying to understand. Moreover, isomorphism is emphatically not a mind-body parallelism in the epistemological sense. The hypothesis takes no stand whatsoever on the question of whether mental processes influence bodily ones, body influences mind, mind is an epiphenomenon of body, or any of the other possible relationships that philosophers have conceived. It comes nearest, perhaps, to what has sometimes been called the "double aspect" theory, the view that cortical events and phenomenal facts are merely two ways of looking at the same natural phenomenon, two faces of the same coin, as it were. But the concept of isomorphism would be banal indeed, were it only that. Instead it proposes that a particular kind of formal relationship holds between the structural aspects of certain psychological events and certain brain events. To be sure, the degree of particularity has sometimes been minimal, and many different brain events might be said, after their discovery, to be in some sense isomorphic with experience. But not all. If, for example, all scalar properties of brain event A are greater in magnitude than those of brain event B, if the experience coordinated with the occurrence of A stands in some measurable relation to that coordinated with B, then the isomorphic hypothesis proposes quite specifically that other events having structural properties between A and B will be coordinate with experiences that lie on the same experienced dimension between the two former ones. Now this might not be so. In fact, if brain models implied by some of the association theories are really adequate, there is no reason at all to suppose that such relations will hold. On the contrary, if experienced properties merely reflected associated contexts or the consequences of previous associations among sensory stimulation, there should be no generalizable order-relationship between neural and phenomenal facts. The only map enabling us to understand the one from the other would be based on the life history of an individual organism.

The concept of isomorphism is thus a working hypothesis that gives structure to the total theory. So long as it is not contraindicated by empirical evidence, it will continue to lead to certain kinds of specific hypotheses and to specific kinds of research. It makes possible the general assumption that the structural properties of brain events must be something like the properties of experience, an assumption that has already led the theory into conflict with views of cerebral activity based on the physiology of the peripheral nervous system. It further makes possible the assumption that the properties and functional dimensions of experience should be sought in the same general orders of relationships that we know in physical fields, an assumption that has led to interpretations of perceptual and memorial facts foreign to much traditional and contemporary theory. So isomorphism is neither a banal and truistic assumption nor a metaphysical notion; it is a genuine scientific hypothesis which has extensive consequences for the biological sciences if it turns out to be true. We are only now reaching the stage where we have investigative tools that may enable us to discover whether it is wholly true, partly true, or false.

In the investigations inspired by such a conception of phenomenal experience, the independent variables are, of course, physical stimuli. And it is essential to emphasize the fact that these independent variables typically lack order in their own right. Because the physical world includes many examples of relational dependence, and because Köhler used them as models for psychology, a common misconception has arisen concerning properties of the world of stimulus variables. Readers have occasionally assumed the gestalt properties are properties of the stimulus and that they are supposed by Köhler to be apprehended by and through some kind of mystical communion. Nothing could be further from the truth. It is easy to show that we can disturb the light rays that correspond to one part of a visually perceived pattern without in any way changing the light rays representing another part; we can, in some cases, be confident that peripheral sensory excitation is equally discrete, so that the stimulus-produced changes in one set of skin receptors are only minimally affected by stimulation in neighboring cells. We discover interdependence and organization in the total experience, and the concept of isomorphism leads us to seek the basis for it in neural events.

Our independent variables are then environmental factors and their various dimensions and relationships. In special cases of the study of learning and memory (and more recently in perception) motivational and attentional variables are also manipulated. But this is terra incognita. The independent variable in these cases is often a verbal instruction; or it may be a sequence of stimuli that establish some kind of "expectation." In a very real sense these experiments are not gestalt-psychological experiments at all, since the variables admittedly have no properties that can yet be understood in the usual organizational terms. And yet, the gestalt point of view does color these experiments and give them a kind of program. For whatever the biological basis of ideationally mediated responses may turn out to be, many of these phenomena can be described as cases of reorganization, cases in which the changed behavior is coordinated with a change in "what goes with what." To a degree, attention and set can change part-whole relations in experience. They can change figure-ground relationships; they can modify the relative obtrusiveness of particular parts, and so on. It is a reasonable hope that the brain model may enable us to work back from these properties of the situation to an understanding of what the instruction or the adapting stimulation has accomplished. As a matter of fact, certain motivational conditions have a genuine structure of their own, and it is not impossible that gestalt psychology may ultimately make some contribution to the understanding of, say, the "directedness" of certain states or the "requiredness" and subsequent resolution of others [12].

What are the dependent variables of gestalt psychology? In a crude sense they are responses, behavings of organisms as experienced by the scientist observer. In that sense, as we all know, psychology has no other raw data. But gestalt psychology has typically concerned itself with observations of behavior in special ways. First, in the important field of perception, the dependent variables have been, for purposes of theory, phenomena. *Experiences* rather than responses are to be correlated with stimulus variables. This approach differs from the kind of modern positivistic one which would correlate stimulus variables only with discriminatory acts, button pushings, verbal responses, and the like. Gestalt psychologists have been willing to make inferences about the phenomenal experience of their observers and try to write laws relating it to the independent variables of stimulation. There are some nice logical issues lurking here, and on occasion perceptual investigation has been tripped up by making such inferences on insecure bases. But by and large this is the procedure traditionally used by the psychophysicist, who has no particular qualms about correlating a wavelength of light to an experience of color—as opposed to a verbal response or a discriminatory act—though he runs exactly the same dangers as the student of more complex perceptual phenomena.

It is at the level of intervening variables that the gestalt psychologist is perhaps most in danger of creating confusion. For the hypothesized intervening events are sometimes phenomena and sometimes brain events. This is not really a confusion. On the contrary, the isomorphic hypothesis implies that the two have the same functional properties and are in some sense two aspects of the same process; at present we know very little about brain events except by hypothetical extension from our knowledge of phenomena. For those reasons it is natural to write as if the hypothesized intervening events were psychological or phenomenal events, even though ultimate coordination with physical and biological theory will require us to discover the neural counterparts of the intervening psychological variables and study them in detail. It is also true that in some few cases these "intervening psychological variables" can be observed about as directly as the dependent variables. In some studies of learning or memory and in special cases of perceptual investigation, the subject's verbal or other reports about processes intervening between the stimulus and the final experience or discrimination can lead to fairly direct inferences about the properties of the physiological processes involved.

At other times, the apparent immediacy of a behavioral result or the lack of discoverable psychological content intervening, or (more positively) the promise of reasonably direct physiological information has led to the construction of hypothetical variables supposed to have independently ascertainable existence in the organism (e.g., "figure currents"). The fact that this has not been done more often is a function of our ignorance about cerebral biophysics. The basic principles of organization in this medium are matters of dispute, and Köhler does not attempt, for example, to predict the laws of perceptual grouping from physical principles. The one recurring principle, the one most clearly associated historically with the notion of gestalt and the one that seems a *sine qua non* of the entire approach, is what has been known as the "Law of Prägnanz." This has never been stated with sufficient precision to justify its acceptance as law. It is rather a general maximum-minimum principle, a proposal that processes in the brain (and hence in experience) distribute themselves in such a way as to produce maximum order and simplicity. Since order, in the sense of articulation, and simplicity, in the sense of homogeneity, may sometimes run counter to each other, it has sometimes seemed that no adequate test of the hypothesis was possible, any result being as satisfactory for the theory as any other. It would probably be possible to deal with such difficulties if we had a more complete and adequate physical model, if, for instance, we knew more about the degree to which the energy systems in question are closed or self-contained and the degree to which energy may be drawn from neighboring systems. At present, it can only be said that the Law of Prägnanz requires detailed reexamination. It does not seem to have contributed greatly to the understanding of psychological facts and has sometimes provided a kind of catchall that serves to obscure real problems. Nevertheless, the idea of dynamic self-distribution according to some kind of precise quantitative principle persists in gestalt psychology and provides a framework of a general kind for more specific hypotheses. A new and revised version of the Law of Prägnanz may yet establish a firmer quantitative basis for psychological theory.

In summary, this is a system in which the model for psychological events is explicitly the field concepts of modern physics. The model is proposed not as a logical fiction but as a scientific construction like any other, subject to independent verification; the system is one in which independent variables are physical events, the dependent variables responses, but the responses are typically taken as grounds for inferences about phenomena, which are then treated as if *they* were the dependent variables. In the last analysis, any intervening variables should be properties of the physical model, but because the isomorphic hypothesis puts those same structural properties into psychological events, one sometimes writes as if the intervening variables were psychological states or events. In other cases, quite explicit and specific brain-physiological events are postulated to bridge the gap between independent and dependent variable. These events are presumed to have laws paralleling the laws of electric current distribution, but they have never been spelled out beyond the statement of a quite general maximum-minimum principle known as the Law of Prägnanz—a principle that needs clarification and reevaluation.

INITIAL EVIDENCE

What kinds of psychological observation led to the adoption of such a point of view? Everyone knows that the major facts were those of perception and that gestalt psychology as a self-conscious theoretical movement is usually dated from Wertheimer's 1912 study of perceived movement [27]. Visual perception lends itself especially well to the demonstration of organizational principles in behavior, but learning and memory and even action have also provided fruitful leads. Let us look very briefly at a few examples.

Movement. An object that moves casts its image on successive retinal cells, and it might be thought naively that this sequential stimulation of a series of elements is the adequate stimulus for the experience of motion. We know, however, that such stimulation is neither sufficient nor necessary for the experience. Objects that move too slowly or too fast do not appear to move. The apparent motion of a retinally fixated automobile, the clear perception of movement in stroboscopic phenomena like the motion picture, or the appearance of movement in the objectively stationary one of two railway coaches that move with respect to each other, all demonstrate the experience without any serial stimulation on the retina. Wertheimer made it clear that the perception of movement is a matter of stimulating discrete elements on the retina with a particular temporal pattern. Korte [22], Duncker, Ternus, and others (cf. Koffka [8]) later showed that matters of intensity, contour, enclosedness, relative size, and "good continuation" all help to determine the character of the experience of movement. The phenomenon is a determinate function of complex relationships in the entire visual field.

Constancy. The apparent brightness of a patch in the visual field varies with the intensity of the light that it reflects. At least it does so when all else is held constant. The fact that two surfaces reflecting the different intensities into the eye may nevertheless look the same raises something of a problem. For example, a white paper still looks white even in very dim illumination. These effects have long been explained as a result of past experience and training; they are said to be a matter of "allowing for" the change in illumination or some other viewing condition which provides a "cue" by which the organism is guided to one or another response to the same stimulation. Cognitive concepts like these provide, however, only partial and unsatisfactory explanations. Although they seem to imply a judgmental process, none is ever demonstrated. Although they imply learning, nothing is said about how the learning occurred; although the supposed learning process is described in rather highly intellectual terms, we know that the phenomenon of constancy occurs in lower animals and in small children. The same data are accounted for much more easily by the rather simple assumption that all the conditions determining the apparent brightness of a given patch are present in the total stimulus field of the moment. On this assumption, gestalt psychologists have sought laws of interaction that could account for the known facts, and the results are promising indeed [25]. Many of the cases that seemed troublesome in the past can now be handled without recourse to other than stimulus parameters.

Size constancy, the tendency for different-sized retinal images to give rise to experience of the same-sized object, lends itself similarly to such analysis, and the nature and kind of stimuli making possible the perception of distance seem to determine apparent size at the same time. Constancy of hue, shape, speed and other attributes of visual experience equally suggest the application of systematic interactions between one part of the visual field and others. The mere existence of constancy phenomena creates great difficulty for any theoretical position that treats the sensorium like a series of push buttons, each sense cell responding to its given physical energy in one and only one way. The solutions provided by concepts of inference, learning, etc., are at best stop-gap solutions that need detailed spelling-out in terms of how constancy is supposed to be acquired. Wherever we can provide evidence that objectively determined stimulus properties will overrule past experience and knowledge, the gestalt solutions look neater.

Form. The perception of form is a logically primitive aspect of gestalt theory. How do objects get their shape? Two common-sense views can be quickly disposed of. First, the objects do not merely look "as they really are." Objects that are not quite circular may look like perfect circles; constellations of dots (or stars) will look like lines or closed figures. Two-dimensional patterns of certain sorts will look three-dimensional, and angles and lines may be distorted by a variety of geometrical tricks in endless well-known optical illusions. Second, they do not necessarily look "as we have learned that they are." The orderly relations between parts and wholes or between parts and parts are not produced in different ways in different people as a function of chance experience, nor does special training have more than a limited influence on the perception of what goes with what in a complex visual field. The really influential factors are aspects of the stimulus configuration, nearness, similarity, common direction, symmetry, and other objective characters of that order. These strongly suggest the operation of forces like those known in certain parts of physics, and a field conception of the phenomena suggests numerous experiments that would not otherwise be suggested [see 28]. The figural aftereffects to be dealt with later are a good example.

Transposition. Ever since the writings of Christian von Ehrenfels, the notion of transposability has been a central one in the study of gestalt phenomena. Certain forms may have all their parts changed and yet retain the characteristic form. A tune transposed into another key may now contain no notes in common with its former playing, but it will still be "the same" tune for most listeners. Even when the change in key is recognized (and for many listeners it will not be), the similarity between the two forms is more striking than the difference. But what is this similarity when everything in the pattern of stimulation has been changed? What remains the same is a set of relationships that inhere in the whole rather than in the parts. When we make a square out of four lines, "squareness" is a property that belongs to the whole but in no sense to any of the parts, just as chemical properties of a certain molecule may not be possessed by any of its elements. The properties of the whole are created by the existence of particular simultaneous relationships. Such facts demand a molar view of experience.

Learning and memory. Many facts about memory, association, and learning have added to the initial evidential push toward a field-theoretical orientation. The earliest observations demonstrated that rote learning raises distinct organizational problems. Little or no learning takes place without rhythmic or other grouping. Difficulty does not increase linearly as items are increased but is a complex function of the length of the list; the serial position gradient has a characteristic form that is "transposable" from list to list.

The role of similarity in recognition and in learning has played a large part in creating a demand for a treatment of these matters in which the role of one part of the task is determined by the whole. What is *similar* for purposes of determining association or isolation can be defined only in terms of the entire list, and yet these relationships are demonstrably important in association, inhibition, and recognition. In short, "relational determination" seems to be as prevalent in the field of learning and memory as in perception.

Köhler's well-known studies of intelligent behavior in chimpanzees [10] provide a further source of stimulation toward the construction of a field theory of behavior. Those observations and many that have followed them seem to provide examples of complex molar behavior that is not subject to simple molecular analysis. First, the behavior itself is controlled by gross relationships between animal and environment; he moves "toward the food" rather than repeating a particular sequence of muscle movements. Second, the animal seems to respond to relationships among parts of his perceptual world; something long or tall is chosen as the appropriate tool in getting a distant banana though other objects might have been chosen equally well by chance. Third, behavior often gives the appearance of being determined by "sudden reorganizations" like those we know in perception, and transfer of training seems to depend on the maintenance of the newly perceived relationship rather than on repetition or reward of particular parts of the original stimulus or response sequence.

Action. A minor but important source can be found in observations of more general aspects of behavior. Reference has already been made to the apparent necessity for describing animal behavior in molar terms —a necessity long since accepted even by conditioning theories. There are related phenomena that deserve comment. Higher animals differ demonstrably from some of the lowest in the degree to which behavior is coordinated and determined "from the top down." It has been aptly observed that in sea urchins the limbs move the animal while in dogs the animal moves the limbs. Certainly in most highly developed animals the latter is the case, and part movements can be understood only in terms of the larger behavior pattern of which they are a part. Certain early observations on the movement of arthropods with amputated limbs played a part in encouraging gestalt conceptions, for they showed that the spider or insect with a leg missing on one side did not move in circles as would a mechanical toy with a built-in pattern of leg movements. And certain insects adapt quite readily by transposing to a different pair of legs the movements ordinarily appropriate to the pair now missing. Some of these observations now seem to have been misinterpreted in part [26], but it is interesting that the contemporary views that are taking their place seem to demand an at least equally molar and dynamic view of biological function.

All these different classes of fact contributed to the development of gestalt theory. The perceptual facts came first and played by far the largest part in the early history of the system, but facts about association and about learning were only a few years behind. Why were these facts considered "strategic?" Why should a theory be built on just these data rather than on facts about color vision or intelligence testing or psychoneurotic phenomena?

Apparently perceptual facts merely seemed to provide the best model. Wertheimer's theoretical interests ranged away beyond perception from the beginning, and the studies of visual patterning and organization were used by him and by Köhler as illustrative of far more general principles. The strategic nature of perceptual facts is perhaps best illustrated by the degree to which the concept of relational determination has been accepted in the study of vision. In the study of learning, where the role of field influences is less directly observable, gestalt concepts have lagged far behind.

GESTALT THEORY IN PRACTICE

How does Köhler, or any psychologist with his point of view, actually proceed in making use of experimental data for theoretical purposes? No explicit rules have been laid down for the establishment of functional relationships between independent and dependent variables or even for connecting either with the hypothesized brain field. In these ways, gestalt theory has been much more programmatic, much more naturalistic, and much more flexible than many contemporary theories in psychology. The choice of experimental problems is very often colored by theoretical concerns; a particular gap in our understanding of some relationship between stimulus and experience or between meaning and association may determine a direction of exploration. A deduction from hypotheses about the nature of brain function may suggest an entire research program. But once the direction has been established, research motivated by this kind of theory has tended to be exploratory and descriptive. The general approach has been one of discovering and describing facts in some area of psychology that has not previously been studied or has been studied without attention to certain variables of stimulation or experience.

Such naturalistic and classificatory investigation is usually typical of a young science. It is characteristic of the gestalt-theoretical approach that its exponents tend to treat psychology as a less mature field of investigation than do some other psychologists. The establishment of special rules or procedures for the "construction of function forms" implies one of two things: perhaps that the forms of science are arbitrary, fictional, and without empirical constraint, or perhaps that we have sufficient data at hand to establish at worst a maximally efficient strategy for approaching new facts. Neither of these views is compatible with Köhler's position as it has developed to date. His is a basically empirical view, departing by virtue of its phenomenological bias to almost the opposite pole from current positivistic notions about scientific philosophy. The gestalt-theoretical position would, I believe, be something like the following: the formal relationships between dependent and independent variables are facts of nature to be discovered, not prescribed, by the scientist; the functions chosen to relate either kind of variable to hypothetical constructs are somewhat more arbitrary but depend in the last analysis on their success in encompassing a large quantity of data, and it is still too early to be rigid about such matters. Instead, the kinds of function chosen will for the time being mirror the stage of maturity of a particular field of investigation and the temporary purpose of the investigator. In the long run, the forms chosen will probably be those most useful in aiding coordination and mutual understanding with the other natural sciences, particularly those that help us to understand behavior and experience in organismic terms.

One effect of such eclecticism in designing and reporting experiments is that relationships may sometimes be stated in entirely qualitative form, as in a report that a recognizable change in the potential difference between two electrodes uniformly follows certain kinds of stimulation. Sometimes they may be stated in the form of a simple quantitative relationship, as when the influence of distance upon the figural aftereffect is investigated; occasionally they may take the form of comparing empirical data to a more general and rational relationship, as in studying the role of stimulus-intensity ratios in constancy and contrast phenomena. Typically, we imply that the stated relationship can ultimately be transposed to the brain field; but in most cases it is clearly impracticable, because of limitations of our knowledge of the psychological facts or the neurological facts or both, to go beyond the establishment of certain relatively direct functions relating independent and dependent variables.

QUANTIFICATION

It is not easy to write about measurement as a special feature of gestalt psychology. On the one hand, the theory has never developed specific enough "function forms" for sophisticated discussions of quantification to have played a real part in the system, even though it is easy to see that many central problems of organization would, in principle, be more sharply delineated in quantitative form. Even the effect of proximity on grouping in visual perception, to take a fundamental example, is typically demonstrated but not measured. We know in a general way that it is a relational phenomenon depending on the proximities of other elements in the field, but its dependence on those other elements is not specified quantitatively. Nor are the possible parameters of size of elements, shape, color, etc., given any kind of quantitative expression. Occasional investigators have made quantitative studies of visual demonstrations used by the gestalt psychologists. In general they translate the demonstration into an empirically derived formula that is then said to "explain" the basic observation. It is easy to see that such formulas in fact leave basic theoretical issues untouched; but they have the advantage of adding precision to our description, limiting the applicable hypotheses about underlying brain dynamics, and sometimes demonstrating similarities among otherwise discrete psychological facts. It is probably fair to say that gestalt-theoretical accounts of learning and memory have suffered even more from this failure of quantitative specification.

On the other hand, it is also clear that most of the kinds of relationship that are envisaged by Köhler as having presumptive *causal* significance are rather complex ones. (He has sometimes used the applicability of Laplace's differential equation as characteristic of what he means by gestalten in physics.) And until preliminary exploratory investigations have made the dimensions and parameters of our subject matter clearer than they are now, we should perhaps resist premature mathematization of the subject. Some branches of psychology have become involved in elaborate quantitative procedures without tangible theoretical or empirical justification, and gestalt psychologists can point to those examples as support for taking an opposite tack.

With respect to statistical analysis of data, the problem is much the same. Some experimental psychologists seem unduly concerned with problems of significance and of statistical inference, and we probably need not provide t tests for every observation in science. On the other hand, many of the studies stemming from gestalt-theoretical interests have been poorly buttressed by statistical information, and a few have turned out to be artifacts that could have been avoided by reasonable attention to quantitative procedures.

THE FORMAL ORGANIZATION OF THE THEORY

It is not too extreme to say that the theory has no formal organization. Neither Köhler nor any of his students and associates has tried to put these matters into axiomatic form or to state with any precision which assumptions are basic and which subsidiary. There has seemed no real necessity (or time) for playing logical games with so much empirical work to be done. The ultimate aim of psychology, from the point of view of gestalt theory, is understanding the relationships among three kinds of fact: independent variables of the physical environment, physical and chemical changes in the organism, and behavior (or the experiences that can be inferred from behavior). These kinds of understanding should ultimately be capable of expression in quantitative terms, and when enough of them are available, it may be possible to see what kind of general theory could help us to deduce large numbers of specific facts from first principles. That time is a long way off, and there is probably no real point in trying to anticipate what such a theory will look like.

SCOPE

To the extent that gestalt theory can be considered a system of psychology, its scope is unlimited. It provides a potential framework for the understanding of all aspects of experience and behavior. How the details of such understanding might look in certain fields is, however, still largely unexamined. There is no gestalt theory of intelligence, for example, and none of neurosis, no special approach to social psychology, and only the outlines of a theory of development. No psychologist who had accepted Köhler's point of view toward general individual psychology could fail to reveal it in his conceptions and approaches in these other fields, and occasional examples can be found in almost any branch of psychology to show how the point of view has in fact spread. Still, gestalt psychology is a theoretical point of view limited in practice to the traditional areas of experimental psychology: sensation and perception; learning, memory, and thinking; and certain aspects of action. The extension by others of some of its concepts into the fields of personality, social psychology, etc., does not change this fact.

THE THEORY AS A MEDIATOR OF RESEARCH

It would take a long and detailed historical chapter to discuss in detail the research that has been inspired and directed by gestalt notions. Instead, let us look at a few indications of its scope. Between 1921 and 1938, the *Psychologische Forschung* devoted 22 volumes to studies that concerned themselves with one or another aspect of gestalt theory. Other German and American journals were publishing such material at the same time, and as long ago as 1935, Koffka published a very large book [8] summarizing the evidence for the point of view. Since that time, the gestalt point of view within perception has become so noncontroversial that it is hard to know what work has been (in any useful sense) mediated by gestalt theory. Köhler's own work perhaps provides the clearest example of the impulsion that a theory may give to scientific discovery.

The idea that a visually perceived figure reflects an active field-process in the brain gave rise to the supposition that the presence of the process should change the properties of the field and hence the organization of new figures introduced into the field. Exploratory studies made it clear that such phenomena do indeed occur, and the next several years were spent in studies of the properties of these changes and their dependence on the prior stimulation. That work culminated in the well-known Köhler-Wallach monograph [20]. But as the monograph makes clear, the facts may lead to deductions about presumptive activities in the visual brain that make the psychological phenomena possible. If the isomorphic hypothesis holds, and if the properties of the brain are those of a volume conductor (as suggested by the nature of perceptual relationships), some shrewd guesses might lead to an understanding of certain aspects of brain activity in this region. The trouble is that neurophysiological investigations had given almost no ground for believing that the brain really works in a way anything like what seemed to be required by the theory. New kinds of electrophysiological investigation were therefore required. Again several years of patient exploration finally made it abundantly clear that there are in fact cortical currents conducted in the brain as a continuum that can be measured and recorded, and that they do behave much as the theory had led Köhler to postulate. There seems no longer any question about the facts: the presence of a segregated contour in the visual field produces "figure-currents" in the visual brain. These currents are self-satiating, i.e., they build up a resistance to themselves; any figure, now presented in the area where such satiation has occurred, will be changed or distorted in predictable ways depending on its characteristics in relation to the satiated field. All these facts flowed directly from the gestalt-theoretical point of view. There can be no doubt that Köhler's views are substantive ones in the sense that they do lead to particular kinds of hypothesis and investigation.

EVIDENCE

The most impressive example of the weight of the experimental evidence that supports the gestalt conception in perception is the cessation of controversy about matters of theory in the study of form and grouping. Wertheimer's "laws" are taught in every textbook, and in general there is nearly universal acceptance of the importance of segregation, figure-ground differentiation, contour formation and the like. These basic descriptive facts of perception are indisputable, and they do not lend themselves to any of the common forms of analysis.

A characteristic piece of evidence is to be found in the study of the time error. The psychophysicist's "negative time error" was a statistical curiosity, something to be allowed for rather than explained until Köhler undertook to treat it in terms of brain field dynamics. His first proposal was that the experience of comparison corresponds to the interaction between the present brain process and the trace or aftereffect of the former stimulus, now diminished by fading with time. Lauenstein, however, proposed an explanation involving even more relational determination. He proposed that the direction of change in time of the trace will depend on the "base level" of excitation surrounding the stimulus in question; instead of simply fading, the trace can be expected to become assimilated to the neighboring intensities. If that were true, the negative time error could be reversed and made into a positive time error by using comparison stimuli less intense than their backgrounds. Under at least some circumstances, this prediction clearly holds true. Later unpublished work indicates that many of the reported anomalies can be explained in terms of satiation effects produced by repeated stimulation and predicted by Köhler's theory of figural aftereffects.

Other aspects of perception are more controversial—the more so in recent years since the revival of experimental interest in perception. There has been an astonishing rebirth of "cue psychology," the view that the organism first receives a signal from one part of the stimulus configuration and then perceives the remainder in one of several ways according to the nature of the cue. This is not the place to discuss the inadequacies of that view, but certain kinds of experimental evidence said to support it do offer a contrast between gestalt and other positions.

If the apparent size and distance of an object are determined entirely by stimulus characteristics, neither "attitude" nor familiarity with the object would seem to enter into the situation. But several recent experiments seem to have shown that two objects exposed under precisely the same conditions will appear to have different sizes if one has always been seen as small in the past and the other large. Similarly, it is maintained that an instruction to think of the stimulus object as a large object will change its apparent distance when compared to the situation where it is considered to be a small one. Comparable claims are made for the influence of familiar shape on the perception of color, of reward on figure-ground organization, of "attitude" on the various constancies. Better phenomenological investigation and less reliance on discriminative responses alone might make it clearer which of these changes are really perceptual ones and which merely different behavior in the presence of the same experience. Meanwhile, however, a real theoretical issue may be joined. Gestalt theory has treated perception as an aspect of general psychology: with the exception of organ anomalies or minor individual constants, the laws of seeing are the same for everyone. Moreover, the laws are laws relating various aspects of stimulation one to another. Now we are confronted with the proposal that different people (or the same person at different times) will see the same set of stimuli differently, not because any stimulative or receptive changes have occurred but because the observer has learned new responses, experienced different sequences of reward and punishment associated with these stimuli, or picked up a different signal ("cue") from associated stimuli or an experimenter's instruction.

These are empirical issues that must be settled. In my opinion, it is too soon to say that any of these experiments provides evidence against gestalt theory. I say that partly because of the reservation above concerning the distinction between perception and response, but also because the experiments referred to almost invariably make use of considerable impoverishment of normal conditions of seeing: tachistoscopic exposure, monocular viewing, chromatic matches with unequally bright hues, etc. The effects are apparently nearly impossible to produce in circumstances where vision is typically reliable, and that fact deserves more attention than it has had. Nevertheless, if it turns out that the claims are essentially sound, gestalt psychology will require some modification.

Interestingly enough, a number of borderline phenomena in this area were first reported by students under the influence of gestalt conceptions. Fuchs [2] reported changes in color when observers voluntarily organized spatially ambiguous figures in different ways. Heider [6] reported that different degrees of organization and different modes of observing colors produced changes in hue. And the simple fact that many ambiguous figures may be voluntarily reorganized was reported as early as the basic work of Rubin. What then is the difference between these studies and the more recent revolt against "autochthonous" factors in perception? In the first place, all the older investigations had to do with organizational changes, with "what goes with what." They were not contending that any and every dimension or characteristic of vision could be determined by need or past experience, but merely that physically neutral patterning could, under balanced autochthonous forces, be determined by attitude or instruction or "set." This is a difference of degree, but it is a genuine difference nonetheless. In the second place, it was clear that these factors were strictly limited in their effect when pitted against the stimulus variables. It is not possible, for example, to change the organization of an ambiguous figure at an indefinitely high rate nor to keep it stable forever.

Even with these differences, gestalt theory sometimes seems to contain a germ of inconsistency. In so far as nonstimulus influences stem from past experience and are contained, therefore, in the memory traces of the observer, it is possible to retain all of the general organizational principles and the isomorphic hypothesis. To the extent that these influences stem from "needs," "attitudes," "attention," and the like, however, present theory cannot yet incorporate them. A major research problem for gestalt theory is the extension of its principles to areas of behavior and experience not mediated by primary sensory projection areas of the brain.

In the past few years, Köhler's work has led to evidence of a different kind, evidence that bears on the general field-theoretical conception of perception and on the hypothesis of isomorphism. That work, discussed briefly above, deserves a more detailed discussion.

Approximately twenty years ago, it had become apparent that certain temporal characteristics of visual organization required explanation. J. J. Gibson [4] and others had shown that some kinds of stimulation resulted in progressive modification of experience through time, and that new stimuli presented after the period of adaptation showed certain kinds of distortions. Köhler, in his work with reversible figures, had come to the conclusion that some process of satiation or self-destruction was operating on particular organizations to make them ultimately too weak to stand the competition of alternate organizations. Following up this lead, he experimented with nonreversible figures to see whether some process accompanying the presence in experience of a segregated object might produce changes in the experience itself. When he found that prolonged viewing of ordinary line patterns does indeed result in progressive changes in the appearance of the patterns, he experimented further to find the spatial and temporal locus of the changes. It quickly became clear that the figure-process has effects that spread throughout the visual field, though weaker at larger distances from the original figure; it developed further that these effects persist in time and operate to distort new figures now inserted in the satiated field.

In the course of these investigations, Köhler came to the conclusion (anticipated in some of his earlier writing) that the underlying neurological counterpart of the phenomena that he observed in the laboratory must be cortical currents corresponding to the figure-process. Such currents could have properties isomorphic with the psychological effects only if they were truly relationally determined processes that spread throughout the visual cortex. Such a notion required the postulation of currents flowing in a continuous medium. Now it is not difficult from the physical point of view to suppose that the brain is a potential volume conductor; all the necessary conditions are known to be present. Nor is it difficult to conceive of nerve cells as sources of EMF, normally so related to their neighbors that no current flows, but subject to the immediate production of currents as soon as an imbalance is established by incoming sensory excitation. Indeed, Gerard [3] had already proposed such an arrangement. These views, combined with the long-known facts of electrotonus, provided a model for a theory of the figural aftereffects. The difficulty lay not in the physical facts, but in the contemporary assumption by almost all physiological psychologists and many neurophysiologists that the important facts of conduction in the brain are essentially like those in the peripheral nervous system. The brain, according to that view, is a complex network or switchboard, the pathways of which are to all intents and purposes (apart from synapses, of course) insulated from each other. Visual facts must be explained in terms of sequences of cells fired in particular orders. Any field effects are at best epiphenomena of some sort and have nothing serious to do with the process of seeing.

It was in order to test this view that Köhler began in 1947 to seek ways of detecting and recording any electrical effects that might accompany visual excitation. When technical problems of amplification, etc., had been conquered, it became apparent that, like alpha waves, direct currents could be detected even through the intact human skull but that these effects of stimulation are soon reduced in intensity, presumably as a result of electrotonic effects. A moving stimulus made it possible to trace the phenomenon through a region of the visual field without being hampered by the virtually immediate self-satiation of the currents concerned.

Further investigation established the fact that regions in which steady figure-currents had been allowed to persist showed disturbed electrical patterns when new stimulation occurred later. These phenomena were consistent with the notion that the very quickly occurring polarization of cell interfaces more gradually affected the property of polarizability and that the medium was hence changed in its intrinsic pattern of resistances. The net result is that a standard stimulus apparently produces a different kind of "figure-current" after satiation of the field than before. The particular directions of change of the electrical effects and some of the quantitative facts discovered in the psychological work may be deduced from the electrotonic model.

Additional investigations have been carried out with auditory stimulation in the intact human being and with both visual and auditory stimulation when recording directly from the surface of the exposed cortex in cats and monkeys. Though certain mysteries remain, these findings are largely consistent with one another and with the original proposals that Köhler made on the basis of psychological evidence in 1944—indeed with proposals made on far more general evidence in 1920. The findings themselves are too technical for presentation within the brief scope of this chapter; the interested reader may refer to recent publications covering the degree to which experimental findings conform to theory [17, 18, 19, 21].

In other words, the phenomenon of figural aftereffect has now progressed from being a curiosity of interest only to specialists in visual perception to being a valuable source of information about the intrinsic nature of neural organization. If the various logical steps have been taken correctly to date, we can feel certain that the visual brain does act as a volume conductor, that it does follow laws of "physical gestalten," and that visual experience does have properties isomorphic with electrical changes in the brain. According to this view, the properties of a visually perceived figure are those permitted by the distribution of current in the visual cortex, and changes in what is perceived are presumably correlated with changes in the distribution of these currents. It now behooves gestalt theory to demonstrate how memories, needs, and attitudes can be represented in this model—or to demonstrate that they do not in fact influence perception.

EXPORTABLE PRINCIPLES

For a psychologist who could not accept all of the postulates and program of Köhler's position, what might nevertheless be of value? In the millennium when theoretical dispute will be a thing of the past, what is most likely to be preserved from gestalt theory? These are questions that are difficult to answer, just because the gestalt position is, as I have reiterated, a point of view much more than a theory. It hangs together in such a way that it is difficult to divorce one aspect from another. Still, it is possible to consider certain aspects as, in principle, separable. The antimosaic attitude, that insistence on the principle of relational determination in psychology, could logically stand alone. This is the most primitive attitude of the gestalt psychologist, and the one for which the evidence from perception is so impressive. It seems likely that this point of view can be carried over into any general psychological theory that attempts to deal with perception. There is evidence of its usefulness in the study of learning and memory. One might urge the eclectic to adopt the principle of relational determination as a basic fact of behavior.

The concept of isomorphism is an independent assumption. The doctrine of relational determination could hold for an "empty organism." It is harder to see how one could believe in a close formal relationship between organism and experience without believing at the same time in relational determination in the nervous system. Some writers do, however, persist in a switchboard kind of model for the nervous system and attempt, for example, to derive the phenomenon of figural aftereffect from assumptions about reverberatory circuits, "peaking," and so on [23]. To the extent that they are successful, it would be possible to maintain some kind of isomorphic notion while holding that both experience and nervous system followed mechanical models. It seems unlikely that there is much to be gained by that procedure.

The antiempiristic aspect of gestalt theory might also be accepted without committing oneself to other parts of the theory. We can adopt Köhler's critical attitude toward easy assumptions about the acquisition of behavior or of experience without becoming gestalt psychologists in any other way.

The phenomenological method is in part connected with the revolt against artificial analysis and "sensationism," but it does not in itself commit one to any particular theories about psychological facts; it is merely one way to start discovering those facts. As such, it offers something of importance to all branches of psychology, particularly those that have become encrusted with traditional techniques, jargon, and systems of analysis, or particularly those in which positivism or radical behaviorism seem to have impoverished the field.

In short, each of the major methodological aspects of gestalt psychology has potential applicability outside the theory. Within the theory, however, they are so closely connected and so much a part of the point of view that colors all psychological investigation that it is not easy to suggest that they be used in isolation from one another.

GESTALT PSYCHOLOGY AS A PROGRAM

If we consider the number of implications of Köhler's point of view that have not yet been finally demonstrated in detail, it is not hard to consider that the theory entails a kind of program of research. The things that still remain to be done are perhaps primarily the following.

The "laws" of grouping require more precise statement, and particularly quantification. The same is true of the many qualitative demonstrations of figural factors in the perception of hue, brightness, distance, shape, and size. A number of facts relating to the perception of movement are also uncoordinated, and it is difficult to make general statements about the parameters of direction, shape, size, similarity of stimuli, and related factors in the study of stroboscopic movement. In other words, the very facts that give the most impressive demonstration of relational determination in perception require more precise statement before we can understand their true nature. Until such time as these facts have led to more easily generalizable principles, both practical and theoretical advances in perception will be delayed. A thorough understanding of the modes of interaction of various stimulus characteristics could lead, if the isomorphic hypothesis stands up, to a far better understanding of brain dynamics than we now have.

A theory of development is needed to complete the structure, if gestalt theory is to be a general theory. At present, we know that the perceptual behavior of adults is different in various ways from that of young children. We do not have a coherent account of the intermediate changes or their causes. Similarly, we do not have a thorough conception of the role of perceptual experience on later perceiving. The figural aftereffect has usually demonstrated relatively short-term influences, though Köhler has shown how much more persistent such changes may sometimes be [16]. What other long-lasting effects may there be, and how are these coordinated with changes in the brain field? What similarities and differences do such phenomena show when compared to the more familiar laboratory facts of learning and memory? Gestalt theory suffers from a kind of confusion engendered by its interest in the phenomena of learning and memory on the one hand and its anti-empiristic bias on the other. Somehow the facts of learning must be brought into some kind of coherence with the study of those psychological and physiological fields that are presumably influenced in some way by learning. Köhler has touched on these problems in a most interesting way [14], but there is still much to be done.

Influences of motivation and attention are similarly in need of investigation. Both concepts have a long history of use as *Dei ex machina*, and gestalt psychologists rightly revolted against the casual attribution of every perceptual problem to these all-powerful forces. But the time has now come when systematic attention must be given to changes in the perception of a constant stimulus configuration, whether those changes are produced by special instructions, "sets" resulting from serial presentation of particular kinds of organization, voluntary shifts of interest, or relatively persistent states of need or motive.

These are matters of implicit program rather than explicit plans for the future. Successful completion of these kinds of investigation would buttress the theory and make it capable of handling all kinds of perceptual phenomena—perhaps any behavioral facts whatsoever. Modifications of the theory and exposure of unsuspected gaps or weaknesses are also most likely to arise in following these lines of investigation.

REFERENCES

1. Focht, Mildred. *What is gestalt-theory?* New York: Columbia Univer. Press, 1935.

2. Fuchs, W. Experimentelle Untersuchungen über die Änderungen von Farben unter dem Einfluss von Gestalten ("Angleichungserscheinungen"). *Z. Psychol.*, 1923, **91**, 145–235.

3. Gerard, R. W. The interaction of neurones. *Ohio J. Sci.*, 1941, **41**, 160–172.

4. Gibson, J. J. Adaptation, after-effect, and contrast in the perception of curved lines. *J. exp. Psychol.*, 1933, **16**, 1–31.

5. Hartmann, G. *Gestalt psychology.* New York: Ronald, 1935.

6. Heider, G. M. New studies in transparency, form, and color. *Psychol. orsch.*, 1933, **17**, 13–55.

7. Katz, D. Die Erscheinungsweisen der Farben und ihre Beeinflussung urch individuelle Erfahrung. *Z. Psychol.* (Ergbnd.), 1911, **7**, 1–425.

8. Koffka, K. *Principles of gestalt psychology.* New York: Harcourt, race, 1935.

9. Köhler, W. *Die physischen Gestalten in Ruhe und im stationären ustand.* Erlangen: Weltkreisverlag, 1920.

10. Köhler, W. *The mentality of apes.* London: Routledge & Kegan aul, 1925.

11. Köhler, W. *Gestalt psychology.* New York: Liveright, 1929.

12. Köhler, W. *The place of value in a world of facts.* New York: iveright, 1938.

13. Köhler, W. *Dynamics in psychology.* New York: Liveright, 1940.

14. Köhler, W. On the nature of associations. *Proc. Amer. philos. Soc.*, 941, **84**, 489–502.

15. Köhler, W. Relational determination in perception. In L. A. Jeffress Ed.), *Cerebral mechanisms in behavior.* New York: Wiley, 1951.

16. Köhler, W., & Fishback, J. The destruction of the Müller-Lyer illuion in repeated trials: I and II. *J. exp. Psychol.*, 1950, **40**, 267–281, 398–10.

17. Köhler, W., & Held, R. The cortical correlate of pattern vision. *cience*, 1949, **110**, 414–419.

18. Köhler, W., Held, R., & O'Connell, D. An investigation of cortical urrents. *Proc. Amer. philos. Soc.*, 1952, **96**, 290–330.

19. Köhler, W., Neff, W. D., & Wegener, J. Currents of the auditory ortex in the cat. *J. cell. comp. Physiol.*, 1955, **45**, Suppl. 1, 1–24.

20. Köhler, W., & Wallach, H. Figural after-effects. *Proc. Amer. philos. oc.*, 1944, **88**, 269–357.

21. Köhler, W., & Wegener, J. Currents of the human auditory cortex. *. cell. comp. Physiol.*, 1955, **45**, Suppl. 1, 25–54.

22. Korte, A. Kinematoskopische Untersuchungen. *Z. Psychol.*, 1915, **2**, 193–296.

23. Osgood, C. E., & Heyer, A. W. A new interpretation of figural afterffects. *Psychol. Rev.*, 1951, **59**, 98–118.

24. Rubin, E. *Visuell wahrgenommene Figuren.* Copenhagen: Gyldenlalska, 1921.

25. Wallach, H. Brightness constancy and the nature of achromatic olors. *J. exp. Psychol.*, 1948, **38**, 310–324.

26. Weiss, P. Experimental analysis of co-ordination by the disarrangenent of central peripheral relations. In Soc. for Exp. Biol. *Physiological nechanisms in animal behavior.* Cambridge: Cambridge Univer. Press, 1950.

27. Wertheimer, M. Experimentelle Studien über das Sehen von Bewegung. *Z. Psychol.*, 1912, **61**, 121–165.

28. Wertheimer, M. Untersuchungen zur Lehre von der Gestalt II. *Psychol. Forsch.*, 1923, **4**, 301–350.

PERCEPTION AS A FUNCTION OF STIMULATION

JAMES J. GIBSON
Cornell University

ORIENTING CONSIDERATIONS

The word *perception* in this essay means the process by which an individual maintains contact with his environment. The word *stimulation* means the kinds and variables of physical energy in the environment to which the sense organs of the individual will respond. The theory to be presented suggests that perception is a function of stimulation. More exactly, it asserts that there is always some discoverable variable in stimulation—in the flowing array of energy at the sense organs of an animal—which determines the character of the perceptual process aroused by it. This variable will usually prove to be one of higher order than are the variables hitherto studied by sensory physiologists, but it is called a stimulus because it is taken to cause perception in the same way that more familiar stimuli are experimentally known to cause sensation.

The theory goes beyond the relation of perception to stimulation, however. It considers also the relation of stimulation to the external environment. The hypothesis is that these neglected but discoverable stimulus variables are generally quite specific to the features of the outer world which are important to the animal in question. The classical variables of stimulation, of course, do *not* indicate the relevant objects and events of the environment with any reliability; hence they are termed "cues." But if the variables of higher order can be shown to specify the world, although not to represent or replicate it, an explanation is possible for perception as defined—the business of *keeping in touch with the world.* If the properties of objects specify the variables of stimulation and these in turn specify the qualities of perception, then percepts will be univocally related to objects within the limits of the combined levels of specificity. Such limits can be determined empirically.

The exposition of this theory seems to require, first, some consideration of what is to be meant by the words *perception* and *sensation,* and the relation of these meanings to introspection on the one hand and to discriminative judgment on the other. Next the relation of stimulation to perception should be elaborated, and then the relation of stimulation to the external environment. The success of the theory in explaining visual perception can then be evaluated by considering a summary of the experiments to which it has led. Finally, the utility of this approach for a theory of perceptual learning should be considered.

The outline does not especially facilitate comparison between this and the other theories of perception gathered together in this book. This theory sets out to redefine the concept of stimulation and reformulate the problems of perception; it probably will not seem to be cognate with the others. For purposes of such comparison, therefore, a final section has been written which follows the editor's list of the features that characterize a psychological theory and which reveals for the reader's benefit the writer's estimation of his own effort.

The function of the perceptual mechanism. Perception was not defined in terms either of consciousness or of behavior, but only by using a metaphor which implies both: an individual is in "contact" or in "touch" with the environment. The fact behind the metaphor is that vision and hearing function in basically the same way as does the sense of touch; i.e., they permit acquaintance with and responses to substantial objects, places, and events. The radiant energy of light or sound, like the kinetic energy of pressure on the skin, may be informative about an object. This is taken to be the central fact of perception. It applies equally to consciousness and to behavior. An individual can both respond to and be aware of an object. In this essay neither capacity is assumed to be prior to the other. The essential part of the perceptual process goes on whether the individual is reacting to his environment or is merely contemplating it.

The fact that one can apprehend things and events at a distance almost as directly as if one could touch them has long been taken to be a paradox in the history of philosophy and psychology. Perceiving things by touch seemed to be self-explanatory (although, of course, it was not). Seeing things seemed to be different, for then one has direct "contact" only with the retinal image. Likewise in hearing only the vibrations from the object "touch" the ear. How is it possible to perceive the distant object with only the information supplied by this proximal stimulus? This paradox, it will be argued, is based on a misconception of stimulation which arose in connection with the study of single receptors. Stimulation is something that excites a whole sense organ, not merely a cell—a mosaic of receptors, not merely a single receptor. *Ordinal* stimulation is vastly richer and more informative than sensory physiologists have realized in the past. The doctrine of sensations or sense data followed from the error of underestimating the stimulus.

The theory to be presented is concerned in the first place with veridical perception and only in the second place with illusions and errors. It presupposes that if a satisfactory explanation of the former can be given, an explanation of the latter will be easy. The explanation will be found in some failure of specificity between perception and stimulation or between stimulation and the external object. This approach contrasts with that of gestalt theory, for instance, which aims to explain both illusions and correct perceptions by the same hypothetical process of sensory organization.

Inasmuch as behavior is connected with perception, this approach also presupposes that adaptive and maladaptive responses differ in being or not being a function of "reality." Hallucinations and delusions are taken to be accompaniments of a response mechanism which has failed somehow to be in correspondence with actual events.

Comparison with existing theories of perception. The simple formula proposed—perception is a function of stimulation and stimulation is a function of the environment; hence perception is a function of the environment—is a radical departure from classical theories of perception. These have taken it for granted that a special psychological or neural process occurs which is not directly dependent on the stimulation of receptors but only indirectly dependent. Perception is based on sensation. The latter depends on stimulation, to be sure, but the former involves some additional or intervening process the nature of which must be discovered.

A large number of processes for converting the data of sense into percepts have been hypothesized over the years. The commonest is association. More recent is sensory organization. Both of these can be conceived as neural processes, if somewhat vaguely, and both suggest experiments which have led to "laws." But neither hypothesis has been sufficiently powerful to exclude the other. Additional processes such as inference, or interpretation, or computation, or categorization, or assimilation, or stabilization have been called upon. The data of sense have been described as cues, clues, signs, indicators, criteria, messages, information, and the like. The processes have been combined in different ways. Some theorists emphasize memory and memory images, others conditioning or response tendencies or motor attitudes. Still others put less emphasis on learning and argue for a spontaneous process. The clearest and most comprehensive recent theories are perhaps gestalt theory as represented by Koffka [28] and modern statistical empiricism as represented by Brunswik [3].

In the present theory, all processes for explaining the conversion of sensory data into percepts are superfluous. No process of conversion is assumed. Not only the qualities of objects but also their very object-character, substantiality, solidity, and the like, are taken to be discoverable in stimulation. Objects are, as it were, "sensed." This approach is not, then, a theory of perception in the ordinary meaning of that word. The proposal is to dispense entirely with the concept of sensation as the basis of phenomenal experience and thereby to rid psychology of the persistent notion that sensory impressions are prerequisite to other impressions. This proposal involves difficulties of terminology for which the reader should make allowances. Terms like "sensing" and "the senses" cannot be abandoned without substitutes, which are not easy to invent.

The status of sensory experience in this theory. It cannot be denied that men sometimes have sensations—pure blues, sour tastes, or bright pressures. At least students in psychological laboratories can be induced to report such experiences, and the habit of describing them can be learned. But this does not mean that the experiences described are the basis of all experience. The phenomenal world is not composed of colors, sounds, touches, tastes, and smells as we have for so long assumed, but of such properties as surface, edge, slant, convexity, concavity, of rising, falling, beginning, ending, moving, and changing. Sensations are the occasional symptoms of perception, not the cause of it.

The supposedly irreducible attributes or data of sensory experience are the products of introspection. Not only this, they are the products of a doctrinal kind of introspection that expects to find them at the core of every perception, that is to say, of structuralism. The danger of structuralism is that a list of modes, attributes, and qualities of experience gets written down and memorized. If these also prove to correspond to simple variables of stimulation which can be conveniently manipulated in psychophysical experiments they achieve the status of a completed theory. The tendency of the theorist thereafter is to find just these listed elements in his description of experience and to overlook experiences which resist this analysis. He will also fail to consider the possible existence of variables of stimulation for the latter experiences. If these potential stimuli are difficult to manipulate in psychophysical experiments the tendency will be all the more pronounced.

The writer has tried to show elsewhere that the array of visual sensations, the sort of experience which can be called the visual *field,* is distinguishable from the experience of the visual *world* [9, chap. 3], and has argued that the latter in no sense depends upon the former. Instead they tend to be alternatives. Although compromise occurs, it does seem that the more one notices the patchwork of colors in the field the less one sees objects in the world, and the more one observes objects the less one sees the patchwork of colors. The field and the world both depend on optical stimulation; the latter is simply the product of a different *order* of stimulation.[1]

The proposal, then, is to relegate the concept of sensation to the status of a psychological curiosity. The term refers to a rare and sophisticated kind of experience, not a basic one.

The validity of introspection in the study of perception. Introspection, when not prejudiced by the theory of sensations, is an excellent guide to the study of perception. A cultivated naiveté about what the world *does* look, sound, and feel like is almost necessary for determining what the problems of perception are, and for inquiring how these are related to problems of behavior. This sort of introspection is a prerequisite to the setting up of psychophysical experiments in perception, that is, experiments to verify the dependence of the qualities of the perceptual world on higher-order variables of stimulation.

On the other hand introspection, however unbiased, is no *more* than a guide to the study of perception. It is no substitute for experiments. Phenomenological description as an end in itself, although an interesting pursuit, is not strict science. It is notably different when performed by different observers because they do not use a common vocabulary. This is necessarily so for any inquiry on the borderline of knowledge, to be sure, but experimentation is the remedy. There have been observers such as Katz [27] who were skillful in using the vernacular to make descriptions which others can recognize, but they are rare. Katz himself was a frequent experimenter. The discipline of public and repeatable psychophysical experiments is an unmistakable vocabulary in which the science of perception should be formulated.

Introspection can set the problems for perceptual research and put

[1] A discussion of the visual field and the visual world is to be found in a paper by E. G. Boring [1], a reply by the writer [11], and a rebuttal by Boring [2].

them into at least a rough classification, and an order or priority. It tells us that what we perceive is not only objects but also places, events motions, and sequences. These constitute a world. There are also organisms, animals, and people as part of this world. And also there are human artifacts, models, pictures, symbols, and other surrogates or signs of absent things as a further subclass of the world. Introspection tells us that the phenomenal world is continuous both in adjacent order and in successive order; it binds objects into the array of space and events into the flow of time. These are problems of perception, and equally they are problems for behavior.

Introspection also tells us that awareness of the world has a subjective as well as an objective pole and it reminds us that proprioception and interoception always accompany exteroception. This poses a difficult problem of the relation between external and internal stimulation. A man always perceives his environment in relation to himself and his body, his own movements and his own internal states. Visual experience, for instance, is inseparably related to the posture of the eyes, and that depends on the posture of the head and body. These involve equilibrium and orientation, which are fundamental to locomotion and action. The latter are initiated by organic sensitivity and guided by kinesthesis. In this circuit of relations, we have passed from consciousness to behavior and back again.

Awareness and discriminative response. Perception has not been defined either in terms of conscious awareness on the one hand or discriminative response on the other because the intention is that the theory shall apply to both. The writer refuses to take part in the debate over whether the language of behavior or the language of consciousness is necessary for the study of perception. In many experiments, one is translatable into the other, and perhaps in all experiments they will ultimately prove to be translatable. In so far as they are not, the writer believes that the formulas of behavior theory and of phenomenal experience are complementary, not contradictory, and that psychologists will have to learn to get along with both of them in the same way that physicists have learned to reconcile the apparent contradictions connected with the notions of wave and particle. It is certainly true that one cannot, *at the same time,* observe a discriminative consciousness and the discriminative judgment or act that goes with it. The first observation is possible to the subject of an experiment, the second to the experimenter. A single individual cannot be expected to take both roles at the same time.[2]

[2] The error (as the writer believes) of assuming that *the psychologist who studies perception is himself perceiving when he does so,* and concluding that *we can know nothing but our perceptions,* is a consequence of trying to take both

In what follows I shall refer either to experience or to behavior, as arity and convenience dictate. An effort will be made in either case mply to avoid assertions which could not lead to experiments.

In this theory, the perceptual process is conceived to be more gen-al than the particular form of it which leads to conscious awareness. perceptual process may or may not have a phenomenal accompani-ent. Discrimination and specificity characterize reactions as well as xperience, and not all reactions are paralleled by experience. There is me reason to believe that any discrimination can be *made* conscious y a sufficient effort of introspective search, but this is another question.

Conscious perception, then, is not a prerequisite to behavior as is taken to be in some forms of gestalt theory. Behavior can go n independently of such awareness and still be more or less specific to e environmental situation. For that matter, behavior can go on with-ut any of the specific inputs which yield contact with the environment –without perception in our sense. But in that case the behavior is likely have painful consequences.

The chain of causation leading to perception. The formula that per-eption is a function of stimulation and stimulation is a function of the nvironment is obviously only a sketch that needs elaboration. The heory assumes a sequence of variables, each being dependent on the revious one. One might think of a sequence of transformations pre-erving a certain correspondence or specificity throughout the different tages. The sequence begins with the environment of the perceiver, con-idered not at the level of molecules, nor that of continents, but at the evel of ecology. There is next the energy at the body surface—light, ound, heat, kinetic energy, and chemical energy, considered at the spe-ial level of the spatio-temporal patterns which can specify the sources f this stimulation and which can also excite receptors. Next is the sen-ory equipment of the perceiver, the anatomy and physiology of the eceptor surfaces together with the exploratory adjustments of the rgans which enable them to register the patterns in question. Here gain the activity of the whole sense organ must be considered, not the ctivity of a single receptor cell. The excitation of these receptors as uch has been much investigated but the effect of discharging them n different distributions over the mosaic of cells is less well understood. Over and above the neural loops that govern sense organ adjustments s the neural transmission, afferent and efferent, through the so-called projection centers of the cerebral cortex. There are various theories of

these roles at the same time. Once having made this argument, a theorist is trapped in a circle of subjectivism and is diverted into futile speculations about private worlds.

what happens in the cortex, and the way in which specificity is preserved to the stimulus pattern is still a difficult problem. But in any case some feature of the neural process results in perception, as evidenced in both experience and behavior. And this perception is specific to the environment only if the above chain of causation remains unbroken. *There is no other avenue for contact with or knowledge of the environment.*

The chain of causation can be considered in two parts—that outside the organism and that inside. A complete theory of perception must deal with both, but each should be made separately explicit. The first part is concerned with the biophysics of stimulation, that is, the nature of the environment and the relation between object and stimulus. The second part is concerned with the variables and properties of stimulation and the relation between these and perception, or what can be called the psychophysics of perception. We will consider the latter first.

OUTLINE OF THE THEORY

Perceptual Psychophysics

Classical sensory psychophysics has accumulated the most solid body of scientific facts to be found in any of the realms of psychology. It has done so by studying the dependence of discriminative judgments on certain stimulus variables, chiefly frequency and intensity. The commonest psychophysical method is to show that differences in experience, as evidenced by judgments, correspond to differences in stimulation experimentally applied. In order to do so, the experimenter must have previously built a device and made arrangements to isolate and control the variable of stimulus energy in which he is interested—light, sound, pressure, or whatever it may be. The essence of the experiment is that a judgment of "greater" is always given when the experimenter sufficiently varies the energy in one direction, and a judgment of "less" when he sufficiently varies it in the other direction.

This method can perfectly well be extended to other variables of stimulation than frequency and intensity. The important ones for perception and behavior are variables of the adjacent and successive order of frequencies and intensities, that is, variables of the stimulus *array* and of the stimulus *flow*. There are gradients, derivatives, ratios, and rates in this flowing array of energy, and these are the higher-order variables of stimulation which the theory postulates. The main requirement for a perceptual psychophysics is that apparatus be constructed for the isolation and control of these variables.

Psychophysical experiments in perception involve the use of artifiial stimulation under the control of an experimenter instead of the natural stimulation of an ordinary environment which, of course, is not under his control. Such experiments induce the phenomenal dimensions of objects, places, events, and the like, without employing an actual object, place, or event. An example is the optical pseudo-tunnel [22]. This is a device for inducing the main properties of the experience of looking into a cylinder (surface, solidity, recession, distance, parallel-sidedness) by presenting a sheaf of light rays to an eye (or two sheaves to the two eyes) the optical texture of which is systematically variable. Another example is the experiments of Michotte [32] in which certain features of the experience of a causal event are induced by systematically varying the motions of black spots in a white field.

The psychophysical experiment and the psychophysical method should not be confused with the theory of sensations, although historically they have been linked. The fact that hue, brightness, saturation, pitch, loudness, timbre, pressure, warmth, cold, and pain are the dimensions associated with psychophysical experiments does not mean that they are the dimensions of phenomenal experience or the components of phenomenal objects. Nor does the validity of the psychophysical method here make it invalid for other more lifelike dimensions of experience.

The generalized hypothesis of psychophysical correspondence. Perception is said to be a function of stimulation. This means that it is exclusively a function of stimulation whenever the conditions of stimulation permit. The explicit hypothesis is that *for every aspect or property of the phenomenal world of an individual in contact with his environment, however subtle, there is a variable of the energy flux at his receptors, however complex, with which the phenomenal property would correspond if a psychophysical experiment could be performed.*

In this form the hypothesis will probably encounter objections at once. What about meanings? What about social objects and events, or esthetic qualities? What about the subjective coloration of our phenomenal world? Before considering these apparent exceptions, closer attention should be given to what the hypothesis does and does not assert. It is a promise of experimental results in the future rather than a synthesis of existing results. Admittedly it aims to open up a new theory rather than to complete an old one.

1. It does not aim to explain all those kinds of experience that have been loosely *called* perceptual. It is a theory of contact with the environment, not of lack of contact with it. Errors, illusions, misjudgments, hallucinations, fluctuating impressions, and misperception in general cannot be explained except by corollaries of the hypothesis, and these have not yet been stated. It does not deny that such experiences occur

or that they are frequent and important. Experience of some sort ma occur in the absence of any pattern stimulation, in silent darkness with the body cradled in cotton wool, for instance. It may occur in the pres ence of impoverished, ambiguous, or equivocal pattern stimulation.[3] Such experience cannot be a function of stimulation; obviously it must be a function of something else.

2. Similarly, the hypothesis does not deny that recalling, recollect ing, and imagining occur, or that they are important. This kind of experience is also not a function of stimulation—at least not a function of the sort that can be established by a psychophysical experiment. This must also be a function of something else. The hypothesis only contra dicts the classical notion that memory in the sense of remembering—the arousal of memory images, for example—is essential for veridical per ception.

3. The hypothesis does assume an unfamiliar concept of stimulation —the notion of a flowing sea of energy, in which the organism is im mersed, whose variations of order are mathematically analyzable. These constitute either effective, or potentially effective stimuli, and the pos sibilities for registering variables of increasingly higher order are taken to be unlimited. There are vastly more stimuli in the world than any one observer is ever likely to respond to. There are the variables of low order known to the experimenters and there are also variables of higher order not yet experimentally isolated. This conception reverses the classical opinion of the matter, which contrasts the poverty of stimula tion for the eye and the ear with the richness of visual and auditory experience. It is here asserted that the light and sound reverberating throughout an ordinary terrestrial environment contain more subtleties of information about the environment than any of its inhabitants can even hope to perceive. There is nothing implausible or contradictory to physical science in this newer conception, as an attempt will be made to show.

4. The hypothesis does not assert that there is *only one* variable of the energy flux with which a given phenomenal variable is in cor respondence. Two or more variables of stimulation can yield the same quality of experience, as in the case of visual depth or the case of kin esthesis where the variables are ordinarily multiple and concomitant. Either one variable in isolation or several in combination will then give the same effect. When, however, a combination of discrepant or con flicting variables is experimentally presented the outcome is unpre-

[3] Clear examples of what is meant by ambiguous and equivocal stimulation may be found in certain optical gradients and combinations of gradients as producers of visual depth, as in the last three experiments with the optical pseudo-tunnel [22, pp. 10ff.].

dictable from the stimulation alone. Experiments on "conflicting cues" are of this sort. But the stimulus combinations of ordinary life are taken to be concomitant, in accordance with a principle of redundant stimulation. The principle is that multiple stimulation normally yields a multiple guarantee of the validity of perception.

5. The hypothesis does not deny that the sensory equipment of the species or the individual determines the kinds of perception that can occur. On the contrary, the receptor and accessory mechanisms determine the modes and variables of stimulation that the individual can respond to or, rather, they limit the variables to which he can *learn* to respond. The mechanisms however deserve more respect than has sometimes been given them by receptor cell physiologists and designers of instruments. It is naive nonsense to conclude, for instance, that perception must be a mental act because the eye is a poor optical instrument, and yet we see well. The eye is not to be compared with an optical instrument.

6. The hypothesis does not deny that perception depends on the attention or "set" of the individual, whatever that may prove to be. Many variables of stimulation are not responded to by an individual at any one time, and different variables are responded to at different times. Both awareness and behavior are highly selective. Potential stimuli become effective stimuli when an individual makes differential reactions to them or perceives them. The phenomenal world of one individual may consequently be rather different from that of another individual in the same environment, and it may be different for the same individual on two different occasions. Attention is supposed to be related to motive, interest, or course of action. The hypothesis only assumes that the energy flux is the same for two individuals in identical situations and that consequently any differences between their perceptions are differences in what the individual is responding *to*.

7. The hypothesis does not deny that perception involves learning, nor assert that perception is innate. The stimuli of which perception is a function undoubtedly change with practice, that is, after repeated encounters with them. Previously ineffective stimulation becomes effective; the individual can respond to variables not previously responded to. More variables in the stimulus flux, and variables of higher order, become discriminated. Phenomenally, the world contains more different objects and more differences between objects than it previously did; it becomes more differentiated and therewith fuller of meaning [18]. The same kind of change in perception occurs with the growth and maturation of the sense organs and the nervous system as occurs with practice and repetition. What the hypothesis does suggest is that perception involves learning of a quite different kind than has been emphasized in

the past. Instead of association it implies discrimination. The phenomenal world is selected, abstracted, and differentiated as a result of repeated stimulation, not built up, constructed, or supplemented as a result of it. Behavior, similarly, involves learning but the kind of learning implied is increased contact with the environment; it is the emergence of new stimuli and new responses of higher order from old ones of lower order, not the connecting of new stimuli to old responses or of old stimuli to new responses.

8. The last three paragraphs may be summarized by saying that an animal or a man may fail to react to some variable in the surrounding sea of energy for any of several reasons. First, he may fail because his species does not possess the necessary neural mechanisms, or because his own are defective at some level, anywhere from the sense organ to the brain. Second, he may fail because the neural equipment is not sufficiently matured to be sensitive to the variable in question or, if an adult, because he has not learned to discriminate the variable. Finally he may fail simply because he is responding instead to some other variable of energy. The way to find out whether an individual is equipped to discriminate, or can be trained to discriminate, or can be "set" to discriminate is to perform an experiment. If differential reactions can be established by speech merely, by "instructing" the observer, we call it a psychophysical experiment. If differential reactions can be established only after associating them with reward or punishment, we call it a learning experiment, but we do not know in that case what part of the learning is discriminating as such and what part is associating. If differential reactions cannot be established even after long training of this sort, we are tempted to conclude that the individual does not have the necessary equipment.

The specificity of perception to excitation and the specificity of excitation to stimulation. The psychophysical correspondence between sensory quality or intensity and the wavelength or amplitude of light and of sound is emphasized in every textbook. The correspondence depends on the receptors and the nervous system; first, on the differences in receptor-excitation which correspond to differences in energy and second, on the differences in phenomenal experience which correspond to differences in receptor-excitation. The first kind of specificity depends on the specialized sensitivity of receptors—their low thresholds for certain energies and high thresholds for all others. This is Sherrington's concept of the "adequate" stimulus for a receptor. The second kind of specificity depends on the specialized sensitivity of the arcs, loops, and circuits of the nervous system. This is the concept that began with Müller's notion of the "specific energies of nerves." There is discriminaon, as it were, at both stages, that of neural excitation and that of neural ransmission, just as there is discrimination in the over-all process of naking psychophysical judgments.

The psychophysical correspondence between the variable of *perceptual* experience and the higher-order variables of light and sound is resumably just as dependent on the receptors and the nervous system s is the classical *sensory* correspondence. The receptor mosaic must have pecialized sensitivity to gradients and transitions, and the nervous system nust transmit these gradients and transitions. A perceptual physiology s distinguished from sensory physiology is required. It should develop n parallel to a perceptual psychophysics as distinguished from sensory sychophysics. After all, light and sound at the eye and ear stimulate he *man* just as truly as they stimulate the cells of his retina and cochlea. The organismic level of stimulation is more in need of study than the ellular level.

The Biophysics of Stimulation

The nature of the environment. The chain of causation beginning vith the environment and ending with perception has stimulation as its niddlemost link. We have so far been concerned with the relation beween stimulation and perception. Let us now consider the relation beween the environment and stimulation.

The environment with which we are concerned is not the one which s measured in microns, nor that which is measured in light years, but hat which is measured in millimeters or meters. The environment which s relevant for stimulation is not that of particles, atoms, molecules, or nything smaller than crystals. Nor is it that of planets, stars, galaxies, r nebulae. The world of man and animals consists of matter in the olid, liquid, or gaseous state, organized as an array of surfaces or nterfaces between matter in these different states. It is the *habitat* of n animal. In some respects it is the world studied by ecology. There is no name, however, for the particular combination of sciences necessary or the study of perceptual stimulation.

Leaving out of account the aquatic and aerial environments of some nimals, let us confine our attention to the terrestrial environment of our wn relatives. Its solid surfaces are arranged in ways of such overwhelmng complexity that they are very hard to classify. We can speak of regions nd places, of objects and things in these places, and of events occurring, ut these words are inexact. We can speak of rocks, trees, and cliffs, of ce, iron, and wood, of brooks, bridges, and mountains, but these words re too specific. Present day physical science is of little help, since it umps from crystals to planets and shows no interest in the entities of the world which we can see and feel with our unaided sense organs—t sources of stimulation.[4] Present-day engineering is no help since it concerned only with creating artificial entities of this sort. Natural o jects have been left to the curiosity of artists.

As a first approximation, it can be suggested that the terrestrial e vironment consists of a gaseous medium (the air) and a solid su stratum (the ground), with other solids which are normally in conta with the ground (objects). The ground and the objects constitute a array of surfaces. These surfaces reflect light, emit sound if they vibrat and radiate or absorb heat if they are hot or cold. They also may ha penetrating edges or points, rounded contours, horizontal or perpe dicular planes relative to gravity, and the like, which determine wheth they can be picked up, walked on, and so forth. Depending on the chemical composition, they may emit gaseous substances, and they ma be edible or inedible, rigid or elastic, living or nonliving.

The air, on the other hand, constitutes a medium for a flux of ligh of sound, and of gaseous emanations. It is also a medium for locomotio or other action of the animal. The surfaces constitute both a support f and obstacles to locomotion but the air constitutes the space of behavio It corresponds to the so called "empty" space of visual perception. Th interrelation between the air and the ground, between gas and soli is a biophysical fact which has governed the evolution of terrestri animals—not only of their action systems but also of their recepti systems. For, as we shall see, the flux of light, of sound, and of od throughout the medium is the stimulus basis for the *guidance* of loc mation toward or away from objects. Or, in the terminology of huma space perception, it is the basis for the perception of objects at a distanc

The environment of man is altered, of course, by the fact that th animal has remade the array of surfaces surrounding him over conside able portions of the earth. He has leveled it, paved it, roofed it, an walled it in, with a strong bias for straight edges, plane surfaces, an right-angled corners. Such a civilized environment differs in many re spects but not in principle from the natural environment in which h species evolved.

The social components of the environment. The environment of an animal contains other animals. These are elastic solids, in general, bein constituted of matter in a viscous state, and they move or deform in variety of ways—in short they behave. These movements and deforma

[4] It is sometimes said that present day physics has "reduced" the world t insubstantial particles or fields. Hence the mystery of how we perceive substanti objects is not only profound, it is insoluble. This nonsense is only plausible becaus the physics appropriate for the study of the perception of surfaces remai undeveloped.

ions are of great import for the animal in question. Actually, they do eem to determine his own behavior—sexual, parental, predatory, or scape—which suggests that the movements must be given to him in ptical stimulation. Now, man's environment, as compared to animals', s enormously complicated by an elaboration of behavior beyond those novements and deformations of the body surface that Darwin called 'expressive of the emotions." In man, vocal sounds evolved into speech ounds. More recently, our species began to make tracings on available urfaces, pictures, and then came writing, and finally we have produced he vast gamut of artificial stimulus sources which we use to interact with ne another—images, models, photographs, music, signs, symbols, and he "media of communication" [13].

These are stimulus objects and events of a special character. The tudy of perception should end with them, not begin with them. Here he involvement of learning with perception is more complex and here he perceptual process merges with reasoning and abstract thinking. Vhether perception is nevertheless a function of stimulation in this ealm, and in what sense it might be a function of stimulation, we shall ot now consider.

The nature of stimulation. At the outset the term *stimulation* was lefined as the kinds and variables of physical energies in the environment o which the sense organs of the individual will respond. Since the word as been employed loosely in the past, and with different meanings by lifferent users, it would be well to elaborate on this definition, even at he risk of repetition.

1. Stimulation is always energy; it should not be confused with the bject which is the source of energy. This fact has long been obvious or light and sound but it is equally true for touch. The stimulus for ouch is not the solid object but the kinetic energy which deforms the kin—either motion of the object (passive touch) or motion of the xploratory part of the body (active touch). Deformation of the skin pecifies the presence of a solid object, to be sure, but so also does a ertain optical texture in the array of light entering an eye. "Contact" vith environmental objects is no more mysterious in the latter case then t is in the former.

2. Stimulation should not be confused with excitation. Even when sort of circular interaction blurs the line between them the distinction s still useful, for stimulation has reference backward to the environment nd excitation has reference forward to the organism.

3. Stimulation for the *animal* is not the same as stimulation for a *ell.* This has been perhaps the greatest source of confusion. We are nterested in the energy that excites a mosaic of cells, not that which xcites a single cell—variables of adjacent and successive order, not

variables of unchanging amount and frequency at a fixed point on th
receptive surface.

4. It is important to realize that the adjacent order of energy value
has reference to one coordinate system, whereas the adjacent order o
cellular excitations has reference to a different coordinate system. In th
case of a motile exploratory mosaic like the retina or the skin, the orde
of excitation may be shifted or transposed with respect to the order o
stimulation [9, pp. 55ff.]. When the eye scans an object, the order o
stimulation remains unaltered but the order of excitation is different
The fact that this makes little difference for perception and behavio
has seemed very puzzling to sensory physiologists. It may prove to b
intelligible to the perceptual physiologists of the future.

All modes of stimulation, not only the optical, can be analyzed a
pattern and as change. Stimulus energy is always an array and alway
a flow. These aspects of stimulation have been separately acknowledge
(as for example, in the concepts of spatial and temporal gestalten) bu
not considered jointly. *Change* of pattern is also a mode of stimulatio
in all probability. Mathematically this is a transformation, and there ar
quite specific families or dimensions of change of pattern. It might b
that the key to an understanding of auditory, visual, and tactual per
ception is the study of such transformations.

5. The stimulus is not a replica of the object perceived. Neither is i
a representation of the event perceived. It is only necessary for per
ception that the stimulus be specific to the object or event. The fallac
involved has been particularly deceptive in theories of vision. Neithe
in the light projected to an eye nor in the retinal image itself, so-called
are there *copies* of objects. There are, however, *correlates* for them [9, pp
53ff.]. The trouble is the frequent assertion that the retinal image is
picture. The optical stimulus is no more a picture in the eye than th
auditory stimulus is a phonograph record in the ear.

6. The stimulus for vision, especially, has always been difficult t
conceive clearly. Is it the retinal image, or the object? Or is it light
Is it the spots or points of the image, or the rays of light? Why, if w
actually see only light (or color, or the retinal image) do we seem to se
objects? According to the present approach, all these are misconception

The optical stimulus can be analyzed at any of several stages o
levels of abstraction before the excitation of receptors. First, there is th
retinal image itself. More generally there is a pair of retinal images at
dual receptor surface. Second, there is the particular sheaf of light ray
entering an eye in a given location at a given time (or a pair of them
entering two eyes). Third, there is the whole array of focusable ligh
converging to *any* given location in the open air. This may be termed th
optical array, one sector of which is picked up by an eye. Fourth, there i

the optical array projected to a *moving* location in the open air, which is important for animals capable of locomotion. Finally, and most abstractly, there is the total flux of light reflected back and forth in all directions throughout an illuminated environment.

Light and sound do travel freely through a medium like air and can be picked up at any point where an eye or an ear might happen to be. This filling of the medium is the physical basis for visual and auditory "contact" with objects at a distance. The optic array with its capacity for projection in accordance with the laws of perspective geometry depends on the rectilinear propagation of light, and is the physical basis of pattern vision. In many respects this is the most convenient stage at which to analyze the visual stimulus. The retinal image, which is usually taken as *the* stimulus, is simply the last stage before excitation. At this stage, the stimulus has been modified by accommodation, convergence, and the exploratory movements of the eyes. Too much preoccupation with the retinal image as the stimulus makes it easy to forget that it is incidental to the process by which the visual apparatus explores the array of focusable light.

The Theory Applied to Visual Perception

The outline has been presented of what might be called a psychophysical theory of perception joined to a biophysical theory of stimulation. In combination they yield a theory of contact with the environment. This theory will in the long run stand or fall only partly on the resolution of old puzzles and mostly on the generation of new experiments. It has been applied, as yet, only to visual problems [9] and tested only with visual experiments [8, 16, 17, 22, 25, 34]. These problems and experiments are perceptual rather than sensory, in the rejected terminology, in that they aim to account for our impressions of the visual *world*. The visual world is a kind of experience which parallels action rather than analytic introspection. It is characterized by a ground which recedes in distance, by other surfaces which face the observer at various slants, and by edges, gaps, and objects of constant size, shape, and color. The visual world includes the point of view itself as one pole of the experience, and admits of a change of the point of view accompanying locomotion of the observer. These properties of the visual world can be studied by psychophysical experiments which aim to isolate their stimuli. A survey of such experiments will summarize the present state of the evidence for the theory.

The optical array and its stimulus gradients. As already suggested, it is just as legitimate to speak of the texture of the optical array as the texture of the retinal image, and more convenient. The various aspects of pattern can be specified on the retina with some difficulty, on a hypothetical "picture plane" with less difficulty, and in the optical array very simply, since angular coordinates can be employed [21].

The natural optical array for a human environment of illuminated surfaces has to be explored by eye movements and by turning the head, a sector of the array being registered at each fixation. Normally we are not limited to the stimulation provided by a single array to a single point; we have two eyes and pick up two arrays at the same time which converge to two somewhat different points. The pattern of one is a perspective transformation of the other. Normally we are also not limited to the array at a motionless point but obtain stimulation from the continuously transforming array to a *moving* point, as we change our location. We thus sample the family of all possible arrays in the environment by moving about.

Experiments are best performed with an artificial optical array. Since one of 360° is difficult to arrange, we must usually be content with a sheaf of rays of lesser scope. One experiment is to "homogenize" the array, that is, to eliminate all texture or transitions of luminous intensity between regions of relative light and dark. The aperture-screen experiment of Katz, although producing film colors under certain conditions [27], does not afford a homogeneous field of wide angle. The attachment of diffusing plastic hemispheres over the eyes of an observer does so; it renders all light entering the eyes unfocusable. The result for perception is that all surface-ness or thing-quality disappears [17, 25]. Other experiments which systematically differentiate the entering optical array in various ways will be described. There are many methods of producing and controlling texture in such an array other than the common-sense method of putting different objects in front of the eyes of an observer. But the application of such an experimental optics to the problems of perception has only begun.

The stimulus variables for vision must exclusively be found in a textured optical array, supplemented by the transformation relating a simultaneous pair of them, and by the transformations relating a continuous sequence of momentary arrays. This assertion substitutes, for the more familiar one that perception depends on pattern vision, binocular disparity and monocular motion parallax. An important variable of texture is its *density*,[5] but the mean density of an array may not be as important as the *variations* of density from place to place. One proof of

[5] Other important variables are probably *alignment* or *continuity* (as witnessed by vernier acuity) and such related variables as *curvature* or *angularity*. There is regular and irregular *spacing* and the whole realm of similarities and differences among geometrical forms. The mathematics of optical texture (in contrast with the mathematics of crystallography, for instance) remains to be developed. The gestalt laws of organization might have served as a point of departure if they had been conceived in terms of optical geometry instead of neurophysiology.

this comes from simple experiments on optical magnification or minification of an array, which preserve the gradations of density between regions but alter the absolute density of every region. The *gradient* of density remains invariant under a size transformation. It seems to be a stimulus for depth perception. It is presumably for this reason that one may look through a telescope (either end as a matter of fact) and perceive a scene equivalent to that perceived with the naked eye.

In the case of a dual optical array projected from the surfaces of a real environment, the gradient of texture density is accompanied by two additional gradients which coincide with it. There is "multiple concomitant stimulation." One of these is the gradient of successive incongruence of the texture (gradations of motion or displacement). The other is the gradient of simultaneous incongruence of one texture relative to the other (gradations of disparity). In the case of artificial optical arrays these three gradients may be "unlinked," as it were, and controlled separately.

Apparent recession and other spatial properties of phenomenal surfaces. Granting that a surface in perception is produced by retinal images which are textured, the recession or increasing distance of the surface should be produced by the triple gradient defined above. There is psychophysical evidence for this hypothesis [8, 22]. Moreover, the specific distance of any point on the surface would be given by the degree of density, disparity, and motility at that point in the array relative to the whole gradient. The distance from "here to there," in short, is probably produced by the difference with respect to these variables between the image of the nose in the field of view (the visual "here") and the image of the object (which is "there"). It would seem that the stimulus variables for the perception of distance in the visual world have been literally under our nose all the time.

The perceived length of a *stretch* of distance along the ground from "there to there," at whatever distance the stretch may lie, probably depends on the number of transitions or texture elements in the stretch relative to the number in the total range of visible distance. Note that a *ratio* of this sort is invariant for different textures of the ground (grass, pavement, bushes). If the impression of length depends on textural "numerosity" instead of empty "visual angle," this would make possible objective comparisons of such distance stretches at different distances. These comparisons are, in fact, possible, as an experiment by Purdy and Gibson has shown [34]. A stretch of grass can be fractionated with some accuracy. The same reasoning should apply to stretches of "width" along the ground at different distances as to stretches of "depth," that is, to the frontal as well as the longitudinal dimension of a receding surface. The surface does in fact possess a phenomenally constant scale or, in other words, constancy of size along both dimensions. This is believed to be the underlying fact which accounts for the size constancy of objects, as will appear later.

The property of the "optical slant" of a delimited surface such as the face of an object, that is, its apparent departure from the frontal plane or its apparent angle to the line of sight, should be given by the degree of "one-way compression" of the texture (the ratio of vertical to horizontal density) along with concomitant degrees of skew of the texture as regards both disparity and motility [9, p. 173]. This implies that constancy of shape of the elements or structure of the texture is a necessary corollary of slant-perception. The direction in which a surface slants or recedes is given by the direction in which the density of its texture increases and in which the supplementary gradients run.

The phenomenal edges of surfaces and objects. An edge in the visual world seems to be characterized by an *abrupt* increase in distance as compared to the *gradual* increase in distance of a receding surface. The quality of depth at an edge should depend on a stepwise discontinuity in the gradients; the amount of depth should depend on the degree of increasing density, disparity, and motility of the texture at the step. Exploratory experiments suggest that they do.

A visual edge should be distinguished from a visual margin. The latter is given by a simple discontinuity of luminous intensity in the optic array, and it does not induce any clear depth impression. An edge is what makes the surface of an object appear in front of the surface of the ground or background. A *closed* visual edge is what characterizes a visual object. This reminds one of the figure-ground phenomenon which was emphasized by gestalt theory. But an edge with depth may also surround a hole or a window, a gap or an interspace. In this case, the surface inside the edge appears *behind* the surface outside the edge, not in front of it. Such a phenomenon has what could only be called a "frontground"; it might be called the "ground-on-figure" phenomenon. The conclusion of gestalt theorists, therefore, that a textureless closed contour necessarily yields a figure-on-ground experience is incorrect. The inference that the difference between figure and ground is a "field phenomenon" is dubious, therefore, and the hypothesis that a form constitutes the prototype of all visual perception is equally dubious.

It might be suggested that the gestalt theorists could not wholly rid themselves of the old doctrine that two-dimensional form is primitive and sensory whereas three-dimensional depth is secondary and perceptual. If, on the contrary, depth is given in stimulation, it need not be derived from sensory organization. The figure-ground phenomenon was established by studies of the perceptions induced by tracings on paper. This is not the way to go about studying the perception of objects; ordinary pictorial stimulation yields only surrogates or ghosts of substantial objects [10]. The seeing of a phenomenal object in the environment involves stimuli for direct impressions of edges and surfaces.

The experimental production of a phenomenal surface. An observer can be made to see a substantial surface where no substantial surface exists by manipulating the array of light to his eyes, that is, by artificially producing the stimulus conditions necessary for the perception. An optical device for this purpose has been constructed [22]. It is called a "pseudo-tunnel," since the perception it induces is that of looking into a long cylindrical space or room. It could be called a "place" as distinguished from an "object." Physically, it consists of circular apertures or edges cut in sheets of smooth material hung behind one another, of alternating low and high reflectance, which are uniformly illuminated. The number and frequency of the sheets in the series can be varied. Optically, it yields an array to each eye consisting of either concentric or skewed circular margins, that is, abrupt alternating transitions of intensity. Perceptually, it yields a solid and substantial tunnel when the transitions are sufficiently frequent. As their frequency decreases, the perception becomes less solid or substantial. The walls of the tunnel then lose the quality which Katz, speaking of color, called visual "hardness" or "inpenetrability" [27]. When the transitions are wholly eliminated (by substituting sheets of the *same* reflectance), the experience is that of fog filling the nearest aperture.

The solid phenomenal tunnel appearing when the over-all texture of the array is dense consists of a surface which recedes as one goes from the periphery of the field of view to the center; it slants inward. It appears thus because the density of the array increases from the periphery to the center and because (if both eyes are open and the head is mobile) there is a decreasing crossed disparity and decreasing crossed displacement of the texture from the periphery to the center. When an observer peers into the pseudo-tunnel, the three gradients coincide. The perspective of the light and dark rings is in geometrical agreement with the perspective of binocular parallax and that of head-movement parallax. In these circumstances, the depth and distance of this synthetic visual space is compelling. Two-thirds of the observers report that the walls of the tunnel seem parallel even when asked if they seem to converge, that is, the far diameter appears as large to them as the near diameter [22, p. 8].

Constancy of the size of objects and constancy of the dimensions of spaces. It is generally recognized that the problem of the size constancy of objects in perception is somehow related to the problem of space perception, but the question is, precisely how? This question might be clarified by digressing to consider the physical distinction between *things* and *space*.

We will only consider things of visible magnitude and we will likewise only consider environmental *spaces,* not abstract space as such. Things (like books, students, trees, and cows) are seen in spaces (like rooms, corridors, gardens, and fields). Spaces are determined by their surfaces. So are things. A thing is physically bounded by its surface. A space *is* a surface; at least an environmental space always has a floor or a ground. Things either rest on the ground or come to rest on it. In general, a space is an unbounded surface. A thing usually intercepts a small angle of the optic array; a space fills the whole array. The biggest space we are capable of seeing is the surface of the terrain; we can only imagine the spherical surface of the planet. In the case of the terrain, half the spherical optic array projected to any standpoint comes from the sky. The sky, paradoxically, presents scarcely any stimulation for space perception although it is what psychologists unfortunately have been tempted to call space. The reasons for this temptation are discoverable in the history of scientific thought.

It should now be clear that space perception, of the kind that is related to the size constancy of things, is concerned with environmental spaces. These are chiefly composed of the interfaces between air and other substances in the solid state. It should also be clear that the difference between a thing and a space in our sense of these terms is not absolute. A thing is normally a part of a space, and a space is a collection of more or less adjacent things. A surface itself is a collection of adjacent elements, which look like things on close inspection. A physical thing, therefore, is located in a physical space relative to other adjacent structures. Consequently, a phenomenal thing is located in a phenomenal space relative to adjacent structures in the optical array and relative to the gradients in it.

The investigators of the size constancy of objects in the past have not paid sufficient attention to the spaces in which they set their standard and variable objects. Instead, they have been concerned with the "cues for depth" of the object, assuming that one must have sensations before one can possibly have a perception. In the present theory, size constancy is a matter of discriminating the surface which lies between the observer and the object, together with the edges which separate the object from the surface, and the gradients and steps of stimulation which determine the surface and the edges respectively.

The problem of size constancy can be put this way: why, when we see an object in space, does it not look smaller when observed from a greater distance in proportion as its retinal image gets smaller? The answer is that, when the object is seen as part of its space, the *space* of which it is a part does not look denser (or more compact or smaller) when that part is observed from a greater distance. A portion of space certainly does not look smaller in proportion as the retinal image gets denser. The density is a stimulus for the impression of increasing distance. This is true so long as the observer attends to the space or "world" and is not reminded that he is supposed to have sensations or to see the perspective of the scene. He usually does not notice the perspective of size and density. The perspectives of double imagery and of parallactic motion are even more rarely observed as such, probably because most of us have not been trained to attend to them as we have to ordinary perspective. The theory suggests, then, that with fixed monocular stimulation *the size of an object is given by the size of its projection relative to the size of the elements of texture or structure in the adjacent optical array*. The stimulus for perceived size is a ratio rather than a simple magnitude, that is to say, a higher-order variable of stimulation. Size is perceived relative to the size scale of the place where the object is seen. When phenomenal objects are seen of constant size, it is because the phenomenal space in question is seen as possessing constant dimensions. When it is not so seen, the objects are not seen as of constant size.

An advantage of this theoretical approach is that it can explain the constancy of *shape* of objects with the same hypotheses. It can also account for constancy of *velocity* in the same way. The phenomenal *rigidity* of the world during locomotion (despite the expansion of the visual field ahead) follows from the same line of reasoning [21]. There is even some promise that constancy of *brightness* and *color* will prove to be consistent with a surface theory of space perception. The arguments will not be extended here.

Is visual space noneuclidean? Some investigators of space perception are convinced that phenomenal space does *not* have constant dimensions at its extremities from the observer. This position is adopted in Dr. Blank's paper in the present volume. In its favor the argument can certainly be made that the environmental spaces of human experience are not like the space of an "empty box without sides," having three dimensions extending to infinity. They are not like the abstract space of euclidean-cartesian geometry. It is therefore easy to make the assumption that phenomenal space is noneuclidean as this term is understood by geometers. This assumption sounds very interesting. Luneburg adopted and elaborated it in the effort to establish a noneuclidean metric for binocular visual space [31].

The essence of the position seems to be that perceived space is finite while physical space is infinite.[6] It is based (as the writer understands it) on two supposed facts about space perception, taken to be grounded on experimental results. The first is that perceived distance reaches a limit asymptotically as physical distance increases without limit. The second is that perceived size approaches zero as physical distance increases without limit. Let us consider these facts. It is true, of course, that the visual field [9, chap. 3] has a horizon. For an unlimited textured surface (a plane, for the sake of simplicity) the phenomenal horizon corresponds to the point in the gradient of the optical array where density becomes infinite. This is the "vanishing point" of classical perspective. It is also true that the optic apparatus is limited by an acuity threshold below which any increase of density of the array becomes indiscriminable. But is it a phenomenal fact that the visual *world* has a horizon? Does the naive uncritical experience of trying to make out something in the distance involve seeing the horizon? The writer doubts it, and the reader should look for himself in order to decide the question.

It seems to me that perceived size does not vanish as one looks at objects farther and farther away. To me, perceived distance does not reach a maximum as one looks into the distance. Instead, both size and distance tend to become indefinite or indeterminable, which is a different matter. They do not approach a mathematical limit but a certain phenomenal (or discriminational) state of affairs. Consider by analogy the perception of very small objects. When a letter of an acuity chart becomes too small to read, it is because the separation of its parts has become imperceptible, *not* because the separation has become perceptually zero.

It can be argued, then, that the limits of phenomenal size and distance on which the Luneburg theory is based are not facts at all.

The basic stimulus for the phenomenal size of an object in the classical theories of space perception, including Luneburg's, is taken to be the retinal size of its image, the visual angle. The latter approaches zero as physical distance increases. The basic stimulus for phenomenal size in the present theory is taken to be a *ratio* of magnitudes in the retinal image, as explained above. This ratio does *not* approach zero as physical distance increases but, on the contrary remains constant. The ratio may become indefinite if the magnitudes on which it depends fall below the acuity of the eye, but it does not vanish.

The experience of the point of view in a space. Every perception or judgment in the so-called third dimension involves, as one pole, the impression of the point of view or the "here." A report that the variable

[6] Note the different assumptions made by the Luneburg theory and the present theory. The former asserts that physical (geometrical) space is infinite; the latter asserts that physical (environmental) spaces are finite but unbounded.

object is more distant than the standard is convertible into the report that "I am more distant from the variable object than I am from the standard." The theory of sensory cues neglects this fact. The theory of stimulus gradients, however, finds it implicit in the gradients themselves. The bottom of the visual field is unique with respect to density, disparity, and parallactic motion. The double image of the nose, for instance, is a prominent feature of the lower margin of the field of view. The nose projects as the largest structure in the field (the minimum of density), as the maximum of crossed disparity in the binocular field, and as the maximum of crossed parallactic motion in each monocular field. According to the present theory it should arouse the maximum possible impression of nearness or, what is the same thing, the zero of distance away [9, p. 228]. The conclusion seems to be that not only visual space but also *the location of oneself in that space* is determined by optical stimulation. The experimental alteration of one's location in apparent space is made possible by optically magnifying or minifying the sector of the optic array which enters an eye, as everyone knows who has looked through a telescope. Psychophysical research on this problem is much needed.

The apparent direction of one's gaze line in the environment. The momentary direction in which one is looking, the "posture" of one's eyes, is not very accurately given by eye muscle kinesthesis. The present theory suggests that it *is* given accurately by optical stimulation. The ground at the point of fixation has a quality which has been termed *optical slant.* It is definable as the apparent inclination of the surface to the plane perpendicular to the line of sight [16]. But it is equally definable as the apparent angle at which I am looking at the surface, this being the subjective pole of the same experience. It is given by the slope (i.e., rate of change) of density of texture at the center of the incoming projection, or concomitantly, by the degree of one-way compression of the texture at that point. (And, moreover, the density variable is normally confirmed by the other two variables). Thus the direction of the gaze line with respect to the ground is given by optical stimulation, whether or not it is also given by postural stimulation. In short, we are sensitive to the particularity of the particular sample of the total optical array which our eyes at the moment are picking up. Since we do sample the total array by exploratory eye movements and head movements—since we look around—we are able to survey the whole of a new environment in a few seconds, and to orient ourselves in it.

The perception of the whole of an environment, including where the observer is and where things are, is not achieved in a single eye-fixation. It depends on stimulation over time and seemingly on stimulation which *changes* with time. Nevertheless what the observer is responding to is the *properties of stimulation which are invariant over time.* H ordinarily pays no attention to the properties which change with time when he is attending to space. These invariants, or high-order variables are the basis for our perception of the world as boundless, permanent concurrent, and objective [9, pp. 160–162].

The perception of moving objects and of one's own locomotion How we perceive motion in an environment has always been puzzling if, as seemed obvious, we have nothing to go on except simple sensa- tions of color and form. Actually, if successive order is a fact of stim- ulation as well as adjacent order, the phenomenal qualties of motion may find their explanation in the resulting variables of higher order and there will be no need to suppose that motion depends on infer- ence or intellectual processes. It will, however, be necessary to discover how a man discriminates, or comes to discriminate, the higher-order variables.

A great deal of confusion has resulted from the seemingly simple assumption that the stimulus for motion is the motion of a retinal image across the retina. This leads into a theoretical morass when eye-movements have to be taken into account. A really simpler assumption, because more general, is that the stimulus is a *family of continuous transformations* in the optic array to the eye [15, 20]. The array is not only fluid as a whole when the observer changes his position; it also includes changes of parts relative to the whole when external objects move relative to their surroundings. The mathematical types of motions and transformations in this array are in a very neat correspondence with types of physical events, as the writer has pointed out [12]. If the parameters of continuous transformation are chosen as variables of stimulation, a psychophysics of motion perception is practicable. A start on this kind of psychophysics has been made [12, 14, 15, 20, 21, 24, 26].

A fundamental distinction needs to be drawn in such research between the visual perception of objective motion and the visual perception of subjective movement [12]. The former is concerned with the displacements of objects, the latter with the displacements of the observer. Both kinds of perception depend on some sort of motion of the pattern of the optic array to the eye. But there is a difference between the modes of stimulation, considering what we know about environmental optics. When an object moves there is motion of only a figure against a motionless background of the optic array. When the observer moves there is continuous transformation of the optic array as a whole. Presumably two quite different modes of experience depend on these two geometrically different modes of optical stimulation. The experimental work just beginning on these problems should be designed with this difference in mind.

Object motion in a stable visual world. According to accepted theory the "stereokinetic" phenomena, or kinetic depth effects, resulting from continuous transformations of a shadow on a translucent screen [20, 38] are the result of a two-stage process: first the discrimination of bidimensional or "sensory" motions in the field of view and second the organization of these into a tridimensional object moving in depth. According to the present theory, however, the seeing of bidimensional motion is only incidental, not necessary, to the seeing of tridimensional motion. Similarly, it has been argued that the seeing of bidimensional *form* is only incidental, not necessary, to the seeing of tridimensional objects. Just as one need not see a stationary object in perspective before one can see it in depth, so also one need not see the *change* in perspective form—the transformation—before one can see a *moving* object in depth. The several parameters of perspective transformation as defined geometrically are taken to be stimuli for corresponding impressions of rigid motion in depth. Any bidimensional form, whether undergoing continuous transformation in time or continuous *non*transformation in time, tends to yield a "virtual" object in three dimensions. When the form is only a shadow on a screen, to be sure, this object may be any member of a family of objects, and its absolute size or shape is accordingly ambiguous, but it has nevertheless the phenomenal properties of an object rather than a sensation.

Using a point-source shadow-casting device, an experiment has shown that judgments of the degree of change of slant of the virtual object are in good psychophysical correspondence with the length of the transformation sequence [20]. This result is independent of the kind of pattern which carries the transformation. The implication of this experiment is, therefore, that a transformation sequence *as such* is a stimulus variable for perception. The variations of the stimulus yield motion in perception; the invariants of the stimulus yield constancy in perception.

Subjective movement in a stable visual world. Just as one can experimentally produce the impression of a moving virtual object in space by manipulating the light to an eye, so one can produce an artificial impression of locomotion in space by such means, as in a motion picture. The impression may be very compelling if the picture is a panoramic one, that is, if a wide sector of the optic array undergoes transformation. The geometry of this motion perspective has been described [21]. The study of this kind of perception is of considerable practical importance for the problem of designing "simulators" of various locomotor situations—automobile, airplane, helicopter—and for the problem of the control of locomotion in such situations by the visual feedback constituted by the optical transformations.

Nowhere is the inadequacy of the theory of sensory cues betrayed more clearly than in research on these problems. To suppose that a transformation of the visual field is first sensed and then perceived as a cue for depth and for a rigid environment with objects of constant size and shape, and is *also at the same time* first sensed and then interpreted as a cue for the perception of locomotion in that perceived space —this involves the theorist in a hopeless multiplicity of hypotheses. To suppose that a transformation constitutes stimuli for perception, however, clarifies the whole set of problems. One can then assume that the phenomenal rigidity or constancy of surfaces and objects corresponds to the invariant properties of the array over time and that the impression of locomotion corresponds to the variation of the array in time. Both aspects of the total perception, the impression of space and the impression of locomotion, are given by the transformation sequence, but by different geometrical aspects of it. The paradoxical impression of an elastic environment as one moves through it, the so-called sensory impression, is irrelevant. It may be a useful clue to the psychologist interested in the optics of stimulation but it is not a necessary clue for the perceptual process.

The dual perception of objective space and subjective locomotion can probably be considered another instance of the fact that experience generally has both an objective and a subjective pole. A continuous perspective transformation of the optic array can serve as both exteroceptive and proprioceptive stimulation at the same time.

The perception of animate movement. Athough the environment is largely composed of surfaces and objects of physically constant size and shape, some of its components are nonrigid objects—clouds, fire, and, above all, organisms. If the motions of rigid objects are projected in the optic array by what can be termed *perspective* transformations, then the deformations of elastic objects must be projected by *nonperspective* transformations. The movements or actions of animals are given by optical stimulation of this sort. The perceiving of such movements can be said to have animate, expressive, or physiognomic qualities. It is at least a reasonable hypothesis that the visual mechanism is capable of distinguishing between perspective and nonperspective transformations and, in fact, of discriminating many kinds of the latter. From the zigzag dance of the three-spined stickleback [36] to the somewhat subtler facial postures of the human male there seem to be a vast variety of animate movements indicating sexual invitation, and the corresponding females seem to be able to perceive them. Whether the identifying of such courtship stimuli is learned or unlearned is another question; the point is that the perceiving animal responds or comes to respond to optical stimuli of a specific geometrical kind.

Consider the facial expressions and other visible movements of persons, leaving out of account speech and its derivatives. We can and do judge their intentions, motives, emotions, and personalities from such behavior. What we can see is literally deformations of the surfaces of their bodies, the facial surfaces being especially important. This seeing depends on coordered changes in the complex pattern of the optic array. What we see is also, of course, meaningful actions and expressions, but they are nonetheless specified in the optic array. Our ability to communicate by pantomime is proof of the richness and complexity of this sort of stimulation. A motion picture screen can be made to reflect pantomime to the eye of an observer. The light *contains* the pantomime by way of variations and invariants of adjacent and successive order of luminous intensity.

It is by no means impossible to carry out psychophysical experiments on the animate, expressive, and physiognomic qualities of optical motions. The kinds of change which can be used to "animate" motion pictures would provide a good beginning for such research.

The problem of meaning. According to the present theory, the meaning of a visual object as well as the topography of its surface is given in stimulation. An apple looks good to eat as well as merely round because of specific ways in which it reflects light. A smiling face looks benevolent as well as merely elastic because of specific transformations in the pattern of the reflected light. The subtleties which specify edibility or benevolence are there to be discriminated whether the observer perceives them or not. Except for rare cases where the apple is made of wax or the smiling face masks a villain, the child, after repeated encounters, *learns* to perceive edibility or benevolence. Meaning, in this theory, is of two sorts, objective and subjective. In the normal course of learning, the latter tends to approximate the former.

LEARNING TO PERCEIVE

The hypothesis that perception is a function of stimulation is easily confused with the hypothesis that perception is innate, and is accordingly regarded with suspicion for, as nearly everyone agrees, perception is learned. The confusion arises from a terminological difficulty which the reader has already been asked to make allowance for: in this essay the word does *not* mean a learned function as distinguished from the innate function of sensation; instead perception means the general function of achieving contact with the environment. This function, like others, develops both by maturation and learning. The dogged conviction that there are innate, physiological, sensory mechanisms and there are also learned, psychological, perceptual processes is wholly inadequate to the experimental facts. This time-honored belief has been here categorically rejected. Consequently perception can be a function of stimulation, as classical sensation was shown to be a function of stimulation, without necessarily being innate as sensation was taken to be innate.

The main tenet of empiricism is the belief that knowledge of the world comes through the sense organs, not from the mind itself. The other tenet of empiricism, that knowledge of the world comes from past experience rather than from innate ideas, is an additional hypothesis necessitated by the seeming fact of the "unreliability of the senses." The present theory accepts the first tenet, but not the second in the form stated or for the reason given. It is in the main tradition of empiricism, therefore, but it escapes getting involved in the futile round of arguments over the remembered components of perception as against the innate components—the classical controversy between empiricism and nativism.

Perceptual learning is taken to be the activity of achieving and improving contact with the environment—of discovering new properties of the world by discriminating new variables in the stimulus flux. Note that the acquiring of new sensitivities and the maturing of new sensitivities go hand in hand, according to this theory, and both begin with the infant. Note also that the *kind* of learning required by this theory is not the same as that required by other theories. If we deny the existence of any fixed set of sensory mechanisms, the sensory *basis* of perception, then all the formulas for enriching, supplementing, interpreting, categorizing, or organizing this sensory material become irrelevant and are equally denied by implication. Granting the assumption of a rich stimulus flux at receptors, learning becomes a matter of differentiating the input, not enriching it [18]. A whole set of psychological concepts about memory, association, and the effect of past experience on present experience needs reexamination. The notion that experience accumulates, that traces of the past exist in the present, and that present incoming material is assimilated to this body of stored information becomes superfluous for a theory of perception once it is granted that high-order variables of stimulation can themselves specify states of affairs in the external world. What does become necessary is some notion of how the receptive system of the individual becomes *tuned to* the variables of high order.

Perception mediated by symbols. A few pages back evidence was reported that one kind of continuous optical transformation had the meaning of a rigid object, and it was suggested that another kind of optical transformation might have the meaning of a smile. Stimulation arising from objects and events can be meaningful as such. But how about stimulation arising from symbols? The meaning of a word, it might be argued, is surely *not* to be found in its phonemes, if spoken, or its letter forms, if written. The meaning is attached or connected to the stimulus by association. It is a contribution of the organism, and this process of association is the process of learning.[7] According to this argument the essence of learning to understand symbols is that some set of organic processes (ideas, mediating responses, or overt responses, according to the taste of the theorist) must be associated with or conditioned to a receptive process which originally *lacked* meaning.

Contrast this view with a discriminational theory of learning to understand written speech. Deposits of ink on paper reflect a differentially patterned array of light. The variables of linear shape specify letter forms, syllable forms, and word forms, each of which is discriminably different from every other. Learning consists of mutually discriminating them and identifying them. Syllables, words, and sentences are all symbols, of increasingly higher order. A child who has only learned the alphabet can make 26 responses to 26 specific patterns. A child who has learned to *read* can make, say, 5,000 specific word responses to 5,000 specific word forms. The variables which differentiate the higher-order shapes of words are of great complexity, no doubt, but they certainly exist and it is these which the reader must learn to discriminate. (Investigators of the process seem to have concluded that a child does *not* learn to associate separate letters in various combinations, but to identify the total word form. This is probably no more difficult than learning to identify the total form of a human face.) There exist in the optic array from a page of print not only word forms, but phrase forms, sentence forms, and even paragraph forms. *The process of learning to read can legitimately be conceived as one of discriminating and abstracting the variables of stimulation in a pyramiding order.* The feedback from speech and the prior auditory discrimination of phonemes, words, and sentences have not been mentioned above, but these facts do not alter the argument.

Even in the case of symbols, then, it can still be asserted that there are discoverable properties in stimulation to which the meaning of the symbol corresponds. Perception mediated by words would depend on the specificity of some particular inner response to a particular outer stimulus. It would also depend, of course, on the specificity of the sym-

[7] Essentially this argument has been made by Postman in a defense of association theory [33] against the claims of differentiation theory [18]. See also the reply by Gibson and Gibson to Postman's criticism [19].

bol to its referent. But the latter is a different matter—one of usage, convention, or the social habits of a communicating human group.

The human species obtains not only knowledge at first hand, but also a sort of knowledge at second hand. We make signs, signals, symbols, images, and pictures of objects and events not presently stimulating receptors. The perceiver of the substitute stimulus gets a kind of indirect perception of the absent object or event. He can be made to apprehend a state of affairs known only to the speaker, writer, or picturemaker.[8] This kind of apprehension is mediated in a literal sense of that term, a second perceiver being inserted in the chain of causation. For this interpersonal process such terms as signs, cues, and messages are appropriate. But the classical theories have assumed that *all* perception is mediated, the "messages of sense" being signs or symbols of the outer world. It is as if the process of perception occurring between an environment and a man could only be understood in terms of the conveying of information between one man and another. True messages are *coded,* which means, to be exact, that their effect depends on a social agreement or consensus represented by a code book or a dictionary. The so-called messages of sense are not coded in this or any meaning of the term. They are *specific* to objects in mathematical and geometrical ways which need to be understood as such.

The effect of earlier stimulation on the perception induced by later stimulation. In the whole history of psychology it has never become clear just what the "effect of past experience" on perception or behavior is. The conflicting psychologies of learning reflect this uncertainty. Various conceptions, old and new, are being reexamined and reformulated—memory, traces, cumulative traces, association between one stimulus and another, association between stimulus and response, reinforcement of the tendency to make a response in the presence of a stimulus, and so forth. Learning itself has proved impossible to define. It has usually been taken to be a *change* of some sort, in experience or behavior, but what *sort* of change it is has not been agreed upon. The kind of change which we call sensory adaptation or fatigue is usually made an exception on arbitrary grounds; it simply does not fit our intuitive conception of learning. The kind of change which ends in hallucinations or delusions is included under learning by some theorists but not by others.

In the face of this unsatisfactory situation, a fresh start seems to be necessary. A helpful procedure might be to forget all terms like mem-

[8] The special problem of pictorial apprehension as distinguished from symbolic apprehension, and their intermediates, will not be treated here since the writer has discussed it in another place [13]. The pictorial surrogate is said to be specific to its object by *projection;* the verbal surrogate by *convention.*

ory, association, reinforcement, insight, or adjustment and to make an empirical survey and a classification of the known *effects of previous stimulation on the activity induced by subsequent stimulation.* This would be a very large undertaking, far beyond the scope of this essay, if it included all the behavioral activity that has ever been studied. For perceptual activity it is worth trying, and the effort may help to determine how the word "learning" can be applied to perception. What are the effects of earlier stimulation on the perception of later stimulation?

The perception of change, difference, motion, or sequence. In the first place it must be realized that earlier and later stimulation often simply constitute stimulation. The "effect" of the earlier on the perception of the later stimulus is then a misnomer; the supposedly two instances should be regarded as one. Stimulus energy is always a flow as well as an array; it varies in successive order as well as simultaneous order, and the neglected variables of succession are unquestionably stimuli for the sense organ. Some visual receptors respond only to an increase or decrease in luminous energy and not at all to a steady application of it. The auditory mechanism responds to a great variety of transitions. The impression of change or difference is just as simple as the impression of unchange or nondifference and this is true at all levels from the "sensory" to the "cognitive."

Change of stimulus pattern is itself a kind of stimulus pattern. The change does not have to be continuous in time to be perceived as a change; the facts of stroboscopic movement prove that a discontinuous transformation may be the equivalent of a continuous transformation. It is unnecessary to postulate for a motion picture that every earlier frame has a distinct "effect" on the perception of every later frame. Is it necessary to postulate that every sequence of 24 frames has an effect on later sequences? Or every sequence of 2,400 frames? Events are divisible into larger or smaller units, like patterns, but questions such as the above raise the issue of where to place the dividing line between perception and memory. So-called primary or immediate memory is actually a manifestation of perception; apprehension has a certain span for successive unrelated details (e.g., letters or digits) as well as for simultaneous unrelated details. How long past must an experience be in order to qualify as a "past experience"?

The recurrence of the same stimulus event after different intervening stimulus events is the condition for recognition. This can be treated as either a perceptual or a memorial process; the judgment of "same" is common to experiments on both perception and memory.

Perceptual adaptation. The application of unchanging stimulation to the retina, the skin, or the chemical receptors (but not some other receptor systems) has the effect of gradually changing the experience originally aroused by the stimulation toward zero intensity or a neutral quality. A prolonged odor vanishes, a constant warm or cool medium becomes neutral, a fixed pressure weakens, and a hue fades—both the color of a fixated patch of surface and the color of the illumination seen when wearing tinted spectacles. The fact has been known for years under the name of sensory adaptation. What the physiologists did not realize, however, is that the phenomenon consists of a *shift of the correspondence between a dimension of stimulation and a variable of experience*. "Chromatic adaptation," said Troland, "operates so as to shift the hue which is evoked by any stimulus in the direction of the complementary of the adapting stimulus" [37, p. 181]. The significant fact about adaptation is not the weakening, fading, or normalizing of experience as such but the tendency of the persisting stimulus to become that which evokes the less intense or neutral experience. As the writer suggested twenty years ago, "it is as if a persistent condition of the environment tended to become the normal quality of the phenomenal world" [6, p. 242]. The negative afterimage of chromatic adaptation and the negative aftereffect of temperature adaptation, on this theory, are the necessary consequences of the shift in psychophysical correspondence. The coordering or covariation of different stimuli and different qualities is preserved, but each stimulus evokes, for a little time, a systematically altered quality. If what was warm now seems neutral, what was neutral must now seem cold and what was cold must now seem colder. The shift can be diagramed [7, p. 566]. The so-called negative aftereffect represents simply a *readaptation* to the condition of stimulation prevailing before the beginning of the experiment. It is noticeable in temperature and color perception because these are "oppositive" dimensions of experience as distinguished from the "intensitive" dimension of pressure.

The fact of a kind of looseness or "play" in the psychophysical relationship may seem reasonable enough for sense impressions. But the writer's theoretical complacency was jolted many years ago by discovering evidence to suggest that it applied also to perceptions of objects and space. The shape of a fixated edge appeared to change in the course of time. A concavity decreased and a straight edge in that region of the visual field then looked convex [5]. Surprisingly, the same thing happened to the curve or bend if the edge were actively felt by a blindfolded subject. The quality of tilt, a departure from the vertical or horizontal, behaved in the same way as did a departure from the rectilinear; and for a felt edge as well as a seen edge [23]. Was it possible that the negative afterimage of motion, the waterfall illusion, was also to be understood as a phenomenal deceleration in the visual field which

hen made stability look like opposite motion? An experiment con-
irmed the hypothesis of velocity adaptation [6, pp. 235–36]. The nega-
ive aftereffects of curvature, tilt, and motion appeared in the corre-
ponding area of the other eye when only one eye had been stimulated.
f the whole visual field were filled with curved lines, as resulted from
vearing spectacle frames carrying prisms, then the whole rectilinear
visual world looked oppositely curved after a sufficient period of adap-
ation. In this situation, moreover, there were changes in the density of
phenomenal space and in the color fringes on phenomenal edges which
were exact reciprocals of the adaptation to the distortion produced by
the prisms.

In this country the early experiments on perceptual adaptation
have not been followed up, unless one includes the research of Helson on
he *adaptation level* (*q.v.*).[9] Instead, an allied phenomenon, discovered
by Köhler and Wallach [30] and named figural aftereffects, has attracted
the interest of experimenters. These effects are distortions or displacements of phenomenal contours or edges which do not seem to be dimensional in character (Prentice on the systematic psychology of Wolfgang Köhler, pp. 427–455). They depend on prior stimulation but
not adaptation in the sense defined above, that is, they cannot be accounted for as a shift in psychophysical correspondence for a dimension
of perceptual experience. It is unfortunate that figural aftereffects and
negative aftereffects have been confused by experimenters since they
represent two distinct methodological alternatives in the study of perception—whether to take the figure-ground phenomenon as basic, or
to search for mathematical variables with which to analyze visual organization.

At Innsbruck, however, the study of perceptual adaptation has been
carried on for many years by the method of imposing an optical transformation on the pattern of light entering each eye. This research has
been reported by I. Kohler [29]. The optical device is worn for weeks
or even months and the aftereffects persist for days or weeks. Kohler
has demonstrated that a persistent abnormality of optical stimulation
leads in the end to a reduction of the phenomenal abnormality of the
world, and that a return to normal optical stimulation then yields a
new phenomenal abnormality of the world of exactly the opposite sort.
One of the most striking aftereffects, obtained on removing prismatic
spectacles, is a different *amount* of apparent curvature of straight lines
when the eyes are turned to the right than when they are turned to the
left. This requires that the stimulating effect of a retinal image be
different for different eye postures. Yet precisely this situation in reverse was what confronted the eye as it explored the optic array behind

[9] Harry Helson, "Adaptation level theory," pp. 565–621 of this volume.

the prism during the adaptation period. There was more curvature o
one side of the array than the other, and the visual system had becom
habituated to this stimulus, not to the retinal image as such.

Another striking effect obtained in the Innsbruck experiments i
the gradual disappearance of the apparent *deformation* of the world a
the head turns from side to side. It reappears in opposite form whe
the prisms are removed, i.e., the scene stretches in front of one's eye
as if things were made of rubber whenever the head is turned. (Strat
ton reported a similar phenomenon in his original experiment.) The ex
planation must be that if an abnormal optical feedback from hea
movement comes to evoke nondeformation of the world, then the rein
statement of normal optical feedback must evoke an opposite deforma
tion of the world. Or, to put it in another way, if what was sensed a
motion of the world is now sensed as mere kinesthesis of the head, wha
was *formerly* kinesthesis of the head must now seem to be an opposit
motion of the world. The suggestion is that even the classical modalitie
of sense, so-called, will give way to this adaptive process.[10]

All these results fit the formula that adaptation is a shift o
psychophysical correspondence such that a persistent value of stim
ulation tends to be that which evokes a normal quality of percep
tion. The phenomenal norm is analogous to Helson's concept of th
adaptation level (*q.v.*). But the more radical concept of an alter
ation of psychophysical correspondence may not be acceptable t
Helson. This theory is strictly psychophysical or dimensional, wherea
Helson, like Köhler, prefers to believe in a spontaneous process of sen
sory organization.

Note what the formula implies: that a psychophysical correspond
ence between *values* of stimulation and *qualities* or *intensities* of ex
perience is not permanent. There are no fixed pairs or connections be
tween them; the connections are altered by a few minutes' exposur
to special stimulation. But the formula equally implies that there i
permanent correspondence between *differences* in stimulus values an
differences in perceptual qualities or intensities. Only so could the neg
ative aftereffect be explained. The correlation or coordering of stimulu

[10] These reports refer to the Innsbruck experiments employing wedge-prism
(optometrist's trial-prisms) rather than to those employing right-angle prisms o
a mirror arrangement. The former device *transforms* the entering optic array wit
respect to rectilinearity, density, "parallelity," etc.; the latter device *reverses* th
entering optic array along one of its meridians without otherwise deforming it
Adaptation also occurs eventually in the latter experiments, but this change i
the psychophysical correspondence cannot be called a *shift;* it is an actual *inversio*
of the up-down (or right-left) dimension of phenomenal experience relative to th
dimension of proximal stimulation. Both kinds of experiment have been performe
and discussed by Kohler [29].

alues and phenomenal impressions must be preserved if what was ormerly neutral is now negative. The suggestion is that the fundamental kind of psychophysical correspondence is one between differnces of stimulation and differences of experience, not one between timuli and experiences.

Is the shift in correspondence which occurs with adaptation proprly to be called learning? It is certainly at least an effect of earlier timulation on the perception aroused by latter stimulation.

The emergence of new phenomenal qualities as a result of repeated timulation. If we now consider instead of continuous unchanging stimlation *recurrent* or *repeated* instances of stimulation, such as occur vhen an animal returns to the same place or is faced more than once vith the same event, we jump to a new level of perception. The activty of recognition or identification (whatever that may prove to be) egins to operate, and in man, verbal naming occurs.

It might be supposed that new phenomenal properties of a thing deelop with repeated presentations merely, whether or not they are interpersed with other things. Conceivably the bare repetition of the same timulus complex permits the receptive system to pick up new variables n the complex by way of sense organ adjustments, affording an opportunity for new ways of fixating, listening, and touching to develop. Perhaps the organism has a *need* to see clearly, hear distinctly, and feel xactly as Woodworth proposed [39, p. 123], and perhaps this involves a seeking out of the subtleties of stimulation which characterize a paricular thing.

On the other hand it is a reasonable hypothesis that the objects, places, and events of the phenomenal world as a whole get differentiated from one another only as the animal encounters and reencounters he *different* objects, places, and events of the physical world. This akes time. The characteristic properties of anything would emerge in perception, then, only as a result of repetition interspersed with other imilar things. A piece of ice, for example, would begin to have visual neaning when it could be discriminated by sight from all the objects hat are *not* ice (glass, cellophane, crystals, etc.). It would begin to ook cold rather than warm and wet rather than dry because it had been distinguished from things that were warm and dry.

These different hypotheses could be tested by experiment. Do the qualities of a thing emerge from repeated impressions of the same thing or only by contrast with different things? The existing evidence on the perception of unfamiliar objects in laboratory situations [4] seems to avor the latter, but no conclusion is possible since the former has not been studied. However, the importance of *comparison* or *discriminative judgment,* whether in life or in the laboratory, is beyond question. A qualitative dimension is probably a dimension of *differences*, not a dimension of *qualities*, as we saw above.

Improvement in psychophysical discrimination as a result of previous discrimination. If we consider the intricacies of past stimulation as opportunities for comparison and discrimination, we reach a level of perception about which there is a great deal of experimental evidence. Psychophysical experiments which use the same observer over many sessions provide facts about just noticeable events and just noticeable differences between events which depend on previous attempts to notice them. This evidence has been surveyed by Eleanor Gibson [4]. With all kinds of stimuli applied to an observer in a great variety of ways, the general fact is that his judgments improve or his errors decrease. The detection of an event with impoverished stimulation and the acuity for slight differences between events both improve.

In some of these experiments, the observer continued to report the presence or absence of something, or the presence or absence of a difference, without ever "knowing" from the experimenter whether his judgment had been correct or incorrect. His "information" had to come wholly from the experimentally isolated variables of stimulation and their succession, not from words. In other experiments knowledge of results, so-called, was given. This is also stimulation, of course, but of enormously higher order than that of the experiment proper. However little we may understand it, such knowledge has a powerful effect on the rate of improvement of the psychophysical judgments. In some experiments, the accuracy of judgments seemed to improve slowly merely as a result of making judgments, but in others to improve rapidly as a result of "correcting" the judgments against some perception of higher order.

We face another question, then, for which an empirical answer i not yet available: do the just noticeable differences between things become smaller with successive discriminations, or only when efforts t discriminate are apprehended as successes or failures? This questio should not be confused with the often-debated issue of whether the impression of a difference comes first and the response of discriminatio later or the response of discrimination first and the impression of a difference later; that issue is probably insoluble. The question is whethe *either* the confirming of a perception or the reinforcing of an act is essential for the improving of an animal's contact with the world, o whether that process is in some degree spontaneous.

The formation of concepts as a result of previous stimulation; th identification of new objects and the abstracting of new properties. Th complex flow of recurrences, transitions, and interpolations of stimulu energy might seem an impossible basis for conceptual knowledge, whic seems to consist of a fairly stable edifice. The empiricist nevertheless accepts this as his basis. The second part of this essay tried to show how a stable spatial environment could be perceived by sensitivity to certain invariant properties of stimulation. It is possible that a stable *conceptual* environment is apprehended by the discriminating of still more comprehensive invariant properties of stimulation.

Admittedly this suggestion is vague, and only experimental work will show whether it fits the facts of concept formation in the child or the laboratory subject. One thing seems to be clear however. The identifying and classifying of things and events, together with the abstracting of similarities and differences between them and the specific application of symbols to them, is not a constructive process but a discriminative process. Cognition may be far from color vision but not as far apart as they have seemed to some psychologists and not separated by a difference in kind. Sensitivity, psychophysics, perception, and concept formation all have reference to the world around us, however different the level of analysis may be.

Learning: conclusions. The attempted survey of the relations between previous and subsequent stimulation for perception has uncovered more questions than it has answered, and it can hardly be considered complete. But it does suggest lines of investigation to take the place of speculations about the effect of past experience on perception. In the first place, we must study stimulation as *change,* realizing that previous and subsequent stimuli can be treated as a single stimulus. Second, we must study the effect of continuous *nonchange* of stimulation on the perception evoked by it, and especially the effect of persistently abnormal values of stimulation on psychophysical correspondence. Third, we must consider what exactly is to be meant experimentally by a *novel* stimulus and by *recurrence* of stimulation. What are the conditions for recognition, and how do identifying responses for things, places, and events develop? Fourth, what are the conditions for perceiving differences among things, their qualities, and how do we perceive the smaller differences after having perceived the greater differences? Fifth, what is the basis for classifying things and perceiving new abstract properties of them?

According to the present theory there occurs an alteration in the capacity of differences in stimulation to evoke differences in the activity of the organism the longer it has been exposed to the stimulus flux of its environment. An *increase* in this capacity might be taken to define perceptual learning, with the qualification that the increase must occur after the organism has reached physiological maturity. The increase in sensitivity probably continues throughout life. There seems to be an increase in the temporal span of stimulation which can be responded to as a single event or a unitary series of events. Also there seems to be an increase in the grasp of patterns of stimulation of higher order, the *patterns* of stimulus pattern, which will account for highly organized behavior and for the phenomenal differentiation of the world.

COMMENTS ON THE SYSTEM PRESENTED

In summary, this essay suggests a theoretical system having three parts as follows:

1. A biophysical theory of the nature of stimulation. This attempts to trace the chain of specificity between the proximal energy at receptors and the objects of the external environment.
2. A psychophysical theory of the basis of perception. This asserts the specificity of perception to stimulation directly, dispensing with any intervening special process.
3. A discriminational theory of the development of perception. This suggests that improvement in perceiving is a matter of discovering meaningful stimuli instead of being a matter of supplementing meaningless stimuli.

The over-all theory implies a program of experimental research. First, it requires that we isolate and control, with the aid of mathematics and undeveloped branches of physics and ecology, the modes of stimulation on which modes of perception might depend. Second, it requires that we verify these correspondences by psychophysical experiments. Third, it requires that we systematically investigate the effect of previous stimulation on the perception induced by subsequent stimulation, or the effect of practice.

Evidence for the system. A start on this experimental program has been made in the field of vision. A number of published experiments were described or referred to which would never have been designed except for the theory. They are psychophysical experiments, and they suggest that the classical puzzles concerning the perception of space, of form, and of motion can be bypassed if one begins to vary systematically the geometrical and sequential properties of a textured optical array. Some of the experiments indicate how one can induce in an experimental observer synthetic perceptions, as it were, of objects and events. If we can discover the *general* rules of how to do so, we will have discovered at the same time the laws of visual perception.

The theory has not been applied to experiments with auditory, tactual, chemical, or other modes of stimulation, although it has here been formulated in such a way that it could be so applied. It is not intended to be limited to vision.

The scope of the system. The three-part theory advanced does not cover all the problems that are related to perception in general. It has little to say about attention or selective perception, about illusions and errors in perception, about the perception of verbal meanings, or about the role of interoceptive stimulation in perception. But the aim has been to formulate principles which may by extension cover these related problems. The theory is not intended to be a "model," in current terminology.

The facts of selective attention, however little they are understood, are consistent with the assumption that the flowing array of energy surrounding an animal is an inexhaustible reservoir of potential stimuli (see above, under "The generalized hypothesis of psychophysical correspondence"). A theory of selective attention remains to be worked out. It will be related to the theory of discriminational learning. It will include the fact that the span of attention depends on the organization of the items perceived—the "higher-order variables" of stimulation responded to. It will have to take into account the facts of sense-organ adjustments and the neural loops which mediate them, the facts of proprioception and the maintenance of posture, and the facts of central neural processes which are only just beginning to be known.

The problem of illusions and errors in perception also demands a supplementary theory. But this can probably be derived from the assumption about levels of specificity—one level between perception and stimulation and another level between the proximal and the distal stimulus. What is required is a study of the kinds of failure of specificity at both levels.

The problem of the perception of verbal meanings cannot be solved without an additional theory of human communication and, below that, a theory of social interaction. But at the more superficial level of the understanding of phoneme sequences or graphic tracings on an otherwise blank surface, the problem is a perceptual one and the hypotheses of discriminational learning should apply (see under "Learning to Perceive").

The problem of the role of interoceptive stimulation in perception is scarcely touched by the theory and this is a real limitation on its scope. It is not even clear whether interoceptive processes should be called *stimulation*. It seems to be a fact, however, that every perception has a subjective pole as well as an objective one, and that an organism which maintains contact with its environment also mantains sensitivity to its own internal conditions. A physiological theory of somaesthesis and motivation in relation to another remains to be formulated.

It will have been noted that the system presented omits reference to the nervous system. This is because our knowledge of perceptual neurophysiology, as distinguished from sensory neurophysiology, is very scant. The existing speculations about the operation of the nervous system in perception are based on either association theory or gestalt theory. The implication of the present theory is that neural mechanisms can be discovered to explain how the system "tunes in" on the variables of stimulation, at first those of simple order and later those of increasingly higher order.

The background of the system. There are, no doubt, a good many presuppositions of which the writer of this essay is unaware. Of those he can formulate, the following seem to be outstanding. First, he has a conviction that the senses are to be trusted rather than the contrary. Second, he assumes that prediction is possible in psychology, and that the activity of perception is a lawful one. He is not attracted by positivism or probabilism. Third, he supposes that perception, considered as contact with the environment, is a biologically useful function. Fourth, he would like to believe that a theory can be at once concrete or practical on the one hand, and abstract or general on the other. Finally, he has a taste for economy in theorizing along with an ambition for comprehensiveness—the classical aim of parsimony and prediction.

The structure of the system. The bare logic of the theory is extremely simple: there are dependent variables of perception and there are independent variables of stimulation. No intervening variables are presumed. This formula gains a great deal of parsimony and the question, of course, is whether it loses thereby in predictive powers. Do the mathematical properties of the flowing array of stimulus energies really specify all the known properties of the phenomenal world of an observer? The writer ventures to suggest that they do because, time and again, unsuspected properties of stimulation have turned up experimentally which *do* specify previously unexplained properties of the phenomenal world.

A variable of stimulation, it must be remembered, is something with respect to which instances of stimulation differ, and ideally it should be capable of isolation and control. It may be as simple as intensity or as complex as the different parameters of a family of optical transformations, but it should be definable in terms of a physical operation or dimension of variation. A variable of perception is something with respect to which instances of stimulation can be compared by an observer. A psychophysical experiment is successful when the judgments of difference are coordered to the differences in stimulation. It is *not* to be assumed that a series of discrete "stimuli" must be connected to a series of discrete "responses."

The possibilities for measurement in the system. It may well be a ong time before perceptual variables can be scaled with the psycho- hysical precision achieved for the low-order variables of frequency nd intensity. Some of the higher-order stimulus variables have not een assigned physical units. Many do not even have names. Important ariables of optical "form," whatever that is, are not yet even clearly onceived. Fortunately, the situation does not prohibit experimentation. The simple coordering of judgments to stimulus variation can proceed vithout the sophisticated procedures of modern psychophysics. It is robably important for experimenters in this field not to apply such laborate methods to their experiments that they forget the primary urpose of the experiments. A concern for exact measurement in psycho- hysics does not take the place of imagination in setting up an experi- nent. Sensory psychophysics seems to have achieved its precision, in art, by the simple expedient of calling difficult or inelegant experi- nents *perceptual* and casting them into the outer darkness of un- onscious inference.

The explicitness of the system. The labor of a hypothetico-deductive xposition has not been attempted in this theory. There are great dvantages in making axioms explicit and theorems rigorous but there nay also be disadvantages. A theory should be vulnerable, but it hould not be forced into conceptual blind alleys by the demand for xplicit formulation. The invention and definition of terminology hould be a progressive affair, especially if the theory, like this one, nust grope its way in novel directions.

The maturity of the system. The theory offered is immature in the ense that the program of investigations called for has only begun. t is also immature in that its potential scope seems to be wider than the cope of the problems to which it has here been applied.

The research potentiality of the system. The theory has been ex- raordinarily fruitful in suggesting to the author hypotheses for experi- nents and in opening up new ways of experimenting on old problems. The important question is whether it will serve the same function for thers.

The difficulties facing the system. The main difficulty in the way f a forthright expansion of the program of experiments is the lack f familiar mathematical procedures for analysing the variables of rdinal stimulation. Psychologists have thought so long of a stimulus s that which discharges a single receptor that they have neglected o develop such mathematical procedures. Transitions, margins, hanges, onsets, motions, and transformations, not to mention forms, atterns, and textures, have no accepted terminology. The gestalt heorists called our attention to these phenomena but failed to conceive them as stimuli in their own right. It is to be hoped that th mathematical difficulty will appear less formidable to others than does to the author.

The problems of experimental control of the variables of high orde can probably be solved if the conceptual difficulties are overcom Nothing else stands in the way of a genuine psychophysics of perceptio

REFERENCES

1. Boring, E. G. Visual perception as invariance. *Psychol. Rev.*, 195 **59**, 141–147.

2. Boring, E. G. The Gibsonian visual field. *Psychol. Rev.*, 1952, **59**, 246 247.

3. Brunswik, E. *Perception and the representative design of psychologic experiments.* Berkeley, Calif.: Univer. Calif. Press, 1956.

4. Gibson, Eleanor. Improvement in perceptual judgments as a functio of controlled practice or training. *Psychol. Bull.*, 1953, **50**, 401–431.

5. Gibson, J. J. Adaptation, after-effect, and contrast in the perceptio of curved lines. *J. exp. Psychol.*, 1933, **16**, 1–31.

6. Gibson, J. J. Adaptation with negative after-effect. *Psychol. Rev* 1937, **44**, 222–243.

7. Gibson, J. J. Adaptation, after-effect, and contrast in the perceptio of tilted lines. II. Simultaneous contrast and the areal restriction of the afte effect. *J. exp. Psychol.*, 1937, **20**, 553–569.

8. Gibson, J. J. The perception of visual surfaces. *Amer. J. Psychol* 1950, **63**, 367–384.

9. Gibson, J. J. *The perception of the visual world.* Boston: Houghto Mifflin, 1951.

10. Gibson, J. J. What is a form? *Psychol. Rev.*, 1951, **58**, 403–412.

11. Gibson, J. J. The visual field and the visual world: a reply to Pro fessor Boring. *Psychol. Rev.*, 1952, **59**, 149–151.

12. Gibson, J. J. The visual perception of objective motion and subjec tive movement. *Psychol. Rev.*, 1954, **61**, 304–314.

13. Gibson, J. J. A theory of pictorial perception. *Audio-Visual Com munic. Rev.*, 1954, **1**, 3–23.

14. Gibson, J. J. *Optical motions and transformations as stimuli fo visual perception.* Film, 16 mm, 1955. Available from Psychological Cinem Register, University Park, Pa.

15. Gibson, J. J. Optical motions and transformations as stimuli fo visual perception. *Psychol. Rev.*, 1957, **64**, 288–295.

16. Gibson, J. J., & Cornsweet, J. The perceived slant of visual surface —optical and geographical. *J. exp. Psychol.*, 1952, **44**, 11–15.

17. Gibson, J. J., & Dibble, F. N. Exploratory experiments on the stimu lus conditions for the perception of a visual surface. *J. exp. Psychol.*, 1952 **43**, 414–419.

18. Gibson, J. J., & Gibson, Eleanor. Perceptual learning: differentiation : enrichment? *Psychol. Rev.*, 1955, **62**, 32–41.

19. Gibson, J. J., & Gibson, Eleanor. What is learned in perceptual arning? A reply to Professor Postman. *Psychol. Rev.*, 1955, **62**, 447–450.

20. Gibson, J. J., & Gibson, Eleanor. Continuous perspective transforma-ons and the perception of rigid motion. *J. exp. Psychol.*, 1957, **54**, 129–138.

21. Gibson, J. J., Olum, P., & Rosenblatt, F. Parallax and perspective uring aircraft landings. *Amer. J. Psychol.*, 1955, **68**, 372–385.

22. Gibson, J. J., Purdy, J., & Lawrence, L. A method of controlling imulation for the study of space perception: the optical tunnel. *J. exp. sychol.*, 1955, **50**, 1–14.

23. Gibson, J. J., & Radner, M. Adaptation, after-effect and contrast the perception of tilted lines. I. Quantitative studies. *J. exp. Psychol.*, 937, **20**, 453–467.

24. Gibson, J. J., Smith, O. W., Steinschneider, A., & Johnson, C. The elative accuracy of visual perception of motion with fixation and pursuit. *mer. J. Psychol.*, 1957, **70**, 64–69.

25. Gibson, J. J., & Waddell, D. Homogeneous retinal stimulation and isual perception. *Amer. J. Psychol.*, 1952, **45**, 263–270.

26. Hochberg, J. E., & Smith, O. W. Landing strip markings and the expansion pattern:" I. Program, preliminary analysis, and apparatus. *ercept. mot. Skills*, 1955, **5**, 81–92.

27. Katz, D. *The world of colour.* R. B. MacLeod and C. W. Fox Trans.) London: Routledge & Kegan Paul, Ltd., 1935.

28. Koffka, K. *Principles of Gestalt psychology.* New York: Harcourt race, 1935.

29. Kohler, I. *Über Aufbau und Wandlungen der Wahrnehmungswelt.* ienna: R. M. Rohrer, 1951.

30. Köhler, W., & Wallach, H. Figural after-effects. *Proc. Amer. philos. oc.*, 1944, **88**, 264–357.

31. Luneburg, R. K. *Mathematical analysis of binocular vision.* Prince-on, N.J.: Princeton Univer. Press, 1947.

32. Michotte, A. *La perception de la causalité.* Louvain: Studia Psycho-ogica, 1954.

33. Postman, L. Association theory and perceptual learning. *Psychol. Rev.*, 1955, **62**, 438–446.

34. Purdy, J., & Gibson, Eleanor. A study of distance judgment by the nethod of fractionation. *J. exp. Psychol.*, 1955, **50**, 374–380.

35. Stevens, S. S. (Ed.) *Handbook of experimental psychology.* New ork: Wiley, 1951. Chap. 1.

36. Tinbergen, N. *The study of instinct.* Oxford: Oxford Univer. Press, 951.

37. Troland, L. T. *Psychophysiology.* Vol. 2. *Sensation.* New York: Van ostrand, 1930.

38. Wallach, H., & O'Connell, D. N. The kinetic depth effect. *J. exp. sychol.*, 1953, **45**, 205–217.

BRUNSWIK'S PROBABILISTIC FUNCTIONALISM[1]

LEO POSTMAN AND EDWARD C. TOLMAN
University of California

[1] No survey of contemporary points of view can be complete without an ex position of Brunswik's systematic contribution. Brunswik's untimely death pre vented him from participating in this project, as he had planned to do. The presen chapter presents a summary of his work based on his published writings. We hav attempted to represent his views as faithfully as possible, without adding interpre tations or criticisms of our own. Whatever errors and inadequacies are present i this account are clearly ours alone.

INTRODUCTION

In presenting this review of Brunswik's systematic position, we hav not followed explicitly the general discussion outline by which th contributors to this volume have been guided. We have, instead, at tempted to reflect in our presentation the organic development of Bruns wik's thinking and research. Brunswik's systematic contribution represent a productive blend of philosophy of science, historical analysis, experi mental methodology, and a functionalist theory of perception an cognition. This broad spectrum of theoretical efforts comes into focus a an integrated and cohesive systematic approach to psychology. Th systematic unity of his approach emerges most clearly if we retain th basic organization which characterized his published work. This we hav tried to do wherever possible.

The first section of this chapter summarizes Brunswik's views on th methodological foundations of an objective psychology, with specia emphasis on the place of psychology in the movement of unified scienc In this context we shall also consider his historical analysis of conceptua developments in psychology which he firmly believed pointed to th ascendancy of functionalism. The next two sections will outline th core of Brunswik's systematic contribution—the conceptual structure c probabilistic functionalism and the method of representative design. Th empirical research which grew out of these approaches will be reviewe next. Here, we shall try to show how inextricably theory and exper mental methodology were intertwined in Brunswik's thinking. In th final section we shall consider some of the criticisms which have bee directed against probabilistic functionalism and Brunswik's evaluation c these criticisms. In an attempt to coordinate our treatment at lea partially with that of the other chapters, we have built our final summar around the formal discussion topics of this volume.

Two major problems have faced psychology in its struggle fc scientific maturity: the development of an objective methodology an the construction of a conceptual framework appropriate to the complexities and subtleties of the behavior of organisms. Historically, these two requirements have often appeared to be incompatible. It was Brunswik's thesis that they could be reconciled in a psychology which (a) rested upon the methodological foundations of the physical sciences and (b) focused its analysis on the achievements of the organisms in adjusting to the environment.

OBJECTIVE PSYCHOLOGY AND PHYSICALISM

Early in his theoretical development Brunswik had come under the influence of Moritz Schlick and the Vienna circle of logical positivists. This influence is reflected in his insistence that psychology be developed as an operational discipline within the methodological limits of unified science. At the same time he emphasized, however, that the methodological requirements shared by psychology with all the other sciences are strictly circumscribed. All scientific disciplines must adopt objective methods of observation and communication, but unity of science implies neither unity of concepts nor uniformity of laws.

Objectivity. Objectivity may be defined in terms of *intraobserver and interobserver reliability*. There must be consistency among the successive observations of a single individual and also consistency among the observations of different individuals. These requirements are met most successfully by the operations of physical measurement, i.e., by the observations of coincidences of points in space-time [31, 58]. Thus, pointer readings have become the basic protocol operations of objective physical measurement. The reliability of pointer readings is well established in experimental practice. Psychologically, point coincidences reflect a unique form of discrimination. Coincidence of points represents an equivalence in *all* respects at the same time. Thus, the judgment can be recorded in "Yes" or "No" form, without reference to any sensory or introspective qualities.[2] In this respect an *operational positivism* based upon the procedures of physical measurement differs radically from the *experiential positivism* in the tradition of Mach which regards sensation as the common basis for the statements of psychology and physics.

Observational reliability decreases as we move from pointer readings to sensory qualities and to the perception of things. This fact is of critical importance for maintaining the distinction between experiential positivism and operational positivism. The distinction should not be

[2] It has also been suggested that judgments of inequality rather than of coincidence provide the highest degree of objectivity in observation [29]. Stevens's emphasis on discriminatory response as the psychological basis of measurement represents a similar position [59].

blurred by the shifts in the doctrine of experiential positivism wit
respect to the immediate givens upon which knowledge is based. Th
punctiform sensations of Mach were discredited by the failure of intro
spectionism and were replaced by Russell's "perspectives" and "aspects'
of things [57], and more recently, by Carnap's "thing-language" [28
and Neurath's "language of daily life" [54]. Thing-language appears t
meet the requirements of objectivity because of the phenomena of per
ceptual constancy: the perceived properties of objects tend to be a con
stant function of the physical (measured) characteristics of the object
rather than of proximal stimulation. Thus, it seemed possible to conside
thing-language as equivalent to physical language. The equivalence i
only approximate and fallible, however, and cannot be defended in prin
ciple. Perceptual constancy is far from perfect and varies with the condi
tions of observation. The fact that identical stimulus patterns may giv
rise to different perceptions, as in figure-ground reversal, underscores th
distinction between the observations of measurement and thing per
ception. The nonequivalence of the two sets of observations is reflecte
in Carnap's distinction between the "predicates of thing-language" an
"perception terms" [27].

Psychology must insist, therefore, on the conceptual separation o
stimulus and perceptual response. The specification of the stimulus mus
be made by means of the operations of physical measurement (pointe
readings). Perceptual responses may be measured in terms of (1) thei
physiological counterparts, (2) verbal responses, and (3) other behaviora
manifestations. In experimental practice, description of stimuli in term
of thing-language is often adequate. Such descriptions must, however
be regarded as temporary substitutes or expedients. All cases of ambiguit
or disagreement must be resolved by operations of physical measurement

Descriptions of responses are also in the last analysis reducible t
physical measurement. This is obvious in the case of motor responses an
their effects, e.g., written protocol marks or settings of the apparatus i
perceptual matches. It is also possible to use verbal responses withou
sacrificing objective reference or falling back upon introspectionism
Objective reference is maintained as long as words remain anchore
in overt behavior by means of correlations between verbal responses an
other overt responses. Thus, verbal estimates of size may be correlate
with motor adjustments of a variable stimulus in a psychophysical ex
periment or with other motor manipulations.

It is clear that the operations of physical measurement, characterize
as they are by the highest possible degree of intraobserver and inter
observer reliability, provide psychology with the objective basis require
for membership in unified science. The fundamental status of physica
measurement must be recognized by those who are concerned with th

formulation of *operational definitions.* The operations entering into the lefinitions must be in principle reducible to the operations of physical neasurement. For example, introspection must not be permitted to egain a foothold in psychological method under the auspices of opera-ionism (cf. the discussion of response measurement above). Within the ramework of physical measurement, it is essential to recognize and to ormalize the equivalence of certain operations, e.g., the equivalence of lirect measurements of length with the results obtained by triangulation. Equivalence of operations may be established on the basis of empirical correlations among results and need not necessarily rest on formal leductive procedures.

Methodological vs. thematic physicalism. Acceptance of the criteria of objectivity in observation and communication constitutes *methodo-ogical physicalism.* Adherence to methodological physicalism, which Brunswik advocates for psychology, must not carry with it commitment o *thematic physicalism.* Thematic physicalism consists in the uncritical mitation of the (real or alleged) aims and procedures of physics. It was Brunswik's belief that the development of psychological theory and re-earch design has been seriously retarded by the widespread and persistent lominance of thematic physicalism. Thematic physicalism introduced everal explicit and implicit biases into systematic psychology.

Elementarism. An outstanding feature of classical physics is the onceptual analysis of matter into small particles or mass-points. Emula-ion of this aim is represented in the history of psychology by the lementaristic sensationism of the structuralists. The analysis of behavior nto reflexes and conditioned reflexes by the classical behaviorists repre-ents a similar elementarism.

Nomothetic bias. In classical physics, analysis into elements is supple-nented by synthesis of the elements in accordance with strict and uni-ersally valid laws. In psychology, elementarism is likewise supplemented y strict laws of synthesis. Such nomothetic principles are exemplified y the traditional laws of association in structuralism and the laws of onditioning in classical behaviorism.

The nomothetic bias has led to the neglect or rejection of probabilistic eneralizations about behavior. The insistence on strict laws to the ex-lusion of probabilistic relationships reflects a confusion between the nivocality of observation and communication (methodological physi-alism) on the one hand, and the univocality of prediction (thematic hysicalism) on the other. It is essential to recognize that probability laws nay be just as objective and precise as strict laws. Whether one or the ther applies is a question of empirical fact.

Emphasis on reductionist analysis. Closely related to the nomothetic ias is the preoccupation with the specific mechanisms mediating response to stimulation. Analysis of these mechanisms is aimed at the reduction of observed stimulus-response relationships to the laws of more "fundamental" disciplines, i.e., physiology, physics, and chemistry. There is a necessary logical connection between the insistence on strict laws and reductionism. As Mises [52] has pointed out, strict laws of nature must be formulated as differential equations stating the relationship of variables within an infinitesimally small spatio-temporal region. "Macroscopic" laws result from a mathematical integration over space and time. Thus, strict laws can in the long run be attained only through microscopic or reductionist analysis.

Reductionism in psychology cannot be defended as a step toward the unity of science. It has already been pointed out that the unity of science rests upon a common methodology and not upon a common set of laws. The fact that psychological or biological concepts *can* be reduced to physical terms does not justify the a priori conclusion that these disciplines share the same laws [28]. Rather, the compatibility of laws is a matter for empirical investigation.

THE CONCEPTUAL FOCUS OF PSYCHOLOGICAL ANALYSIS

We now turn to the second major issue in the development of psychological theory, viz., the construction of a conceptual framework which can handle the full complexity of behavior without sacrifice of methodological rigor. It was Brunswik's view that the conceptual developments in psychology show a gradual but inevitable convergence toward a functionalist, "achievement-centered" formulation. The place of such a functionalist position can be best understood with the aid of a comparative analysis of psychological systems. The theme of this analysis is provided by the criterion of *regional reference*.

Regional reference. Consider Fig. 1 which represents an organism within its surroundings, as it might be described by an objective observer using the methods of physical measurement. The environment may be regarded as a *causal texture* providing the conditions and supports for the organism's behavior. Such a classification yields a number of *regions* which are represented in Fig. 1. The regions to the left of the organism refer to physical features and events which ordinarily would be treated as antecedent conditions in the analysis of behavior. The regions to the right of the organism represent reactions of the organism and their effects on the environment. The figure brings out the fact that psychological analysis may focus on events of different degrees of remoteness from the organism. The interest may be *central, proximal,* or *distal.* "Central" refers to events within the organism, "proximal" to events at the boundaries of the organism, and "distal" to events with which the organism is not in immediate contact. This scheme shown in Fig. 1 is symmetrical (as indicated by the choice of letters) with respect to the central region. Corresponding letters indicate events of roughly equivalent degrees of remoteness from the organism.

Central and proximal emphases. The historical development of psychological systems is characterized by an increasing degree of distal reference, i.e., extension of description and analysis beyond the segment *a*-O-*A* of Fig. 1.

Classical psychophysics was concerned with the relationship between proximal stimulation (*a*) and sensation (O). The stimulus was measured

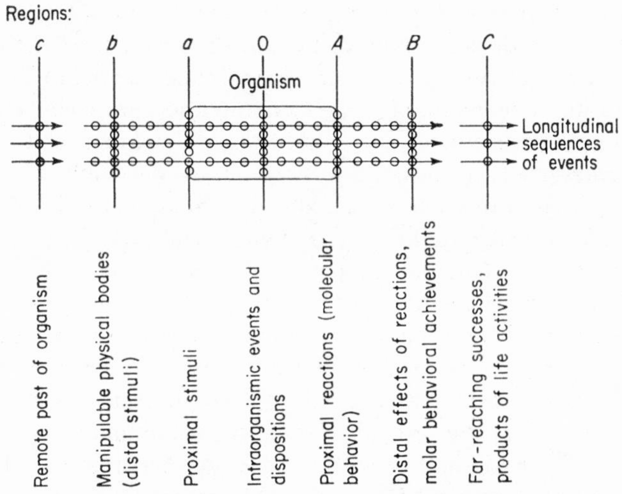

FIG. 1. The regional reference of psychological systems: a classification of variables in terms of their distance from the organism. *From Brunswik* [11].

in terms of its effect on the sense organ. The response was a central state of the organism—conscious content or sensation. The introspective analysis of central states was based on the assumption that there exists a strict one-to-one relationship between verbal statements and inner events.

There were two antithetical departures from the tradition of classical sensationism—gestalt psychology and classical behaviorism—but neither of them extended significantly the regional reference of psychological analysis. In defining the stimulus, gestalt psychology shifted from punctiform excitation to stimulus pattern, and the resulting central state was treated as a response to the total sensory configuration. In its treatment of response, gestalt psychology remained basically introspectionistic. It is true that in gestalt phenomenology the elements of the structuralist were replaced by a self-conscious use of everyday language. The functional analysis remained confined to the *a*-O segment, however, and the assumption of one-to-one correspondence between verbal utterance and conscious experience continued to be made. Thus, classical sensationism and gestalt psychology were alike in their neglect of central-distal relationships (O as a function of *b*). Both equally failed to concern themselves with behavioral achievement (*B*).

Classical behaviorism continued to define the stimulus in proxima terms, but it introduced a radical change in the treatment of response Central mental states were rejected, and "response" was considered synonymous with bodily movement. The focus of description and analysis was on sensorimotor relationships (*a*-*A*), and the central region (O) was essentially bypassed. The analysis did not, however, extend beyond the periphery of the organism either on the stimulus side or on the response side. Sensation was replaced by reflex, but there was concern neither with the distal environment nor with behavioral achievement.

The emergence of distal reference. Two developments must be credited with the extension of psychological analysis to distal variables the study of the perceptual thing-constancies and molar behaviorism. In both these developments the emphasis shifts away from peripheral event to organismic achievement.

In the study of the thing-constancies the stimulus is defined in dista rather than proximal terms; i.e., it is specified in physical units rathe than as an effect on the sensory surface of the subject. The experimenta analysis is aimed at the organism's ability to estimate or "attain" the distal value of the stimulus in spite of variations in proximal stimulation Response is evaluated in terms of achievement. The phenomena o constancy highlight the fact that perceptual achievement is largely in dependent of specific proximal events; i.e., the same achievement can be mediated by different constellations of proximal stimuli. In term of the scheme of Fig. 1, the primary interest is in O as a function of *b* with *a* varying over a wide range of values. Since achievement is in ferred from overt reactions of the organism (*A*), the measurement o constancy is fully compatible with the methodological requirements o behaviorism.

The perceptual constancies show that the organism can maintain a stable perceptual environment in spite of variations in proximal media tion. In its manipulation of the environment, the organism can similarl attain constant effects by means of varying proximal movements. Thi fact finds explicit recognition in Tolman's molar behaviorism [60]. In order to attain a given goal (*B*), the organism must manipulate (*A* the means-objects which enable it to gain access to the goal. In man environments, there are alternative means-objects and hence alternativ anipulations providing access to the same goal. Alternative routes lead o a constant behavioral achievement, just as alternative patterns of roximal mediation may result in a constant perceptual achievement. Thus, molar behaviorism focuses on the relationship between central dis-ositions (O) and distal achievements (*B*), allowing specific manipula-ions (*A*) to vary over a wide range. In accordance with behaviorist nethodology the central dispositions (O) are operationally defined in erms of antecedent conditions (*a*).

The symmetry of the conceptual analysis in constancy research and nolar behaviorism is apparent and was thoroughly explored in a joint ublication by Tolman and Brunswik [61]. In both cases, the analysis ocuses on the achievements of the organism as it deals with the distal eatures of the environment—perceptual attainment of the distal prop-rties of objects or the behavioral achievement of environmental changes. And again in both cases, distal achievement is seen as relatively in-lependent of specific proximal processes of mediation.

PROBABILISTIC FUNCTIONALISM

Emphasis on achievement or "distal focusing" is the central theme f Brunswik's psychology. The elaboration of this theme into a general ystematic position—*probabilistic functionalism*—involves (1) the par-llel analysis of perceptual and behavioral achievement within a unitary onceptual framework, (2) the assessment of the organism's achieve-nents in adjusting to an environment which remains to an important legree unpredictable, and (3) a sustained emphasis on "vicarious func-ioning," i.e., the mediation of perceptual and behavioral achievements y multiple and interchangeable processes.

The lens model. The principles of probabilistic functionalism can be nost clearly understood in terms of the *lens model* presented in Fig 2. This model, which is an elaboration of the general scheme of Fig. 1, ighlights distal achievement and the vicarious functioning of proximal timuli and responses. We shall exhibit the features of the model by first pplying it to the analysis of the perceptual thing-constancies.

The formal features of the model are those of a double convex lens. A bundle of light rays emanating from an initial focus is brought back o convergence at a terminal focus. The initial focus represents a distal timulus, i.e., a measured physical property of an object in the environ-nent. The rays emanating from this initial focus, labeled "process de-ails," represent the energy changes produced by the source. The energy hanges result in a pattern of proximal effects on the sensory surface f the organism. These proximal effects function as *cues* and are repre-ented in the central column (surface of the lens). The presence of the proximal stimuli on the sensory surface of the organism gives rise to a series of processes within the organism (again labeled "process details") which mediate the final perceptual response. The perceptual response, which constitutes the achievement of the organism with respect to the distal stimulus, is represented as the terminal focus.

This analysis brings to the fore three distinct functional relationships, viz., those between (1) distal variable and proximal effects, (2) proximal effects and perceptual response, and (3) distal variable and perceptual response. Examination of these relationships will serve to bring out the essential uncertainty of causal linkages in the environment and the probabilistic nature of psychological laws.

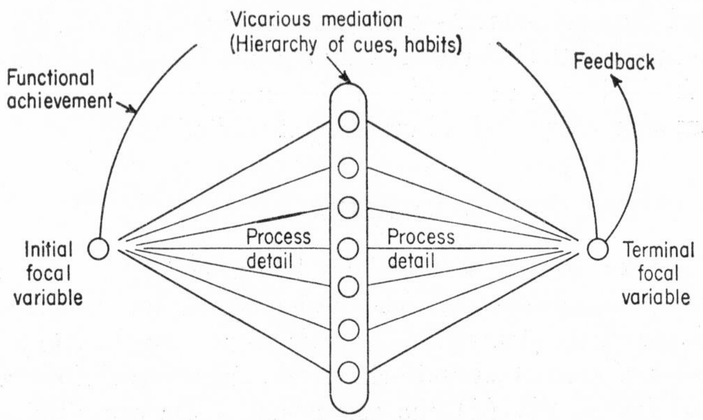

FIG. 2. The lens model: a representation of the functional unit of behavior. *Adapted from Brunswik* [17].

Relationship between distal variable and proximal effects: ecological validity. The presence of a given distal property does not imply a specific, predictable pattern of proximal effects. Consider, for example, the distal variable of distance from the eye. It is conventional to list a series of proximal "distance cues," including retinal disparity, convergence, accommodation, linear perspective, and other visual cues. None of these proximal variables can be regarded as *the* cue to distance. In any given instance, some of these may be present whereas others may not.

By the same token, it is not possible with certainty to infer the nature of the distal variable from a specific pattern of proximal stimulation. Retinal disparity is usually the result of differences in depth but can be produced under artificial laboratory conditions by two flat pictures presented in a stereoscope. The trapezoidal shape of the retinal image which functions as a cue to depth is, indeed, often produced by a rectangular object tilted in the third dimension. It may well be produced, however, by an actual trapezoid form in the frontal plane. There is uncertainty, then, in (1) predicting proximal effects from distal causes and (2) inferring distal causes from proximal effects.

Some proximal cues are much more likely than others to vary systematically as a function of distal stimulus changes. The degree of covariation between a proximal cue and a distal property defines the *ecological validity* of the proximal cue with respect to that property. Variations in ecological validity may again be illustrated in terms of proximal cues to distance. Retinal disparity tends to be in close correspondence with distance and thus has high ecological validity as a cue to distance. Perspective, on the other hand, has already been shown to have an ambiguous relation to distance and hence has lower ecological validity than does retinal disparity. Since the ecological validities are less than perfect, the relationship between the distal variable and its proximal mediators is one of "probable partial causes and probable partial effects" [56].

Relationship between proximal effects and perceptual response: the utilization of cues. In adjusting to distal events, the organism utilizes whatever proximal cues are available to it. Confronted with cues of limited validity, the organism is forced to adopt a "probabilistic strategy," i.e., to combine and weight proximal cues so as to make the most likely inference about the distal object. The best the organism can do is to make, as Reichenbach put it, a posit or wager [56]. In making its "bets," the organism can use different proximal cues and combinations of cues interchangeably. Since the pattern of cues produced by a given distal object is variable, flexibility in the utilization of cues is essential to adjustment.

As we have seen, proximal cues vary with respect to ecological validity; i.e., they are more or less likely to be regularly associated with particular distal events. For maximal effectiveness in adjustment, different cues should be weighted by the organism in accordance with their validity. To determine whether such is, indeed, the case we must (1) make an independent determination of the ecological validities of different proximal cues, and (2) ascertain the weight given to these cues by the organism.

Relationship between distal variable and perceptual response: functional validity. We now turn to the relationship between the two focal variables, viz., distal variable and perceptual response. This relationship measures the degree of the organism's perceptual achievement. To the extent that the organism is successful, the distal variable may be called "functionally attained." To determine the degree of attainment, we can correlate distal (physical) value with perceptual response. This correlation measures the *functional validity* of the perceptual response.

As the perceptual thing-constancies demonstrate, functional validity is normally high though by no means perfect.

The fact that perceptual attainment falls short of perfection is an inevitable consequence of the environmental uncertainties with which the organism must cope. Since the association between distal and proximal events is probable rather than certain, foolproof perceptual achievement is *in principle* impossible for an organism that must depend on proximal cues. The manner in which a fallible organism utilizes the available cues may result in further interference with perceptual achievement. The major source of error in perceptual achievement lies, however, in undependable object-cue relationships rather than in the organism's utilization of cues.

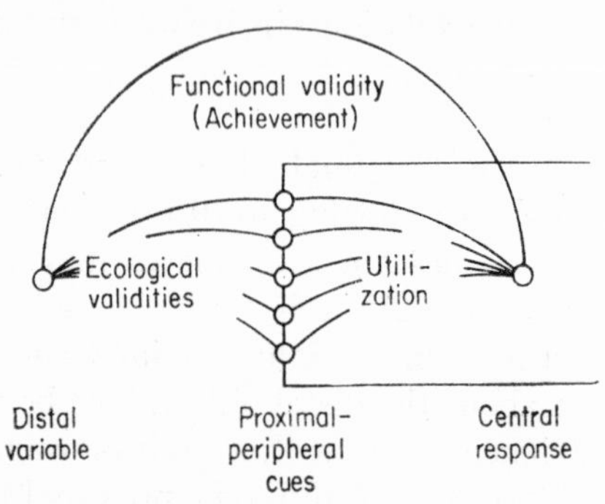

FIG. 3. Application of the lens model to perceptual constancy. *From Brunswik* [19].

The analysis of perceptual achievement in terms of the lens model is summarized in Fig. 3. Here the general classes of variables and relationships of Fig. 2 have been specified for the particular case of perceptual constancy. Note by way of summary that the relationship between distal variable and proximal cues measures ecological validity and that the correlation between proximal cues and perceptual (central) response represents utilization of the cues. The relationship between distal variable and perceptual response represents the functional validity of the response, i.e., the degree of achievement with respect to the distal variable.

Application of the lens model to behavioral achievement. The analysis represented by the lens model applies to behavioral as well as to perceptual achievement. Return to Fig. 2. Let the initial focus stand for a condition of the organism, e.g., state of food deprivation. This condition activates a family of habits. The hierarchy of habits associated with the condition of hunger is formally analogous to the pattern of proximal stimuli in the case of perception. Confronted with a particular environmental situation, the organism may perform or "utilize" one or the other, or a combination, of these habits in order to achieve the end state of hunger reduction. This end state is represented by the terminal focus in the lens model. A series of such behavioral units may precede the attainment of the end state. As the arrow labeled "feedback" indicates, the consequences of past acts may influence the nature of the subsequent units of behavior.

Uncertainty of causal linkages obtains in molar behavior, just as it does in perception. No single habit or group of habits is uniformly associated with the initial condition of hunger. The correlation of means and ends equally falls short of perfection. There is a probable rather than an invariant relationship between any specific bodily action and the achievement of the end state. When a particular action is unsuccessful in achieving the end state, the organism will shift to an alternative one and continue to do so until the end state is achieved. Just as proximal cues are weighted and utilized according to their "assumed" probabilities, so alternative actions are performed according to "expected" probabilities of success.

The emphasis on the use of alternative means in the achievement of an end is closely related to Tolman's definition of purpose as persistence and docility of behavior with respect to some end [60]. A description of behavior as purposive in Tolman's sense is thoroughly consistent with Brunswik's pervasive interest in the adaptive properties of behavior.

The application of the lens model to behavioral achievement is as yet fragmentary and lacks the specificity of the analysis of perceptual achievement.[3] In illustrating the potential applicability of the model, we have chosen as the "focal variables" an initial condition of deprivation and the end state of need-reduction. The relationship between these variables was treated independently of the specific physical situation, and the analysis bypassed the interaction between perceptual and behavioral achievement. This latter interaction would have to receive extensive attention in the further development of probabilistic functionalism.

REPRESENTATIVE DESIGN AND PROBABILISTIC THEORY

The theoretical orientation of probabilistic functionalism has far-reaching implications for psychological methodology. The analysis of

[3] In his most recent work Brunswik became increasingly concerned with the application of his systematic position to molar behavior as well as to perception. See especially [19].

organismic achievement cannot be pursued within the confines of experiments which are based on the rigorous control and isolation of variables. At the sacrifice of experimental control, organismic achievement must be studied in situations representative of the natural habitat of the subject. Thus, *systematic design,* which has been modeled after the procedures of physics, must be replaced by *representative design.* And the general laws tested in classical experiments must be superseded by statistical generalizations. The argument for a change in methodology proceeds from a critique of systematic designs to a positive program for representative design.

Analysis of systematic experimental designs. Experimental designs may be evaluated with respect to the following criteria: (*a*) choice of variables, (*b*) manner of variation of the variables chosen, and (*c*) manner of covariation of the variables chosen. In practice, these characteristics of experimental designs are, of course, not independent. Rather, they supplement each other as expressions of a general philosophy of design.

Choice of variables. The crucial decision here concerns the number of variables chosen for investigation in a given design. The classical ideal was the "rule of one variable." One variable was to be considered at a time, with all other variables either held constant or assumed to be irrelevant. With the introduction of analysis of variance there has been a trend toward multivariate design. The number of variables included in any one systematic design has, however, remained small both for practical reasons and because of the difficulties in interpreting higher-order interactions.

The choice of variables also involves decisions with respect to regional reference (in the sense of Fig. 1). As we have seen, there has been a long history of preoccupation with central and proximal events. Interest in distal variables is of more recent origin. The study of distal variables calls for multivariate designs since distal achievement usually depends on a multiplicity of factors rather than upon a single factor.

Manner of variation of the variables chosen. In a typical systematic experiment the values of the variable or variables fall within a restricted range. Within this range, the values are usually spaced in even, discrete steps, e.g., a set of weights or sizes differing from each other by equal amounts. Values of other variables which are recognized as potential determinants of the response under investigation are either held constant at some finite value or reduced to zero.

Manner of covariation of the variables chosen. Experimental control determines not only the manner of variation of each individual variable but also the nature of covariation among the variables. Within the limits of systematic design three methods of controlling covariation nay be distinguished: (1) *artificial tying* of variables, (2) *artificial 'nterlocking* of variables, and (3) *artificial untying* of variables.

1. An illustration of *artificially tied* variables is provided by a classi-:al psychophysical experiment—the measurement of length discrimina-ion on the Galton bar. A standard length and a comparison length are :xposed side by side, and the subject is required to adjust the two 'engths to equality. In this arrangement the distal variable of physical ;ize and the proximal variable of retinal size are artificially tied, and it)ecomes impossible to determine the extent to which the judgments (achievements) of the subject are related to each of these two variables. Physical size and retinal size are tied together because a third variable, viz., the difference in distance between standard and comparison stim-ılus, has been held constant at zero. Thus, it becomes apparent that :he holding constant of one variable may have important effects on the :ovariation among other variables.

With distal and proximal variables artificially tied, the Galton bar :xperiment yields little information about the factors governing the liscrimination of length. In fact, the experimental situation closely ap-proaches the conditions of physical measurement. The only difference is that in the experiment the lines are put side by side, whereas in neasurement proper they would be superimposed. Under highly con-trolled conditions (maximal tying of variables) psychophysics and measurement tend to become indistinguishable.

2. *The artificial interlocking of variables* may again be illustrated with a reference to the perception of length. Suppose that the stand-ard and comparison lengths are not exposed side by side but at different distances. This arrangement is typical of constancy experi-ments. The variables of physical and retinal size have now been sep-arated and their relative weight in determining perceptual discrimina-tion can be assessed. Equality of retinal sizes now requires inequality of physical sizes; conversely, equality of physical sizes now entails in-equality of retinal sizes. Note, however, that this arrangement imposes drastic restrictions on the possible range of covariation of physical and retinal sizes. As long as the distance between the two lengths remains constant, any given setting of the comparison stimulus can produce only *one* value of retinal size. Thus, the restriction on the range of covariation of distal and proximal size results from the holding constant of a third variable, viz., distance at some arbitrary value. The range of covariation can be extended to the fullest possible extent only by allow-ing distance to vary freely. When covariation is present but is restricted in range, we speak of the artificial interlocking of variables.

From the point of view of functional analysis the exposure of the standard and comparison lengths at different distances makes it possible to "confront" distal size and retinal size as determinants of perceptual discrimination. The subject's responses can now show relative invariance with respect to the one or the other. To the extent that constancy obtains, judgments will be found to be an invariant function of physical rather than retinal size. When two alternative determinants of behavior are thus pitted against each other, the experimental design is designated as *diacritical*. Diacritical design is, of course, a special case of systematic design.

The use of diacritical design for disentangling tied variables may be illustrated further by an example from molar behavior. According to Holt, the movements of an individual should be defined in terms of "that object, situation, process . . . of which his behavior is a constant function. . . . So in behavior, the flock of birds is not, with any accuracy, flying over the green field; it is, more essentially, flying southward" [42, pp. 161–166]. This statement asserts a specific hypothesis: the behavior of the birds is a constant function of geographical direction (south) and not of local conditions (green field). By way of analogy to the perceptual case, geographical direction may be considered the counterpart of distal size and local conditions as the counterpart of retinal size. Holt's hypothesis cannot be tested as long as geographical direction and local conditions remain tied variables. Thus, if we move the birds backward along the line of their flight (Position I in Fig. 4) and observe that they persist in their original direction, the only conclusion we may draw is that their behavior is reliable. We still cannot decide whether the direction of flight is a function of geographical direction or local conditions. Testing additional groups of birds ("responder replication") is equally futile; we should be merely getting information about the generality of the behavior in the population. Holt's hypothesis can be tested only by confronting geographical direction and local conditions in a diacritical design, just as distal size and retinal size are confronted in the perceptual constancy experiment. Such a confrontation can be achieved, for example, by starting the birds from a position parallel to the field (Position II in Fig. 4) and observing whether the flight will move southward or toward the green field. Since the two responses are now incompatible, the two variables have been disentangled. As in the perceptual case, however, such an experiment would be characterized by an artificial interlocking of vari-

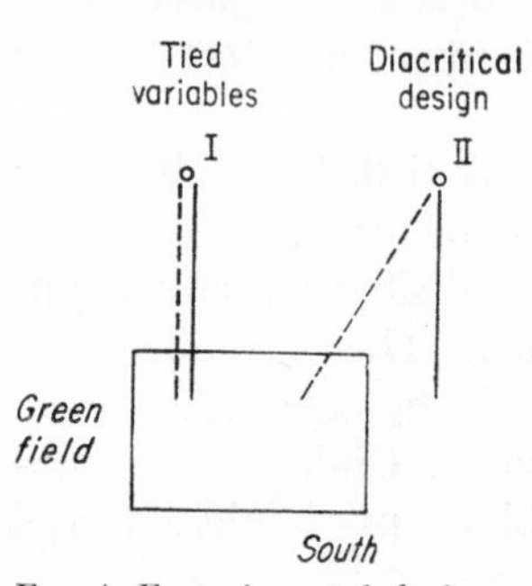

FIG. 4. Experimental designs in the study of behavior constancy. For explanation, see text. *From Brunswik* [19].

ables. By limiting the starting point to Position II we restrict the range of covariation of geographical direction and local conditions.

Although diacritical design makes it possible to pit two variables against one another, it does not lead to the *isolation* of variables in the full sense of the term. In the size-constancy situation, differences in distance are accompanied by differences in surround, brightness, etc. In the test of Holt's hypothesis, geographical direction remains confounded with such factors as temperature, topographical landmarks, magnetic cues, etc.; and the greenness of the field is similarly confounded with such variables as shape and size. By moving from Position I to Position II we have split an aggregate of tied variables into two clusters of tied variables. Strictly speaking, diacritical design is only partially effective in pitting the two critical variables against each other. We cannot conclude with certainty, therefore, that the organism's response is a constant function of either one or the other variable.

3. *Artificial untying of variables* is accomplished when natural covariations among variables are eliminated by means of experimental control. The more fully the investigator succeeds in reducing the correlation among variables to zero, the more closely the design approximates the ideal of the rule of one variable. Manipulation of the independent variable then does not carry with it systematic changes in any other variable.

An example of the artificial untying of variables comes from an experiment on social perception [21, p. 27]. The individuals whose personality traits were to be judged were required to wear identical clothing and to assume identical postures. Thus, attitudes aroused by clothing and posture could not interfere with the judgments of the personality traits. This control was achieved, however, only at the expense of eliminating whatever correlation naturally obtains between clothing habits and muscular tonus on the one hand, and personality traits on the other.

Critique of systematic designs. If psychological research is to center on organismic achievement in a probabilistic environment, the inadequacies of systematic design must by now be apparent. With respect to the *choice of variables,* systematic design must make arbitrary decisions about the nature and number of variables to be included in the design. With respect to the *manner of variation* of the variables chosen, systematic design is typically limited to a few carefully chosen values within a limited range. These values usually are not representative of the range and distribution of values which the organism encounters in its natural habitat. Finally, with respect to the *manner of covariation* of variables, all the procedures discussed (artificial tying, untying, and interlocking) eliminate or restrict covariation and thus render it unrepresentative of the organism's habitat. In short, the formal structure of systematic design and the requirements of representativeness are incompatible.

As the discussion of diacritical designs has shown, systematic design is likely to fail in its aim of *isolating* the variables of which behavior is a constant function. This failure is a consequence of the multiplicity of variables which are potentially relevant to almost any response of the organism. When two variables are diacritically separated (i.e., when the response to one is made incompatible with the response to the other), both variables remain tied to a number of other factors whose contribution cannot be assessed. Complete isolation of a variable as the crucial determinant of response would necessitate the diacritical confrontation of that variable with a large and, indeed, indefinite number of other variables. Such a procedure would not only be unrealistic but, if carried out literally, would serve to obscure the organism's capacities for achievement. Take the determinants of perceived size, for example. The diacritical separation of all possible determinants of size would require us to pit against distal size the very variables which make constancy possible. Thus, distal size would have to be confronted with the indirect cues to size and distance on which the mechanism of constancy must depend. In the study of *achievement* it becomes meaningless to isolate the distal variable from its proximal mediators.

Representative design. Systematic design has failed in its attempt to isolate crucial variables and to find strict laws of behavior. By its very nature, it does not concern itself with partial causes and partial effects and cannot reflect the probabilistic character of psychological laws. Yet, if psychological research is to deal with the essential features of behavior, it must be focused where the organism itself is focused, viz., on adjustment to an uncertain environment.[4] Thus, systematic design must be replaced by *representative design*. The basic aims of representative design are (1) to reflect accurately the probabilistic nature of environmental circumstances, and (2) to exhibit the full measure of the organism's ability to cope with environmental contingencies. These aims are served by the representative sampling of situations from the organism's ecology.

The universe of situations: ecology. An *ecology* may be defined as the natural-cultural habitat of the organism. It constitutes the universe of situations which the organism is likely to encounter in the course of daily living. An ecology is defined independently of the organism's responses; it is an objective description of the stimuli and "behavior sup-

[4] The requirement that psychological description concern itself with the same order of events as does organismic activity represents the principle of *behavior-research isomorphism.*

ports" offered to the organism by the environment. In surveying and measuring the ecology, the independent observer can abstract and specify certain features of the environment. The features selected for description—*ecological variables*—are those deemed relevant to the organism's adjustment and survival. The nourishment value of food, specified regardless of the reactions of organisms, is an example of an ecological variable. Object size and its associated system of proximal cues constitute a set of ecological variables which are of special interest because of their significance for manipulation and orientation.

The representative sampling of situations. A situation encountered within the ecology is formally analogous to an individual in a population of responders. Just as each respondent represents a more or less incidental combination of traits, so each situation may be regarded as a more or less incidental constellation of ecological variables. There is, however, an obvious and important difference between the two kinds of instances. The individual responder must be taken as he is, and we cannot alter the particular constellation of traits which characterizes him. Situational instances, on the other hand, *can* be manipulated and changed, taken apart and created *de novo*. Such active manipulation of situations is the earmark of systematic design. By contrast, representative design rejects interference with environmental situations. Patterns of ecological variables must be left undisturbed and studied as they occur in natural situations. Experimental control is abandoned in favor of representativeness.

"Representative design" thus refers to investigations in which the external ecology of the organism is studied in a sample of situations. It should be clearly distinguished from the representative sampling of subjects in which the traits of a population of organisms are studied in a sample drawn from that population. One of the burdens of the present argument is that psychological research has too long neglected the sampling of situations in favor of the sampling of individuals. It must also be emphasized that representative design does not refer to the sampling of *variables;* when situations are sampled, each instance constitutes a "variate package" which is left undisturbed. When variables are sampled, there are as many universes as there are variables. But there is only one universe of environmental situations; i.e., there is only one ecology for a given organism.

Representative design and statistical analysis. In recognizing the probabilistic nature of the environment and of behavioral laws, psychology necessarily becomes a statistical discipline. The use of statistics is, of course, commonplace in psychology. In the context of functionalist analysis, however, the purposes and methods of statistical analysis are altogether different from what they are in systematic experimentation and in differential psychology.

There have been three major uses of statistical methods in psychology: (1) the error statistics of classical psychophysics, (2) the statistical analysis of uncontrolled variation in systematic experiments, and (3) the measurement of individual differences.

As was pointed out earlier, a highly controlled psychophysical situation such as the Galton bar experiment closely approximates the conditions of physical measurement. Thus, it was no accident that the normal law of error, which had been developed with reference to physical observation, became the basis of psychophysical measurement. As the procedures of psychophysics diverged from those of measurement, e.g. in constancy research, the use of error statistics declined correspondingly. Special indices had to be devised, for example, to measure the degree of perceptual constancy.

Statistics must be used in the evaluation of systematic designs because there are sources of variability beyond the experimenter's control, particularly those which come under the heading of "individual differences." The disturbing influence of individual differences can be partly eliminated by stating general relationships in terms of group averages. As long as the group remains the same, the pattern of individual differences can be treated as a *quasiconstant* parameter, e.g., in comparing the performance of a group before and after an experimental treatment. When more than one group is under investigation, techniques of matching may be used to hold the effects of individual differences constant. Tests of significance are used to evaluate systematic experimental effects against error variance. The important point is that the statistical analysis of systematic experiments seeks to minimize, or to hold constant, differences among individuals subjected to controlled changes in environmental conditions.

By contrast, the typical procedure of differential psychology is to hold the environmental conditions ("test") constant and to concentrate on the analysis of individual differences. Thus, the problem of representativeness arises in connection with mental testing, but the concern is with representative samples of individuals rather than of situations. To the analysis of *variability,* differential psychology adds the analysis of *covariation,* i.e., correlations among traits and performances of individuals. Correlational analysis has, indeed, become the quantitative mainstay of differential psychology, ranging all the way from determinations of test reliability and validity to the factorial analysis of abilities and traits.

Like differential psychology, probabilistic functionalism uses the correlation coefficient as the major tool of statistical analysis. There is, however, an all-important difference between the two approaches. As we move from differential psychology to the functionalist analysis of achievement, *individuals and situations shift places.* The correlations now are (1) between objective characteristics of situations and (2) between objective characteristics and the responses of the organism. In principle, such an analysis can be carried out without replication of subjects; it is "object-centered" rather than "subject-centered." Thus, functionalist analysis uses the formal quantitative techniques of differential psychology but applies them to objects rather than subjects. Unlike systematic experimental psychology, functionalist analysis is not concerned with the statistical control of differences among individuals, although exploration of individual differences in achievement may be of interest.

Correlational analysis of ecological variables and organismic achievements. We shall now summarize the main uses of correlation coefficients in the analysis of environmental features and organismic achievements.

1. Correlation coefficients are used to measure the degree of dependence among environmental events, thus giving intraecological correlations. Of particular interest for the study of perceptual achievement is the degree of association between distal variables and proximal cues; the correlation between distal and proximal value of a stimulus measures the *ecological validity* of the proximal cue. The precise description of ecological conditions depends, of course, on the stability of physical measures of environmental features. The correlation between successive measurements of an environmental stimulus establishes the *ecological reliability* of that stimulus, just as repeated administrations establish the reliability of a test. Such features as the physical size of rigid bodies (except those that are apt to grow or shrink) and the albedos of their surfaces tend to have high ecological reliability. Ecologically reliable features provide the organism with stable points of orientation.

2. The *basic measure of perceptual achievement* is the *correlation* between the distal value and the "attained" value of a stimulus, e.g., the correlation between the physical size and the estimated size of objects. This correlation measures the *functional validity* of the perceptual response. (Corresponding measures of behavioral achievement have not been worked out as yet.) Once the functional validity of an individual's responses has been determined, we may inquire about the reliability of that response. For purposes of measuring *intraindividual observational reliability*, the same individual responds repeatedly to the same sample of situations and the correlations among successive series of responses are determined. If one is interested in the agreement among individuals, one may, of course, obtain responses to the same sample of situations from more than one subject. The correlations

among their responses measure *interindividual observational reliability* This last problem is, however, outside the scope of functionalist analysis proper and is concerned with generalization across individuals rather than situations. It is included here to show that the exploration of individual differences is fully compatible with representative design. At the present time, however, the measurement of the functional validity of responses in a limited number of subjects represents a more urgent and more challenging task than the analysis of individual differences. When research is directed to significant problems of functional achievement, it may well be that individuals will be found to be more homogeneous than the results of many systematic experiments had led us to expect.

A representative design in the study of size constancy. The most complete illustration of representative design and of the statistical procedures associated with it is provided in one of Brunswik's studies of size constancy [15]. A single subject (a woman graduate student) was used. The experimenter accompanied her on her daily rounds and periodically requested her to judge the linear dimensions of the objects at which she happened to be looking at the moment. A total of 93 such judgments were obtained. The objects were sampled at random, and the judgments were in a natural setting, without interference with available depth cues. The subject made judgments under various attitudes, but we shall be concerned with only two of these: (1) the "naive-realistic" attitude directed toward the attainment of bodily size and (2) the "painter's attitude" directed toward the attainment of retinal or photographic size. These two attitudes represent the two major "poles of intention" of perception—the distal and the proximal. Note that there is only one subject but a large sample of situations, reflecting an emphasis on the situational generality of perceptual achievement and a relative indifference to individual differences among subjects.

Ecological validity of size cues. The results of the experiment afford an opportunity to determine the relationship between physical size and one of its major proximal cues, viz., retinal size. Figure 5 shows the degree of covariation between proximal size (P) and bodily size (B) for the objects included in the experimental sample. Both variables are plotted logarithmically, B in terms of millimeters, and P in terms of millimeters at an assumed projection distance of 1 m from the eye. The product-moment correlation between log B and log P is .70 and is an index of the ecological validity of retinal size per se as a cue to physical size. Since the judgments were made at varying distances, this correlation shows that in general large retinal images tend to be associated with large physical objects. Even though the correlation is considerable, it falls far short of accounting for the nearly perfect accuracy of the subject's judgments. Clearly, the judgments are based not only on retinal size but also on distance cues. Independent studies have shown that the common cues to depth have moderate ecological validities lower than that of retinal size. It is clear, then, that no single proximal cue has an ecological validity high enough to account by itself for the subject's achievement. Such achievement must be based on a combination of proximal cues.

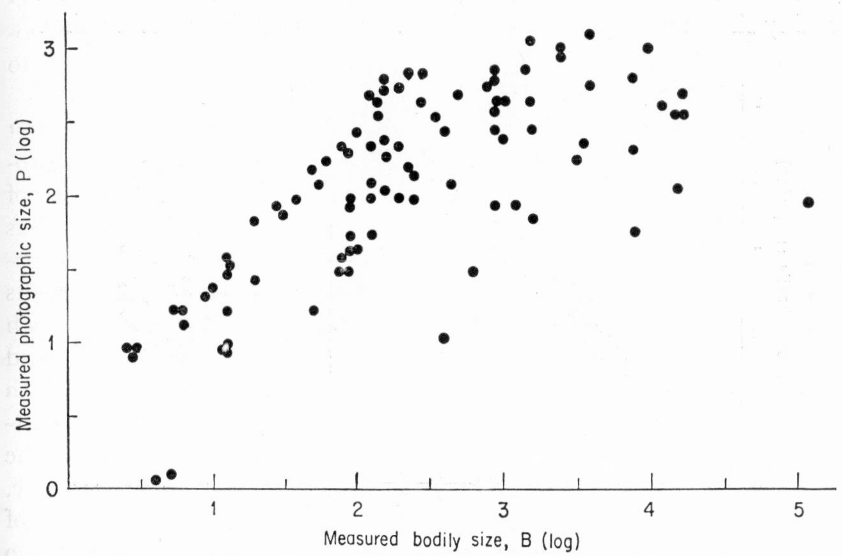

FIG. 5. Photographic (projective) size as a function of bodily size. Data from a representative survey of size constancy in a single subject [15]. *Adapted from Brunswik* [19].

Functional validity of size judgments. The main results of the experiment are presented in Fig. 6. All the judgments plotted in the figure were made with a naive-realistic attitude. The scattergram on the left shows the covariation between bodily size (B) and estimated bodily size (b). Most of the judgments fall close to the diagonal. The correlation coefficient of .99 measures the functional validity of the judgments, which is thus seen to be very high indeed. The high correlation is in part a result of the extremely wide range of values sampled. Some of the individual judgments are far off the mark; occasionally sizes are over- or underestimated by a factor of three or four. Nevertheless, the over-all achievement is quite impressive.

The scattergram on the right-hand side of Fig. 6 shows the covariation between projected or photographic size (P) and estimated bodily size (b). The functional validity of the judgments, as measured by the product-moment correlation, is now reduced to .73; i.e., the judgments correspond much less closely to projective size than they do to bodily size. It is interesting to recall that the correlation between bodily size (B) and projective size (P) is .70. Thus, the correlation between projective size and judged bodily size is only a little higher than would be expected from a system that responded exclusively to bodily size.

The judgments plotted in Fig. 6 were obtained when the subject's attitude was naive-realistic, i.e., when she "intended" to estimate the bodily size as closely as possible. When the subject shifted to a painter's

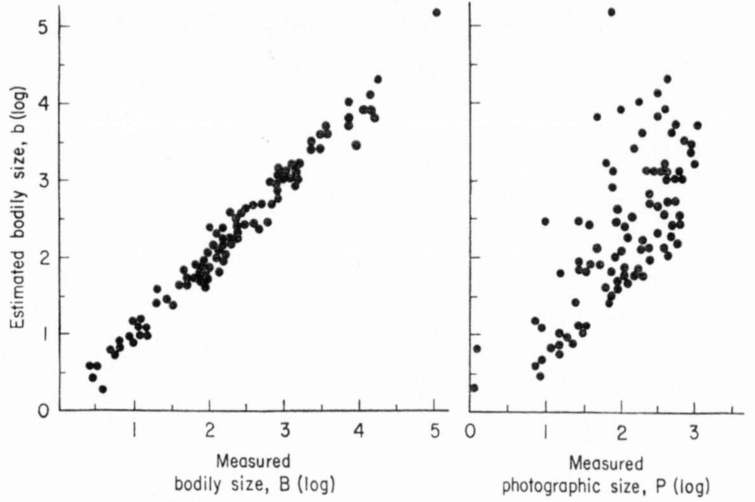

Fig. 6. Estimated size as a function of bodily and photographic size. Data from a representative survey of size constancy in a single subject [15]. *Adapted from Brunswik* [19].

attitude and "intended" to estimate the photographic size, the correlation between projective size (P) and estimated projective size (p) was .85. The achievement with respect to projective size is, therefore, considerably below that for bodily size (.99). Judgments of projective size have lower functional validity than judgments of bodily size.

Perceptual compromise. A detailed analysis of the size judgments made it possible to check on the situational generality of the principle of *perceptual compromise* which had been suggested by laboratory studies of the thing-constancies. In a constancy experiment, the subject's judgments can vary between two extremes—from complete determination by the distal stimulus value (e.g., physical size, albedo) on the one hand, to complete determination by the proximal stimulus value (e.g., retinal size, intensity of reflected light) on the other. In ther words, degree of constancy may vary all the way from 1.00 to).00 [21, p. 21f.]. The degree of constancy is influenced by the subect's attitude. A naive-realistic attitude favors constancy. An analytic ttitude reduces constancy and moves the judgment in the direction of he proximal stimulus. Even a naive-realistic attitude, however, rarely esults in truly perfect constancy. Estimates of distal values are, to ome degree, affected by proximal values; to a considerably greater exent, judgments of proximal values are affected by distal values. If the listal and proximal values be regarded as the alternative "poles of inention" of the perceptual system, the judgments represent a *compronise* between these poles. It is important to note, however, that the ompromises are biased in the direction of constancy. As we have seen, chievement with respect to the distal stimulus exceeds that with respect to the proximal stimulus. The perceptual apparatus is geared to ommerce with the distal environment, and an analytic attitude can nterfere with this general organismic aim only to a limited degree.

The representative study of size constancy includes evidence for the generality of the principle of perceptual compromise. It was found that amount of overestimation varied inversely with the distance from the subject (or, conversely, that amount of underestimation varied directly with the distance from the subject). Objects close to the subject produce relatively large retinal images, and the value of the proximal cue would, therefore, favor overestimation. Similarly, objects far from the subject produce relatively small retinal images and the value of the proximal cue would favor underestimation. The results of the representative survey show that perceptual compromise occurs over a wide range of situations.

Representative design and statistical significance. The results of the experiment were obtained with one subject ($n = 1$) and with one sample of situations ($N = 93$).[5] In evaluating the significance of the results, two distinct sets of problems arise: (1) those related to ecological generality and significance and (2) those related to generalization across subjects.

The perceptual judgments were obtained for a sample of objects chosen at random from the subject's environment. The generality of the results would be increased by replications of the experiment. Such replications would not, however, be carried out with the identical sample of objects. Rather, *ecological replications* would use successive random samples from the same environment. For each of these replications, scattergrams like those shown in Fig. 6 and coefficients of functional validity would be obtained. In the context of representative design,

[5] In his discussions of sampling Brunswik used N to refer to the size of a sample of objects, and n to the number of respondents.

replication refers not to the reproduction of identical external conditions but to the accumulation of successive random samples from a universe of situations.

One may also ask whether the results of the representative study are significant in the sense of yielding relationships which are reliably different from zero. To answer this question, the correlation coefficients measuring ecological and functional validity can be evaluated by conventional tests of significance. Note, however, that the number of cases used in the test of significance is the number of situations (N), and not the number of subjects (n). For all the correlations cited, the null hypothesis can be rejected at a high level of significance.

With only one subject, the results of the experiment cannot be generalized to a population of individuals. Although the ecological generality is high, "responder generality" is nil. As usual, generalization to a population of individuals would depend on the representative sampling of subjects. Each of the subjects would have to be tested in a comparable sample of situations. Some steps in this direction have already been taken. In the present study, the recorder was used as a second subject. The functional validity of his judgments of bodily size was almost identical with that of the subject. Dukes [30] has independently obtained highly similar results in a study using a different sample of situations and a six-year-old boy as subject. These repetitions still do not provide a firm basis for generalization to a population of subjects. As was pointed out, however, problems of situational generality should be assigned a high priority in psychological research, and differences among individuals may turn out to be unexpectedly small in studies of functional achievements.

Statistical isolation of variables. Representative design self-consciously avoids isolation and control of the variables which determine the subject's response. As a result, data such as those shown in Fig. 6 yield no information about the association between any one isolated variable and perceptual response. Whatever isolation of variables becomes necessary for analytic purposes may be achieved, after the fact, by statistical means. For example, partial correlation can be used to hold a given variable constant. Thus, in evaluating the correlation between bodily size (B) and estimated bodily size (b), we can hold the projective size (P) constant by means of partial correlation. This is tantamount to reducing the ecological validity of retinal size to zero. Under these circumstances the functional validity of size judgments remains very high ($r = .98$). Combinations of other cues appear to be sufficient to sustain highly accurate size judgments.

Interpretation of mediating mechanisms. Recently Hilgard [39] suggested that under representative conditions the size estimates may have

een significantly influenced by the subject's *knowledge* about the con-
entional sizes of objects, such as houses, trees, books, etc. If this as-
umption is correct, a blindfolded subject whose estimates were guided
nerely by the names of objects could achieve a high degree of size
onstancy. In an experiment stimulated by Hilgard's suggestion, Bolles
nd Bailey [3] were able to show that such is, indeed, the case. The
onvisual estimates of a sample of sizes were almost as accurate as the
isual estimates of the same sizes. This finding should not, however, be
nterpreted to mean that representative design is vitiated by a failure to
solate the variables relevant to purely perceptual response. Words and
ounds are legitimate cues to perceptual size, just as are visual cues and
actile-kinesthetic cues. Normal perceptual function does not depend on
urely sensory cues alone, and this fact is properly reflected in the
ituations sampled under representative design.

It is interesting to note, however, that in the experiment of Bolles
nd Bailey there was only a moderate correlation between the errors
nade in visual and nonvisual estimates of the same objects. Yet there was
ittle difference in the over-all accuracy of judgments under the two
onditions. The two performances are, therefore, based on systems of
ues which overlap only in part but are equally effective.

Range of application of representative design. The need for repre-
entative sampling of objects and situations is not limited to the area of
perception. Such sampling is required in principle whenever the investigator wishes to generalize his results beyond the specific conditions
of the experiment. Thus, it will be necessary to sample means-end
relationships (habits) in order to understand the conditions of behavioral
achievement, but the specific methods of attack on this problem remain
to be developed.

Urgent problems of representativeness arise in such applied fields as
social psychology, clinical psychology, and mental testing. Whenever
persons function not only as responding subjects but also as stimulus
variables, the necessity for representative sampling becomes immediately
clear. There has been a traditional imbalance between the effort devoted
to the representative sampling of respondents and the casual and inadequate sampling of persons in the role of "objects." The implications
for social perception will be discussed in detail later. In the area of
clinical research, Hammond [37] has pointed out that investigations of
diagnostic techniques have failed to sample adequately the conditions
of administration and the characteristics of examiners. Nevertheless, the
results of such studies have been generalized not only to a population of
respondents (which had, indeed, been sampled more or less adequately)
but also to a universe of situations and examiners which had been
represented by only a few arbitrarily selected instances. These deficiencies

can be remedied by the representative sampling of examiners and methods of administration.

In mental testing, little or no attention has been paid to the use of representative samples of the stimulus patterns used in tests. Frequently the tendency has been to draw on current laboratory experiments in compiling materials for test construction. True, there have been informal efforts to use test materials relevant to "real life," but no explicit attempts to achieve a truly representative coverage of situations. As a result, generalizations from test performance are subject to the same limitations as are the conclusions of systematic laboratory experiments.

The problem of ecological validity and of the utilization of cues arises not only in perception proper but wherever judgments must be made. The utilization of cues in clinical diagnosis is a case in point. Hammond [38] was able to show, for example, that in clinical diagnosis there may be gross discrepancies between the ecological validities of cues and the weights assigned to them by the diagnostician. Valid cues may be ignored or reversed in application, and cues of low validity may be given excessive weights. Here, as in perception, the full exploration of these facts will be made possible only by the use of representative designs.

PROGRAMMATIC RESEARCH AND METHODOLOGICAL DEVELOPMENTS

There was a constant interplay between Brunswik's theoretical development and his experimental research. Probabilistic functionalism and representative design are inextricably interwoven, and there is no sharp line between general theory and methodology in Brunswik's work. Recognition of the intimate association between the conceptual and methodological aspects of Brunswik's position helps us to understand the pattern and direction of his experimental research. Many of the empirical studies carried out by Brunswik and his students were programmatic in the sense that they were designed to focus on a theoretical point or to demonstrate the potentialities of a new method of experimental or quantitative analysis. The content area in which Brunswik's empirical contributions were most continuous and most numerous was that of the perceptual thing-constancies. It is clear by now that the procedures and results of constancy research provided him with a central point of departure for both his functional analysis of behavior and his critical evaluation of experimental method. His interest in social perception was sustained by similar considerations. In his more recent efforts, he showed increasing interest in the application of his general point of view to problems of molar behavior in general, and learning and thinking in particular. In surveying the empirical studies of Brunswik and his associates, we have found four major areas of activity: (1) experiments on the perceptual constancies, with special emphasis on the wide range of distal achievements, (2) studies of social perception, which were of value in exploring problems of representativeness in research design, (3) extension of probabilistic analysis to other functions of the organism, notably learning and thinking, (4) studies of the ecology, i.e., analysis of the environmental patterns to which the organism must adjust.

Analysis of the perceptual thing-constancies. The perceptual thing-constancies bring into bold relief the capacity of the perceptual system for discriminating the distal features of the environment and the equivalence of widely varying patterns of proximal cues in mediating such distal achievement. The experimental studies of constancy carried out by Brunswik and his students were in the main concerned with one of four objectives: (1) determination of constancy under normal environmental conditions, (2) the effect of attitude (intention) on constancy, (3) demonstration of the generality of constancy in the perception of distal properties, and (4) exploration of genetic and learning factors in the development of constancy.

The environmental conditions of constancy. Such classical psychophysical investigations of the constancies as the "alley problem" and the "thread problem" [see 62, p. 475f.] used an experimental technique which may be described as the *successive accumulation of cues.* To determine the crucial determinants of constancy, all but one or a few of the potential cues were eliminated and the degree of constancy measured. Increases in the degree of constancy could then be related to the introduction of additional cues. Starting with a maximally impoverished situation, the experimenter was free to add further cues and to observe their effect. This procedure reflects the investigator's interest in the isolation of the specific cues mediating constancy. Brunswik's concern with perceptual functioning in lifelike situations led him to favor the reverse procedure, i.e., the *successive omission* of cues. Constancy is first measured in a situation in which the subject is not deprived of any of the cues which are available to him under normal conditions. The available cues are then progressively reduced and the resulting changes in constancy are observed. Although the two sets of experimental procedures may overlap, the difference in the definition of the base situation reflects important differences in theoretical orientation.

A study conducted by Holaday [41] under Brunswik's direction illustrates the technique of successive omission in the investigation of size constancy. In the "normal" or base situation cubes were placed at varying distances on the floor of a large auditorium. Under free conditions of viewing, a constancy ratio of .88 was obtained. The procedures used for progressive impoverishment of the situation are summarized in Table 1. Note that a high degree of constancy is maintainec even when some of the major cues such as retinal disparity are elim-inated.[6] The results of the experiment demonstrate the adequacy o greatly impoverished proximal cues in maintaining perceptual constancy The great advantage of the technique of successive omission is that i preserves intact the multiplicity of minimal proximal cues, many of which are unknown, and evaluates the contribution of the major well-establishec cues against this background of subtle but effective mediators of per-ceptual achievement.

TABLE 1. DEGREE OF SIZE CONSTANCY AS A FUNCTION OF AVAILABLE DISTANCE CUES

(Technique of Successive Omission)*

Condition of stimulus exposure	Mean logarithmic constancy ratio	
	Binocular judgment	Monocular judgment
Cubes with most favorable, "normal" conditions of the experiment	.88	.88
Cubes viewed through tubes restricting the visual field	.81	.79
Cubes barely discernible in natural twilight	.78	.74
Dim squares in darkroom, slight head move-ments	.75	.52
Dim squares in darkroom, head on chin rest	.67	.15

* From E. Brunswik, *Perception and the representative design of psychological experiments* Berkeley, Calif.: Univer. California Press, 1956. P. 25. Data taken from B. E. Holaday Die Grössenkonstanz der Sehdinge, *Arch. ges. Psychol.*, 1933, **88,** 419–486.

Brunswik's investigations of the constancy problem showed a gradua shift from systematic designs featuring close to life experimental arrange-ments to representative surveys of objects and situations. A step towarc representativeness was taken in a study in 1940 [13], in which object varying in size were scattered at different distances in a room. Size and distances were uncorrelated, and judgments were made under un-restricted normal conditions. Thus, the arrangement allowed the specifi pattern of proximal cues to vary from object to object. In this study correlation coefficients were first used to measure the functional validit of size judgments. Nevertheless, the procedure still fell short of Brunswik' requirements of representativeness because the general background wa

[6] The technique of successive omission of cues has been used in other moder experiments on perceptual constancy, e.g., in the study of size constancy by Holwa and Boring [43].

fixed, and objects, sizes, and distances were restricted to a limited number of predetermined values. The final step toward representativeness was not taken until 1944 [15] when size judgments were obtained for a random sample of objects and situations encountered in daily life. That is the study which we have discussed in detail in the section on representative design.

Attitude as a determinant of constancy. The degree of constancy depends on the subject's attitude. This fact is of systematic significance because it shows that the organism can be directed towards different kinds of perceptual achievement. For an individual engaged in manipulating environmental objects, the distal value of the stimulus provides the perceptual aim. The closer the perceptual judgment comes to the distal value of the stimulus, the higher is the achievement. For an individual concerned with the projection of the stimulus on the sensory surface, e.g., a painter, the criterion of achievement is the proximal value of the stimulus. The subject's attitude thus represents one of the criteria against which perceptual achievement is to be evaluated. In this sense attitude is essentially synonymous with "pole of intention"; i.e., it designates the perceptual aim toward which the organism is directed at a particular time. The influence of these alternative attitudes or "intentions" on perceptual judgment has already been illustrated under Functional validity of size judgments. It remains here to present a more detailed discussion of the effects of attitudes on perceptual constancy.

The usual experimental procedure was to induce different attitudes by means of verbal instruction and to examine resulting shifts in the distribution of *errors* in perceptual judgment. In a constancy experiment, these errors can be readily evaluated with respect to two criteria—deviation of the judgment from the point of objective bodily (distal) equality and deviation of the judgment from the point of objective retinal (proximal) equality.

An experiment by Klimpfinger [47] on shape constancy may serve as an illustration. The standard stimulus was an ellipse 20 cm high and 30 cm wide, rotated 33.5° about its vertical axis. A series of ellipses in the frontal parallel plane served as comparison stimuli. A horizontal axis of 25 cm defined the point of objective retinal equality. Objective bodily equality was, of course, defined by a horizontal axis of 30 cm. Two attitudes—the naive-realistic and the analytic—were used. All judgments were converted into constancy ratios (the higher the ratio, the closer the judgment is to objective bodily equality). The distributions of constancy ratios obtained under the two instructions are shown in Fig. 7. A composite curve combining the frequencies obtained under the two attitudes is also shown.

Consider the composite curve first. Its bimodality constitutes ob-

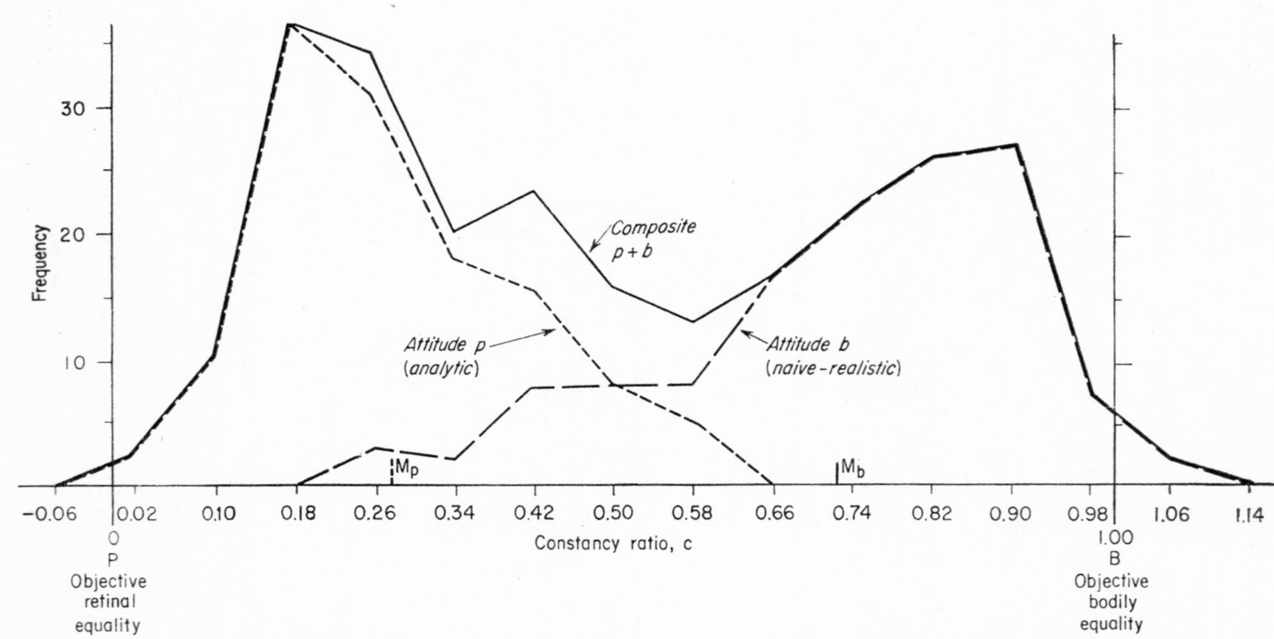

FIG. 7. Distribution of constancy ratios as a function of attitude. *From Brunswik* [21]; *data from a study of shape constancy by Klimpfinger* [47].

:ctive evidence for two distinct kinds of stimulus evaluation or per-
:ptual achievement. This assertion is supported by the shape of the
istribution independently of introspective evidence concerning the at-
tudes adopted by the subjects. The shapes of the component distri-
utions do, however, give some indication about the subjects' interpreta-
on of the instructions. The curve yielded by the naive-realistic judgments
skewed significantly to the left. In fact, some of the constancy ratios
ll at the mode for the analytic condition. This fact suggests that a few
the subjects misunderstood or disregarded the naive-realistic instruc-
ons and considered the analytic attitude as appropriate to the ex-
:riment. The curve obtained with analytic instructions is less skewed
id thus suggests fewer cases of misinterpretation. The point to be em-
hasized is that the subjects' attitudes can be evaluated by analysis of the
stributions of errors without recourse to introspective evidence. We
all return to the problem of attitudes when we discuss the relationship
:tween perception and thinking.

Extension of the constancy problem. In exploring the organism's
pacities for distal achievement, Brunswik and his associates extended
e analysis of constancy beyond the classical trio of size, shape, and
lor. Effective adjustment to the environment requires perceptual
nstancy. Hence, constancy should obtain for a multiplicity of distal
operties with which the organism must deal in its physical and
ltural environment. We shall survey briefly some of the perceptual
mensions to which the traditional constancy design was applied.

1. The formal features of the design dealing with *loudness constancy*
e analogous to those of experiments on size constancy. The distal
mulus variable is the intensity of sound at the source. It is measured
placing a microphone next to the source. The proximal stimulus
riable is the intensity of sound at the ear, measured by the microphone
aced at the position of the observer. As in the case of size constancy,
e distal and proximal variables are "confronted" by placing the source
different distances from the subject. Again analogously to size con-
ancy, two attitudes are possible—a naive-realistic attitude toward the
udness of the sound at the source and an analytic attitude toward the
ipact of the sound at the ear. Proximal cues are clearly not limited
the auditory modality. Visual cues to the distance of the source play
important part in estimates of loudness.

In an extensive study of loudness constancy Mohrmann [53] sampled
fferent types of auditory material as well as different amounts of in-
rmation about the spatial position of the source. The stimuli varied
dely in complexity and meaning (see Fig. 8). Subjects were tested
ider one of three visual conditions: (a) in the dark without any prior
quaintance with the spatial arrangement; (b) blindfolded but free to

view the situation between tests, and (c) with a full view of the situation throughout. Figure 8 shows the degree of loudness constancy as a joint function of type of stimulus, visual conditions, and attitude. As usual the naive-realistic attitude results in considerably higher degrees of constancy than does the analytic (sensorial) attitude. The presence of visual cues favors constancy. There is a tendency for speech and music to yield somewhat higher constancy ratios than are obtained with

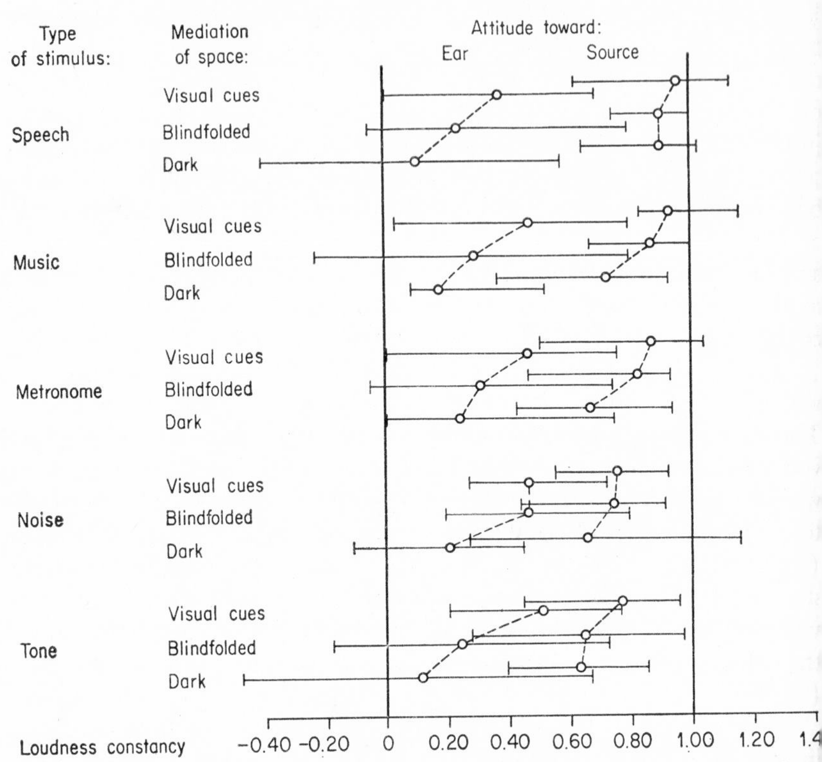

FIG. 8. Loudness constancy with distance variant. *From Brunswik* [21]; *adapted from Mohrmann* [53].

meaningless sounds. The differential effects of the stimuli are, however, largely limited to the realistic attitude. Joint variation in the three sets of variables results in a wide range of constancy ratios. The perceived loudness of speech under unrestricted visual conditions and with a naive-realistic attitude is virtually independent of distance. When tone is presented in the dark and the subject adopts an analytic attitude the degree of constancy is close to zero.

Mohrmann's study has been presented in some detail because it illustrates the application of constancy design to a new modality and brings out the generality of "distal focusing" in perception. The wi range of distal achievements is illustrated further in additional constancy experiments.

2. An experiment carried out by Schreiber under Brunswik's direction [7, p. 161 f.] extended the constancy problem to the tactile-kinesthetic area of *weight, density, volume, and surface.* Balls of different weights were dropped from varying heights onto the hand of the subject; thus, the objects impinged upon the receptors at varying speeds. The subjects made three types of judgments, viz., of weight, speed, and force of impact (kinetic energy). If we regard weight as the distal variable, the experiment may be considered as one on weight constancy with impact variant. There was some degree of weight constancy, although the judgments of speed and energy were actually more accurate than those of weight. This result is understandable in view of the fact that the ball was never allowed to come to rest on the hand. There was, therefore, only a tenuous connection between the proximal conditions of impact and the distal variable of weight. Whatever constancy there was attests to the organism's capacity to respond to subtle proximal cues in discriminating distal properties.

Weight constancy was also studied by Izzet [45] in the situation which has conventionally been used to investigate the size-weight illusion. The standard and comparison objects were of the same shape, but their volumes stood in a ratio of 1:2. The weights of the comparison objects were varied systematically. Two perceptual attitudes were induced, one toward matching weights and the other toward matching density (weight/volume). Thus, there were two distal variables and two constancy problems, viz., weight with volume variant and density with volume variant. There was considerable constancy in both respects, but the constancy ratio for weight (about .8) was higher than that for density (about .5).

There is an important difference between weight constancy with impact variant and weight constancy with volume variant. This difference lies in the nature of the stimulus changes used in testing constancy. When impact is varied, the association between a given weight and a particular impact is merely transitory, just as is the association between a particular physical and retinal size. Volume, on the other hand, is a permanent characteristic of the objects judged. Thus, constancy may be maintained relative to two classes of variants: characteristics which are temporarily and characteristics which are permanently associated with the distal objects. Constancy relative to permanent features of distal objects is further illustrated in the experiment of Stevenson [cf. 7, pp. 152–155] showing volume and surface constancy with the height and width variant.

3. Brunswik's investigations of *perceptual constancy* were not limited

to the physical properties of objects but were extended to culturally defined characteristics such as the monetary *value* of stamps and coins. Constancy in the perception of such attributes is of especial theoretical interest because it is necessarily mediated by acquired cues. Experiments carried out under Brunswik's direction demonstrated value constancy for aggregates of stamps and coins with number and area variant. In a study by Fazil [7, pp. 147–150], for example, the standard stimulus consisted of a group of 40 2½-cent coins. The comparison stimuli consisted of varying numbers of 25-cent coins. Perceptual judgments were made under conditions which prevented explicit counting. When subjects were instructed to equate the standard and comparison stimuli for monetary value, a considerable degree of constancy was shown. On the average, slightly fewer than five 25-cent coins were perceived as equal in value to the standard. The deviation from objective equality (four 25-cent coins) indicates that the judgments were biased in the direction of equalizing number and/or area. Thus, there was a perceptual compromise between value on the one hand and number and area on the other. By the same token, judgments of area and number were biased in the direction of equalizing value. Value constancy for aggregates of stamps was demonstrated by Zuk-Kardos [7, pp. 140–149], and more recently by Ansbacher [1].

The concern in these investigations is with value constancy as a perceptual *achievement* rather than with value as a determinant of perceptual *error*. The theoretical object is, therefore, quite different from that of experiments aimed at the analysis of motivational biases in perception. Within the functionalist framework the emphasis is on positive achievement, i.e., "veridical" perception. It is interesting to recall in this connection that the perceptual disposition known historically as the size-weight *illusion* was reinterpreted as evidence for the perceptual *constancy* of weight and density. Here again there is a shift of emphasis from error to positive perceptual achievement.

The ecological generality of constancy. The exploration of constancies across sense departments and with respect to a variety of distal properties shows that the organism is capable of considerable perceptual achievement in dealing with many different classes of objects in its environment. The series of studies which we have just reviewed was designed to ascertain the pervasiveness of distal achievement in perception, and the results contribute a preliminary "mapping" or "canvassing" of the ecology. That is, they provide us with general information about the range of perceptual achievement. The experiments fall short, however, of the requirement of representativeness, for neither objects nor situations were adequately sampled. Research aimed at "canvassing" the ecology is a preliminary to truly representative surveys.

Developmental and learning factors in constancy. Like other instrumental dispositions, the constancies should reflect the organism's past experiences and be subject to modification by training. In a series of related experiments Brunswik and his associates explored the developmental changes in the three classical constancies—size [2], shape [48], and brightness [4]. The age groups included in the studies ranged from two- or three-year-olds to adults. The developmental trends are shown in Fig. 9. The trends for the three attributes are quite similar. When degree of constancy is plotted as a function of age, the curve rises, reaches a peak around ten years of age or in the early teens, and then flattens out or declines. The terminal level is, however, never as low as the initial level.[7] It appears as though the attainment of constancy depends on experience and on the full development of a distal (realistic) attitude. In maturity, however, an analytic attitude competes increasingly with the distal attitude and causes a deceleration or reversal in the developmental trend.

The studies also reveal important differences in the absolute levels of constancy. The constancy ratios for size are considerably higher than those for shape and color. Although these results may be in part a function of the specific experimental procedures, it is probable that differences in the intrinsic difficulty of the perceptual achievements are responsible. Size constancy benefits from gross depth cues; shape and color constancy depend on more subtle patterns of proximal mediation.

The developmental studies suggested that experience results in a gradual differentiation of the distal and analytic attitudes. Such a differentiation was demonstrated for shape constancy under controlled conditions of training in an experiment by Klimpfinger [47]. In the practice sessions, which were spread over a month, subjects alternately assumed a naive-realistic and an analytic attitude. As a result of the training, there was increasing divergence between the judgments made with the two attitudes. With a naive-realistic attitude, judgments showed an increasing degree of constancy as a function of practice, whereas there was some trend in the opposite direction for judgments made with an analytic attitude.[8] The results of the experiment confirm the view that the effects of practice on perceptual constancy stem, in part, from changes in the attitudes ("intentions") of the organism.

The developmental changes in constancy are in harmony with the functionalist analysis of perceptual processes. The ability to discriminate the physical features of the environment increases with experience,

[7] As Fig. 9 shows, the decline of constancy in the older age groups is pronounced for shape and color but is negligible for size.

[8] In the case of loudness constancy, Mohrmann [53] did not find comparable trends. Klimpfinger's results may, therefore, have only limited generality.

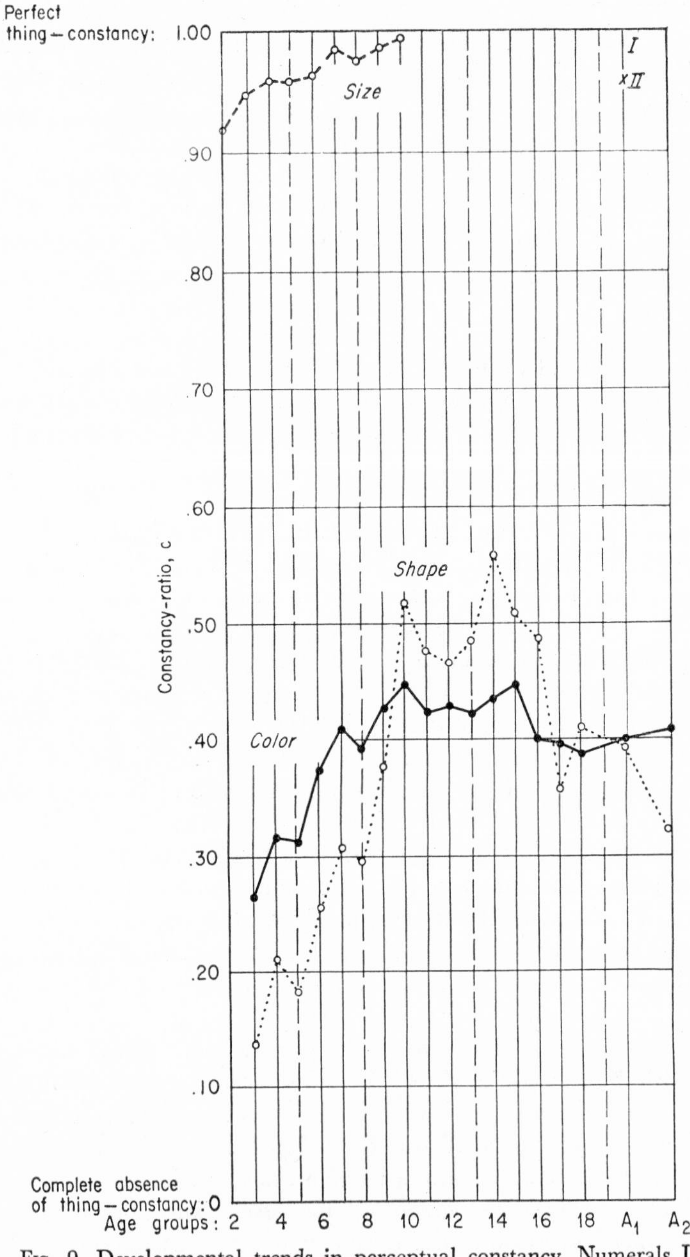

FIG. 9. Developmental trends in perceptual constancy. Numerals I and II refer to two different samples of subjects. *From Brunswik* [21].

and the distal orientation of the organism becomes firmly established. The distal orientation does not, however, remain free from competing dispositions. In the human subject, at least, the development of analytic reactions to the environment counteracts the progressive increases in constancy.

Social perception and approaches to representativeness. A series of experiments on social perception provided Brunswik with an opportunity to develop some of his methodological arguments in detail and to illustrate the difference between systematic and representative design.

Representative features of experiments on social perception. When persons are the objects of perceptual judgment, representative features are necessarily built into the design. Consider, for example, an experiment on the perception of social traits from photographs [21, pp. 26–39]. A group of Army students was photographed in identical clothing and posture under uniform physical conditions (illumination, distance, etc.). The photographs were used to obtain judgments of such traits as intelligence, energy, and likability. It was clearly impossible, however, to isolate the traits in question one at a time. To isolate the variable of intelligence, for example, one would have to choose a group of individuals systematically varying in measured intelligence but alike with respect to all other social traits. Such a selection would, of course, be impossible in practice, but even if it were feasible, it would yield combinations of social traits which are quite atypical of social reality. The investigator must, therefore, allow social traits to vary together in a natural unrestricted manner; to that extent the procedure is a step in the direction of representativeness of design. The holding constant of clothing, posture, and external background is, on the other hand, still in accordance with the requirements of systematic design. This procedure serves to focus the judgments on the traits themselves, to the exclusion of irrelevant external conditions and gross socioeconomic differences which might have influenced judgment. Such controls parallel the technique of "successive omission of cues" in size-constancy experiments (cf. the discussion above on the environmental conditions of constancy). Although the covariation of many variables is thus left undisturbed, the imposition of the controls nevertheless detracts from the representativeness of the design. The experiment represents a compromise between representativeness in the choice of social traits and restrictive control of the context of judgment.

Ecological validity of cues and functional validity of judgments in social perception. Social traits such as intelligence or energy are *covert distal variables,* as distinguished from such *overt distal variables* as size or shape. The distinction between covert and overt variables refers to the directness of the association between the distal feature and the proximal sensory events. In the case of size or shape, changes in distal features are directly reflected in the pattern of proximal stimulation. Covert distal features are, so to speak, one step further removed from changes in the proximal stimulus pattern: i.e., the judgments of social traits are themselves mediated by distal features like size, shape, etc. The object-cue relationships significant for social judgments are, therefore, the associations between the true degree of the trait on the one hand and external characteristics such as facial features and body build on the other.

The true value of the traits was estimated from the ratings of close acquaintances; in the case of intelligence, these could be supplemented by measures of test performance. It then became possible to assess both the *ecological validity* of various external characteristics and the accuracy or *functional validity* of the judgments. The ecological validities of external cues were found to be uniformly low. No one physical feature correlates significantly with the presence of any one social trait. One of the highest relationships found is a correlation of about .25 between height of forehead and measures of test intelligence. Most of the other correlations between social traits and external characteristics were considerably lower.

It is not surprising, therefore, that the functional validity of the judgments was generally low. Judgments of intelligence had a validity close to zero. The coefficients for personality traits such as energy and likability tended to be higher and statistically significant. Whatever functional validities were obtained represent a considerable achievement in view of the extreme tenuousness of the external cues.

The utilization of cues. The low ecological validity of external cues is paralleled by the low correlations between specific cues and judgments of social traits. Thus, there is in this case good correspondence between the ecological validities of external features and the subjective weights which the judges assign to such cues. In another respect, however, the pattern of judgments is at variance with the objective facts. There are high correlations among the judgments of various traits, i.e., substantial "halo effects" which are not justified by the relationships among the criterion measures. The presence of a halo effect undoubtedly contributes to the low functional validity of the judgments. In general, it is clear that perceptual achievements with respect to social traits (covert distal variables) are much lower than with respect to the major physical dimensions of objects (overt distal variables).

Representative design vs. factorial design in social perception. As we have seen, the use of persons as objects of judgment makes it virtually impossible to isolate one trait or characteristic at a time. Thus, in the experiment just described, there was no attempt to control the covariation among traits. At first glance it might appear that the use of factorial design might restore systematic control over the covariation of traits and provide for the statistical evaluation of interactions. A factorial design would comprise all possible combinations of traits; i.e., all the "plots" would be filled. If one wished to do so, one could then extract a representative sample from the factorial design; in doing so one would be armed with knowledge about the nature of the interactions among variables. Unfortunately, however, such a procedure is not likely to work in practice. At least some of the combinations of variables in a factorial design are likely to be impossible or unrealistic.

This limitation of factorial designs is well illustrated in a study of Brunswik and Reiter [26] which investigated the perceptual impressions produced by schematized faces. Five features of facial geometry were selected for study: (1) height of forehead, (2) separation between the eyes, (3) distance of mouth from the point of the chin, (4) length of the tip of the nose, and (5) length of the bridge of the nose. Three values were assigned to each of the variables so that a $3 \times 3 \times 3 \times 3 \times 3$ factorial design was generated. In carrying out the design, it became apparent, however, that two combinations of features of the nose —a long tip with a short bridge, and a short tip with a long bridge— resulted in bizarre and ridiculous facial patterns. Inclusion of these cases probably would have made the judging task appear unrealistic. These two combinations were, therefore, omitted from the design. The symmetry of the design was sacrificed to the requirements of representativeness, and application of analysis of variance was made difficult. The case is cited in detail because of its general methodological implications. Although multifactorial design may often be a step in the direction of representativeness, its symmetrical structure is likely to be incompatible with the demands of representativeness. Representative samples of situations, moreover, are likely to vary in many more dimensions than factorial designs can encompass in practice. By the same token, the statistical techniques of analysis of variance, which are coordinated to factorial design, are not directly applicable to the results of representative surveys. New statistical techniques will have to be developed to evaluate the interaction of variables in representative samples of situations.

The process of cognitive achievement: perception and thinking. Perception is only one process which is instrumental in the discrimination of distal properties. Knowledge about the properties of the environment can also be attained through intellectual processes. Functionalist analysis, which focuses on the cognitive capacities of the organism, thus becomes concerned with the relationship between perception and thinking.

Perceptual and intellectual attitudes in perception. The relationship between perception and thinking may be first considered in connection with the effects of attitude on constancy. The distinction between the naive-realistic and analytic attitude was discussed earlier (cf. the material cited under Functional validity of size judgments). The differential effects of these two attitudes are probably limited to perceptual functioning proper. The determinants of judgment may, however, be complicated further by deliberately encouraging the subject to give some weight to purely intellectual considerations in arriving at his estimate. Specifically, factors of reasoning are superimposed upon perceptual responses when subjects are instructed to take a *critical* or *betting* attitude, i.e., to make use of whatever knowledge they have about the physical situation. By appropriate instructions both the naive-realistic and the analytic attitude may be made critical. In both cases, the critical approach serves to bring the subject closer to his perceptual aim (pole of intention). In other words, the addition of a critical component enhances the normal effects of attitude. Table 2 shows the effects of

TABLE 2. THE EFFECTS OF ATTITUDES ON SIZE CONSTANCY*

Attitude	*Logarithmic constancy ratio*
Realistic	.86
Critical-realistic	.94
Analytic	.39
Critical-analytic	.25

* Adapted from E. Brunswik, *Perception and the representative design of psychological experiments*, Berkeley, Calif., Univer. California Press, 1956. P. 98. Data from B. E. Holaday, Die Grössenkonstanz der Sehdinge, *Arch. ges. Psychol.*, 1933, **88,** 419–486.

attitude on the constancy ratios obtained in Holaday's study of size constancy (cf. discussion under The environmental conditions of size constancy). A critical-realistic attitude results in greater constancy than a "purely perceptual" realistic attitude. With an analytic attitude, instructions to be critical serve to reduce constancy, and the judgment comes closer to the proximal value of the stimulus.

Judgments made with a critical attitude represent an interaction of perception and thinking. The continuity of the results obtained with "purely perceptual" and critical attitudes indicates that the perceptual process is not entirely autonomous but can under some conditions be influenced by intellectual processes.

The distribution of errors in perception and thinking. There are important differences between the kinds of knowledge that can be attained through perception and through thinking. Perception depends on cues of limited ecological validity. No one cue is a reliable indicator of the distal event, and different patterns of cues may be used interchangeably. As a result, the knowledge about distal variables that can be attained through perception is necessarily uncertain and variable. In thinking and measurement, on the other hand, it is possible to solve for the distal value by applying a general physical law, e.g., a law of optics. The situation may, to be sure, have to be manipulated in order to make the application of the law appropriate. Once the conditions specified in the law are met, however, the distal values in question can be determined with absolute precision. As a result, thinking and measurement are "certainty-geared," whereas perception is forced by the limited validity of proximal cues to be "uncertainty-geared."

This analysis has definite implications for the *distributions of responses* that should be obtained in perceptual and intellectual solutions of problems. Perception, which reflects the utilization of probabilistic cues, should yield a continuous distribution of errors around a mode representing some approximation to the distal value. In measurement and thinking, the solution is apt to be either completely right or wrong. The distribution of errors will depend on the opportunities for false assumptions and false inferences afforded by the problem. If there is one particular false step which is commonly taken, the errors should be concentrated at one value. In any event, the distribution of errors should be discontinuous. To test these implications, an experiment was conducted in which the *same* problem was solved by perception and by reasoning, and the distributions of errors were compared [21, pp. 89–93].

The problem involved a typical size-constancy situation. The perceptual version was presented under conventional laboratory conditions, with the normal array of distance cues left undisturbed. In the "thinking" version, which was presented as part of an examination, the subjects were supplied with all the physical measures required for determining the distal value of the stimulus. The correct distal value was 8 cm, while the proximal value was 16 cm. Figure 10 shows the distributions of errors obtained from groups of subjects under the two conditions. The perceptual results show the usual trend toward approximate size constancy. The geometric mean (8.95 cm) is displaced from objective equality (8 cm) in the direction of proximal equality, in accordance with the principle of perceptual compromise. This corresponds to a logarithmic constancy ratio of .84. The distribution of responses is compact and continuous. The frequency of precisely correct answers is not outstandingly high. The distribution of responses obtained through explicit reasoning is strikingly different. Almost half the answers are precisely correct. A secondary mode is represented by the value of the proximal stimulus—a precise answer to the wrong question. The rest of the responses are widely scattered and include some bizarre errors.

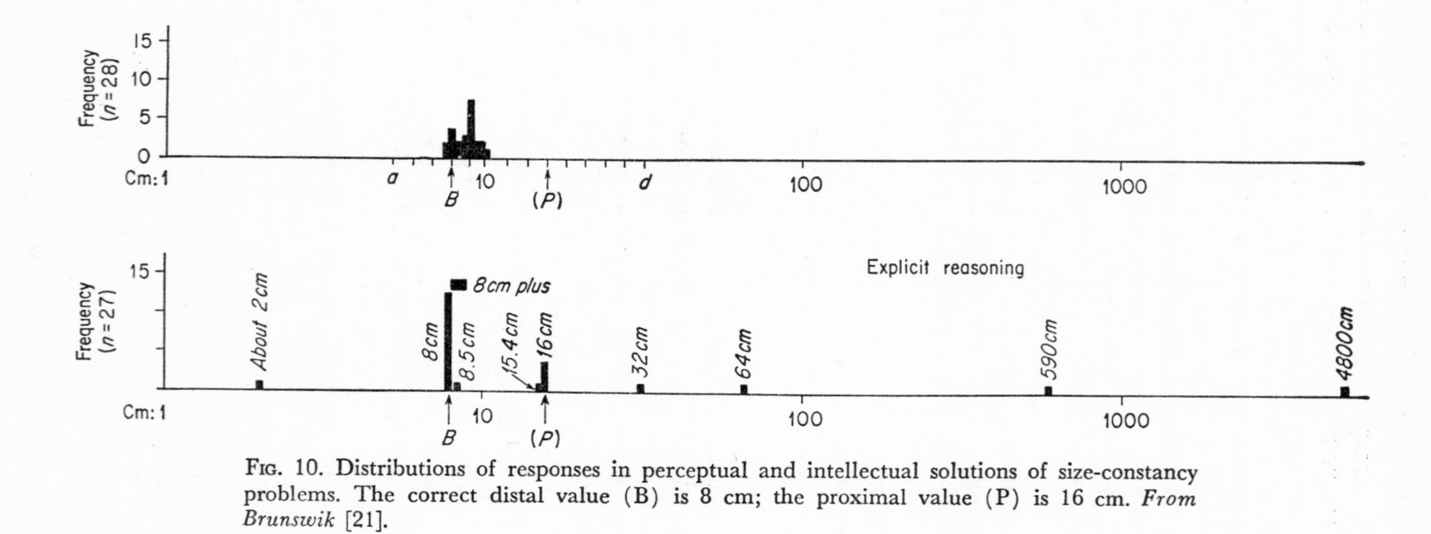

FIG. 10. Distributions of responses in perceptual and intellectual solutions of size-constancy problems. The correct distal value (B) is 8 cm; the proximal value (P) is 16 cm. *From Brunswik* [21].

To the extent that it is successful, explicit reasoning can achieve the ends of perception with considerably higher precision than that of which perception itself is capable. At the same time, the errors produced by unsuccessful reasoning may be vastly greater than those ever encountered in perception. Reasoning typically depends on a relatively small number of basic cues,[9] and one misstep may be sufficient to shunt the process onto an entirely incorrect track. In perception, on the other hand, the very multiplicity of probabilistic cues which precludes certainty and absolute precision protects the process from drastic error.

The presence of multiple cues probably contributes to the speed of perceptual response, which is almost instantaneous. The immediacy of perceptual reactions suggests that available cues are utilized in a stereotyped and, as it were, superficial fashion. Such stereotyped utilization of cues makes perception vulnerable to error and resistant to change. As Brunswik put it earlier, the perceptual system is characterized by a certain degree of "stupidity" [7, pp. 119f., 128, 223ff.] as compared with the reasoning process. Stupidity is the price paid for speed of reaction, and such speed is often essential in adjusting to sudden dangers and fleeting goals in the environment.

In conclusion, the approximate success of perception based on interchangeable probabilistic cues is more fully geared to the adaptive requirements of the organism than are the precise but precarious achievements of reasoning. Drastic errors of reasoning would often lead to catastrophic failures of action, were it not for the corrective influence of perceptual estimates.

The acquisition and extinction of perceptual cues. The major object-cue relationships on which perceptual achievement is built are learned early in life. Many of these relationships (ecological validities of cues) remain stable throughout the lifetime of the individual. Nevertheless, the ecological validities of cues do change sometimes, particularly with shifts in habitat, and the ability to learn new cues may be of considerable adaptive significance. Several experiments by Brunswik and his associates were concerned with the acquisition and extinction of cues under controlled conditions of training.

Perceptual learning in constancy experiments. Evidence for perceptual learning came to light early in some of the experiments on thing-constancy. In studies of size constancy [41] and shape constancy [32] subjects were occasionally required to look at the experimental arrangement in the viewfinder of a camera. Under these conditions extremely low constancy ratios were obtained. This finding was surprising

[9] This statement applies to explicit, more or less formal, reasoning. There are, of course, cases of thinking in which a multiplicity of cues is taken into account.

in view of the fact that size constancy is known to be high when photographs are used as stimuli [36, p. 212]. The explanation lies in the fact that the standard and comparison stimuli shifted their lateral positions when viewed through a camera. In the rest of the series the lateral position of the near and far object had remained constant. Thus, lateral position had become an effective cue to depth in the context of the experiment. Further observations showed that such cues are readily unlearned [32].

The acquisition of cues for constancy was investigated more fully in an experiment by Fieandt [34, 35]. The concealed-shadow demonstration of brightness constancy provided the experimental setting. A light-gray disk was exposed in the aperture of a screen of the same albedo. A concealed shadow caster was then introduced between the source of illumination and the screen in such a way that only the disk was shaded. Under these circumstances there was no brightness constancy and the disk appeared gray. When the shadow caster was moved closer, the penumbra of the shadow on the screen provided an effective cue to illumination and the disk brightened dramatically. When the shadow caster was moved back to its original position, the disk darkened again. In spite of full intellectual understanding of the situation, the subjects' perceptual system continued to respond autonomously and, so to speak, stupidly (cf. discussion under The distribution of errors in perception and thinking). The perceptual response did, however, prove capable of modification by training. By frequent alternations between presentations of the disk in concealed shadow and in full shadow, Fieandt was able to condition the increase in brightness to a minimal amount of penumbra. As a result of the training, the disk began to brighten just as soon as a mere tip of the penumbra became visible. In a further extension of this experiment, it was possible to establish a differentiation between the disk in concealed shadow and an unshaded dark disk reflecting an equal amount of light. The minimal penumbra cue was made effective for the former but not for the latter. Even after 80 training trials, however, the association between the minimal cue and the perceptual response remained rather weak and was subject to rapid extinction. The experiment has systematic significance for two reasons: it provides an illustration of the autonomy of perception. The shadow cue continues to function independently of intellectual insight into the situation. Secondly, it shows that new perceptual cues are acquired slowly and laboriously, and even after having been "stamped in" by frequent repetition are unlearned rapidly.

The acquisition of cues of limited validity. The probable rather than uniform association between distal features and cues has been stressed repeatedly. Experiments on perceptual learning are, therefore, made representative of conditions in daily life when cues of limited validity are used, i.e., when partial rather than continuous reinforcement is used. The acquisition and functioning of such cues are illustrated in a study by Brunswik and Herma [23]. The subjects were presented with pairs of weights which were lifted simultaneously. On two-thirds of the trials, the heavier of the two weights appeared on the same side. On the rest of the trials, the position of the heavier weight was reversed, or the two weights were equal. Thus, position could serve as a cue to weight, and this cue was valid in two-thirds of the cases. To determine the cumulative effects of training, the two weights were compared on test trials in which the two stimuli were objectively equal. As a result of the training, there was a significant tendency to judge the weight on the "heavy" side as *lighter*. The effects of the training manifested themselves in the form of a successive weight contrast. (This tendency did not, however, persist indefinitely but declined toward the end of training in spite of continued reinforcement.) An additional finding of the experiment again demonstrates lack of correspondence between perceptual functioning and explicit conceptualization. At the end of the experiment the subjects were asked to name the side on which the heavier weight had appeared more frequently *during the training trials*. In four-fifths of the cases the answer was *incorrect;* i.e., it agreed with the contrast effects expressed in the verbalized judgments, and not with the sequence of physical events. Yet, the emergence of the contrast effect reflects a significant effect of the bias in the distribution of physical weights.[10] There was not only "learning without awareness," but, indeed, "learning against awareness." In fact, the results suggest that two kinds of learning were occurring simultaneously —one perceptual and unverbalized and the other verbalized.

Probability learning of instrumental responses. The analysis of probability learning was extended by Brunswik and his students from perceptual responses to instrumental acts. The association between means-objects and goals is apt to be probable and not certain, just as is the correlation between distal features and proximal cues. Thus, a situation in which reward uniformly follows the instrumental act is not representative of daily life; in the organism's habitat rewards are frequently exhaustible or intermittent. Brunswik early recognized the theoretical significance of partial reinforcement schedules. His special interest, however, was in the organism's ability to *discriminate* among means-objects which lead to a goal with *different probabilities.* The problem was explored in a study of probability learning in rats. In a simple T maze the two arms led to reward with different relative probabilities. For different groups of animals the relative probabilities

[10] Similar results were obtained in an experiment by Levin [50].

of reward were: 100 per cent:00 per cent; 75 per cent:25 per cent 67 per cent:33 per cent; 100 per cent:50 per cent. The correction method was used. For all combinations except 67 per cent:33 per cent the animals learned to go to the more profitable side; i.e., in all cases but one the difference was above the animals' threshold of probability discrimination. When conditions were ranked with respect to degree of learning, the following order was obtained: (1) 100 per cent:00 per cent was highest, followed by (2) 50 per cent:00 per cent, (3) 75 per cent:25 per cent, and (4) 100 per cent:50 per cent. It appears that preference for the more profitable side is a function of both the absolute difference and the ratio of probabilities. Thus, for both the 75 per cent: 25 per cent and the 100 per cent:50 per cent combinations the absolute difference in probabilities is 50 per cent, but the ratio of probabilities favors the 75 per cent:25 per cent group which does, indeed, show a higher degree of learning. The animals' choices may, therefore, be regarded as a compromise between responses to *absolute* differences and responses to *ratios* of probabilities. (This analysis is, however, complicated by the fact that it involves comparisons between conditions which use partial reinforcement on both sides with conditions in which continuous reinforcement is pitted against partial reinforcement.)[11]

Probability learning in human subjects was demonstrated in an experiment by Jarvik [46] conducted under Brunswik's direction. This study was concerned with the discrimination of the relative frequencies with which one of two symbols—a "check" and a "plus"—appeared in a series. Probability ratios of 60:40, 67:33, and 75:25 were used. Subjects gradually learned to predict the symbols in accordance with their probabilities in the series. As in the experiment of Brunswik and Herma [23], there was a terminal decline in performance in spite of continued reinforcement. Again, as in the perceptual experiment, learning was independent of the subjects' understanding of the situation. Jarvik's results also brought to light a phenomenon which may be specific to probability learning, viz., a "negative recency effect" in the subjects' choices. That is, whenever there was a randomly determined run of one kind of symbol, there was an increase in the anticipation of the other alternative. The longer the run, the greater was the tendency to guess the opposite alternative. Clearly, the negative recency effect interferes with the orderly progress of probability learning.

Brunswik attached considerable importance to features of the learning process which appear to be peculiar to probabilistic situations, such as the "paradoxical" terminal decline in the curve of probability learn-

[11] After the end of training the probability ratios were reversed. The 100 per cent : 00 per cent group again showed fastest learning. Only the 75 per cent : 25 per cent and 67 per cent : 33 per cent groups failed to relearn.

ing and the negative recency effect. Since probabilistic situations are representative of learning in daily life, these effects may, in turn, be characteristic of learning under natural conditions. Such properties of learning cannot be discovered as long as acquisition and performance are studied under unrealistic or limiting conditions such as, for example, 100 : 0 ratios of probability.

Partial reinforcement and probability learning have, of course, received considerable theoretical and experimental attention in recent years. As we have noted, Brunswik was among those who early recognized the importance of these problems. At the same time it is clear that many other investigators came to these same problems by a very different route; both partial reinforcement and probability learning have become critical issues in learning theory. It is of considerable interest to note the convergence of probabilistic functionalism and "mediational" theories of learning on a set of common empirical problems.

Empirical studies of the ecology. It is clear that the organism can discriminate among environmental probabilities and give weight to them in responding to objects and to patterns of events. In order to specify with precision the nature of the environmental regularities to which the organism must adjust and to assess the adequacy with which cues are utilized, it becomes necessary to measure the relationships among the environmental events themselves. Analysis of the interrelationships among external variables ("textural ecology") thus becomes propadeutic to the full development of a functionalist psychology. Such analysis is, of course, carried out entirely by means of physical measurement, in complete independence of the responses of the organism. The inclusion of ecological analysis among the research areas of probabilistic functionalism is a logical consequence of the commitment to representative design as the basic tool for the investigation of organismic achievement. Among the foremost tasks of textural ecology is the measurement of the ecological validities of proximal cues in perception.

Some conclusions concerning the ecological validities of perceptual cues have already been mentioned in connection with specific experiments, viz., the limited validity of retinal size as a cue to depth (see under Ecological validity of size cues), and the low validities of physiognomic features as cues to personality traits and intelligence. We now turn to investigations the main purpose of which was to obtain information about the ecological validities of perceptual cues.

Ecological validity of cues to depth. Frequent reference has been made to the fact that there are a number of probable cues to depth which function interchangeably in the perception of depth. A study by Seidner [21, p. 49f.] undertook to measure the ecological validities of some of these cues. Seidner's materials consisted of a random selection of pictures from a popular magazine. Objects in these pictures were in turn selected at random for purposes of measurement. The real distances of these objects were roughly but reliably rated on a five-point scale. The distances were then correlated with features of the projections of the objects in the photographs, e.g., location, color, etc. The correlations represent estimates of the ecological validities of such features as cues to depth. The following validity coefficients were reported: .6 for vertical position, about .4 for the number of objects filling the space between two points, and about .2 for brightness. The method of measurement was, of course, quite rough, and no great significance should be attached to the precise values of the coefficients. The results do indicate, however, that cues differ widely in validity, and that the validity of any one cue considered by itself is apt to be low. These conclusions were borne out in an extension of Seidner's study [21, p. 123] in which the sample of measures was obtained from photographs of scenes in the daily routine of one individual.

Nearness as a cue to manipulability. Functionalist analysis focuses on those distal features of objects which are of adaptive significance. Distal features are not limited to such physical properties as size, shape, or color; they include complex variables which are relevant to the instrumental activities of the organism. One such complex distal characteristic is *manipulability.* Manipulability refers to those properties of objects which make locomotion and handling possible. Tolman early drew attention to these variables when he spoke of the manipulanda properties of objects [60]. Brunswik and Kamiya [24] advanced the hypothesis that one of the traditional "principles of organization," viz., nearness, may function as a cue to manipulability. Using a sample of photographs depicting a variety of situations, they correlated the distance between adjacent parallel lines with the "mechanical coherence," i.e., manipulability, of the regions bounded by these lines. Thus, distance between adjacent parallel lines was treated as a proximal cue and mechanical coherence as the distal variable. When the regions were dichotomized into coherent and noncoherent (manipulable and nonmanipulable) ones, a low but significant point-biserial correlation with nearness (separation of parallel lines) was obtained. It appears that nearness does, indeed, have some limited validity as a cue to manipulability. Some preliminary work has indicated even higher ecological validities for other principles of organization, e.g., symmetry and closedness.

It is possible to speculate that the so-called gestalt factors of organization may turn out to be acquired cues that owe their potency to generalized probability learning. Such a view is, of course, directly opposed to an interpretation of perceptual organization in terms of brain dynamics. As acquired cues, principles of organization would be "imposed from the outside" rather than generated autochthonously within the organism. The demonstration of ecological validities for principles of organization does not in itself constitute evidence for their acquired character but merely points to an objective basis for their acquisition. The known ability of the organism to discriminate and utilize ecologically valid cues makes the functionalist reinterpretation plausible.

CURRENT ISSUES IN FUNCTIONALIST THEORY

Summary of basic generalizations. Our survey of experimental studies has served to highlight and illustrate the main points of Brunswik's theoretical position: (1) Psychological analysis must focus on the organism's achievements in adjusting to its environment. Adaptive significance is the yardstick by which the importance of psychological problems is measured. (2) The environmental regularities to which the organism can adjust are probable rather than certain. (3) Perceptual discriminations may be regarded as responses to patterns of probabilistic cues. The organism accumulates, combines, and weights these cues in order to maximize the validity of its discriminations. (4) Cues can be used interchangeably so that different patterns of cues can lead to equivalent results. Similarly, different motor responses can result in equivalent behavioral achievements. This is the principle of vicarious functioning which is the essential underpinning of adjustment to an environment which remains partly erratic. (5) Because of the uncertainties inherent in environmental conditions, stimulus-response relationships are necessarily probabilistic in nature. However high distal achievement may be, it is never certain.

Critical discussions of this system in relation to other prevailing theories have centered around three main issues: (1) the rationalistic orientation implied by the description of the organism as pursuing strategies based on the evaluation of probabilistic cues, (2) the abandonment of universal laws in favor of mere probabilistic relationships, and (3) the deliberate neglect of specific mechanisms of mediation. We shall now attempt to present Brunswik's evaluation of these issues.

Reasoning as a universal model of behavior. In speaking of the "utilization of cues" Brunswik treated the organism's responses as dependent on a process akin to statistical reasoning.[12] Thus, there is an obvious similarity between Brunswik's views and Helmholtz's theory of

[12] That the organism is, indeed, something of an intuitive statistician was demonstrated in an experiment by Hofstätter [40]. His subjects (even those who were statistically naive) achieved considerable success in estimating such values as means, standard deviations, and coefficients of variation.

unconscious inference. Brunswik's position differs from that of Helmholtz, however, in important respects. First, it is free of introspectionist implications. Helmholtz assumed that inferences such as those mediating the thing-constancies are automatized versions of processes which had been originally conscious. Brunswik always insisted that the analysis of perceptual processes can be made without reference to the problem of conscious experience. Secondly, Brunswik did not accept Helmholtz's assumption that perceptual inferences are essentially rational. On the contrary, he emphasized the differences between perception and reasoning with respect to both achievement and mediation. He pointed repeatedly to the autonomy of perception and its resistance to intellectual influences. Thus he thought of perception as a quasi-rational rather than a rational system.

Perception and reasoning do, however, share a common purpose, viz., the attainment of knowledge ("distal achievement"). The formal characteristics of reasoning provide a model to which the processes and achievements of both perception and thinking can be referred. Thus, perception and reasoning can be measured by a common yardstick and the similarities *and differences* between them can be exhibited. Such a model, which applies the formal criteria of reasoning to both perception and thinking, Brunswik designated as *ratiomorphic*. The model may be used for the "rational reconstruction" of behavior, regardless of whether the behavior is in fact rational. Application of the model has shown perception to be a stereotyped and imperfect quasi-rational process.

Universal laws vs. probabilism. A recurrent criticism [44, 55] of Brunswik's position has been that it renounces one of the basic aims of science—the formulation and testing of universal laws—in favor of probabilistic relationships. In response to this criticism Brunswik emphasized three points: (1) the propositions of probabilistic functionalism neither deny, nor are incompatible with, the existence of general laws; (2) the principles of molar behavior are necessarily probabilistic and this fact must be recognized by psychological theory; (3) probabilistic generalizations can supplement and enrich general physical laws insofar as they apply to the ecology of the organism.

1. Probabilism in psychology should not be construed as a denial of universal laws of nature. The assertion that there is uniformity in nature is a statement about reality. With such an assertion or belief about reality probabilistic functionalism has no quarrel. The disagreement with nomothetic theory concerns the aspects of reality which are to be represented in scientific generalizations. Thus, the assumed opposition between the uniformity point of view and the probability point of view [51] represents a confusion of the existential with the representational. Accepting the existence of universal laws in principle, one

may still insist that only probabilistic relationships can be adequately represented in the propositions of a science.

2. Psychological generalizations are of necessity probabilistic because those features of the ecology which are *accessible* to the organism are, as a matter of empirical fact, not uniform but to a significant degree unpredictable. Even though general laws may be revealed by highly controlled physical measurements of the environment, the behaving organism is in no position to impose the necessary conditions of control and to apply these laws. Rather, the organism must respond to the more or less dependable regularities that it encounters in its environment. And if the psychologist is to describe what organisms do, in fact, do, he must relinquish his quest for univocal stimulus-response laws. As has already been emphasized, this is not a negation of law per se but merely a recognition of the fact that certain classes of events cannot be described by universal laws.

3. In descriptions of the environment, physical laws and ecological correlations supplement rather than contradict each other. Physical laws refer to relationships which obtain under ideal conditions; i.e., they are strictly valid only when all disturbing and irrelevant conditions have been eliminated. Ecological correlations indicate the degree to which the relationships asserted in the law do, in fact, obtain under the less than ideal conditions which make up the organism's habitat. Table 3 brings out the ways in which physical law and ecological cor-

TABLE 3. RELATIONSHIP BETWEEN ECOLOGICAL VALIDITIES AND PHYSICAL LAWS

Variables correlated	Ecological validities	Partial correlations		Law of physical optics
		Variable held constant	Coefficient	
B × P*	.70	D	1.00	
B × D	.77	P	1.00	B = PD
D × P	.08	B	−1.00	

* B = bodily size; P = projective size; D = distance.

SOURCE: E. Brunswik, Representative design and probabilistic theory in a functional psychology, *Psychol. Rev.*, 1955, **62,** 209. Data from E. Brunswik, Distal focussing of perception: size-constancy in a representative sample of situations, *Psychol. Monogr.*, 1944, No. 254.

relations supplement each other. The data presented in the table are drawn from the representative survey of size constancy discussed earlier (see under A representative design in the study of size constancy). Consider first the intercorrelations among the three environmental variables, bodily size (B), projective size (P), and distance (D). Under normal environmental conditions all three correlations fall short of

unity. Each coefficient represents the (limited) ecological validity o
one of the variables as a cue to one other. Note, however, that the
correlation between any two variables becomes unity when the third
variable is held constant. The holding constant of the third variable
provides the conditions of control which are required for the determina
tion of a physical law but which do not actually obtain in the ecology
The perfect partial correlations in turn reflect the familiar proportion
ality law of physical optics. Far from contradicting the physical law
the ecological correlations merely show that the ideal conditions necessary for application of the law are not uniformly met in the organism's normal environment.

The role of mechanisms of mediation. Brunswik's position has been
criticized by those who consider reduction to physicochemical processes
as the basic aim of psychological science (for discussion of this problem
see [33 and 49]). We have already stated the reason which led Brunswik
to take issue with this orientation. Mediational analysis is concerned with
specific chains of events leading from stimulus to response. Dista
achievement, however, can usually be mediated in many different, and
frequently equivalent, ways. Concentration on a "single track" of mediation is apt to lose sight of the organism's capacity for achievement.

It should be emphasized, however, that Brunswik was in no sense
opposed to the analysis of mediational processes. His argument concerned the degree of priority which should be assigned to such analysis
at the present state of psychological knowledge. In order to reduce we
must know what to reduce. What we must first know, therefore, are
(1) the nature of the organism's achievements and (2) the varieties of
proximal patterns which make the achievements possible. Armed with
this information, we can seek for reductionist explanations which will
be continuous with the functional analysis of behavior. An analogy
may help to clarify the argument. When we study vicarious functioning, i.e., the gross characteristics of alternative proximal patterns
(cues), we are concerned with the grand strategy of the organism in
attaining its ends. When we address ourselves to the microscopic details
of the several specific chains of mediation within the organism, we deal
with problems of tactics within the grand strategy. The rational course
of analysis is to proceed from the mapping of grand strategy to the detailed examination of tactics.

SUMMARY

By way of a final summary and conclusion, we shall now comment
explicitly on some of the major questions in the discussion outline which
has guided the contributors to this volume.

Orienting attitudes. Brunswik's systematic approach represents the integration of two basic attitudes—methodological physicalism and functionalism. The methods and procedures of psychology must be continuous with those of the other sciences. Such continuity emphatically does not entail adoption of the aims or imitation of the procedures of the physical sciences. Rather, the unity of sciences is based on a common foundation of objective methods of observation and measurement. Within this framework, psychology must be free to develop its own analytic tools and concepts.

The conceptual structure of psychological theory must be built around the analysis of the organism's achievements in adjusting to the environment. It is in reference to these achievements that the stability of behavior patterns can be understood as well as the flexibility and variability of the mechanisms which sustain stability. The emphasis on achievement clearly identifies Brunswik as a modern representative of the functionalist movement.

The functionalist emphasis dictates a "molar" level of analysis. Segments of behavior are defined relative to the solution of problems faced by the organism. The specific problems with which Brunswik's analysis has been concerned are largely in the areas of perception and thinking. The treatment of cognitive processes as organismic achievements is the hallmark of Brunswik's functionalism.

The analysis of achievement remains at the behavioral level throughout. Consideration of specific physiological processes of mediation is rejected, or at least indefinitely postponed, in view of the compelling evidence for the essential equivalence of different mediating mechanisms. Reductionist interpretations cannot, therefore, throw light on the conditions and processes of achievement.

Prediction is limited to probabilistic generalizations. The sequences of environmental events to which the organism must adjust are probable rather than certain. Hence, the achievements of which the organism is capable are in principle probable rather than foolproof. Psychological prediction must explicitly recognize the semierratic nature of the environmental setting in which behavior evolves. Just as the organism must react to probable rather than certain events, so the predictions of behavioral achievement are necessarily probabilistic rather than certain.

No limitation should be put on the range of behaviors subjected to functionalist analysis. Insistence on comprehensiveness of empirical exploration follows directly from Brunswik's emphasis on achievement and the adjustive properties of behavior. Although the basic development of his system was rooted in the psychology of perception, he attempted to apply its basic concepts and methods to the analysis of thinking and learning. He also advocated and supported applications of probabilistic functionalism to social and clinical psychology.

Structure of the system, as thus far developed. The systematic core of Brunswik's position is revealed by the classification of variables entering into the functionalist analysis of behavior. This classification rests on the criterion of regional reference, i.e., the degree of remoteness from the organism represented by a given variable. The antecedent conditions of behavior are specified in terms of distal and proximal variables. Distal variables are events in the environment, e.g., the measured objects of physics, with which the organism is not in immediate contact. Proximal variables are events at the boundaries of the organism, e.g., the retinal image produced by a distal stimulus. Events within the organism are classified as central variables. The observable effects of the antecedent conditions are again divided into proximal and distal. Specific movements of the organism exemplify proximal effects; the resulting changes in the environment, e.g., the change in position of a manipulated object, constitute the distal effects.

Thus, distal and proximal stimuli are the systematic independent variables. Proximal effector responses and distal environmental effects are the systematic dependent variables. Central events, e.g., perceptual judgments, have the status of intervening variables in the sense that they are inferred from correlations between independent and dependent variables. The identification of central events as intervening variables must, however, be made with considerable reservations. Brunswik has not specified general functions relating central events on the one hand and independent and dependent variables on the other. As Fig. 2 shows, such functions (in this case the function relating central events to the chain of independent variables) are not elaborated but are subsumed under the heading of "process details." Qualitatively, central events such as perceptual judgments are conceptualized as reflecting the utilization of cues by the organism.

Relationships between the two classes of independent variables and between the two classes of dependent variables are of considerable significance for functionalist analysis. The degree of association between distal and proximal stimulus variables defines the ecological validity of cues, i.e., indicates the extent to which the proximal value can be validly inferred from the distal value and vice versa. Similarly, the degree of association between proximal movements and distal effects indicates the amount of uncertainty which attaches to the attainment of goals through specific classes of manipulations.

Initial evidential grounds for assumptions of system. The system has its conceptual and empirical roots in the analysis of the perceptual constancies. The constancies clearly exemplify (1) the extent to which the organism is geared to the discrimination and manipulation of distal events, (2) the probable rather than univocal linkages between distal and proximal events, (3) the equivalence of widely varying constellations of proximal stimuli in mediating a constant perceptual achievement. Thus, the emphases on achievement, probabilistic laws, and vicarious functioning, which are the key features of the system, derive directly from the study of the perceptual constancies. Much of the later work was devoted to a generalization of the constancy model to other areas such as thinking and learning.

The arrangement of the constancy experiment dictated the choice of empirical variables in much of Brunswik's research. On the independent side, physical measurements of size, weight, brightness, etc., are used to measure the distal variables. The traditional family of sensory cues represents the proximal variables. It should be noted, however, that Brunswik and his associates have significantly extended the range of distal and proximal cues used in the analysis of the perceptual constancies.

The dependent variables are in general the conventional responses of the psychophysical experiment, e.g., matches and verbal reports. Brunswik did not, however, assume a one-to-one correlation between verbal utterances and experience. The dependent variables, like the independent variables, were in the last analysis reducible to the operations of physical measurement. Thus, the study of perceptual achievement could be carried out without reference to conscious experience.

Construction of function forms. The probabilistic nature of psychological laws is reflected in the statement of functional relationships. Relationships among distal and proximal variables are expressed almost exclusively in terms of correlation coefficients. Correlation coefficients are also used as indices of achievement, e.g., the correspondence between the measured physical properties of an object and perceptual estimates. Higher orders of correlational analysis, e.g., multiple and partial correlations, can be used to measure more complex forms of functional relationships.

It must be emphasized that correlations are used to express the relationships among independent and dependent variables and not to measure the covariation among the responses of individuals. In Brunswik's usage of the correlation coefficient, objects and individuals have changed places since it is the "tests" that are varied and the individuals that are held constant. Functional relations can, and have been, determined on the basis of data obtained from one individual in a sample of situations.

Measurement and quantification. Brunswik's primary concern was with the experimental designs which provide the data for psychological measurement. He rejected the classical ideal of the one-variable design and found modern multivariate design inadequate. In such systematic designs, both the values of the independent variables and the manner of covariation among variables are arbitrarily and artificially restricted. Systematic design must be replaced by representative design in which situations characteristic of the organism's natural-cultural habitat are sampled. Measurement must not be allowed to interfere with the patterns of variables which occur in uncontrolled environmental situations.

Thus, the representative sampling of situations becomes a necessary condition for the determination of valid functional relationships. It is important to understand that the requirement of representative sampling applies to situations rather than variables. Once a sample of situations has been obtained, the relationships among specific (distal and proximal) variables can be determined from the instances included in the sample and expressed as correlation coefficients.

Whereas representative design foregoes experimental manipulation and control, it allows of the isolation of variables by statistical means. Partial correlation can be used to hold a given variable or set of variables constant and thus to determine the relationship between an isolated cue and perceptual response. Similarly, the effects of particular combinations of variables can be gauged by means of multiple correlation.

Formal organization of the system. Brunswik was inclined to regard his system of analysis as satisfying the criteria of a model in the broadest sense of the term. Thus, his lens model (see under Probabilistic Functionalism above) specifies the basic variables to be used in the analysis of achievement and points to the empirical functions which make it possible (1) to measure the degree of achievement, and (2) to reconstruct the sequence of processes which make the achievement possible. The model does not, however, do more than provide a general framework for experimental inquiry and measurement. A detailed model of specific mechanisms of mediation is eschewed, just as are reductionist interpretations, and on the same grounds.

Using the concept of model in its most general sense, we note that the formal characteristics of reasoning—the "ratiomorphic model"—provided Brunswik with a set of criteria for the evaluation of cognitive achievement. In the application of these criteria there is no less concern with deviations from the model than with conformance to it. In the "rational reconstruction of behavior" no assumption is made that behavior is, in fact, rational. Unlike Helmholtz, whose theory of unconscious inference also applied principles of reasoning to the analysis of perception, Brunswik did not consider perception as a fully rational process. On the contrary, he emphasized the intuitive nature of the perceptual process and its lack of docility.

History of the system to date in mediating research. As has already been indicated, the major application of the system has been to the study of the perceptual constancies. Brunswik and his students have made major methodological and empirical contributions to the analysis of the constancies. The basic aim of the research was to study the conditions and scope of perceptual achievement under conditions representative of daily life. The range and flexibility of perceptual achievement were abundantly demonstrated in extensions of the constancy paradigm to new dimensions of discrimination. The sensitivity of the constancy process to the changing conditions of the organism was demonstrated in studies of the effects of attitude. The modification of perceptual constancy by experience was explored in studies of developmental trends and of the effects of training.

Studies of social perception—judgments of facial expressions and personality traits—form a second cluster of empirical investigations. These studies were used by Brunswik primarily as vehicles for the exposition of his theory of experimental design. When persons are the objects of judgment, the limitations of systematic designs and the need for representative sampling are brought sharply into focus. At the same time, the results of the experiments illustrate the organism's ability to utilize subtle cues of low validity in attaining its perceptual aims.

Brunswik's later experimental efforts were increasingly directed at the extension of probabilistic functionalism beyond the area of perception. The similarities and differences of perception and thinking as processes instrumental in the attainment of knowledge were compared. Recognition of the essential uncertainty of linkages among environmental events led Brunswik to an early realization of the systematic importance of partial reinforcement. He was clearly one of the pioneers in the flourishing new area of probability learning. Although the basic theoretical assumptions remained rooted in a theory of perception, the range of their application was expanded steadily.

Evidence for the system. Brunswik's approach combines a general theory of behavior with an experimental methodology which grows organically out of that theory. The orientation toward achievement and the emphasis on vicarious functioning reflect a systematic attitude toward psychology and a reasoned preference for a particular strategy of research. The method of representative design translates this preference into concrete experimental operations. The experimental work of Brunswik and his associates has demonstrated the productivity of this point of view. The work also has served to bring to the fore the high degree of perceptual achievement of which the organism is capable in the face of changing stimulation and the organism's capacity to discriminate, and adjust to, probabilistic relationships among events. In this general sense the theory can claim a broad range of empirical support. Its further support must rest upon the fruitfulness of the experimental methods and designs which grow out of its functionalist and probabilistic orientation.

REFERENCES

1. Ansbacher, H., Perception of number as affected by the monetary value of the objects. *Arch. Psychol.,* 1937, No. 215.

2. Beyrl, F., Über die Grössenauffassung bei Kindern. *Z. Psychol.,* 1926, **100,** 344–371.

3. Bolles, R. C., & Bailey, D. E., Importance of object recognition in size constancy. *J. exp. Psychol.,* 1956, **51,** 222–225.

4. Brunswik, E., Zur Entwicklung der Albedowahrnehmung. *Z. Psychol.,* 1928, **109,** 40–115.

5. Brunswik, E., Über Farben-, Grössen- und Gestaltkonstanz in der Jugend. In H. Volkelt (Ed.), *Bericht über den XI. Kongress für exper. Psychol.* Jena: Fischer, 1930. Pp. 52–56.

6. Brunswik, E., Die Zugänglichkeit von Gegenständen für die Wahrnehmung und deren quantitative Bestimmung. *Arch. ges. Psychol.,* 1933, **88,** 378–418.

7. Brunswik, E., *Wahrnehmung und Gegenstandswelt.* Vienna: Deuticke, 1934.

8. Brunswik, E., *Experimentelle Psychologie in Demonstrationen.* Vienna: Springer, 1935.

9. Brunswik, E., Psychology as a science of objective relations. *Phil. Sci.,* 1937, **4,** 227–260.

10. Brunswik, E., Das Induktionsprinzip in der Wahrnehmung. In H. Piéron & J. Meyerson (Eds.), *XI*[e] *congrès international de psychologie.* Paris: Alcan, 1938. P. 346 f.

11. Brunswik, E., The conceptual focus of some psychological systems. *J. unified Sci.* (*Erkenntnis*), 1939, **8,** 36–49. Republished in P. L. Harriman (Ed.), *Twentieth century psychology.* New York: Philos. Library, 1946. Pp. 49–63.

12. Brunswik, E., Probability as a determiner of rat behavior. *J. exp. Psychol.,* 1939, **25,** 175–197.

13. Brunswik, E., Thing constancy as measured by correlation coefficients. *Psychol. Rev.,* 1940, **47,** 69–78.

14. Brunswik, E., Organismic achievement and environmental probability. *Psychol. Rev.,* 1943, **50,** 255–272.

15. Brunswik, E., Distal focussing of perception: size-constancy in a representative sample of situations. *Psychol. Monogr.,* 1944, No. 254.

16. Brunswik, E., Points of view. In P. L. Harriman (Ed.), *Encyclopedia f psychology*. New York: Philos. Library, 1946. Pp. 523–537.

17. Brunswik, E., The conceptual framework of psychology. *Int. Encycl. nified Sci.,* 1952, **1,** No. 10.

18. Brunswik, E., "Ratiomorphic" models of perception and thinking. In J. Mailloux (Ed.), *Proc. 14th int. Congr. Psychol.,* Montreal, 1954.

19. Brunswik, E., Representative design and probabilistic theory in a unctional psychology. *Psychol. Rev.,* 1955, **62,** 193–217.

20. Brunswik, E., In defense of probabilistic functionalism: a reply. *Psychol. Rev.,* 1955, **62,** 236–242.

21. Brunswik, E., *Perception and the representative design of psychological experiments*. Berkeley, Calif.: Univer. California Press, 1956.

22. Brunswik, E., & Cruikshank, R. M., Perceptual size-constancy in arly infancy. *Psychol. Bull.,* 1937, **34,** 713 f. (Abstract)

23. Brunswik, E., & Herma, H., Probability learning of perceptual cues n the establishment of a weight illusion. *J. exp. Psychol.,* 1951, **41,** 281–290.

24. Brunswik, E., & Kamiya, J., Ecological cue-validity of 'proximity' and of other gestalt factors. *Amer. J. Psychol.,* 1953, **66,** 20–32.

25. Brunswik, E., & Kardos, L., Das Duplizitätsprinzip in der Theorie der Farbenwahrnehmung. *Z. Psychol.,* 1929, **111,** 307–320.

26. Brunswik, E., & Reiter, L., Eindrucks-Charaktere schematisierter Gesichter. *Z. Psychol.,* 1937, **142,** 67–134.

27. Carnap, R., Testability and meaning. *Phil. Sci.,* 1936, **3,** 419–471; 1937, **4,** 1–40.

28. Carnap, R., Logical foundations and the unity of science. *Int. Encycl. unified Sci.,* 1938, **1,** No. 1.

29. Dubislav, W., *Naturphilosophie*. Berlin: Junker and Dünnhaupt Verlag, 1933.

30. Dukes, W. F., Ecological representativeness in studying perceptual size-constancy in childhood. *Amer. J. Psychol.,* 1951, **64,** 87–93.

31. Eddington, A. S., *The nature of the physical world*. New York: Macmillan, 1928.

32. Eissler, K., Die Gestaltkonstanz des Sehdinge. *Arch. ges. Psychol.,* 1933, **88,** 487–550.

33. Feigl, H., Functionalism, psychological theory and the uniting sciences: some discussion remarks. *Psychol. Rev.,* 1955, **62,** 232–235.

34. Fieandt, K. v., Dressurversuche an der Farbenwahrnehmung. *Arch. ges. Psychol.,* 1936, **96,** 467–495.

35. Fieandt, K. v., *Über Sehen von Tiefengebilden bei wechselnder Beleuchtungsrichtung*. Helsinki: Psychol. Institute, Univer. Helsinki, 1938.

36. Gibson, J. J., *The perception of the visual world*. Boston: Houghton Mifflin, 1950.

37. Hammond, K. R., Representative vs. systematic design in clinical psychology. *Psychol. Bull.,* 1954, **51,** 150–159.

38. Hammond, K. R., Probabilistic functioning and the clinical method. *Psychol. Rev.,* 1955, **62,** 255–262.

39. Hilgard, E. R., Discussion of probabilistic functionalism. *Psycho Rev.*, 1955, **62**, 226–228.

40. Hofstätter, P. R., Uber die Schätzung von Gruppeneigenschafte Z. *Psychol.*, 1939, **145**, 1–44.

41. Holaday, B. E., Die Grössenkonstanz der Sehdinge, *Arch. ge Psychol.*, 1933, **88**, 419–486.

42. Holt, E. B., *The Freudian wish.* New York: Holt, 1915.

43. Holway, A. H., & Boring, E. G., Determinants of apparent visu size with distance variant. *Amer. J. Psychol.*, 1941, **54**, 21–37.

44. Hull, C. L., The problem of intervening variables in molar behavic theory. *Psychol. Rev.*, 1943, **50**, 273–291.

45. Izzet, T., Gewicht und Dichte als Gegenstände der Wahrnehmun *Arch. ges. Psychol.*, 1934, **91**, 305–318.

46. Jarvik, M. E., Probability learning and a negative recency effect i the serial anticipation of alternative symbols. *J. exp. Psychol.*, 1951, **41**, 291 297.

47. Klimpfinger, S., Ueber den Einfluss von intentionaler Einstellun und Uebung auf die Gestaltkonstanz. *Arch. ges. Psychol.*, 1933, **88**, 551–59

48. Klimpfinger, S., Die Entwicklung der Gestaltkonstanz vom Kind zur Erwachsenen. *Arch. ges. Psychol.*, 1933, **88**, 599–628.

49. Krech, D., Discussion: theory and reductionism. *Physiol. Rev.*, 195 **62**, 229–231.

50. Levin, M. M., Inconsistent cues in the establishment of perceptu illusions. *Amer. J. Psychol.*, 1952, **65**, 517–532.

51. Marx, M. H., *Psychological theory: contemporary readings.* Ne York: Macmillan, 1951.

52. Mises, R. v., *Probability, statistics and truth.* New York: Macmillan 1939.

53. Mohrmann, K., Lautheitskonstanz im Entfernungswechsel. *Z Psychol.*, 1939, **145**, 146–199.

54. Neurath, O., Unified science as an encyclopedic integration. *Int Encycl. unified Sci.*, 1938, **1**, No. 1.

55. Postman, L., The probability approach and nomothetic theory *Psychol. Rev.*, 1955, **62**, 218–225.

56. Reichenbach, H., *Experience and prediction.* Chicago: Unive Chicago Press, 1938.

57. Russell, B., *Our knowledge of the external world.* Chicago: Ope Court, 1935.

58. Schlick, M., *Allgemeine Erkenntnislehre.* Berlin: Springer, 1925.

59. Stevens, S. S., The operational basis of psychology. *Amer. J. Psychol.* 1935, **47**, 323–330.

60. Tolman, E. C., *Purposive behavior in animals and men.* New York Century, 1932.

61. Tolman, E. C., & Brunswik, E., The organism and the causal textur of the environment. *Psychol. Rev.*, 1935, **42**, 43–77.

62. Woodworth, R. S., & Schlossberg, H., *Experimental psychology.* Ne York: Holt, 1954.

ADAPTATION LEVEL THEORY[1,2]

HARRY HELSON
University of Texas

[1] Although this presentation is not cast explicitly in the form suggested by the editor, it has profited greatly from his outline and logical analysis of conceptual models and also from a number of specific suggestions which he made after submission for publication.

[2] The preparation of this chapter was supported in part by funds provided under Contract AF 18(600)-916 with the School of Aviation Medicine, USAF, Randolph Air Force Base, Texas, and by a grant from the Graduate School of the University of Texas. I am indebted to Dr. R. R. Blake for numerous discussions of AL theory, particularly with reference to implications for social psychology, and for critical reading of the ms. and to Dr. Louis Moran for discussion of several problems in which he called my attention to pertinent sources in the literature.

INTRODUCTORY

Personality, interpersonal behavior, and deviant states on the one hand and psychophysics, perception, and judgment on the other are governed by common underlying principles when viewed as acts of adjustment of the organism to external and internal forces. Hitherto, attempts at conceptualization of problems of adjustment have been one-sided and incomplete largely because they have been concerned only with borderline or deviant behavior and have not included the normal range of behavior. As a result of recent advances in psychophysics and perception, it is now evident that sensory processes represent the results of organic adjustment just as much as do personality and interpersonal behavior. Any general theory must therefore be applicable to all behavior whether studied in the laboratory, in the clinic, or as it occurs in everyday life. It is the purpose of this paper to delineate the broad outlines, and some specific applications, of adaptation level (AL) theory in the main areas of psychology.

Adjustment and organization. To be most fruitful for scientific purposes the concept of adjustment, like other concepts, must be formulated in quantitative terms and must be capable of experimental manipulation. In approaching problems of adjustment by quantitative and experimental methods we may seem, at first sight, to be narrowing our field of interest and to be excluding important problems from consideration. Concentration on aspects of behavior which can be investigated by quantitative methods often yields a frame of reference in which a far wider variety of phenomena may be ordered and understood than was originally contemplated. This has proved to be true in the development of the theory of adaptation level which began as a generalization covering the relations between spectral energy of sources of light and reflectances of backgrounds and of objects to perceived colors [34, 44]. The theory was extended to lifted weights and auditory data [35], then to psychophysical judgments in general [36, 62]. With certain methodological modifications it now has been applied to learning [52, 53, 80], to personality and interpersonal relations [7, 23, 41], to semantic behavior [42], and finally to behavior involving such everyday activities as volunteering [74], gift-giving [9], and signing petitions [8].

Coordinate with the concept of adjustment is the concept of organization. The importance of whole properties arising from pattern of stimulation was recognized by the gestalt psychologists who made organization a cardinal postulate of their system of psychology [54]. As a postulate the concept of organization was obviously not subject to analysis; indeed it was maintained that analysis destroys the properties of organized wholes. Although this emphasis was valuable in establishing the importance of organization in all behavior, little progress was made in developing an analytical and quantitative approach to problems of patterning. Once it was recognized that organization depends upon the adjustment level of the organism to the conditions confronting it at any time, the way was opened for a quantitative treatment of organization and patterning.

AL theory. The first problem that confronts the systematist who attempts to deal with adjustment in a quantitative way is to find an operational criterion or measure of it. From the results of numerous experiments it was apparent that the level of performance is reflected in responses to situations indicating neutral, indifferent, or balanced states of the organism. These responses, it was found, could be closely approximated as a weighted geometric mean of all stimuli affecting the organism within certain time limits. It is convenient to distinguish three broad classes of stimuli operative in all behavior: (1) the stimuli being responded to and in the immediate focus of attention; (2) all other stimuli immediately present and forming a background or context for focal stimuli and often affecting them profoundly; and (3) all determinants of behavior having their locus within the organism, such as effects of past experience and constitutional and organic factors which interact with present stimulation and are treated as residuals since they are not ordinarily under experimental control. These three classes of stimuli pool to form a single level to which all responses are referable. This level we call the adaptation level because it represents the adaptation or adjustment of the organism to given conditions of stimulation.

The concept of AL is, in current parlance, an "intervening variable" but it differs from many intervening variables in being operationally defined in stimulus terms. Even residuals may be evaluated in terms of equivalent stimulation when experiments are designed with this end in view.

On the positive side, AL theory makes explicit the relations existing between focal and background stimuli, and in turn, the relations of these to factors operative within the organism. On the negative side, AL theory excludes the notion of a bare stimulus-response relation such that responses can be predicted from knowledge of stimulation alone or without the necessity of knowing what occurs between stimulus and response. Nor does AL theory admit internal factors like need, drive, or motive independent of the conditions in which they are manifested. The concept of adaptation level provides for the interaction and interdependence of both inner and outer determinants of behavior, while at the same time permitting evaluation of the relative contributions of each. How this is done will be made clear in the section dealing with quantitative aspects of the theory.

Significance of acceptance and rejection in behavior. From the point of view of dynamics of adjustment all forms of behavior involve acts of acceptance, indifference, or rejection. That is to say, in varying degrees every response can be regarded as indicating either a positive, negative, or neutral adjustment of the organism. Almost all terms having to do with sensory processes, feelings and emotions, and with cognitive expectancies have reference to the bipolar nature of experience which ranges from pleasantness to unpleasantness, good to bad, beautiful to ugly, large to small, far to near, and so on through the whole gamut of continua expressing human discrimination. As Woodworth has formulated it: "Lines can be arranged in order of length, time intervals in the order of their duration, boxes in the order of their weight, sounds in the order of loudness, tones in a pitch series, colors in a circular chromatic series. . . . Historical personages can be arranged, roughly at least, in the order of their eminence" [85, p. 393]. To Woodworth's statement must be added the all-important additional characteristic of such behavior, namely, that in ordering objects every continuum contains a neutral or transitional region, corresponding to the adaptation level of the organism, such that if lines are arranged in order of length, some are short, some are long, and some are *medium* in length. If objects are arranged in order of preference, some are pleasant or beautiful, some are indifferent, and some are unpleasant or ugly.

The position of the neutral region is of utmost importance, for it determines what reactions will be made to the various specific members of any class of objects. Thus Bishop [5] found that school teachers and college students ordered asocial acts essentially the same as inmates of a prison, but the point at which the groups separated good from bad acts differed importantly. Similarly, Hovland and Sherif [50] found that the order of items regarding attitudes toward Negroes was very similar in the case of pro-Negroes and anti-Negroes, but the absolute scale positions of many of the items differed markedly for the two groups. The individual rater's own position determined whether the items were rated near the unfavorable or favorable ends of the scale along which the items were ordered. Hence the determination of the adjustment level as exemplified by the position of the neutral region is as critical in the study of attitudes as in psychophysics and perception.

In maintaining that all responses are relative to the adjustment level of the organism we do not mean to imply there are no differences among them. Although we agree with writers who make perception a central concept in psychology we do not assert, as some have done, that all forms of behavior are perceptual in character. Rather we agree with Sherif and Sherif when they say: "Frame of reference does not denote a specific psychological item . . . the concept denotes a system of relations operative at a given time which determines perceptual structuring and hence behavior. Here perceptual structuring is taken as the prototype of all psychological processes . . . " [78, p. 138]. Once the structural identity of conditions determining behavior is recognized it is unnecessary to resort to analogical thinking in order to discern common features in different types of behavior. One investigates effects of, and interactions among, stimulus variables, background variables, and personal or residual variables in psychophysical studies, in social situations, and in psychotic behavior, because these sources of variance are present no matter what types of behavior are in question. Perception is, therefore, not an inclusive category of analysis but, rather, refers to one aspect of the total situation that requires consideration in analyzing behavior.

ASSUMPTIONS OF AL THEORY

The postulates underlying AL theory are as follows:

1. All behavior centers about the adaptation level or equilibrium level of the organism. (Paralleling physiological homeostasis there is behavioral homeostasis.)

2. Behavioral equilibrium depends upon interaction of all stimuli confronting the organism (simultaneous pooling), and between present and past stimulation (successive pooling).

3. The adaptation level is approximated as a weighted log mean of all stimuli affecting the organism.

4. All dimensions of present and residual stimuli are related to the AL. In some cases, only frequency, intensity, area, order, and spacing of stimulation need be taken into account in determining AL; in others, properties such as difficulty, beauty, prestige, significance, quality, affective value, and so on, must be included. (In the case of stimuli which cannot be physically measured, resort must be had to various types of calibration such as are common in psychophysical scaling methods, attitude scaling, and the like.)

5. The existence of an equilibrium level immediately indicates the bipolarity of behavior. Stimuli above AL elicit one kind of response, stimuli near AL evoke indifferent responses, and stimuli below AL elicit opposite types of response. (In the field of color vision, stimuli

above AL are tinged with illuminant hue, stimuli near AL are achromatic or weakly saturated, and stimuli below AL are tinged with the complementary hue; in the expression of attitudes, propositions near the individual's indifference point are neutral whereas all others are either accepted or rejected, depending on which side of the indifference point they fall.)

6. Unless counteracting residuals are strong, the value of AL tends to be a weighted mean of the stimuli confronting the organism in accordance with 3 above. For example, the weight stimulus evoking a medium response in a series of stimuli ranging from 200 to 400 g is about 250 g, a value within the series. But if one has had experience with heavier weights before the presentation of the 200 to 400 series, none of the series weights may be called medium, and the value of AL will correspond to some value of stimulus outside the series range owing to the influence of the residual stimulation.

7. From 6 it follows that fixed stimuli do not have constant effects on the organism. Properties of stimuli, we must assume, depend upon the relations of stimuli to the prevailing AL.

8. The assumption that AL is the result of averaging mechanisms in the organism immediately implies that AL is the end result of integration since, mathematically, averaging operations are special cases of integration.

9. Behavior of groups, as well as of individuals, we assume, expresses group levels. Since it is not always possible to define group actions by reference to physical measures, it is necessary to resort to other criteria. Thus, the conditions in which 50 per cent of a group of individuals agree to take part in a psychological experiment may be defined as the neutral level for this action situation. These conditions were found by Rosenbaum and Blake [74] to involve a moderate request to volunteer, with no other social pressure exerted in addition to the bare request. Stronger request and the example of willingness to participate by another person increased the percentage of positive responses. (This experiment is discussed in greater detail below.) Groups, like individuals, may be said to exhibit various levels of response with regard to all types of situations.

10. We assume that learning, acquisition of skilled acts, and all manifestations of capacity or ability represent ways in which the organism adjusts to the problems and tasks confronting it and that it is therefore meaningful to handle them within the structure of AL theory. How this is done will be shown in the sections which follow.

From a consideration of the assumptions underlying AL theory, it is apparent that its usefulness is limited neither to sensory processes nor to external determinants of behavior as some have supposed [1].

The concept of AL refers to states of the organism which have an objective equivalent or measure. Inner determinants of behavior are given as much importance as outer determinants, since the definition of AL includes both sets of factors. In AL theory, the relative importance of inner and outer determinants of behavior is treated as a question of fact to be determined experimentally by evaluating the weighting coefficients for focal, contextual, and residual stimuli in specific cases. Finally, AL theory is not limited to behavior involving responses only to physically measurable dimensions of stimuli since it is feasible to evaluate other dimensions of situations in order to determine how adjustment levels affect all forms of behavior.

ADAPTATION LEVEL AND RELATED CONCEPTS

Homeostasis. Following Cannon, Fletcher was one of the first psychologists to acknowledge the importance of homeostasis as an explanatory principle in psychology [21]. He gave, among others, the following examples of psychological homeostasis: afterimage of motion, constancy of color, size, shape, weight, and distance, negative distractors where there is a tendency to maintain work level even under distraction, ego and aspiration levels with rationalization as a defense against ego disturbance, maintenance of social status or position, and operation of defense mechanisms. He also pointed to the fact that both Hering's and Hecht's theories of vision utilized the concept of equilibrium in explaining visual phenomena. Like the writer, Fletcher recognizes adaptive processes at work in all behavior, in personality and social behavior, as well as in sensory processes.

Homeostasis as conceived by Fletcher is essentially Cannon's point of view. There is, however, one important way in which the writer's concept of adaptation level differs from Cannon's [11] concept of homeostasis. Cannon's definition of homeostasis stresses the "tendency to uniformity or stability in the normal body states of the organism." Cannon's position is essentially comparable with Katz's view of perceptual constancy wherein objects maintain apparent size, shape, and color under changing conditions of stimulation. According to the view adopted here, adaptation levels are involved when objects do *not* present constant characteristics as well as when they do. Cannon was impressed by the fact that bodily mechanisms negate as far as possible disturbing forces so as to maintain normal states. Hence he stressed the stable or uniform aspects of homeostasis such as normal body temperature, normal acid-base equilibrium of the blood, etc. Thus it is not possible for blood temperature to depart too far from 98.6°F if bodily health is to be mantained nor for the pH of the blood to vary much from its normal value of 7.40. Homeostasis has stressed preservation of such physiological constants as these and thus emphasized the striving toward equilibrium in organic functions. To be sure, adaptation and compensation play their part in maintaining homeostasis: thus, if the oxygen tension drops markedly the heart pumps faster in order to make up the lack of oxygen per unit volume of blood by getting more blood to muscles and tissues. But here also homeostasis stresses equilibrium and constancy as end results of alterations in function.

Whereas AL theory is concerned with behavioral homeostasis, it also is concerned with the wider range of phenomena in which constancy cannot be said to exist.[3] Thus in monochromatic light, object colors are not "normal" yet they can be accounted for in terms of the adaptation level which is established under such conditions of viewing. Adjustment levels differing widely from "normal" levels may be maintained for considerable periods and it is with these as well as with normal cases that AL theory is concerned. Although it is maintained that all responses are referable to an equilibrium or neutral point, AL theory does not assume that all behavior represents a striving toward equilibrium. The more one departs from purely physiological manifestations and considers behavioral phenomena, the wider is the range of ALs underlying individual behavior.

Adaptation with negative aftereffect. This principle, as formulated by Gibson [25], has much in common with AL theory though the two differ in important respects. Gibson restricted negative aftereffect of adaptation to sensory processes which have opposites or which can form bilateral or oppositional series; unilateral or intensive series like pressure, size, and olfactory intensity, he maintained, do not have opposites and would, therefore, be exempt from the operation of the principle. Gibson also pointed out that among the properties of an oppositional series the neutral quality becomes the norm or the standard of the series for absolute judgments and that the average or most frequent stimulus determines the neutral quality. While recognizing the validity of each of these principles it is necessary, in our view, to modify and extend them to cover all the facts. It is assumed in AL theory that all behavior involves adaptation; adaptation has not only negative aftereffect but positive and negative effects simultaneously:

[3] My colleague Dr. R. R. Blake suggests in this connection that human organisms might be made to function at temperature levels higher or lower than 98.6°F by means of chemical intervention. This point illustrates the difference between homeostasis as usually conceived and AL theory; whereas the former is concerned with preservation of relatively fixed levels of activity, or the preservation of certain constants, the latter is concerned also with problems of changing levels.

high AL sensitizes to negative qualities, low AL to positive qualities, and intermediate AL to both positive and negative qualities, as shown in the writer's studies of the colors seen in strongly chromatic sources of illumination [34]. AL theory assumes that relative types of judgments made with respect to explicitly given standards are influenced by the adjustment level no less than judgments of the absolute type, and this assumption has been verified experimentally in recent work [49]. Furthermore, the neutral state is determined not only by the frequency with which stimuli impinge upon the organism, but also by all properties of stimuli and, in addition, by residual stimuli which may be more important in some situations than focal stimuli. A final point of difference between AL theory and Gibson's view is the broader meaning given to adaptation as a dynamic state which changes with every change in the environment and with every change in the organism.

Kohler's theory of adaptation. Ivo Kohler has formulated a theory of adaptation [55] which is very close to the position taken by this writer in his papers dealing with psychophysical data [34, 35, 36]. Kohler assumes that when there is interaction in time between different components of stimulation an equilibrium will be established. If any of the components is changed, readjustments occur until a new stationary state of the system is reached. What we have called contextual and background stimuli, Kohler refers to as the "stimulus milieu." He points out there is a difference between saying that a certain perception is more or less independent of immediately present stimuli and saying that a given perception is independent of the stimulus milieu in which the individual having the perception lives and develops. The first statement may be true; the second is not. One must therefore distinguish between a momentary present single stimulus and the stimulus milieu in which the organism exists. Kohler then suggests that the gestalt tendencies found in perception and often taken to be nativistic in origin may actually have arisen from constant stimulus milieu. To the old concept of stimulus-sensation he would add the concept of durative-stimulus-sensitivity, for stimuli not only have the power of arousing sensation but they may also affect subsequent sensitivity.

What we have called the adaptation level Kohler calls the null point. He argues that the more one leaves the concept of punctiform stimulation and recognizes summative effects the more one finds something which plays the role of a null point which acts as the reference point for a whole series of aftereffects of adaptation. Correctly understood, says Kohler, the null point is the first step in the direction of organization within perception. In a brilliant series of observations involving double adaptation followed by double aftereffects, Kohler has shown that shift in the null point is responsible for the effects found. In one of his experiments, for several days glasses were worn which were half yellow (on the right) and half blue (on the left). After removal of the glasses, looking to the right gave a yellowish hue to objects and looking to the left gave a bluish hue, *but if a gray was fixated to the right it looked bluish and if fixated to the left it looked yellowish!* The same local region, he points out, gives different aftereffects depending upon the previous stimulus milieu. When glasses with half-prisms were worn, similar distortions of perceived forms were observed and when empty frames were worn the mere tactile feel of the frames helped restore the visual aftereffects of adaptation. The last observation points to sensory interaction. These and many other phenomena, Kohler points out, show that more than two dimensions are necessary to take account of contextual effects of adaptation since an additional axis is necessary for each covariant boundary condition.

In common with the writer, Kohler envisages the mechanism of adaptation as automatic and physiological in nature. Although he points out that phenomena of adaptation are not limited to laboratory observations and are to be found in everyday life, his own experiments have thus far been confined to sensory processes. His own results, he states [55, p. 414]: "bilden . . . eine ganz konkrete Bestätigung der Helsonschen Theorie. Es ist tatsächlich so, als würde der einzelne Reiz nach dem Durchschnitt seiner Wirksamkeit in ähnlichen vergangenen Situationen 'eingeschätzt' werden." Kohler has developed an electrical model for adaptation which merits further elaboration. The similarity of Kohler's and the writer's views is quite remarkable since the two positions have been developed independently.

Varieties of adaptive phenomena. Adaptation is often regarded only as the result of durative, steady stimulation, it being forgotten that effects of transient stimulation depend upon momentary states of the organism and therefore as much upon adaptation level as phenomena following long-continued stimulation. Thus the negative afterimage following fixation of a stimulus (20 to 30 sec) is generally regarded as an aftereffect of adaptation but so also must be the fleeting afterimages following momentary stimulation and the many other brief effects following fast stimulation. Simultaneous contrast effects have been called "lateral adaptation" by Evans [18], and as pointed out earlier, successive contrast has been called "negative aftereffect of adaptation" by Gibson. The figural aftereffects attributed by Köhler and Wallach to satiation [56] fall easily under daptation. The heteromodal figural aftereffects studied by Jaffe [51] re believed by him to be interpretable in terms of quantitative AL heory, and since these involve intersensory interaction, we are justified n regarding this class of phenomena as adaptation effects.[4]

Shifts in judgment, affectivity, and cognitive states are formally imilar to the changes in sensory processes arising from adaptation and nay be included among them. Phenomena of affectivity and of learnng have been described in terms of "expectancy levels" which in turn re special cases of AL phenomena [58]. In so far as past stimulation nfluences present behavior and there is interaction between focal and contextual stimuli, we are justified in including such interactions mong AL effects. The varieties of adaptation are, therefore, many nd each type must be investigated with appropriate concern for its ikenesses to and differences from other types. It may be necessary to ormulate different definitions of AL when dealing with different areas of behavior, and quantitative formulations may have to be adapted to pecific subject matters. Thus in applying the concept of adjustment evel to group behavior, we shall find it necessary to use a statistical criterion of group action or norms of group behavior as the definition of level. Group adjustment is a reality and has certain properties not unlike individual adaptation although it may have to be differently defined for specific situations.[5] We shall return to this problem in the discussion of personality and social behavior.

[4] Lest it be thought that the concept of adaptation employed here is too broad consider the following definition taken from the *Encyclopedia Britannica* [14th ed., vol. 1, p. 160, 1940]: "Adaptation, a process of fitting, or modifying a thing to other uses, and so altering its form or original purpose. In biology, adaptation plays a prominent part as a process by which an organism or species becomes modified to suit the conditions of life. *Every change in a living organism involves adaptation; for in all cases life consists in a continuous adjustment of internal to external relations.*"

[5] The extension of AL theory to personality and interpersonal relations has been criticized as follows: "Adaptation level sounds like a good physiological concept, something that might correspond to the momentary concentration of photoreceptive substances in the retina. But when Helson attempts to apply the same concept to all the facts of constancy and contrast, to lifted weights and even to social phenomena, there is little left of physiological value" [86, p. 449]. It is difficult to see why extension of a physiological concept to social phenomena impairs its physiological value. Indeed, Cannon [11] and following him, another physiologist, Dempsey [16], find homeostatic mechanisms at work in political, economic, and sociological phenomena. Dempsey after referring to the "homeostatic aspects of intellectual functions" says: "The suggestion that homeostatic principles govern sociological as well as physiological forces implies that parallel or analogous mechanisms should be demonstrable in both fields." " . . . in social terms homeostasis is a guiding principle directing the evolution of a social organization that will sail on an even keel in the face of the buffetings by disruptive forces" [16, pp. 232–234].

QUANTITATIVE THEORY

A quantitative theory of behavioral phenomena must contain more than mathematical relations. It must have psychological content. The degree of mathematical sophistication in a theory is not necessarily positively correlated with its power of interpreting extant data or its power to suggest new experiments or to yield new psychological information. A simple mathematical formulation may have more power than a complicated mathematical model if the former deals with fundamental mechanisms of behavior and the latter is concerned with minutiae or trivia. Examples of each are not difficult to find in contemporaneous theorizing. If the theorist expresses fundamental facts, relations, or principles in quantitative form, when these facts, relations, or principles have been handled only verbally or in qualitative terms, then the way is opened for further advances. The Weber and the Fechner laws are examples of simple quantitative theories which have decisively influenced thinking in psychology by showing that certain aspects of sensory phenomena were subject to measurement and mathematical treatment.

In quantitative theorizing, one may put into quantitative form a fundamental general characteristic of behavior and then subsume specific cases under it or one may begin with the minutiae of some domain and by successive postulations work up to more general phenomena. There is no a priori way of assessing the relative merits of these two approaches. They can be judged only by their results. The present writer's preference has been for the broad type of generalization in which particular phenomena and laws find their place as specific instances. Color vision, brightness discrimination, psychophysical judgments, the varieties of learning, and even personality and interpersonal relations appear to him to be expressions of a unitary, single, organic system manifesting itself in different ways. Whether this system can best be understood by beginning with phenomena basic to all its manifestations or by first considering each of its manifestations singly is a pragmatic matter.

As will be seen in the discussion dealing with the beginnings and development of AL theory, a general formulation translated into quantitative terms has proved applicable to a wide variety of behavioral phenomena when appropriately modified to suit particular problems. Though a single basic underlying concept has been employed in the various applications of AL theory, it has yielded a number of different mathematical expressions made necessary by different approaches, problems, and subject matters. Let us turn, therefore, to some of the more important applications of AL theory, beginning with sensory processes and psychophysical problems and following on through applications to personality, social behavior, learning, and cognitive states in order to see how the concept has made possible quantitative treatment of various types of behavior.

BEGINNINGS OF AL THEORY

Adaptation level theory had its beginnings with the formulation of the principle of color conversion, a generalization covering phenomena of constancy, contrast, and adaptation. In 1924, I decided to test the assertion frequently made in textbooks that after colored glasses are worn for a time objects appear in their "normal" colors as a result of adaptation. To make this test, D. B. Judd and I constructed a 36-in. sphere coated with orange-red paper and illuminated by a 100-watt clear Mazda lamp. We acted as our own observers by placing our heads in the sphere for periods ranging from 5 to 75 min. This method of providing constant light flux to the whole retina in spite of eye movements was the prototype of the large present-day spheres in which observers can sit in comfort and report what they see. The results with the sphere were later confirmed with colored goggles [45] and led us to raise the question: "How can we account for the colors of objects when the whole eye is flooded with chromatic light and there is no 'constancy' to speak of?"

In the studies which followed we made the mistake of using stimuli having a large variety of hues, lightnesses, and saturations in the belief that sampling the whole gamut of colors was the best way to find out what colors are seen when the eyes are adapted as completely as possible to chromatic light. We found that reds in monochromatic red light might look red, white, or blue-green; greens might look reddish, achromatic, or bluish; and so on through the hue circle. Our results were as confusing as the observations reported in the literature, and for nearly two years it seemed as if there was neither rhyme nor reason to the colors of objects when the color of the illumination differed radically from daylight. We were further bothered by the fact that the CIE specifications of the colors agreed with our observations in some instances and not in others, and we properly attributed the breakdown to the fact that the Standard Observer on which the CIE specification was based was not adapted to chromatic light.

The insight that proved decisive and fruitful now seems so obvious and simple that the reader may wonder why it took so long to achieve. It consisted simply in using *achromatic* stimuli instead of *chromatic* stimuli. The former have the advantage of differing from one another in only one dimension—reflectance. Consequently, any differences found among (daylight) achromatic stimuli can only be due to differences in the intensity (luminance) of the light, not to differences in spectral energies. The data in Table 1 show how beautifully ordered are hue, lightness, and saturation of stimuli in strongly chromatic light when nonselective (daylight achromatic) stimuli are employed: the stimuli of highest reflectance take the hue of the illuminant, some intermediate stimulus is achromatic, and the remaining stimuli have one or both components of the afterimage complementary to the hue of the illuminant. The stimulus which is achromatic on daylight white background is seen in Table 1 to have a reflectance of 27 per cent, on

TABLE 1. HUE, LIGHTNESS, AND SATURATION OF 19 DAYLIGHT GRAY SAMPLES HAVING REFLECTANCES FROM 3 TO 80 PER CENT VIEWED IN MONOCHROMATIC RED ILLUMINATION ON DAYLIGHT WHITE, GRAY, AND BLACK BACKGROUNDS

Reflectances, in per cent		Background				
		White	Gray		Black	
80	R*	9.0/2.0	YR	8.0/8.0	R	8.0/8.5
52	R	7.0/3.0	YR	7.5/6.0	R	8.0/8.5
39	R	7.0/1.0	YR	7.0/4.0	R	7.0/8.0
34	R	7.0/1.0	YR	7.0/4.0	R	7.0/8.0
27	A	5.0/0.0	yR	6.5/4.0	R	6.0/7.0
23	rB	5.0/1.0	yR	6.5/4.0	R	6.0/8.0
22	rB	5.0/1.0	yR	6.0/3.0	R	6.0/8.0
17	rB	4.0/1.0	yR	5.5/3.0	R	6.0/7.0
16	rB	4.0/1.0	yR	5.5/3.0	R	5.0/7.0
15	B	5.0/2.0	yR	5.5/2.0	R	5.0/6.0
13	B	4.0/2.0	yR	4.5/2.0	R	5.0/6.0
13	B	3.0/2.0	yR	4.5/1.0	R	5.0/6.0
11	B	3.0/2.0	yR	4.0/1.0	R	5.0/6.0
10	BG	3.0/4.0	A	4.0/0.0	R	4.0/4.0
7	BG	2.0/4.0	BG	3.0/2.0	R	3.0/4.0
7	BG	2.0/4.0	BG	3.0/4.0	R	3.0/4.0
5	BG	2.0/4.0	BG	2.5/4.0	yR	4.0/4.0
3	BG	1.0/4.0	BG	2.0/6.0	yR	2.0/1.0
3	BG	0.5/4.5	BG	1.0/8.0	A	0.0/0.0

* R, G, Y, and B indicate Red, Green, Yellow, and Blue. Small letters indicate minor components in binary hues. Lightness (numerator) and saturation (denominator) are in terms of a 0–10 scale.

SOURCE: H. Helson, Adaptation-level as a basis for a quantitative theory of frames of reference, *Psychol. Rev.*, 1948, **55,** 299.

gray background it is a stimulus of 10 per cent, and on black background a stimulus of 3 per cent is achromatic. Obviously, the neutral or achromatic level is largely determined by the reflectance of the background. It is now clear why the CIE specification of hue is correct in some cases and not in others; the Standard Observer gauged the spectrum against a completely dark surround and hence with a "low" AL. The CIE specification will, therefore, not yield a correct indication of hue or saturation in the case of stimuli having reflectances below adaptation reflectance.

The data in Table 1 are typical of many observers and yield a generalization which brings illuminant, background, and adaptive state of the eye together under a single principle which I have called the principle of color conversion: in every viewing situation there is established an adaptation level such that stimuli above adaptation reflectance are tinged with the hue of the illuminant, stimuli below adaptation reflectance are tinged with the afterimage complementary to the hue of the illuminant, and stimuli at or near adaptation reflectance are either achromatic or weakly saturated colors of uncertain hue. This principle holds not only for strongly chromatic sources of light but also for weakly chromatic illuminants: thus shadows on snow are bluish because the eyes are somewhat yellow-adapted because of the strong yellowish component in sunlight. The Bezold-Brücke effect is now seen to be a special case of the operation of the principle of color conversion. Whether stimuli will keep their daylight color when the illumination departs from daylight, therefore, depends upon many factors, chief of which is the relation of the stimulus to the achromatic point of the eye.

Since AL was found to be all-important in predicting the colors of objects under different viewing conditions, it was necessary to be able to specify it quantitatively. Adaptation reflectance (or in luminance terms, adaptation luminance) was found to be a weighted geometric mean of the reflectances of all stimuli in the field of view weighted according to area, nearness to fixation point and, in special cases, to other factors. Assuming momentary fixation of particular parts of the visual field, adaptation reflectance was closely approximated [34, 44] as follows:

$$A_r = k(\bar{R}_s R_b^3)^{1/4} \qquad (1)$$

where A_r is adaptation reflectance, $\bar{R}_s$ is the log mean reflectance of the stimuli other than background, assuming them to be of equal areas, R_b is the reflectance of the background, and k is a fractional constant. Writing (1) in log form we have:

$$\log A_r = \log k + \frac{\log \bar{R}_s + 3.0 \log R_b}{4} \qquad (2)$$

Since formulas (1) and (2) refer only to brightness adaptation, to derive the chromaticity coordinates of the stimulus which will be neutral we take a weighted mean of the trichromatic coefficients of the stimuli and background as follows:

$$x_A = \frac{\bar{x}_s + 3.0x_b}{4} \tag{3}$$

$$y_A = \frac{\bar{y}_s + 3.0y_b}{4} \tag{4}$$

where x_A and y_A are the CIE trichromatic coefficients representing the "white point" or neutral stimulus, $\bar{x}_s$ and $\bar{y}_s$ are average x and y chromaticity coefficients of all stimuli in the field, and x_b and y_b are the chromaticity coefficients of the background. Weighting the background three times as heavily as all other stimuli in the field of view was found to give a close approximation to the neutral stimulus actually observed in strongly chromatic sources of illumination but the relative weights of stimuli and background may turn out to be different under other conditions of viewing.

The data in Table 1 show that the pattern of colors perceived in strongly chromatic illumination, no less than in white and nearly white sources of light, depends upon the chromatic adaptation of the visual receptors even though the stimuli as such remain unaltered. We find that the organization of the perceptual field mirrors the adjustment level of the eye and is determined by it. The formulas defining the AL for given conditions of viewing have so far employed only the reflectances and chromaticity coefficients of the stimuli and background, but if we are to account for individual differences in color vision among observers, it is necessary to take into account a number of residual factors which differ from person to person such as macular pigmentation, transmittance of the ocular media, color sensitivity, and perhaps set and other "subjective" factors. We may therefore expand Eq. (2) to include residual factors by adding a third term as follows:

$$\log A_r = k_1 \log \bar{R}_s + k_2 \log R_b + k_3 \log R_r \tag{5}$$

where the k's are weighting coefficients, R_b and $\bar{R}_s$ are defined as in the preceding equations, and R_r is the residual factor. If residuals are isolated and measured they may be specified by expanding Eq. (5) to as many terms as necessary. Similar extensions can also be made in Eqs. (3) and (4) specifying the chromatic AL if residuals are found to be important in determining chromatic adaptation.

The principle of color conversion was established with nonselective (achromatic) stimuli in strongly chromatic illuminants, but it laid the foundation for a quantitative theory of chromatic as well as achromatic object colors in all illuminants [46].

With the realization of the importance of shifting level in vision, it was natural to attempt to deal with problems of psychophysics which transcend particular sense modalities such as the decentered position of the point of subjective equality, time-order errors, effects of standards, "anchors," and interpolated stimuli, likenesses and differences between the absolute and relative methods of judging stimuli, and the general problem of "frames of reference." Many studies in the literature were concerned with these questions, but each one was treated more or less in isolation from the others and there were no unifying principles for treating them systematically within the framework of a single theory. Such hypotheses as there were were qualitative so it was not possible to devise crucial quantitative tests of their validity.

The first extension of the concept of AL was from vision to lifted weights where a cross between the absolute and relative conditions of judging was employed in order to see if a "background" weight would behave like a visual background and if the weighted log mean formula developed for the achromatic point in vision would predict the stimulus judged "medium" in lifted weight experiments. In the classical lifted weight experiments, subjects judge a set of stimuli with respect to a standard, which is usually identical with the middle stimulus, and in the method of absolute judgment, subjects judged each weight on an absolute scale, e.g., from very, very heavy through medium to very, very light. In our experiments, subjects lifted a given weight before each series stimulus and gave judgments of the series stimuli in terms of an absolute scale. The effect of the background stimulus on the series stimuli could thus be studied when it was far above or below the series stimuli or when it was one of the series stimuli. It was found that when no background stimulus was present the stimulus judged medium was the logarithmic mean of the series stimuli minus a value which was three-fourths the size of the step interval between the stimuli (the "d" factor). This factor parallels the fractional constant multiplying the weighted log mean of object and background reflectances which was found necessary to predict the achromatic point in vision. With a background stimulus, and using absolute judgments, the stimulus judged medium proved to be the weighted log mean of the series and background stimuli minus the d factor. Whereas in vision it was necessary to weight the background by three and the log mean of the stimuli by one, in lifted weights the reverse weighting was necessary: the log mean of the series stimuli had to be weighted by three and the background stimulus by one in order

to approximate the ALs actually observed. Other extensions of th
weighted log mean formula to double anchors, to judgments of sound
with interpolated intensities, and to a variety of other types of psycho
physical judgments were made and furnished the basis for concludin
that the organism establishes its neutral level in accordance with th
weighted log mean formulation [35, 36, 39, 62, 64, 65, 66].

The weighted log mean formula was important not only in provid
ing a quantitative method of dealing with many psychophysica
phenomena, but perhaps even more important, it made explicit th
fact that pooling or interaction of focal, background, and residua
stimuli actually occurs. Since the weighted log mean formula yields
single value, the AL, the quantities entering into AL must interac
or enter into a common pool representing the level of functioning of th
organism. Furthermore, since the three sets of factors must be evalu
ated in the same dimensions in order to be commensurate, th
weighted log mean formulation brings residuals into the same univers
of discourse as focal and background stimuli. This means that residual
can be objectively evaluated and their stimulus equivalents deter
mined when experiments are designed with this purpose in mind.

The wide applicability of the weighted log mean formula spring
from the fact that, like many laws, it is in reality a *definition* and like al
definitions it is neither true nor false as it stands. It becomes true wher
specific values assigned the weighting constants are verified by experimental data and it is false if the constants do not yield ALs approximating observed ALs. As additional factors are found to influence AL,
they can be incorporated into the weighted log mean formula. The
simple weighted log mean formulas employed by the writer and his
coworkers may be modified to take into account cases more complicated than the ones with which we have so far dealt. Thus in a theory
of rating which employs a weighted mean containing 11 terms its
author says: it " . . . may appear long and involved. It is replete
with unknown constants. Despite certain simplifying assumptions it is
still quite complex. However it represents fairly well the actually
complex response which rating involves . . . its consideration and
manipulation lead to many believable and practical theorems and
corollaries about ratings" [84, p. 7]. Similarly, the author's simple
weighted log mean formula proved capable of yielding a number of
deductions which would not have been made without its aid, for
example, the source of the potency of background and anchor stimuli
in the larger number of times they stimulate (or the larger areas
they occupy) as compared with series stimuli; the possibility of quantitative evaluation of the role of previous stimulation and of other
residual factors; the role of AL as the frame of reference when no

explicitly given standards are present; and the time-order "error" as a natural consequence of the logarithmic formulation.

The use of the weighted log mean equation in a study of judgments of time is illustrated by Philip [71] using data previously published by Turchioe [83]. Turchioe required subjects to duplicate time intervals of 780, 1,010, and 1,390 msec. The average intervals reproduced by the subjects for each comparison stimulus *C* were taken by Philip to be the observed ALs. The time interval between cessation of the standard and the reproduction was first 1 sec and later 2 sec, S_1 and S_2. Since the comparison or standard stimuli were presented in random order, Philip assumed they pooled as series stimuli and their log mean was taken as a series effect. Since the observations were made in two sessions, the data of each session were evaluated separately according to the following equations:

$$\log A_1 = k_1 \frac{\Sigma \log X}{3} + k_2 C + k_3 S_1 \tag{6}$$

$$\log A_2 = k_1 \frac{\Sigma \log X}{3} + k_2 C + k_3 S_2 \tag{7}$$

Setting $k_1 + k_2 + k_3 = 1$ and substituting experimental values for A_1 and A_2, X, C, S_1, and S_2, Philip found the following weighting coefficients for each of the experimental variables by solving the resultant simultaneous equations:

$$\log A_1 = 0.3068 \frac{\Sigma \log X}{3} + 0.6549 \log C + 0.0383 \log S_1 \tag{8}$$

$$\log A_2 = 0.3604 \frac{\Sigma \log X}{3} + 0.6015 \log C + 0.0381 \log S_2 \tag{9}$$

From the values of the constants, it is apparent that the comparison stimulus immediately being judged is about twice as important in determining the time-interval reproduced by the *S*s as the pooled effect of all the standards, and that the interval from the end of the comparison stimulus to the beginning of the response has a constant but very small effect. Furthermore, the change in the series and comparison constants in the second session shows that with increasing practice the other comparison stimuli exert somewhat more effect on the judgments at the expense of the comparison stimulus in the immediate focus of attention. Philip states that "these conclusions could not have been made if the usual methods had been applied to Turchioe's data" [71, p. 79], and he agrees with the writer that "An important use . . . of these equations concerns the evaluation of factors which hitherto have not been given quantitative expression and so have not been capable of experimental verification. Assumptions concerning remote anchors, general frames of reference, and past experience can now be tested and quantitatively evaluated" [35, p. 7].

As a final example of the generality of the weighted log mean function let us consider Attneave's derivation of Guilford's "*n*th power law": assuming that the jnd is proportional to some average of the stimuli being judged, or their pooled effect regarded as the adaptation level A and the standard, we may write:

$$\frac{\Delta R}{f(R,A,)} = K \tag{10}$$

where ΔR is the jnd, R is the standard, and K is the Weber constant. If the function f is a weighted log mean we may write Eq. (10) as:

$$\frac{\Delta R}{(R^n A^{1-n})} = K \tag{11}$$

Since A^{1-n} is a constant, it may be combined with K giving:

$$\frac{\Delta R}{R^n} = K' \tag{12}$$

which is Guilford's "generalized *n*th power law" [2, p. 86].

Guilford [26] shows that according to the various values given n we obtain the Weber law, the Fullerton-Cattell square root law, and other psychophysical laws from his generalized power function. He also points out that there are many special effects in psychophysical work which must be taken into account, such as the influence of context, or background, and residual stimuli from past experience. It is possible to include such additional factors by breaking A down into its components as we did above, with the result that instead of a single term A we have:

$$A = S^p B^q R^r \tag{12a}$$

where S is the log mean of the stimuli being judged, B is the background stimulus, R is the residual, and the exponents p, q, and r are the weighting coefficients whose sum is 1.

EXTENSIONS OF THE QUANTITATIVE THEORY

The weighted log mean formula defines the value of AL and makes possible determination of the relative contributions of focal, background, and residual stimuli to resultant ALs. It does not yield an exact prediction of responses to particular stimuli since all that we know at this stage is that stimuli above AL elicit positive responses, stimuli below AL elicit negative (or opposite) responses, and stimuli at or near AL are indifferent or elicit no response. To obtain quantitative predictions of responses to specific stimuli, it is necessary to derive equations embodying the relations between stimuli, AL, and responses. The first such equation was derived by the writer [36] on the following assumptions: (1) the response to any stimulus with respect to any attribute depends upon the distance of the stimulus from AL; (2) the greater the distance of the stimulus from AL, the larger the number of jnds from AL; (3) the magnitude of the perceived difference is not, as in the Weber law, a constant fraction of the standard nor, as in Fechner's law, a function of only the stimulus and its distance from absolute threshold but rather depends upon both the stimuli being judged and the value of AL. It was assumed that the jnd could be closely approximated by taking as the base on which the Weber constant operates the average of the AL and the stimuli being judged. The assumption of *equal* weighing of series stimuli and AL proves to be unnecessary as will be shown below. Furthermore, the number of jnds between AL and the stimuli being judged does not have to be known, with the result that stimuli may be judged in terms of rating scale categories which can be translated into a numerical scale for purposes of computation. The equation derived on the assumptions made above is:

$$J = \frac{K(X - A)}{X + (1 + b)/(1 - b)A} + 0.5K \tag{13}$$

where J is the judgment in numerical terms, K is the top of the numerical scale into which the rating categories have been translated and is equal to twice the value assigned the middle category of the scale, A is the AL, and b is a constant which proves to be the y intercept of the linear form of the equation which is as follows (when the constant $0.5K$ is omitted):

$$\frac{K + J}{K - J} = \frac{X}{A'} + b \tag{14}$$

where the symbols have the same meaning as in Eq. (13) with the exception of A' which is a value such that $A = A' - bA'$. Transformation of Eq. (13) into linear form makes possible determination of A' (hence of A) and b by means of the normal equations for the slope and y intercept of linear functions by the method of least squares.

From Eq. (13) it is seen that when $X = A$, J is the judgment corresponding to the category denoting the indifferent, zero, or neutral response. The constant $(1 + b)/(1 - b)$ shows the contribution of A

to the judgment relative to unit weighting of the series stimuli since the coefficient of X is 1. This equation has proved useful in obtaining the best values of A and b from a variety of experimental data obtained by employing either absolute or comparative rating scales as described elsewhere [36, 49, 43, 64]. The curve yielded by Eq. (13) is a negatively accelerated curve resembling a logarithmic function and hence requires increasing increments of stimulation for equal differences in judgment.

One of the most important quantitative generalizations in psychology is the Fechner law, and many publications have been devoted to its generality, the limits within which it holds, and the propriety of regarding jnds as elemental units which can be integrated to form larger units. By making entirely new assumptions which do not require jnds to be equal or to be "integrated," Michels and the writer [62] have proposed a reformulated Fechner law in which the magnitude of response stems from the distance of stimuli from AL rather than from the absolute threshold as in the original law. The new law takes into account the condition of the observer (residuals) and the influence of all stimuli, series and background stimuli as well as the standard stimulus, in determining the nature of responses. The modified Fechner law replaces the absolute threshold of the Fechner law by AL as shown in the following expression:

$$J = K \log X - K \log A \tag{15}$$

where J, X, and A refer to judgment, stimulus, and AL, and K is the slope. Since A depends upon all stimuli affecting the organism (and residual stimuli also) the judgment of any stimulus depends upon AL rather than on the absolute threshold which is fixed under restricted conditions.

The reformulated Fechner law provides a quantitative theory for the use of both absolute and comparative rating judgments in psychophysics [49, 65]. It has also accounted for time-order errors [64] and for a number of other phenomena which have been reported in connection with construction of such sensory scales as the veg scale [65], the bril scale [66], and loudness scales [67]. When subjects are asked to divide a sensory interval fixed by two end stimuli or to determine the stimulus that is a given fraction of a fixed stimulus, certain effects have been found showing the operation of levels in this type of psychophysical judgment as well as in the older procedures. Garner [24] found that subjects choose the mean or median stimulus from among the series presented them as the half-loudness of a given stimulus (90 db re 0.0002 microbar) thus demonstrating a strong series effect in this method of scaling. Canter and Hirsch [13] report that the half-judgments of weights obtained in the construction of the veg scale agree with calculated values of the ALs for each weight level and they conclude that "the method of fractionation may be a special case of the adaptation-level judgment" [13, p. 649].

In establishing sensory scales, it has been customary to take the stimulus chosen from among a series of stimuli as a given fraction of a standard (one-half, for example) as the new standard for determining a second fraction. It is assumed that the second interval is one-fourth the original interval and that by such successive fractionations the points on the sought-for scale can be determined. But a stimulus as a member of a series does not have the same sensory value as the same stimulus presented as a standard [35] or, stated in other words, "a fixed physical stimulus cannot be assumed to be equivalent to itself when presented under different circumstances" [65, p. 682]. In spite of the complications introduced into scaling methods by recognizing effects of series stimuli, order of presentation, and many other factors influencing judgment, AL theory has provided a quantitative theory by which they may be evaluated, and in addition, it has been able to reconcile discordant results obtained by various workers [30, 67].

Treatment of multidimensional phenomena. Except in certain laboratory experiments the stimuli to which we react are not unidimensional in character. The response of like or dislike for a painting depends upon its use of color, composition, balance, subject matter, and our knowledge about painting in general and this one in particular. It is a remarkable fact that individuals can respond to complex objects and events as wholes. We must assume that the organism pools incoming data of all kinds, with the result that ensuing behavior represents some "net" effect of all the attributes of the stimuli taken in conjunction with the prevailing state of the organism.

Even in cases where a single judgment can be made concerning the combined effect of many simultaneously operating factors, it may be of interest to determine the relative contributions of the individual factors to the total impression. In principle, the problem of multidimensional psychophysics is no different from the problem of determining the contributions of various factors to unidimensional judgments in AL theory. Whether there is one AL or as many ALs as there are dimensions entering into the total must be decided in individual cases. It may also be a matter of convenience whether one chooses to think in terms of one adjustment level in which several factors are operative or in terms of interacting levels forming a single AL. Thus Guilford [28] in calculating an AL in which effects of previous experience must be taken into account treats them in terms of a previously established AL which interacts with present stimulation to form a new

AL. Similarly, it is possible either to combine interacting factors into a single value representing their pooled effect or to regard each factor as having its own level and to think in terms of interacting levels. Still other possibilities are open, some of which will be discussed below in dealing with complex behavioral situations.

SOME SYSTEMATIC ISSUES CLARIFIED

The problem of constancy with shifting AL. Since the adjustment level of the organism varies from moment to moment, it may be asked how can we perceive the constant properties of objects and how do individual behavior patterns persist over periods of time if the organism is so variable? We must account for the fact that the organism adjusts to changing conditions while maintaining its own stability and that it can remain aware of the invariant properties of objects while responding to specific differences among them. The paradox of sameness in difference and of difference in sameness characteristic of organic functioning was recognized long ago by Richet when he wrote: "By an apparent contradiction it [the body] maintains its stability only if it is excitable and capable of modifying itself. . . . and adjusting its response . . . to stimulation" [quoted by Cannon, 11, p. 21]. The resolution of this paradox can best be discussed by reference to the definition of the adjustment level of the organism as a weighted log mean of internal and external stimuli.

Mean values are affected by all values entering into them, but they are less variable than are their component quantities. Although AL moves in the direction of every stimulus it does not, as a rule, completely overtake even steady-state stimulation. Complete adaptation is found only with weak stimulation. AL usually assumes a value well within the range of present stimuli. Stimuli in the immediate vicinity of AL are most affected by changes in AL and this has been found true of cognitive as well as sensory and affective stimuli. Thus visual stimuli near the chromatic threshold shift easily from one hue to another, as shown by the data in Table 1, whereas extremely bright and dim stimuli are comparatively unaffected by quite large changes in value of AL [cf. 48]. Similarly, it has been found that when the statements in the Thurstone-Chave Attitude toward War Scale are made predominantly militaristic or pacifistic the extreme statements are only slightly affected but the intermediate statements shift significantly [20].

We have already seen how a shifting zero can result in unwanted complications in psychophysical scaling methods and that AL theory, by recognizing the sources of the shifts, has made it possible to order them within a theoretical framework. On the other hand, many of the perceptual constancies arise from the very fact that the zero of organic function does shift with changing conditions, thereby preserving invariant relations between the stimulus field and the organism. If the visual AL were not so labile, white surfaces in dim illumination would appear black and in high illumination would be so dazzling as to lose surface character entirely. Differences among the various sense organs in amount and speed of adaptation are related to their relative sensitivities and the total range of energies to which they can respond. As Michels and the writer have pointed out:

> An interesting compensating effect enters here, with the result that organs with high static sensitivity show great adaptive shifts and those with low static sensitivity show low shifts. Thus a hundred-fold variation in the intensity of light uses up the full scale of responses in a rating scale with the eye in a given state of adaptation. Actually we find it necessary to respond to intensity over a million-fold range. Changes of the adaptation level allow us to make judgments over any part of this range. On the other hand, in hearing we need a range of ten thousand-fold to evoke the full range of responses and adaptive effects are much less marked than they are in vision [63, p. 6].

The fact that all conditions of stimulation pool in establishing AL makes it possible to have the same AL with different constellations of conditions provided that their net effect is the same. Thus Bevan and Darby [4], noting the reciprocity between magnitude and frequency of presentation of stimuli possible according to the weighted log mean definition of AL, calculated the number of times various stimulus magnitudes could be presented without affecting the position of AL and performed experiments to test the agreement of the theory with observed data. Using a set of "core" weights of 220, 260, 300, and 340 g, they explored the limits of the reciprocity law and found it to be

> . . . between 312.1 grams presented 200 times for each core and 314.4 grams presented 100 times for each core at one extreme, and 1,010 grams presented 1.16 times and 1,231 grams presented once for each core at the other extreme. . . . It . . . can be confidently stated that all magnitude presentation values between 314.4/100 and 1010/1.16 constitute a family of equivalent stimulus conditions

so far as preserving the same value of AL [4, p. 580]. Even though the added weights extended far beyond the series weights, the agreement between observation and theory was remarkably good in the case of three groups and off only by about 15 per cent in the case of three other groups of subjects. Here we have an example of a new type of "constancy" which involves equivalent stimulus conditions over an extraordinary range of stimulus magnitudes.

The type of constancy just discussed concerns maintenance of constant AL with changing stimuli. An invariant stimulus, in the sense of eliciting the same response, with changing AL, has also been discovered. In a study of the time-order error by Michels and the writer [64] it was found that the curves of judgment against stimulus in the two usual time-orders—standard-first, variable-second (SIV2) and variable-first, standard-second (VIS2)—intersect, showing that there is one judgment that is identical in the two time-orders even though AL with SIV2 is different from AL with VIS2. Reference to Fig. 1 shows that the constant judgment stimulus (CJS) is the standard

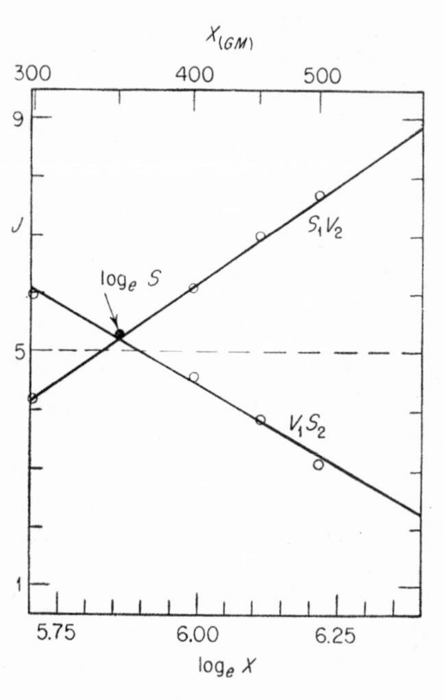

FIG. 1. Comparative judgments of five stimuli (350-g standard). The solid lines are least square fits to the experimental points. The average judgment shown by the black circle was identical for the two orders. The J values for S_1V_2 represent judgments of X relative to S; the J values for V_1S_2 represent judgments of S relative to X. *From Michels and Helson* [64, p. 331].

when it is employed as a variable and compared with itself. The significance of the present finding lies in the fact that although the judgment of the standard compared with itself is not the "equal" judgment (denoted by a value of 5) it nevertheless is the same (5.3) in both time-orders. The values of PSE are also the values of AL and are given by the intersections of the two curves with the 5 ordinate in Fig. 1.

Looking at the curves in Fig. 1, it appears that both time-orders with their different values of PSE or AL may be regarded as biased orders since in the one case the standard always precedes the variables and in the other case it always follows the variables. Since AL is affected by order of presentation, we would expect that, if a completely randomized order of standard and variables were employed, the AL resulting from this condition should lie between the ALs from the two biased orders. A further question presents itself: in such a completely randomized set of presentations, in which the judgments would refer to the standard as often as to the variables, what would happen to CJS and AL? Would they become identical? If so, then the time-order error would vanish since it is equal to the standard minus PSE (AL).

Anchoring, predominant, and background stimuli. According to the theory advanced here, responses to stimuli depend upon their relation to the AL prevailing at the moment of stimulation making AL the "frame of reference" of all behavior. In many experimental situations, certain stimuli may be designated as anchors or standards to serve as a basis for comparison with other stimuli. The question then arises: do anchoring stimuli become the frame of reference to the exclusion of all else in the field and regardless of the state of the organism? AL theory provides an operational answer. *If*, in any situation, a standard stimulus, or an anchor, or a background stimulus, proved to be equal to AL, *then* all other stimuli, including residuals contributed by the organism, would be found to have zero weight in determining AL. In such a case, it could be asserted that the standard or anchor alone provides the measure of AL. But if other stimuli are present and if the individual has had any previous experience with the class of stimuli under consideration, it is extremely improbable that they would have no affect on AL.

Data are available concerning this systematic issue. In numerous visual experiments [34, 44, 39], it has been found that the background must be weighted about three times as heavily as all other stimuli in the field to approximate AL. For lifted weights, the log mean of the series stimuli must be weighted about three times as heavily as the background stimulus to predict the value of stimulus which will elicit the medium judgment when "absolute" judgments are made. On the other hand, if the series stimuli are directly compared with a standard and the judgments are relative to the standard, such as heavier, lighter, then the standard stimulus must be weighted about 5.7 times the log mean of the series stimuli to approximate the "comparative" AL [49]. Thus, the question as to whether behavior is determined primarily by anchoring stimuli or by AL can only be answered by determining the relative weights for series, anchoring, and residual stimuli in specific situations.

Modification of perception vs. modification of response. Since the concept of AL defines the state of the organism as the central factor in determining effects of stimulation, the question arises: do predictions from AL theory refer to "inner" states or to responses?

This question involves the relation of responses to inner states. Doe changed response necessarily imply modification of inner state? W touch here upon the extent to which any response is a "true" reflectio of internal states. It is doubtful if the problem as just stated is capabl of scientific answer, but an operational solution is possible: whether o not a given proposition refers to perception, attitude, emotion, or t response depends upon the operations defining the behavior in ques- tion. Internal states must be operationally defined by means o behavioral criteria. Inferring internal states correctly from over behavior, including verbal behavior, is difficult. Thus, if an individua habitually drives through red traffic lights we may certainly infer tha he is a lawbreaker and probably that he is color blind, but this be- havior does not univocally imply that he is color blind. It is obviou that additional operations are necessary if we are to know about th nature of his color vision. We may give the traffic violator various colo blindness tests and from his responses to them determine more or les surely whether or not he distinguishes red from green colors.

Let us consider still another example. In experiments in whic individuals are subjected to group pressures, it is legitimate to as whether conforming subjects merely express agreement with the grou while holding different attitudes or whether their responses can b taken at face value as indicating their inner convictions. In some situa- tions, e.g., in voting, the response is sufficient indication of inner con- viction although different inner states may underlie identical responses. On the other hand, in public opinion polling it is important to be sur that expressions of attitudes at one time (before election) will be tru indications of behavior at another time (at the polls). Different AL may be operative in these cases and the problem, therefore, become one of defining the correct adjustment level involved in each type o behavior.

PAST EXPERIENCE, LEARNING, AND EXPECTANCY LEVELS

The effect of past experience on present behavior is an old problem in psychology and has been dealt with in many ways. Past experience has been assigned various roles in behavior ranging from complete denial that present behavior is to be explained by past events (e.g., in the ahistorical approach) to the assertion that no understanding of behavior is possible without reference to the past history of the organ- ism. Contradictory results in the literature regarding effects of pre- vious experience may be traced to the fact that in many cases where there has been previous experience with stimuli its influence does not appear in experiments designed to show its effects. The assumption

hat past experience will manifest itself in specific experimental situa-
ions is unsafe owing to the lack of knowledge concerning essential
haracteristics of the original stimuli, of their background accompani-
nents, and of the state of the organism at the time of the experience
s compared with the state of the organism at the time of the test.

In spite of the difficulty of dealing with differences among individu-
ls arising from different past histories, it is possible to study past
timulation as an experimental variable under laboratory conditions
 advantage is taken of the fact that controlled stimulation at one time
unctions as "past experience" at a later time. This was done in a
tudy by Nash [69]. Effects of past stimulation were quantitatively
valuated both with and without accompanying background stimula-
ion. Two groups of subjects judged lifted weight stimuli as follows:
he first group began with a set of five weights ranging from 400 to
00 g in 50-g steps and after five presentations of each weight in ran-
om order the heaviest weight was discarded and replaced by a 350-g
timulus. After this series was completed, the heaviest weight was again
iscarded and replaced by a 300-g weight. This procedure was re-
eated until a set of weights ranging from 100 to 300 g had been
udged. The second group of subjects began with the 100 to 300 set of
veights and the opposite procedure was followed: the lightest weight
vas discarded and a heavier weight (350 g) was added and new sets
f weights were formed until the second group ended with the 400 to
00 set. In other terms, the first group was given descending sets of
veights and the second group was given ascending sets of weights as
hown in Table 2. The judgments were made in terms of a nine-step
cale ranging from very, very heavy through medium to very, very
ight. Numbers were assigned to the qualitative categories and the
alues of AL calculated according to Eq. (13). The stimuli were first
udged singly and on another day with a 900-g background stimulus.
Calculated values of AL for the two orders of presentation by method
f single stimuli are given in columns 2 and 3 and with 900-g back-
round stimulus in columns 4 and 5 of Table 2.

Comparison of the values of AL in Table 2 for the same sets of
timuli in the ascending and descending orders of stimulation shows
learly the effects of "past experience" on succeeding judgments.
Thus the AL for the 400 to 600 g set without previous experience is
18 g. Following six sets of preceding lighter stimuli, the AL for the
00 to 600 set is 361 g, a difference of 57 g. On the other hand, the AL
or the 100 to 300 set without previous experience is 165 g, but after
ix sets of preceding heavier weights it is 186 g, a difference of 21 g.
Since higher AL means lighter judgments, and lower AL means
heavier judgments, it is evident that experiencing heavier sets of

weights results in making succeeding sets lighter and experiencing lighter sets makes succeeding sets heavier than they would have been without previous experience (barring individual differences in pre-laboratory stimulation). Residual effects of previous stimulation are cumulative under the conditions of these observations. There can be no doubt of the efficacy of "past experience" in this experiment, and it is possible to evaluate the residual effects of preceding sets of stimuli upon succeeding sets quantitatively by methods described elsewhere [35, 62].

TABLE 2. EFFECTS OF PRECEDING STIMULATION AND OF BACKGROUND STIMULI UPON PERCEPTION OF WEIGHTS*

Stimuli, in g	Method of single stimuli		900-g background stimulus	
	AL_D (descending)	AL_A (ascending)	AL_D (descending)	AL_A (ascending)
(1)	(2)	(3)	(4)	(5)
400–600	418	361	452	409
350–550	384	332	458	415
300–500	356	301	460	398
250–450	315	257	437	380
200–400	269	227	442	404
150–350	232	202	404	357
100–300	186	165	371	317

* Data from M. C. Nash, A quantitative study of effects of past experience on adaptation-level, unpublished doctoral dissertation, Bryn Mawr College, 1950.

When a background stimulus is employed the effects of previous series weights are profoundly modified—in general they are reduced. The higher values of AL with 900-g background stimulus in both orders of presentation show that all the stimuli were judged lighter than they were judged without background stimulus. The reduction in range of ALs with background stimulus shows the "series effect" has been markedly reduced. Thus, the range of AL_D with single stimuli is 232 and drops to 81 with 900-g background stimulus although the same type of judgment was called for in the two cases. Similarly, the range of AL_A is 196 with single stimuli and drops to 92 when the 900-g background stimulus is employed. A strong background can thus counteract effects of previous stimulation to a considerable degree.

The effects of the 900-g background stimulus are largely owing to the fact that it is far beyond the range of even the heaviest series stimuli (400 to 600 g). Background stimuli exert their effects either because they are larger, more intense, or are presented more frequently, or ecause they differ in some important property from other stimuli. onversely, any stimulus may become an anchor stimulus by being resented more frequently or by being made a standard with respect o which other stimuli are judged. Whatever enhances a stimulus in he present tends to strengthen its subsequent influence as a residual.

It is apparent that the role of past stimulation cannot be deter-nined without knowledge of the contextual stimuli accompanying he focal stimuli and of the state of the organism at the time of stimula-ion. When, therefore, individuals are called upon to report on "past xperience" in clinical, counselling, interviewing, and questionnaire ituations, it is doubtful if they give all the material necessary for omplete evaluation of the effects of the focal stimuli which stand out in nemory. Furthermore, since the dynamic interactions of focal and ontextual stimuli with various organic states have yet to be deter-nined under experimental conditions, it is difficult to utilize informa-ion maximally or reliably regarding influence of past history on resent behavior merely from knowledge of past experience as such. f focal and contextual effects do not wholly account for behavior, hen the influence of past experience may be evaluated as a residual actor.

Consideration of effects of past experience on perception leads aturally to problems of learning. Learning defined as the modifica-ion of behavior resulting from experience or practice can be regarded ssentially as a matter of the relative contributions of residuals and resent stimulation to various forms of behavior. Immediate, insightful earning finds a place in AL theory as learning in which the contribu-ion of residual factors is minimal as compared with the influence of resent stimulation. Such problems as continuous versus abrupt learn-ng, learning in accordance with the structure of the situation (insight) ersus mechanical learning, can be reformulated in terms of the rela-ive contributions of focal and background stimuli on the one hand ersus residual stimuli on the other hand.

The importance of contextual stimuli has so far escaped learning heorists, and the state of the organism has usually not been of interest o perception theorists, with the result that the influence of those factors n perception and learning has only recently begun to receive system-tic treatment. Several studies demonstrate this point clearly. The irst study, by the writer and Kaplan [47], concerns transfer of a light-ess discrimination. The stimuli were the same in the learning and ritical trials, but the background against which they were viewed vas changed. Subjects were shown five grays having reflectances of 5, 20, 28, 50, and 62 per cent on black background in random order. The gray of 28 per cent was designated correct, the only reinforcement necessary since the subjects were all adults. After five consecutiv correct responses to this gray, the stimuli were then presented o white background. According to both elementaristic and configura tional theories of transfer, the gray of 28 per cent reflectance shoul have been chosen on the white background albeit for different reasons because it was the identical stimulus in the training and transfe situations according to the former and because it was the middl stimulus in the two situations, hence having the same position in th lightness structure, according to the latter. Actually, only 32 per cen of the 62 subjects chose the middle stimulus. The stimulus of 50 pe cent reflectance was chosen by 53 per cent of the subjects and th stimulus of 62 per cent by 8 per cent, the remaining subjects choosin the stimulus of 20 per cent reflectance. According to AL theory, subjects choose the stimulus most like the training stimulus they shoul choose either the stimulus of 50 per cent or 62 per cent reflectance since these stimuli have approximately the same lightness, by calcula tion, on the white background that the training stimulus had on blac background. Hence 61 per cent of the subjects chose in accordanc with the assumption that transfer of training would be based o similarity of *perceived* quality. Even the choices of the middle stimulu can be subsumed to AL theory if we follow McClelland and his co workers [58] and Smedslund [80] in their use of the concept of "ex pectancy levels" as special cases of AL phenomena. We shall return t this point below after considering the problem of transfer of discrimi nations involving two stimuli.

James has tackled the problem of transfer of training when one c two stimuli is positive in the training trials and two different stimu are presented in the critical trials. In applying AL theory to this cas he makes four assumptions:

1. In the process of training there is established in *S* a neutra level corresponding to the adaptation level when one of the two stimu is reinforced.

2. *S* learns to avoid stimuli which are less (or more) intense tha the neutral and to approach those which are more (or less) intense tha the neutral.

3. The process of establishing a neutral point is independent c reward and punishment although reward and punishment may affec the character of responses on either side of the adaptation level.

4. When new stimuli are presented to *S*, they will produce a grad ual change in the position of the adaptation level with the rate of shi depending upon such factors as number of trials, distribution of prac tice, intelligence, and so on.

From these assumptions it follows, James points out, that if th

·itical stimuli fall one on either side of the adaptation level perfect ·ansfer will result. If both fall on the same side of the AL, then re- ›onses will be random with respect to the critical cue until continued xperience with the test stimuli has shifted AL in the appropriate irection. By means of the weighted log mean formula, James cal- ulates the value of stimulus that is neutral, i.e., neither positive nor egative, and succeeds in accounting for most cases of positive transfer s well as a number of negative cases reported in the literature [52].

The effects of previous amounts of reinforcement on rate of subse- uent learning are nicely demonstrated in a study by Elam [17]. He eports that rats given 100 per cent reinforcement on both sides of a ' maze, regardless of right or wrong choices, later learned to choose ie correct side of the maze faster than did rats given 10 per cent or 0 per cent reinforcement on either the correct or incorrect side. His iterpretation of these results is that the 10 per cent and 50 per cent roups develop a lower expectancy level than does the 100 per cent roup and consequently work for a lower reward.

The concept of expectancy levels has been elaborated in a number f hypotheses by Smedslund [80] working with human subjects. Since pace does not permit description of his experimental conditions and esults let us consider only his generalizations as indicative of new irections in which AL theory may be applied. Probability adaptation ; defined by Smedslund as "the level of probability expectation that is ffectively neutral to the person involved at a given time and it is onceived as a special case of the phenomena of adaptation level." 'revious experience affects the probability level for it is "to some ex- ent a function of the levels of probability expectation of all the erceptual hypotheses that have been tried out in the situation, in- luding the one that is at the moment activated." This final general ypothesis, although couched in terms of pooled or interacting resent and past levels, is very much like the writer's view of the inter- ction of stimulus and residual determinants of behavior: "The level f probability adaptation is displaced in the direction of some kind f weighted average of the levels of probability expectation of all the erceptual hypotheses that have been tried out in a given situation ut not below a given minimum value" [80, p. 49].

Smedslund has formulated the concept of probability levels and xpectation levels in a clear and decisive fashion making it possible o apply the concept of adjustment levels to domains where cue, erbal, and symbolic stimuli play an important role in behavior. For xample, we can translate Merton's and Lazarsfeld's concept of relative group deprivation" into Smedslund's terms which are more ynamic than relative deprivation and its cognate terms "frame of reference" and "patterns of expectation." Merton and Lazarsfeld [61 point out that *felt* deprivation is more important than actual reinforce ment. They found that men in the Air Corps, where the rate of pro motion was conspicuously high, were far more critical of chances o promotion than were men in the Military Police, where chances o promotion were about the worst in the military service. Yet men in th Military Police complained less than did men in the Air Corps. Dif ferences between prevailing level and one's expectations, which wer to some extent determined by prevailing level, account for the differ ence between complaints in the two branches of service. Relativ deprivation, a result of the discrepancy between expectancy level built up by experience and actual rewards, is therefore subsumabl under the concept of level of probability adaptation.

In closing this section it should be borne in mind that applicatio of the concept of AL to phenomena of learning, motivation, and inter personal relations is a recent development, but from progress alread made it gives promise of further interesting extensions beyond th original formulation. In the next section, we shall discuss a theor of motivation having much in common with the theory of Smedslun but developed quite independently by two workers who have ap proached their problems from a consideration of sensory ALs and th relations of these to motivation and learning.

AFFECTIVE AND MOTIVATIONAL BEHAVIOR

We have so far discussed effects of stimulation without reference t some of its most important characteristics, viz., its affective, emotional and motivating aspects. Hardly any stimuli or situations are com pletely neutral or indifferent, and therefore, they call forth approac or avoidance, acceptance or rejection responses. Harlow has bee foremost recently in stressing "external stimulation as the primar motivating agency in animal behavior" [32, p. 23]. He finds the locu of the motivating power of stimuli to be "differential responsiveness t external stimulus patterns" [32, p. 29] and has presented evidenc demonstrating that monkeys solve mechanical puzzles when n motivation is provided other than presence of the puzzle. Similarly Harlow and others have found that monkeys learn to discriminat between different colors or other properties of objects merely for th privilege of being able to see out of a confining box. From such result as these, it appears entirely possible to order stimuli with respect t strength of affective arousal or motivating power and thus to stud this aspect of behavior quantitatively.

A significant approach toward scaling hedonic aspects of sensor stimuli has been made by Guilford in his construction of isohedon lines for various combinations of frequency and intensity of pure-tone stimuli [29] as shown in Fig. 2. The plane defined by the isohedon lines contains three regions: a neutral region above which is the region of unpleasant intensity-frequency combinations and below which is the

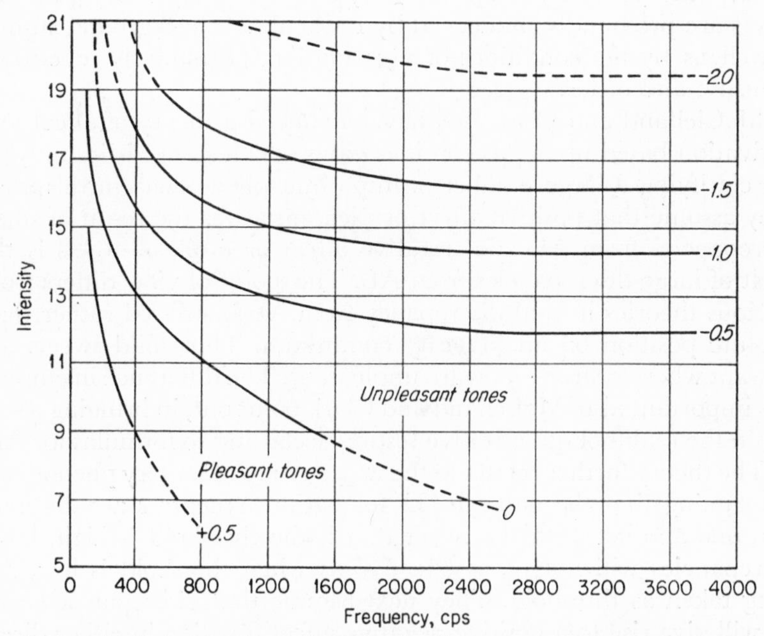

FIG. 2. An isohedon chart, showing the lines of constant affective value levels at one-half sigma intervals for various combinations of frequency and intensity of pure-tone stimuli. *From Guilford* [29, p. 694]; *based on data from Singer and Young* [79].

region of pleasant intensity-frequency combinations. The neutral curve starts

> . . . with a tone of 100 cycles per second at an intensity level designated as 19, and ends by extrapolation with a tone whose frequency is approximately 2,600 with an intensity level of 7. . . . For all tones with combinations of frequency and intensity above and to the right of this curve we would predict a judgment of "unpleasant." For all tones with frequency and intensity below and to the left of this curve we would predict a judgment of "pleasant" [29, p. 694].

The locus of indifferent combinations of frequency and intensity is a curve, not a point, in Guilford's isohedon chart and is exactly analogous to the locus of achromatic points found in vision as the ratio of stimulus-background luminance varies [48]. Affective states are thus seen to behave in much the same way that sensory dimensions do and to be closely dependent upon them. Like sensory dimensions, affects "above" the indifference region have one quality and affects "below" the indifference region have the opposite or complementary quality just as stimuli above AL have one hue and stimuli below AL have the (roughly) complementary hue. And like sensory qualities, affects are profoundly influenced by residual and background stimuli as well as by the conditions of presentation, particularly repetition, intensity, and order.

McClelland and Clark [58] have advanced a theory of affect and motivation based upon AL considerations which succeeds in unifying and clarifying a large number of important phenomena in this area. They assume that positive affect or pleasantness is the result of small discrepancies from AL and negative affect or unpleasantness is the result of large discrepancies from AL. This point of view differs from previous theories in that discrepancy from AL is stressed rather than absolute position on an intensity continuum. Thus mild sweets are pleasant whereas strong ones are unpleasant. The difference in emphasis is important also, McLelland and Clark point out, in bringing affect within the realm of quantitative testing according to formulas for AL.

The theory further relates to the wider group of sensory phenomena in assuming that the natural ALs for various receptors are different from one another with the result that if the threshold is high, large discrepancies will not be as effective as when threshold is low, AL being taken as threshold. They next assume that discrepancies from AL will give rise to a positive-negative affect function in either direction along a continuum, and it is recognized that some changes are unidirectional, others bidirectional. Increases or decreases in stimulus intensity can be related to motivation, they state, only if adaptation level and learning are taken into account. This view of motivation differs from that of Miller and Dollard in two ways: first, change of intensity by itself is not sufficient to account for affectivity and must be related to the existing AL; and second, such changes produce affect immediately and become motives only through learning. ALs are affected by learning and experience but the affective reactions to discrepancies from AL are native. It is through changes in AL that stimuli change their affective value and hence their power of motivating action.

McClelland and Clark do not restrict their theory of motivation to purely sensory aspects of stimulation. They point out that changes in patterns of stimulation and in the expectations aroused by stimulation involve hedonic and motivational effects. Differences from expectations, if not too large, are pleasurable as shown by the variety of behaviors adopted by rats after a problem is learned. Rats will take different paths to food if all lead to food and they may eat the food where it is or carry it elsewhere. After learning, it appears as if the animal introduces variation to increase uncertainty to a pleasurable level. Before learning, the uncertainty is too great to be pleasurable. If expectations are exactly confirmed repeatedly, boredom results, with the tendency to discontinue the act. To predict specific affects it is also necessary to know the level of certainty of expectations: if expectations are of low probability, confirmation produces negative affect, as in fear of the strange; if of moderate probability they produce pleasure, as in reading a detective story; and if of high probability, precise confirmation produces boredom, as in rereading a story or playing with a toy that has been thoroughly explored. In this theory, it is also recognized that adults may be motivated by higher, cognitive expectation levels, or structures, which may lead in direct opposition to simple sensory pleasures or pains.

The full explanatory power of the theory can best be appreciated by recourse to the original presentation. The systematic implications of the McClelland-Clark theory of motivation are summarized by them as follows:

> . . . we have redefined the whole problem of so-called primary and secondary drives. . . . *all drives (motives) are learned.* Affective arousal, on which motives are based, is essentially primary (unlearned), although adaptation levels which govern can obviously be changed by experience. So the traditional distinction between primary (biological) need and motives, and secondary (learned or social) motives has disappeared. Instead we may speak of primary affect and secondary motives [58, p. 83].

Although McLelland and Clark deal with the problem of rate and amplitude of affective change and with the role of frequency and contiguity of cues associated with affective change, it is not clear to me how high intensities of pleasant affective experience are explained in their theory. If objects such as works of art or advertisements are arranged from the least pleasant through the indifferent ones to the most pleasant, they are ordered according to gradations in intensity of affective arousal. We can visualize such an affective continuum by denoting the ends of a straight line "most pleasant" and "most unpleasant" and the middle by "indifferent." On such a continuum the most pleasant and the most unpleasant stimuli are *most discrepant* from the indifferent stimuli which coincide with AL. According to the McClelland-Clark theory, it is difficult to account for as great intensity of pleasantness as unpleasantness since, once the smaller discrepancies from AL are exceeded, increasing discrepancy should be accompanied only by increasing unpleasantness. Although the McClelland-Clark model works without difficulty for pleasantness arising from small discrepancies from AL, it is not clear how the theory accounts for intense pleasant states that are many steps removed from *affective* neutrality.

PERSONALITY AND SOCIAL BEHAVIOR

It has been possible to apply the paradigm found useful in the study of sensory processes to problems of personality and social behavior with due regard to the differences in the subject matters of the different areas. At first sight it might appear that transfer of AL theory from study of sensory responses to social behavior is merely by way of analogy, but consideration of the studies dealing with such social acts as volunteering [74], gift-giving [9], and conformity to social pressures [41] shows that this is not the case. Personality traits are manifested only in response to prevailing stimulus-background conditions,[6] and group behavior is also a function of the field conditions confronting the individuals composing the group coupled with whatever influence personal factors (residuals) may have in social contexts. In applying AL theory to personality and interpersonal relations, it is necessary to evaluate stimuli in other than energy terms, and the concept of "level" of group action requires a somewhat different definition from individual adjustment level though the two are closely related.

Individuals in groups are influenced by focal, background, and residual stimuli and though the stimuli are interpersonal, emotional, and cognitive in nature they may be ordered in continua no less than physical stimuli. Level of group action may be defined in terms of the number of individuals in the group taking positive or negative action on various issues or remaining neutral. The conditions giving rise to predominantly positive or negative actions or to equal numbers of positive and negative acts by the members may be designated as high, low, or neutral levels just as individual levels are specified in stimulus terms. In some social situations, for example, as in contributing a gift for a member of the group, all individuals may give something and the neutral level must be arbitrarily defined, perhaps as the average amount contributed by the group when there are no pressures to donate a given amount. This amount may be taken as the neutral

[6] Not so Carr and Kingsbury [14] who exclude situational factors in identifying traits and who regard the maladaptiveness of behavior as most indicative of the existence of traits, e.g., the host who is rude to his guests. This point of view is diametrically opposed to our fundamental premise that operationally nothing can be known about inner factors of personality apart from the interaction with the situations in which they are manifested.

level or norm by which to gauge the effect of various conditions. In short, we are here maintaining that social stimuli can be ordered with respect to the degree to which they influence behavior; hence, they may serve as independent variables in the study of interpersonal relations. The results of experiments dealing with personality and social variables can thus be brought methodologically into the same universe of discourse as data obtained in psychophysics or in learning experiments through the establishment of quantitative, functional relations between stimulus and behavioral variables. We believe this is ultimately the only way of gaining insight into the dynamics of personality and interpersonal behavior.

To see concretely how stimulus, background, and residual factors have been studied as personal and social variables let us consider experiments having to do with such everyday activities as gift-giving, volunteering, expression of attitudes, and yielding to social pressures.

In an experiment by Blake, Rosenbaum, and Duryea [9], gift-giving (generosity) was studied as a function of ostensible group standards by varying the background stimulus. According to a trait theory, it might reasonably be assumed that individuals possess varying degrees of generosity which may be measured by means of a properly designed test of the paper and pencil variety. Individuals standing high in the test would be expected to give more toward a gift than individuals low in the test—if not on one occasion then at least on the average. The results of this study point, however, in another direction. It was conducted as follows: graduate students were asked by the experimenters to make a donation to buy a gift for a departmental secretary. The students were also told that they could give as much as they liked, but at the same time a clip sheet was exposed to their view showing amounts ostensibly contributed by others. In the case of 10 individuals, amounts averaging 25 cents were shown; 10 other individuals saw amounts varying about a mean of 75 cents; and in the case of another group of 10, serving as a control group, nothing was shown to indicate what others might have given. The average amounts donated by the three groups of subjects were 32 cents, 63 cents, and 75 cents respectively. It is evident that background factors were more powerful than a trait of generosity which might have been operative in the situation, especially in view of the fact that the control group, left to itself, donated *more* than either of the experimental groups.

An experiment by Rosenbaum [73] on volunteering to take part in a psychological experiment illustrates the interaction of stimulus and background strengths in determining group behavior. Graduate students studying in the departmental library at the University of Texas were requested to take part in a short psychological experiment under nine combinations of stimulus and background conditions: three degrees of request, ranging from a weak invitation to a strong plea were employed with positive, neutral, and negative backgrounds. Background conditions were created by having an assistant, seated next to the test subjects, agree or refuse to volunteer for the experiment under the three conditions of request just before the test subjects were approached. With neutral background, the students were approached directly. One hundred and thirty-five individuals, picked at random in groups of fifteen for each of the nine conditions, took part in the experiment.

TABLE 3. VOLUNTEERING AS A FUNCTION OF STIMULUS AND BACKGROUND FACTORS*

Background	Stimulus strength					
	Strong		Moderate		Weak	
	Yes	No	Yes	No	Yes	No
Positive	12	3	12	3	6	9
Neutral	12	3	7	8	0	15
Negative	11	4	1	14	1	14
Total	35	10	20	25	7	38

* From M. Rosenbaum, The effect of stimulus and background factors on the volunteering response, *J. abnorm. soc. Psychol.*, 1956, **53,** 120.

The results in Table 3 show that, in general, strong stimulus and positive background produce overwhelming positive responses[7] and weak stimulus and negative background produce overwhelming negative responses, whereas the moderate request and neutral background result in an almost 50:50 division between those who volunteered and those who refused. Moderate request and neutral background, therefore, represent the neutral level of stimulation for this group. As the stimulus increases in intensity, more individuals accede to the request and as the stimulus decreases in intensity and the background changes from positive to neutral to negative more opposite types of response are found. We find here little evidence for the opera-

[7] That these findings are close to real life is borne out by a remark made by one of the writer's colleagues just after the above was written. This colleague possesses a rare type of blood and is often called upon to be a donor. He complained of being extremely tired after giving a pint of blood and added that he had been a donor only a short time previously. When asked why he had consented to be a donor so soon again he replied, "They said they were *desperate*." Who can doubt that social stimuli are graded in intensity?

tion of traits, or other residual factors, among the majority of *S*s. They are important in the case of the small number of individuals who either refused under conditions in which the majority responded positively, or volunteered under conditions in which the majority refused. From the results in Table 3, it appears that the act of volunteering is a special case of conformance to a social background "rather than an individualistic act conditioned by an essentially undefinable complex of inner tensions, needs" or traits [74, p. 193].

Although recognizing the importance of environmental (stimulus) determinants of individual and group behavior, AL theory also recognizes the importance of internal determiners in personality and the actions of groups, and it provides a model for simultaneously evaluating both sets of factors. But AL theory insists that internal factors, whether they be conceived as traits, attitudes, sets, motives, excitatory or inhibitory potentials, habit strengths, drives, instincts, or residuals of whatever kind, have no operational meaning apart from the situations in which they are called forth. Traits inferred from paper and pencil or projective tests may have little or no situational validity simply because the test situation does not test the same organism that is responding in a life situation. Conversely, situational factors may influence responses given to the Rorschach ink blots as pointed out by Miller [68] and by Sarason [75]. Thus the sex of the examiner, the "appearance" of the examiner (Jewish appearance, or even name), and certain intangible personality characteristics affect the protocols, not to mention their interpretation. Similarly certain factors operating in the testee, such as temporary frustrations, may affect his responses "in ways that are not typical of his usual behavior," Miller points out. Probably no one is more aware of all the extraneous factors that influence Rorschach protocols than the skilled examiner, but our point here is that *conceptually* responses to ink blots or to test items in personality scales are no different from psychophysical judgments in being influenced by situational factors and momentary adjustment level of the organism.

We have next to consider studies involving residual factors in behavior. Residuals are undoubtedly as numerous as stimuli. Although it is possible to control stimuli for experimental purposes, this is not always true of residuals. Indeed, we have defined residuals as all determinants of behavior not accounted for in terms of focal and background stimuli. According to this definition, although the contributions of residuals may be measured they cannot always be identified. Nevertheless, the possibility of measuring residuals represents an advance since effects often attributed to external sources, or confused with effects of stimulation, can now be isolated and assigned their proper locus within the individual. Stimulus sources of variance and residual sources of variance should be separated and the contributions of each to behavior must be evaluated if the interaction of situational and personal variables is to be understood. We shall now discuss studies showing different approaches to, and treatment of, residuals.

In a study by Ball [3] effects of a previously experienced verbal background were found to influence the attitudes of test subjects toward statements concerning war and peace. Three groups of 100 individuals were asked to express their agreement or disagreement with 38 statements selected from the Droba Attitude toward War Scale [19] by placing a cross on a line underneath each of the statements. The line was 5⅝ in. long and marked "strongly disagree" at the left end, "indifferent" in the middle, and "strongly agree" at the right end. The position of the cross with respect to these three anchor points indicated the extent of agreement or disagreement with each of the 38 statements. Measurement of the position of the crosses was to the nearest one-eighth in. making a maximum of 45 for strongest agreement, 1 for maximal disagreement, and 23 for indifferent.

TABLE 4. ORDER OF BACKGROUND FOR M, F, AND C FORMS*

Statements	M	F	C
1–19	Most people think that . . .	Only a few people think that . . .	No background
20–38	Only a few people think that . . .	Most people think that . . .	No background

* From J. H. Ball, The influence of background and residual stimuli upon the measurement of attitudes, unpublished master's thesis, Univer. of Texas, 1953.

From the design of the experiment given in Table 4 the manner in which the influence of background as a contextual stimulus and as a residual stimulus was studied can be seen. In the case of the first group, statements 1 to 19 were preceded by the phrase "Most people think that," and the last 19 statements, 20 to 38, were preceded by the phrase "Only a few people think that." With the second group the reverse order of background phrases was used: statements 1 to 19 were preceded by the phrase "Only a few people think that" and statements 20 to 38 were preceded by the phrase "Most people think that." The third group, acting as the control, were given the 38 statements with no preceding background statements.

From Table 5 it is seen that the immediate effect of the background statements was to raise the ratings in the case of the favorable background (24.78 for "most people believe") and to lower them in the case of the unfavorable background (21.43 for "few people believe"). The ratings of the control group lie between the ratings of the two experimental groups as expected.[8] The second backgrounds also pulled the ratings in their direction: "few" following "most" background caused a downward shift from 24.78 to 21.43, and "most" following "few" background caused an upward shift from 20.35 to 23.46. But the second ratings are neither as high in the case of "most" background nor as low in the case of "few" background as the first ratings with these backgrounds. There is thus a double effect in the second set of ratings: effect of the residuals left by the first background plus the effect of the second background. The fact that the second ratings of each group plot nearer the first ratings of the other group in most cases (Fig. 3) shows that the backgrounds presented simultaneously with the stimuli are more effective than the residuals left by the first backgrounds.

TABLE 5. MEAN RATINGS OF TWO SETS OF 19 STATEMENTS BY THREE GROUPS*

Statements	Group I	Control	Group II
	"Most" bkgd.	No bkgd.	"Few" bkgd.
1–19	24.78	23.96	20.35
	"Few" bkgd.	No bkgd.	"Most" bkgd.
20–38	21.43	22.75	23.46

* From J. H. Ball, The influence of background and residual stimuli upon the measurement of attitudes, unpublished master's thesis, Univer. of Texas, 1953.

Another approach to the study of residuals is exemplified by a study in which 45 men were classified into ascendant, average, and submissive categories according to their scores on the Allport and Allport A-S reaction study [41]. Individuals with decile scores ranging from 1 to 4 were classed as ascendant, those with scores of 5 and 6 were classed as average, and those with scores from 6 to 10 were classed as submissive. Each of the subjects expressed extent of agreement with various statements taken from the Thurstone-Chave militarism-pacifism scale [82] after hearing four other individuals give their judgments. The test subjects believed the other subjects were present in adjoining rooms, but actually they were a simulated group on a tape recording [6]. Comparison of the subjects' responses to the statements in private with their responses in the simulated group condition shows the extent to which they were influenced by the group (background) opinion. The responses were made in terms of a seven-

[8] Details of results of tests of significance of the differences between values in Table 5 are given in the original study.

category scale ranging from strongly disagree (1), through neutral (4), to strongly agree (7). The data in Table 6 show that the submissive subjects shifted toward group opinion to a significantly greater extent than did ascendant subjects (17.1 as against 10.5 category steps).

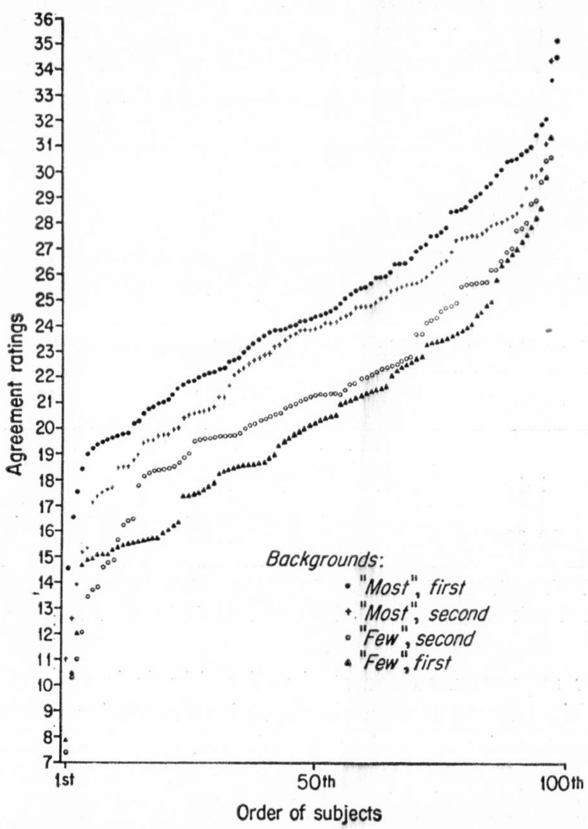

FIG. 3. Effects of backgrounds and of residuals on expression of attitudes. Mean ratings of statements 1–19 and 20–38 by 100 subjects in each of two groups. The order of subjects on the abscissa is the order of ratings from lowest to highest on the first set of 19 statements as judged by each individual. The four plotted values for each abscissa rank represent the mean ratings of the two sets of statements by two subjects judging the statements in opposite orders. *From Ball* [3, p. 42].

Subjects rated average in the A-S test moved toward the group opinion an amount intermediate to the other two groups (15.5 category steps).

In this study it is obvious that the residual factor was not experimentally controlled to the extent that it was in the preceding study by

Ball. Yet the results are noteworthy in that the *presumed* residual, degree of ascendance or submissiveness, measured by the A-S test, correlated highly with yielding behavior in what for the subjects was a lifelike group situation.

We have been able in this section to give only a partial account of the systematic approach to problems of personality and social behavior undertaken within the framework of AL theory. Many questions immediately present themselves concerning the nature and role of focal stimuli, background factors, and residual or personal contributions. Investigations have already been completed showing that yielding to group pressures depends upon the type of task and content of

TABLE 6. AVERAGE CHANGE OF THE ASCENDANT, AVERAGE, AND SUBMISSIVE SUBJECTS TOWARD OR AWAY FROM BACKGROUND GROUP OPINION*

Subjects	Toward group	Away from group
Ascendant	10.5	2.2
Average	15.5	1.3
Submissive	17.1	1.7

* From H. Helson, R. R. Blake, Jane S. Mouton, and J. A. Olmstead, The expression of attitudes as adjustments to stimulus, background and residual factors, *J. abnorm. soc. Psychol.*, 1956, **52,** 321.

the material which subjects are required to deal with—for example, factual versus attitudinal materials, and easy versus difficult tasks. Similarly, we have investigated effects of variation in background conditions such as degree of discrepancy of group opinions from subjects' opinions, and the effect of having one member of the group a high-prestige individual whereas the other members are peers of the test subjects. And finally there are many questions concerning more complicated stimulus-background relationships some of which have already been investigated, for example, the effect of focal and background stimuli which conflict with each other and therefore create tensions within the individual.[9]

There are important differences between the approach represented by these studies of personality and group behavior and other approaches. Instead of requiring people to report how they *think* they behave in various situations, or to imagine what is given in certain types of test materials, they are here responding in lifelike situations

[9] Studies dealing with these and other questions are in press and will appear as a monograph entitled "Situational and personal factors in conforming behavior," a project report to be issued by USAF School of Aviation Medicine, Randolph Field, Texas.

which are under experimental control. The actual behavior of subjects reveals the dynamics of their personalities. Under such conditions much is learned from individuals of which they themselves are unaware. Take, for example, this finding in the study by Helson, Blake, Mouton, and Olmstead [41] discussed above: subjects who yield more *frequently* to group opinion also move closer to the group position than do subjects who yield less frequently; and subjects who react against the group more frequently also move farther away from the group position than do subjects who react against the group less frequently. Moreover, some individuals who reject group opinions do so at the expense of self-consistency since they often reject a position held by the group identical with their own opinion expressed in private. (These are the "ornery" individuals.) It is difficult to believe that individuals would report such modes of behavior even if they were aware of them and it is doubtful if some of these findings can be known in advance of experimentation.

In concluding this section, the basic issues can be briefly recapitulated by asking, can personality be regarded as a totality or patterned whole of *inner* traits, drives, attitudes, or other residuals, conceived to be more or less independent of situational factors? When stated in this way, most workers would reject such a concept of personality yet many of them proceed as if there are purely internal determinants of behavior which are merely triggered by environmental forces.[10] Perhaps the question at issue is one of relative emphasis on internal versus external determinants of behavior. AL theory maintains that inner determinants such as needs, values, drives, and traits can be studied and understood only as they interact with concrete situations, and operationally such concepts have no meaning apart from situational factors. This position requires an *experimental* approach to personality and interpersonal relations no less than to perception and learning if we are to understand and predict behavior in social contexts.

VERBAL BEHAVIOR AND INTELLIGENCE

That the concept of AL can be fruitfully applied to the study of verbal behavior and cognitive functions has been shown in several studies only two of which, however, will be discussed here for purposes of illustration.

[10] That the very yardsticks of personality measurement are subject to context effects is beautifully shown in a study by Young, Holtzman, and Bryant [88] in which the composition of the items employed in scaling was found to influence raters' judgments, made with respect to the items, in systematic ways.

The first study, by Helson, Dworkin, and Michels [42], was designed to test the hypothesis that background number would influence the numerical connotations of common words and phrases implying quantity or amount. There are many words in every language which denote quantity without however being numerical terms, such as "many," "few," "everybody," "a considerable number," "most," and "almost no one." Words and phrases denoting amount can be studied quantitatively and were therefore chosen to test the hypothesis that a high background number, by raising AL, would lower estimates of such words and a low background number, by lowering AL, would increase the estimates.

Four groups of 75 subjects each were asked to specify the numbers denoted by 26 terms while keeping a given number in mind as the population to which the terms applied. The background numbers were 100, 1,232, 144,690, and 1,728,583 and were chosen to prevent use of round numbers and per cents except in the case of the lowest background number which served as the control. Each group judged the terms with a different background number.

TABLE 7. AVERAGE AMOUNTS IN PER CENT DENOTED BY 26 COMMON WORDS AND PHRASES AS A FUNCTION OF THE BACKGROUND NUMBER*

	Background numbers			
	100	1,232	144,690	1,728,583
Average per cent......	43.5	43.8	40.1	39.0

* From H. Helson, R. S. Dworkin, and W. C. Michels, Quantitative denotations of common terms as a function of background, *Amer. J. Psychol.*, 1956, **69**, 197.

The results, given in Table 7, show that the hypothesis underlying the study was verified. The average amounts denoted by the 26 terms decrease as the background numbers increase, with one exception. The differences between the two smaller backgrounds on the one hand and the two larger backgrounds on the other are not statistically significant. Of equal importance with the main finding is the finding that not all the words and phrases behave alike with respect to background influence. The 26 terms divide into three groups: the first group, containing terms such as "many," "a lot," "some," "several," "few," and "hardly anybody," changes significantly percentagewise from background to background; the second group, containing terms such as "all," "everybody," "generally," "too few," "nobody," and "none," maintains percentage constancy relative to the background numbers; and the third group of terms is intermediate between the other two groups in amount of change. It contains such terms as "too many," "a considerable number," "quite a few," "practically nobody," and "almost no one." The quantitative treatment of the data based on the reformulated Fechner law provides a technique for determining whether or not various terms are employed as synonyms. It was found that terms which appear to be synonymous in denoting the same absolute number with one background, e.g., "many" and "a considerable number," may denote different amounts with other backgrounds and hence are not always synonymous. In common with judgments of psychophysical stimuli, estimates near the middle of the list, or near AL, change more than do estimates at the end of the list. It is thus evident that in investigating effects of background a number of unexpected and interesting results were obtained regarding the behavior of the terms employed in this study.

In the second study of interest to us, Heim [33] shows that measures of intelligence are influenced by both contextual and residual items employed in the test. In her study, subjects were given easy tests of intelligence in which hard items were included and hard tests in which easy items were included. She was thus able to study the effect of level of difficulty on test performance. She distinguishes between immediate adaptation to level of difficulty and successive adaptation. Evidence of immediate adaptation to level of difficulty was found in the fact that subjects did less well with difficult items in an easy context than with items of equal difficulty in a hard context. Subjects become attuned or adapted to the level of difficulty as they work through a test since hard questions tend to be answered more correctly in a hard context than in an easy context. Successive adaptation was shown by the fact that subjects who take a hard test first do better later with hard items in easy context than do equated subjects who begin first with the easy test and take the hard test second.

The consequences of Heim's findings have both theoretical and practical importance. She says:

> It would follow that the notion of one intelligence scale along which the total population can be distributed is untenable. Such a notion implies that every individual possesses a constant amount of a static quality, measurable by standard tests of intelligence . . . the findings of this paper . . . would suggest that the subject's response to the same test problems will vary: he will sometimes do himself less than justice (still on the *test* criterion) and he will sometimes do "surprisingly well" [33, p. 221].

The two papers dealing with effects of contextual and residual factors on meanings of everyday terms and measurement of intelligence demonstrate that cognitive functions no less than sensory processes are affected by changing level of adjustment. It is sometimes assumed that "higher" cognitive functions are less dependent on stimulus conditions than are sensory and affective processes, but the studies discussed in this section, as well as many others in the literature,[11] show that this is not the case. By bringing cognitive and other inner determinants of behavior into systematic relationship with stimulus conditions the way is opened for many fruitful investigations.

TRAUMATIC AND PSYCHOTIC BEHAVIOR

The manner in which deviant behavior is envisaged in AL theory can perhaps be summarized best by repeating what I said on this subject in an earlier publication:

> The normal individual is centered in the temporal present and in his immediate spatial environment. While cognizant of past and future, he weights stimuli in accordance with their nearness, frequency, intensity, and, even more importantly, in accordance with their significance or value for him as a person. Other things being equal, objects in his special areas of interest, or occupying a high place in his affections, will be weighted more than objects having less interest or less affective value for him. The presence of a loved one in a far-off place may bring it psychologically near but, in general, the here-now represents the reference point for normal orientation.[12] Psychotics, on the other hand, are typically disoriented either in time or space, or both, and their cognitive-affective balance suffers as a result. Thus, in general paralysis of the insane the patient is disoriented in space whereas in schizophrenia he may be spatially oriented but the here-now no longer has a normal feeling tone and objects and events lose whatever real character they formerly possessed.
>
> We thus envisage personality in much the same way as we have treated perception—namely, as a system in which the energies released by internal and external forces are balanced, giving rise to ordered responses. External objects, and events, as well as internal states, are differentially weighted and responded to accordingly. Overweighting of internal states, of past or imagined happenings, of "things which can't be helped," of events far removed in space or time, or which the individual cannot change, leads to worry and neuroticism, and may even be a manifestation of psychosis. The normal individual adjusts to extreme stimuli in such a way as to ameliorate their severity. Just as the physiology of the organism is directed toward preservation

[11] Studies of cognitive functions by McReynolds [59] and by Sells [76] stress still other approaches to thought processes which are germane to AL theory.

[12] The studies by Marks [60] of judgments of skin color and by Rethlingshafer and Hinckley [72] of judgments of age and height demonstrate how one's own personal characteristics, acting as background, influence judgments of characteristics of other individuals. The general tendency found in these studies is to take one's own skin color, height, or age as "average" or the norm by which to judge others.

of normal temperature, normal pH content of the blood, and the preservation of the numerous other constants characterizing a state of health, so at the behavioral level we postulate a psychological homeostasis that parallels the well-known physiological homeostasis which governs organic activities. The critical problem for personality theory is to understand how residuals develop, how they interact with present stimulation to modify behavior, and how they can be modified or counteracted by appropriate control or manipulation of environmental factors to make possible adjustment of the organism to changing internal and external conditions [40, pp. 98–99].

The pooling and interaction of stimulus effects with organic states is probably nowhere better exemplified than in the field of experimentally induced trauma and in certain aspects of psychotic behavior. Whether or not various conditions will be traumatizing depends largely on the frequency, recency, intensity, and spacing with which they occur.[13] Thus Stone [81] found a gradual lowering of maximal cognitive level with repeated electroconvulsive shocks. Working in the same area, Worchel and Narciso [87] report that a single electroconvulsive shock does not obliterate traces of material learned immediately prior to shock. However, after 5 shocks in a period of 8 days the subjects were not able to learn a series of 10 nonsense syllables to criterion of one perfect repetition in 45 trials. The effects of shock were cumulative. But it was also found that memory ability 5 to 9 days after the last shock was equal to the ability before the first shock, showing that the effect of this amount of shock was reversible after a time.

Animals as well as human beings give evidence of the influence of spatio-temporal factors on emotional adjustment. Changes in mere spacing of emotion-producing conditions may have very important effects. Fredericson [22] found greater traumatic effects in massed confinements of dogs than in spaced confinements. Dogs confined continuously for 10 min in a box gave from 680 to 1,822 responses, whereas dogs confined for 1 min at a time and then released for 1 min gave 21 to 916 responses in the 10-min total time of confinement. The difference between the two groups is even more striking when we compare their averages: the massed group averaged 1,104 yelps per puppy, the spaced group averaged 347 yelps per puppy. There was thus a highly significant difference between the traumatizing effects of the massed and spaced conditions of confinement.

That establishment and maintenance of a stable adjustment level are necessary for normal ordered reactions is shown in a study by

[13] The theory of the general adaptation syndrome, formulated by Selye [77] as a result of studies of autonomic and endocrine functions, stresses physiological effects of intensity, frequency, and spacing of traumatic stimuli in much the same way that these are envisaged at the behavioral level in AL theory.

Kaplan and the writer [53] investigating the ability of psychotics to judge lifted weights before and after lobotomy. It was found that these subjects did not respond like normal individuals before operation and sometimes afterward as well. Among the atypical responses the following stood out: (1) confusion of the weight serving as a background stimulus with the weight to be judged; (2) inversions of judgment, e.g., a stimulus of 350 g was judged to be lighter than a stimulus of 300 g; (3) a tendency to restrict the range of responses to about half as many categories as normal individuals use under similar circumstances; and (4) failure to differentiate effects on series stimuli of different background stimuli. The psychotic subjects fail to preserve a stable reference level and so do not discriminate among stimulus conditions which are clearly different to normal subjects. In many cases, notable improvement followed at various periods after operation.

Perhaps the most important consequence of the theoretical position advocated here consists in the formulation of a conceptual model for thinking about personality (abnormal as well as normal) from the standpoint of determining what aspects of a total situation should be selected for experimental or clinical analysis and study. The emphasis is upon concretely specifiable variables which can be quantitatively evaluated in social and dynamic contexts as well as in "alone" situations. With this model, we can look forward to the development of a way of relating personality variables to one another and to the simpler forms of behavior which proved amenable to experimental control long ago. We hope thus to find common concepts and approaches for all domains of psychology.

SUMMARY

The concept of adaptation or adjustment level (AL) as the fulcrum around which all responses pivot provides an analytical approach to problems of organization and patterning. In making explicit focal, background, and residual stimuli as three sources of variance which pool to determine level, it becomes possible to isolate and evaluate the relative contributions of external and internal factors in all behavior. The quantitative definition of level brings together a number of disparate phenomena within the framework of a single theory. The theory has proved capable of extension from problems of psychophysics and perception to problems of learning, semantic behavior, the evaluation of intelligence, deviant behavior, and behavior in social contexts. With further methodological advances in the various areas, adaptation level theory can provide a basis for the integration into a unified and coherent whole of the various fields which now stand apart.

The various applications of AL theory show that it consists, not of an a priori system which is forced on the facts of behavior, but rather that it furnishes a conceptual model useful in the investigation and systematic interpretation of many different problems. Thus the weighted log mean definition of AL is applicable in various areas when appropriate values of the component factors entering into it are determined. Similarly a number of equations embodying various relevant parameters but having AL as the common zero of function have been developed for the purpose of dealing with interactions of stimulus, background, and residual factors in different areas. The theory has been found applicable to a large variety of phenomena, not because of the predilections of the writer or the others who have found AL theory useful, but because basic features of organic behavior are incorporated therein.

Since it stresses methodological considerations and is operational in character, AL theory may serve to indicate where certain theories need supplementation or where certain approaches need to make explicit how they deal with the interactions of stimulus, background, and residual factors. Two examples from opposite extremes of the behavior continuum illustrate what is meant here. At the present time, most personality theorists have not dealt with the problem of the relations between traits (inner, residual factors) and situational determinants of behavior; some sensory psychologists, on the other hand, have not realized the necessity for incorporating residual and adaptational factors into their systematic thinking.

If it is asked: "What is the unique contribution of the point of view advocated here?" the reply is that a number of important considerations have been brought together into a single systematic structure which is operationally useful. Considered separately, the ingredients of the theory may be found here and there, for psychologists have long been aware of adaptation, of focal and contextual stimuli, and they have realized that inner factors also play a role, sometimes a very significant one, in determining behavior. They have also employed quantitative methods as far as possible within the limits of their subject matter. Yet psychology has been divided by different philosophies with the result that one often hears questions like what does sensory scaling have to do with counseling or with interpersonal relations? What does knowledge about deviant behavior contribute to the study of sensory processes or cognitive functions? The compartmentalization of psychological problems stems from the fact that workers in the various fields have not taken seriously the basic truth that all approaches deal with the same essential materials and processes, whether the individual is lifting weights or functioning as a member of a committee. Such lacunae in thinking, I believe, have been largely overcome in AL theory which proceeds on the basic premise that all life consists of reactions to external and internal stresses, with the specific character of responses determined by the prevailing adjustment level of the organism. Putting this proposition into operational and quantitative form for all substantive areas of psychology is, I believe, the unique contribution of AL theory.

REFERENCES

1. Allport, F. H. *Theories of perception and the concept of structure.* New York: Wiley, 1955.

2. Attneave, F. Psychological probability as a function of experienced frequency. *J. exp. Psychol.,* 1953, **46,** 81–86.

3. Ball, J. H. The influence of background and residual stimuli upon the measurement of attitudes. Unpublished master's thesis, Univer. of Texas, 1953.

4. Bevan, W., & C. L. Darby. Patterns of experience and the constancy of an indifference point for perceived weight. *Amer. J. Psychol.,* 1955, **68,** 575–584.

5. Bishop, R. Points of neutrality in social attitudes of delinquents and non-delinquents. *Psychometrika,* 1940, **5,** 35–45.

6. Blake, R. R., & Brehm, J. W. The use of tape recording to simulate a group atmosphere. *J. abnorm. soc. Psychol.,* 1954, **49,** 311–313.

7. Blake, R. R., & Mouton, Jane S. Present and future implications of social psychology for law and lawyers. *J. pub. Law,* 1955, **3,** 352–369.

8. Blake, R. R., Mouton, Jane S., & Hain, J. D. Social forces in petition-signing. *Southwestern soc. sci. Quart.,* 1956, **36,** 385–390.

9. Blake, R. R., Rosenbaum, M., & Duryea, R. A. Gift-giving as a function of group standards. *Human Relations,* 1955, **8,** 61–73.

10. Caldwell, R. E. The mathematical formulation of a unified field theory. *Psychol. Rev.,* 1953, **60,** 64–72.

11. Cannon, W. B. *The wisdom of the body.* (2d ed.) New York: Norton, 1939.

12. Cannon, W. B. The body physiologic and the body politic. *Science,* 1941, **93,** 1–10.

13. Canter, R. R., & Hirsch, J. An experimental comparison of several psychological scales of weight. *Amer. J. Psychol.,* 1956, **68,** 645–649.

14. Carr, H. A., & Kingsbury, F. A. The concept of traits. *Psychol. Rev.,* 1938, **45,** 497–524.

15. Christman, R. J. Shifts in pitch as a function of prolonged stimulation with pure tones. *Amer. J. Psychol.,* 1954, **67,** 484–491.

16. Dempsey, E. W. Homeostasis. In S. S. Stevens (Ed.), *Handbook of experimental psychology.* New York: Wiley, 1951.

17. Elam, C. Personal communication.

18. Evans, R. M. *An introduction to color.* New York: Wiley, 1948.

19. Droba, D. D. A scale of militarism-pacifism. *J. educ. Psychol.,* 1931, **22,** 96–111.

20. Fehrer, E. Shifts in scale values of attitude statements as a function of the composition of the scale. *J. exp. Psychol.,* 1952, **44,** 179–188.

21. Fletcher, J. M. Homeostasis as an explanatory principle in psychology. *Psychol. Rev.,* 1942, **49,** 80–87.

22. Fredericson, E. Distributed versus massed experience in a traumatic situation. *J. abnorm. soc. Psychol.,* 1950, **45,** 259–266.

23. Freed, A., Chandler, P. J., Blake, R. R., & Mouton, Jane S. Stimulus and background factors in sign violation. *J. Pers.* 1955, **23,** 499.

24. Garner, W. R. Context effects and the validity of loudness scales. *J. exp. Psychol.,* 1954, **48,** 218–244.

25. Gibson, J. J. Adaptation with negative after-effect. *Psychol. Rev.,* 1937, **44,** 222–244.

26. Guilford, J. P. A generalized psychophysical law. *Psychol. Rev.,* 1932, **39,** 73–85.

27. Guilford, J. P. *Psychometric methods.* (1st ed.) New York: McGraw-Hill, 1936.

28. Guilford, J. P. *Psychometric methods.* (2d ed.) New York: McGraw-Hill, 1954.

29. Guilford, J. P. System in the relationship of affective value to frequency and intensity of auditory stimuli. *Amer. J. Psychol.,* 1954, **67,** 691–695.

30. Guilford, J. P., & Dingman, H. F. A validation study of ratio-judgment methods. *Amer. J. Psychol.,* 1954, **67,** 395–410.

31. Guilford, J. P., & Park, D. G. The effect of interpolated weights upon comparative judgments. *Amer. J. Psychol.,* 1931, **43,** 589–599.

32. Harlow, H. F. Mice, monkeys, men, and motives. *Psychol. Rev.,* 1953, **60,** 23–32.

33. Heim, Alice W. Adaptation to level of difficulty in intelligence testing. *Brit. J. Psychol.,* 1955, **46,** 211–224.

34. Helson, H. Fundamental problems in color vision. I. The principle governing changes in hue, saturation, and lightness of non-selective samples in chromatic illumination. *J. exp. Psychol.,* 1938, **23,** 439–476.

35. Helson, H. Adaptation-level as frame of reference for prediction of psychophysical data. *Amer. J. Psychol.,* 1947, **60,** 1–29.

36. Helson, H. Adaptation-level as a basis for a quantitative theory of frames of reference. *Psychol. Rev.,* 1948, **55,** 297–313.

37. Helson, H. Design of equipment and optimal human operation. *Amer. J. Psychol.,* 1949, **62,** 473–497.

38. Helson, H. "Perception and personality—a critique of recent experimental literature," Project Report No. 1, Project No. 21-0202-0007, Air Univer., USAF School of Aviation Medicine, Randolph Field, Tex., 1953.

39. Helson, H. Color and seeing. *Illum. Eng.,* 1955, **50,** 271–278.

40. Helson, H. An experimental approach to personality. *Psychiat. Res. Rep.,* 1955, **2,** 89–99.

41. Helson, H., Blake, R. R., Mouton, Jane S., & Olmstead, J. A. The expression of attitudes as adjustments to stimulus, background and residual factors. *J. abnorm. soc. Psychol.*, 1956, **52**, 314–322.

42. Helson, H., Dworkin, R. S., & Michels, W. C. Quantitative denotations of common terms as a function of background. *Amer. J. Psychol.*, 1956, **69**, 194–208.

43. Helson, H., & Himelstein, P. A short method for calculating the adaptation-level for absolute and comparative rating judgments. *Amer. J. Psychol.*, 1955, **68**, 631–637.

44. Helson, H., & Jeffers, V. B. Fundamental problems in color vision. II. Hue, lightness, and saturation of selective samples in chromatic illumination. *J. exp. Psychol.*, 1940, **26**, 1–27.

45. Helson, H., & Judd, D. B. A study in photopic adaptation. *J. exp. Psychol.*, 1932, **15**, 380–398.

46. Helson, H., Judd, D. B., & Wilson, M. Color rendition with fluorescent sources of illumination. *Illum. Eng.*, 1956, **51**, 329–346.

47. Helson, H., & Kaplan, S. A preliminary study of background effect on transposition of a lightness discrimination. Unpublished manuscript.

48. Helson, H., & Michels, W. C. The effect of adaptation on achromaticity. *J. opt. Soc. Amer.*, 1948, **38**, 1025–1032.

49. Helson, H., Michels, W. C., & Sturgeon, Artie. The use of comparative rating scales for the evaluation of psychophysical data. *Amer. J. Psychol.*, 1954, **67**, 321–326.

50. Hovland, C. I., & Sherif, M. Judgmental phenomena and scales of attitude measurement: item displacement in Thurstone scales. *J. abnorm. soc. Psychol.*, 1952, **47**, 822–832.

51. Jaffe, R. The influence of visual stimulation on kinaesthetic figural after-effects. *Am. J. Psychol.*, 1956, **59**, 70–75.

52. James, H. An application of Helson's theory of adaptation-level to the problem of transposition. *Psychol. Rev.*, 1953, **60**, 345–352.

53. Kaplan, S., & Helson, H. A study of judgment in pre- and post-lobotomized patients. Unpublished manuscript.

54. Koffka, K. *Principles of gestalt psychology.* New York: Harcourt, Brace, 1935.

55. Kohler, Ivo. Die Methode des Brillenversuchs in der Wahrnehmungspsychologie mit Bemerkungen zur Lehre der Adaptation. *Z. f. exp. u. angew. Psychol.*, 1956, **3**, 381–417.

56. Köhler, W., & Wallach, H. Figural after-effects. *Proc. Am. philos. Soc.*, 1944, **88**, 269–357.

57. Lewin, K. *Field theory in social science.* New York: Harpers, 1951.

58. McClelland, D. C., Atkinson, J. W., Clark, R. A., & Lowell, E. L. *The achievement motive.* New York: Appleton-Century-Crofts, 1953.

59. McReynolds, P. Thinking conceptualized in terms of interacting moments. *Psychol. Rev.*, 1953, **60**, 319–330.

60. Marks, E. S. Skin color judgments of Negro college students. *J. abnorm. soc. Psychol.*, 1943, **38**, 370–376.

61. Merton, R. K., & Lazarsfeld, Paul F. (Eds.) *Continuities in socia research.* Glencoe, Ill.: The Free Press, 1950.

62. Michels, W. C., & Helson, H. A reformulation of the Fechner lav in terms of adaptation-level applied to rating-scale data. *Amer. J. Psychol.* 1949, **62**, 355–368.

63. Michels, W. C., & Helson, H. Man as a meter. *Physics Today,* 1953 **6**, 4–7.

64. Michels, W. C., & Helson, H. A quantitative theory of time-orde effects. *Amer. J. Psychol.,* 1954, **67**, 327–334.

65. Michels, W. C., & Helson, H. A reconciliation of the *veg* scale wit Fechner's law. *Amer. J. Psychol.,* 1954, **67**, 677–683.

66. Michels, W. C. An interpretation of the bril scale of subjectiv brightness. *J. opt. Soc. Amer.,* 1954, **44**, 70–74.

67. Michels, W. C., & Doser, B. T. Rating scale method for comparativ loudness measurements. *J. acoust. Soc. Amer.,* 1955, **27**, 1173–1180.

68. Miller, D. R. Predictions of behavior by means of the Rorschac test. *J. abnorm. soc. Psychol.,* 1953, **48**, 367–375.

69. Nash, Myrtle C. A quantitative study of effects of past experienc on adaptation-level. Unpublished doctoral dissertation, Bryn Mawr College 1950.

70. Nash, Myrtle C. An experimental test of the Michels-Helson theor of judgment. *Amer. J. Psychol.,* 1950, **63**, 214–220.

71. Philip, B. R. The frame of reference concept. *Canad. J. Psychol.* 1949, **3**, 73–79.

72. Rethlingshafer, D., & Hinckley, E. D. Influence of characteristics o judges on their psychophysical judgments. *Amer. Psychologist,* 1954, **9**, 454 (Abstract).

73. Rosenbaum, M. The effect of stimulus and background factors or the volunteering response. *J. abnorm. soc. Psychol.,* 1956, **53**, 118–121.

74. Rosenbaum, M., & Blake, R. R. Volunteering as a function of fiel structure. *J. abnorm. soc. Psychol.,* 1955, **50**, 193–196.

75. Sarason, S. B. *The clinical interaction.* New York: Harpers, 1954.

76. Sells, S. B. The atmosphere effect: an experimental study of reason- ing. *Arch. Psychol.,* 1936, **29**, 5–72.

77. Selye, H. Stress and the general adaptation syndrome. *Brit. Med. J.* 1950, **1**, 1383ff.

78. Sherif, M., & Sherif, Carolyn W. *Groups in harmony and tension.* New York: Harpers, 1953.

79. Singer, W. B., & Young, P. T. Studies in affective reactions. II. De- pendence of affective ratings upon the stimulus-situation. *J. gen. Psychol.* 1941, **24**, 303–325.

80. Smedslund, J. *Multiple probability learning.* Oslo: Akademisk For- lag, 1955.

81. Stone, C. P. Losses and gains in cognitive functions as related to electro-convulsive shocks. *J. abnorm. soc. Psychol.,* 1947, **42**, 206–214.

82. Thurstone, L. L. (Ed.) *Attitudes toward war.* Scale No. 2, Forms

A & B (1930); Scale No. 34, Forms A & B (1931). Chicago: Univer. of Chicago Press, 1930–31.

83. Turchioe, R. M. The relation of adjacent inhibitory stimuli to the central tendency effect. *J. gen. Psychol.*, 1948, **39**, 3–14.

84. Wherry, R. J. "Control of bias in ratings. VII. A theory of rating," Final Report, Sub-Project 9, Department of the Army, PRB Report 922 Project No. 29545100 Subtask 75, Research Contract No. DA-49-083 OSA 59, Personnel Research Section PR 4575, Ohio State Univer., Columbus, 29 Feb., 1952.

85. Woodworth, R. S. *Experimental psychology.* New York: Holt, 1938

86. Woodworth, R. S., & Schlosberg, H. *Experimental psychology.* (Rev. ed.) New York: Holt, 1954.

87. Worchel, P., & Narciso, J. C. Electroshock convulsions and memory: the interval between learning and shock. *J. abnorm. soc. Psychol.*, 1950, **45**, 85–98.

88. Young, H. H., Holtzman, W. H., & Bryant, N. D. Effects of item context and order on personality ratings. *Educ. psycholog. Measmt.*, 1954, **14**, 499–517.

A NEUROPSYCHOLOGICAL THEORY

D. O. HEBB
McGill University

INTRODUCTION

As far as possible this report will answer the questions posed by Dr Koch and his committee with respect to the way in which my theory o behavior [8] came into being. The great difficulty is that I cannot alway reconstruct accurately, cannot be sure when afterthoughts and self-justification have crept in to contaminate my account of the *status quo ante* —*ante* theorizing, that is, not *ante* writing. By the time the book wa being written it was clear that the theory could not be as satisfactory a at times in the construction it had promised to be, and some protective maneuvering had no doubt begun.

My "orienting attitudes" in the first place were those of a naive realism, and still are, when trying to work out mechanisms of behavior I enjoy playing the game of epistemology and the logic of science, bu this is apart from the serious business of trying to understand learning o perception. (The serious business of psychology, that is; epistemolog is serious enough, but a sideline for the student of behavior.) We still d not have a good enough understanding of the logic of science to allow it to shape the theory of behavior completely, any more than we can allow physiological conceptions to do so.

Further, one does not self-consciously list one's postulates and so on when absorbed in problem solving; and after a conclusion has been reached one can no more go back and make an accurate account of the factors entering into it than one could reliably analyze a complex social perception. I cannot specify how "the independent-intervening-dependent variable function specifications were constructed" any more than I can reinstate my thought processes in yesterday's game of chess and see how my opponent's attack could have been so underestimated. Finally, some of my orienting attitudes have changed in *consequence* of theorizing, and I cannot be sure of not mixing up present views with those of the past. If the hope of the committee is to discover what attitudes lead to what sort of theory, there is bound to be (in my case at least) an unknown degree of contamination from later attitudes.

With this understood, let us consider the Committee's proposed topics.

BACKGROUND FACTORS AND ORIENTING ATTITUDES

It is suggested by the committee that discussion of background factors might begin autobiographically. So: B. A., Dalhousie, 1925, with a distinguished record (lowest course average without actually failing) and the intention of writing novels. This did not pay off—writing all day was too painful—and I began to think of the possibility of returning to college and actually working. About this time, also, I ran into some of Freud's work, which appeared to be a fascinating and cogent set of ideas in need of being made rigorous (it may be relevant that math and physics were the only subjects in which I had made respectable marks). I had had almost no psychology before, but McGill was persuaded to accept me as a part-time graduate student, despite my earlier record. There a friend drew my attention to Pavlov's recently published English translations.

Pavlov was even more fascinating than Freud, as a way of getting at the mechanisms of what Freud was talking about. I was now earning my living as a teacher, and of course was becoming increasingly interested in learning. Professor Boris P. Babkin arranged an unpaid assistantship with Dr. L. A. Andreyev, one of Pavlov's collaborators on temporary research appointment at McGill. After two years' intensive work, however, I began to feel that there were fatal limitations in Pavlovian thought; though I could not specify what they were, the whole thing became less convincing the farther I got into it. Also, much of Pavlov's theory depended on his quantitative data, and I had discovered that the method of measuring salivary secretion was intrinsically unreliable; the idea of estimating reliability, or the error of measurement, did not enter into Pavlov's thinking.

Thus was I softened up for my encounter with Köhler's *Gestalt Psychology* and Lashley's critique of reflexology (in that order). Accordingly, when at last (in 1934) I decided that full-time graduate work was necessary, I managed to get accepted in Lashley's laboratory in Chicago. The order of these decisions is important, in evaluating later attitudes: I decided first that physiological psychology was the ticket for me, secondly where and with whom to study, rather than becoming a physiological psychologist because of having happened to work with one. I had had no experience with physiological method; I anticipated great difficulty in getting up the necessary anatomy and physiology; and I took a financial beating to study at Chicago and later Harvard without an assistantship, instead of going where I could have got one. At this time I was thirty years old and presumably knew what I was doing.

So much for predoctoral history. Only one postdoctoral experience need be listed as having a major effect on my preconceptions. This was the profound upset in my ideas following failure to find any sign of mental defect produced by Penfield's frontal-lobe operations, with removals running up toward 20 per cent of the mass of the human cerebrum. This broke up some elaborate research plans, which took for granted that loss would be easily demonstrated. By early 1938 it was clear that the relation of brain and intelligence, in man, was quite different from what it was supposed to be. I found the facts extremely puzzling, but failed to interest others in them; there was polite incredulity instead. The problem preoccupied me until 1942 when I published a possible line of explanation, again without any panic on the stock market [7]. The idea was that neural tissues needed for the development of intellectual function might not be equally necessary for its maintenance.

But this line of thinking raised more problems than it settled, and it was the attempt to deal with them that led eventually to the theory that was published in 1949. Some of the features of my book are undoubtedly due to the fact that when writing I expected it to meet a rather complete lack of interest, and that it would take years of experimentation to win a hearing for the theory. Though confident that it was following a sound line, I was unhappy about the form it had to take—the misleading degree of specificity in some places, the vagueness in others—and was quite unprepared for the generous reception that it actually received. Apparently it met a long-unfelt need.

That covers the autobiographical side. As far as possible, I will try to reconstruct the theoretical opinions which immediately preceded contruction of my theory, which began in early 1944. My earlier reaction rom Pavlovian theory made me certain, beyond question, that Hull's ap-roach could not be successful in the long run. His modifications of Pavlov and Watson were not getting at the root of the trouble; and the uman brain-operation data had reinforced my conviction that *radical* hanges were needed to make existing theory work. I had all the fervor f the reformed drunk at a temperance meeting; having been a fully onvinced Pavlovian, I was now a fully convinced Gestalter-*cum*-Lash-eyan. Though I saw that the configurational theories were not satis-actory, I thought they pointed the direction for better theorizing in the uture. The theory of which I found myself eventually the author did eal violence to these a priori convictions. Theory it seemed must begin vith (1) perception, and take in (2) learning in such a way as to en-ompass (3) ideation, and attention or set. Here my thinking stalled. I could find no mechanism of learning that was consistent with my ideas bout perception. The breakthrough came in playing with a crude nalogy for attention: that it is like a process in the brain that opens ne afferent pathway, leaving others blocked. Treating attention or set n this way suggested interesting possibilities; though they depended on a kind of connectionism which, I was convinced, was untenable, I was nterested enough to go back and look at the whole question of con-ections in the light of recent physiological ideas.

As noted above, all this was carried out in a spirit of naive realism, eeking answers to the questions: How does the brain work in thought? What happens in learning? What pathways are concerned in visual per-eption?

The "limits of prediction" in psychology, I would probably have said, re about the same as in any other science; that is, they are set by our wn intellectual capacity. Maybe there are intrinsic limits to scientific rediction—that is, we may not be dealing with a fully deterministic niverse—but it seems to me that the scientific method is to make the vorking assumption of determinacy up to the point at which it is con-lusively refuted. Though it has *possibly* been reached by physics, in the o-called indeterminacy principle, this point is still far removed in bio-ogical research of any kind.

As to the "fruitful level of analysis," no conscious consideration was given to such a question in theorizing. It is evident to me *post hoc* that I theorized at several levels (see below), and my present answer to the question is that *all* levels of analysis are fruitful, complementing one nother and equally necessary for theoretical progress.

Concerning the "comprehensiveness of empirical reference": the riginal intent was narrow (as noted above). What happened was that he system of ideas as it developed took on relevance to wider problems.

When it was finally worked out I considered it to have "unrestricte generality of scope"; not that it is successful over this wide range, bu that when it does not account for a behavioral phenomenon—any be havioral phenomenon—this is evidence that the theory is unsatisfactor on that point (at the best incomplete, but probably needing changes a well).

Finally, I do not recall raising in my own mind the questions o the fruitful degree of formalizing a theory, in the sense of "hypothetico deductive axiomization." My guess is that I would have opposed goin far in this direction. It seems obvious to me that overformalization ca be sterile and cramping, both in thinking and in experiment. But whe is theory too formal? I don't know; clearly some formalization is neces sary, and one must be definite and precise—up to a point. Beyon that, elaboration of details of definition and the like becomes logicall equivalent to carrying an answer to too many places of decimals.

Such views, however, were certainly not explicit at the time o writing. They have developed as a result of a difficulty encountered sinc 1949. I have repeatedly been asked whether my theory is definite enoug to be testable, and have come to the conclusion that, as it stands, thi question cannot be answered.

"Testable" in what respect? There is no need to test the theory t see whether it is "true": there is already plenty of evidence, on specifi points, to show that my theory is at best incomplete, and wrong i detail. But so of course are other theories. Can one then test the theor in comparison with others, to see which is better? But this would be o specific points, one after another; it would not amount to assessing th general validity of the theories being compared. When a theory prove wrong on specific points, its adherents do not accept defeat, throw ou the theory, and start afresh. If illustration is needed, consider th Tolman-Hull battle—but really, this is and always has been characteristi of theorizers in any field, as Conant [4] has emphasized. What th theorizer does is to revise an assumption or two and keep on going Logically, one cannot test the validity of a theory as a whole if it i based on a number of separate postulates and (in effect) consists of a network of more specific hypotheses. The *experimentum crucis* ide applies only to the single hypothesis of the type that links two in dependently identifiable entities.

I had not got far before I knew that my speculations must be wron in many respects even before they were put on paper—though I coul not say just *which* respects. All that could be hoped was that the genera line was right. I had to be specific on many points, just to show it wa possible. The situation was this.

In 1945 Lashley and the Gestalters had abolished connectionism; th eflexologists no longer defended it but had withdrawn into the never-ever land of the empty organism, miniature systems, and as-if theory. Iull was balanced on the dividing line between physiological conceptions nd ones with behavioral reference only (between "hypothetical contructs" and "intervening variables"), apparently inclined toward physilogizing but unwilling to commit himself, so that he was not vulnerable o a physiological critique. In short, connectionism had no defenders, and he psychological world had tacitly conceded the argument that such exlanations of behavior were not possible.

To show on the contrary that they were quite possible in the light f newer ideas of nervous function, I had to carry one out—making arbirary assumptions whenever evidence was lacking—to show that a *coneivably* true theory, as far as existing evidence was concerned, could be nade specific and detailed. Now if in constructing a theory you come to a oint at which, let us say, any one of three assumptions is possible, your robability of being right after you have made the choice is at best 0.33. After you have done this a second time, your probability has shrunk to .11. And so on.

Thus there is no need to test the specific implications, the possible letailed predictions to be extracted from the statements of *The Organizaion of Behavior*. The problem in writing was to find a balance between eing vague and general on the one hand, and on the other of giving he endless elaboration of detail (including alternate formulations) vhich in fact I had worked out in the course of theorizing. What I tried o do was to make the general propositions as clear as possible, and to laborate detail that would show what kind of specificity they might be iven. One could have been much more detailed, but this, besides making ne look foolish, might have seriously clogged the wheels of thought nd communication, and interfered with what values the theory did ave.

Surely in our theorizing we work by a series of approximations, very ough in the early stages. As we find evidence that we are getting closer o the bull's-eye, as theory develops, much more precision of statement nd formalization of assumptions will be in order. Each theorist has to lecide for himself what the fertile degree of formalization is at the resent stage of knowledge, but it cannot be assumed that it is always etter to increase the degree of elaboration in detail (or equally, the legree of quantification).

STRUCTURE OF THE SYSTEM, AS THUS FAR DEVELOPED

The committee's request for "exhaustive itemization of systematic ndependent, intervening and independent variables," "major interrelations among constructs," and "discussion of order of determinacy . . . c construct linkages" is a large order. Perhaps the best way of answerin is first to outline the main structure of the system, then try to deal wit some of these individual points.

The key conception is that of the *cell assembly,* a brain proces which corresponds to a particular sensory event, or a common aspec of a number of sensory events. This assembly is a closed system i which activity can "reverberate" and thus continue after the sensor event which started it has ceased. Also, one assembly will form con nections with others, and it may therefore be made active by one of then in the total absence of the adequate stimulus. In short, the assembl activity is the simplest case of an *image* or an *idea:* a representativ process. The formation of connections between assemblies is the mecha nism of association.

The way in which the connections are established, between singl neurons to form the assembly in the first place, or between neurons con necting one assembly with another, is as follows. If a neuron, *A,* is nea enough to another, *B,* to have any possibility of firing it, and if it doe take part in firing it on one occasion (it often requires two or mor neurons working together to trigger the response in another), th probability is increased that when *A* fires next *B* will fire as a result. I other words, "synaptic resistance" is decreased, by a microscopic growt at the synapse or some chemical change in one of the two cells. Th assembly might be made up of perhaps 25, 50, or 100 neurons, an building it up in the first place would be a very slow process, requirin many repetitions of the stimulating conditions. These conditions might b a particular pattern of pressure in a small area of skin, exposure to particular vowel sound, or an optical contour of a particular slop falling in the central foveal area; or they might be "relational," consist ing of a decreased illumination as the eye moves from a lighter to darker area, or of the common property ("hardness") of a series c tactual stimulations as the infant's hand touches a rattle, a bar of hi crib, the milk bottle, and so forth.

It is proposed that these representative activities, each correspondin to some property of environmental stimulation, would form connectin links with each other and with concurrent motor activities, on the basi of the "synaptic resistance" postulate referred to above. Most assemblie would be established during the occurrence of particular motor activitie (visual stimulation and eye movements, tactual stimulation and move ment of the corresponding part of the body, auditory stimulation an vocalization); each would therefore establish neural connections wit and tend to produce, its own motor activity. However, actual muscl contraction would often not occur, because some other assembly activit

ccurring at the same time might inhibit the motor path, or simul-
ineously active assemblies might have motor effects that were physically
icompatible with each other (e.g., flexing and extending a limb at the
ime time). Overt movements would result whenever such inhibition or
onflict was absent.

The *phase sequence* is a temporally integrated series of assembly
ctivities; it amounts to one current in the stream of thought. Each as-
embly activity in the series might be aroused (1) sensorily, (2) by ex-
itation from other assemblies, or (3) in both ways. It is assumed that
ie last, (3), is what usually happens in an organized flow of behavior.
ach assembly must establish connections with a number of other as-
emblies, at different times; which of these others it will arouse on any
pecific occasion will depend on what other activity, and especially what
ensory activity, is going on at that moment. Assembly *A* tends to excite
, *C*, and *D;* sensory activity tends to excite *D* only, so *A* is followed
y *D*. At each point in time, behavior would thus be steered both sensorily
nd centrally, jointly controlled by the present sensory input and the im-
iediately prior central activity.

The possibility—or the inevitability, on the assumptions already
iade—that two or more phase sequences may run concurrently opens
p the possibility that one may conflict with the other, in the sense that
iey may produce incoordinated behavior, motor components belonging
) one sequence perhaps alternating randomly with those belonging to
ie other; or if one is inhibitory of the other, all motor outflow might be
ullified. This, it is assumed, is what happens in gross emotional dis-
irbances. The later development (since the theory was first published)
f knowledge of the brain-stem arousal system on the whole fits in here
ather well. Higher levels of arousal would increase the probability of
icompatible assembly actions, or "conflicting" phase sequences in this
ense, and hence contribute to the incoordinations of strong emotion [9].

A closely related possibility is that the occurrence of two phase
equences simultaneously, which have never occurred with just that
ming before, will produce new combinations of motor components that
ave adaptive value. This is considered to be insight behavior, and the
ew combination of assemblies at that moment means seeing the situation
i a new way.

Set, in this scheme, is the influence of the preexistent central activity
n the next link in the phase-sequence chain. The animal is presented
ith a stimulus situation that can arouse different central activities, each
ieaning a different motor response; which will occur is in part deter-
iined by excitation from assemblies already active. The significance
f the theory, as I see it, is principally in trying to get these central
rocesses out of the bushes where we can look at them. Everyone knows

that set and expectancy and the stimulus trace exist. How are we to learn more about these ideational or mediating processes, and the limits on their role in behavior, except by forming hypotheses (as explicit as we can reasonably make them) and then seeing what implications they have for behavior, and whether these implications are borne out in experiment? By all means, if you will, call these central events mediating processes instead of ideas or cell assemblies, but let us get busy and investigate them.

Variables dealt with, and level of analysis. It is clear that this theorizing is at several levels. The hypothesis about synaptic change is a very "molecular" one indeed. Each neuron might have up to a thousand such contacts with other neurons. The cell assembly might comprise something of the order of a hundred neurons. The perception of a simple object, or the "idea" or "image" of such an object, is supposed to consist of the activity of a number of assemblies, corresponding to its various properties, occurring within a time period of a second or so. A phase sequence, or series of assembly activities, would comprise a large number of assemblies.

Much of the theorizing is at the very molar level of assuming the existence of the phase sequence, with properties defined in rather general terms and no reference to constituent cellular activities. That is, the theory might be divided roughly in two parts. The main part, as far as actually dealing with behavior is concerned, assumes the existence of ideational elements renamed with a physiological reference (cell assemblies) and a stream of thought, also renamed (phase sequence). A logically separate part of the theory attempts to show how the ideational element would come about, on the basis of existing anatomical and physiological knowledge. This is the molecular aspect of the theorizing; the main part is molar.

Similarly, the variables dealt with are at different levels. The *independent variables* are: sensory excitations, at varying levels of complexity of patterning, temporal as well as spatial; direct neural stimulations; content of blood stream and plasma, stimulating neural cells or modifying their excitability; and the structural and functional properties of the nervous system, controlled by using animals of different heredities, animals suffering from disease, or animals subjected to surgical injury.

The *intervening variables* are: unobserved functioning of sense organs, nervous system or effectors (e.g., gut movements, or changes of skeletal-muscle tension producing no overt change of posture), and activity of glands of internal secretion. In short, unobserved processes inside the skin which, one supposes, mediate the observed response.

Here particularly, it is important to be clear that different levels are involved, and one may get very far from what is reasonably considered to be a "hypothetical construct"—i.e., something potentially observable.

For this and other reasons (see below), a "phase sequence" or "emotional disturbance" or a "conceptual activity" is a psychological construct, too complex to be directly examined; ten thousand electrodes, with simultaneous recordings, might be too few for the purpose—even if we knew where to place them.

The *dependent variables* are observed muscular and glandular activities, treated again at different levels of complexity. Also, such things as the EEG, EMG, and GSR may be dependent variables, but according to the context as well as the level of analysis, they may at other times be independent or intervening variables. The EEG, for example, would be an independent variable if one were to study intelligence in epileptics during subclinical attacks, comparing test performance in the subject when the EEG was abnormal and when it was not. At a low molecular level, an independent variable might be the punctate, momentary stimulation of a specific receptor group, and the dependent variable a single integrated movement of a limb or an eyeball. More frequently, however, discourse is at the level of making the sight of a particular object the independent variable and the dependent variable a movement of the whole animal toward or away from it. "The sight of an object" can be made more molecular, reduced hypothetically to a series of stimulations and responses in rapid sequence as the animal looks at the object. But only one such reduction would be possible at a time; in practice one could not deal with a maze run (e.g.) at this level, and would have to deal with such larger segments of behavior in more molar terms. More and less molar accounts of behavior are related in that one is prepared at any point to (hypothetically) make a reduction from the higher to the lower level, considering one of the higher items at a time.

It was said above that a phase sequence is a psychological construct, not a physiological one. The statement, which applies also to the cell assembly, needs explanation. Not only are these hypothetical processes too complex to be recorded physiologically; they also relate primarily to the behavior of the whole intact animal, and exist as constructs whose necessity is found only in the attempt to explain such behavior. It is the evidence of behavior that led Pavlov and Hull to the stimulus trace, not physiology; the physiological evidence, by itself, and for traces with time period of 10 or 15 secs, almost rules this out. It is behavior alone that justifies the conception of expectancy. When behavior indicates the existence of such forms of ideation or mediating process, we reconsider the evidence of anatomy and physiology and, with hindsight, see how the constructs may, conceivably, be made compatible with what we know of brain function; but this does not change the fact that they originated as *behavioral* constructs, nor the fact that the knowledge we have of their properties is still derived mostly from behavior.

This becomes very clear indeed when one tries to translate them into physiological terms, as I did. I started with the preconception that ideation existed; the difficulty was to see what brain process could have the properties that ideation implies, in relation to behavior. The assembly did not follow logically from the neurological evidence; on the contrary, its specifications put a heavy strain on the evidence, and only the known existence of delayed response, expectancies, imagery, and so forth made the argument even remotely plausible.

What I mean by a psychological as opposed to a physiological construct, therefore, is that its referents are primarily in the behavior of the intact animal. One may name it, and hypothetically describe it, in physiological terms; but this is in the effort to maintain communication between different levels or universes of discourse. My theory is not an attempt to substitute physiology for psychology. No theory of the behavior of the whole animal could be, because in such a theory one is trying to deal with the functioning of the whole brain and nervous system, as influenced moment by moment by the whole internal environment, and the kind of construct one must work with ("learning capacity," "anxiety," "intelligence") takes one at times completely out of the universe of physiological method and its concentration on the functioning of part systems rather than of the whole body over extended periods of time.

INITIAL EVIDENTIAL GROUNDS OF THE SYSTEM

From here on my report is increasingly in danger of being repetitious. The request to "identify the chief classes of . . . data," and to say why this material was considered "strategic" or "fundamental," has been partly answered. To amplify:

It always seemed to me that learning is the crucial question in psychological theory. Even in talking about the innate or instinctive, one is concerned in a sense with delimiting the role of learning. But as has been said, all lines of thought about learning and memory seemed nullified by the facts of perception. It seemed certain to me that this hurdle would have to be crossed first.

This was not what happened. Without meaning to, I bypassed the strategically important perception. The solution found was one that married ideation and learning, and gave perception the second-rate status of a concubine. That is to say, the main structure of the theory was such as to provide for the acquisition (learning) of ideational processes, and for their part in subsequent modifications of behavior. Only then did I turn to the question of the equivalence of stimuli—the great stumbling block for learning theory—and the rather implausible treatment of this question was largely dictated by the direction the theory had already taken. When they were reexamined in detail, however, the facts of perception were not as clearly opposed to this line of speculation as I had thought—some of them seemed instead clearly to support it—and so, as other facts began to fit together, it began to be possible to take all this seriously.

Constructing the theory was at first playing a little game, not a very serious undertaking. The idea about attention and set as being the selective action of some sort of self-maintaining (reverberatory?) process in the brain seemed a neat one, but unreal, because of failing to provide for sensory and cortical equipotentiality. But it had interesting possibilities when I went further, so a mechanism was worked out by which a "cell assembly" (though at that time it was referred to as a "lattice") might develop, in accord with what I knew about the anatomy and physiology of the visual system.

Here a check was encountered. The assembly would take a considerable time to develop, which implies that some of the most important aspects of perception and of learning would be delayed for an equally long time. The game was finished at this point—it seemed—because the implication was contrary to fact. Before giving it up, however, I cast around in an attempt to see how an experiment might be devised to test the question again, in the light of these new ideas, and then recalled vaguely the evidence compiled by von Senden [25] from all the cases of congenitally blind persons given their sight after they were old enough to report what they saw. I looked his monograph up again; what he reported, in short, was that the patient could not perceive patterns as normal persons do until he had been exposed to the visual world for a period of months, that there was no stimulus equivalence in this period, and that visual memory for patterns was almost at a zero level. Subsequently, if the patient kept on trying, these capacities showed a sharp rate of improvement, all about the same time. This evidence of course was very exciting; it fitted closely into the conception of a first period of slow development of assemblies and a subsequent period of normal performance (or nearly so) after the assemblies had reached an adequate level of functioning. At this point, then, I began to take the game seriously.

Almost at once, however, another difficulty arose. As the functioning of assemblies was thought of, it would have to occur in a perceptual environment in which most of the stimulus combinations were familiar; otherwise cells would fire chaotically and organized sequences of assembly action ("phase sequences") could not occur. Thus behavior would be random and uncoordinated in a strange environment, since an orderly progression of muscular movements would depend on an orderly sequence of brain events. Clearly—it seemed again—the idea that unfamiliar stimulus combinations would disorganize behavior was contrary to fact.

Now it happened that my serious research in the preceding months had dealt with the emotional sensitivity of the chimpanzees at the Yerkes Laboratories of Primate Biology, Orange Park, Florida. I had, as a matter of fact, just completed a paper reporting data for which I could find no rationale but which seemed too significant not to publish. When the idea occurred to me to identify chaotic assembly activity with emotion and when this, in a general way, made sense of a lot of facts about emotion that had made no sense before, I felt sure at last that I was in business as a theorist. If perception happened to get manhandled in making it accord with the rest of the theory, so much the worse for perception as the key determinant. But in fact, when I now went back over the perceptional evidence that had seemed so decisive before and looked at it from the new theoretical point of view, there were obviously large holes in it.

These incidents, in each of which a necessary implication first seemed a fatal flaw and then, when the behavioral evidence was looked at from the new point of view, became instead an asset, extending the scope of the theory, gave me confidence that the line pursued was sound. It also seemed quite clear that "physiologizing," if one physiologized on the right lines, could be broadening instead of narrowing, and could stimulate purely behavioral research as well as research employing physiological methods. The research in this laboratory on the adult's perception of printed words [19, 21, 11], for example, or the child's perception of inverted pictures [12], arose from the considerations just dealt with, as well as the larger program studying restrictions of the early environment and the development of intellectual and motivational processes [13, 6, 3, 17, 24, 15]. Certain other physiological considerations were at the bottom of the study of restriction of the later environment [2, 5, 9]. It is also relevant to point out that the reevaluation of man's emotionality as a factor in his social behavior by Dr. Thompson and me [10] was specifically initiated by trying to see whether the implications of the physiologizing about emotion, referred to above, were (as they seemed) contrary to the facts of adult human behavior.

CONSTRUCTION OF FUNCTION FORMS

The committee's questions under the heading of "construction of function forms" are mostly not relevant here, implying as they do too much sophistication on my part at the time of theorizing. One point however may be dealt with: the "grounds for favoring employment or nonemployment of intervening variables."

I did not consider such questions in writing my book, but have since worked out some sort of rationale for my procedure. I can summarize by saying that any theory of the behavior of the whole animal must employ intervening variables or dispositional concepts. As I have already said, a physiologically oriented theory of behavior must remain a *psychological* theory. It will have to employ constructs derived from behavior which could not have originated with neurological data, even if subsequently one finds a way of relating them to such data.

One cannot analyze higher behavior without recourse to such intervening variables, though one can develop hypotheses as to the relations between them and the data of anatomy and physiology. Knowledge of behavior may lead to the inference that there are such things as "ideas"; given this as an essential starting point, one can try to build something up from the neurological data that will have the same properties. Then one looks at the discrepancies between the neurological construct, and the original construct derived from behavior (including any "extra" produced by the neurologizing). Perhaps the discrepancies are only apparent: the revisions suggested by the neurologizing may be found to be justified by existing behavioral data, or by new experiment. If so, the neurologizing has shown its value, and one is left in possession of an improved construct—but still fundamentally a psychological one.

It is evident that such a method of analysis is not an attempt to substitute physiological ideas for psychological ones, or hypothetical constructs for all intervening variables. Certainly, if "intervening variable" includes the dispositional concept, then it seems clear that physiological psychology must always make essential use of intervening variables—must remain completely dependent on them—in dealing with the larger aspects of behavior. It differs from other psychology in making more *explicit* use of physiological ideas, in trying to maintain communication (translatability) with the physiological universe of discourse, and in using the translation into neurological terms and back again as a means of clarifying present conceptions and developing better ones at about the same level. It does not aim at getting rid of "emotion," "memory," or "perception" entirely, but at making such conceptions more precise and effective.

MENSURATIONAL AND QUANTIFICATIONAL PROCEDURES

There are of course no precise quantitative aspects of my theorizing. The committee requests that one express one's views nevertheless on the place of mensuration in psychology.

First, it is clear that psychology would hardly exist without its quantitative experimental methods, as in the comparison of learning rates by counting errors, the analysis of animal perception by counting the number of choices of one stimulus pattern and rejections of another, measurement of amount of autonomic activity in the GSR, and so on.

It seems to me to be less fertile, however, to do much assigning of precise quantitative properties to our intervening variables at present.

The problem is the relation of qualitative to quantitative analysis, and this is, in brief, the problem of the hen and the egg. We cannot profitably refine our quantitative values to a much greater degree than the refinement of our qualitative conceptions. The two must develop hand in hand. Before one can measure profitably one must know what one is measuring, or find the right things to measure. In this sense, qualitative analysis must precede quantitative. When the quantification is done, it is likely to react upon, and improve, the ideas that preceded it. New qualitative analyses then lead to better ideas of what to measure, and so forth. Trying to short-circuit this process, when dealing with a system in which the variables involve a large number of dimensions, inevitably rigidifies one's present theoretical ideas and tends to prevent growth, rather than stimulate it. Precise quantification with respect to theoretical entities should be expected only in late stages of development of the science.

Meteorology is one example of the difficulties of quantifying the behavior of complex systems; even though the analyst has available a number of precise measurements, which he knows are reliable, he cannot at present do much quantifying of some of the things he is most concerned with: the direction, and speed, of the future movement of weather systems. A very nice example of the interaction of quantitative and nonquantitative conceptions is the improvement in forecasting that was made by introducing the nonquantitative construct of the weather "front." The meteorologist's primary problem is to find such conceptions, which show him how to combine the available quantifications and what new ones to ask for.

I think we have generally underestimated the role of qualitative analysis in the physical sciences, and forget how often it was the development of a new *idea* that made quantification possible thereafter (of course, quantitative discrepancies also lead to revision of existing ideas; my point is that the process works both ways). Think, for example, of the effect of the isotope idea in clarifying the quantitative conceptions of chemistry, and to what an extent chemistry (especially organic chemistry) is concerned with the *structure* of molecules whose over-all quantitative properties are already known.

At any rate, I see quantitative and qualitative thinking as going hand in hand, not opposed to one another, and feel that in psychology we must always be as much concerned with the question of what to quantify as with quantification of presently known variables. We are dealing with an *n*-dimensional system (*n* being a large number) when we theorize about our intervening variables. We may expect that the effective level of quantification will be relatively low for some time to come, corresponding to the very rough approximations of our qualitative conceptions, and that the degree of precision will increase at about the same rate in both. We should be as sophisticated about the probable error in theory as we are in experimentation.

THE MEDIATION OF RESEARCH

Two topics raised by the committee ("formal organization of the system" and "range of application") are pretty well covered in the preceding sections, and so omitted at this point.

The "history of the system to date in mediating research" is hard for me to see in perspective, and the relation of the system to the research not too clear. I shall not try to cover work in other laboratories that may have been stimulated by it [1, p. 240]. The work in our own laboratory has been done by graduate students and research associates, and it is most important to say first that the work is theirs, not mine; so it is very difficult for me to say to what extent or in what way my theorizing affected it. I have consistently discouraged experiments designed as a test of my theory in a narrow sense, feeling that this would limit the student's research too much. Much better is the experiment that aims from the first to give a chance of getting at better ideas. This, of course, means an incidental testing of present theory, but it does not merely ask whether the theory is right or wrong.

The connection of my theory to some of the work is fairly clear: the studies of visual perception of Mishkin and Forgays, Orbach, Heron, and Hunton [19, 21, 11, 12]; the effects of perceptual isolation by Bexton, Heron, Scott, and Doane [2, 5]; the role of the infant environment in mental development by Hymovitch, Forgays and Forgays, Clarke et al., Thompson and Heron, Melzack, and Mahut [13, 6, 3, 24, 17, 15]; and the reexamination of the mass-action and equipotentiality conceptions by Lansdell and Smith [14, 23].

Apart from these studies, the theory as far as I can see had its effect by raising rather general questions and promoting argument in the laboratory. Theory inevitably has a sort of restricting effect on ideas; one tends not to follow up, even in thinking, the avenue that is clearly "impossible." My coworkers have been in general vigorously critical of much of my theory, but they accept the validity of the sort of questions that it raises, as objects for research. Indirectly, therefore, it has played a significant part in some of the studies to which it did not give rise directly.

EVIDENCE FOR THE SYSTEM

The committee asks next what evidence there is for the system, and what evidence is opposed. I would apply here the same criteria as in discussing earlier the question of the crucial experiment. If it is true that only a specific hypotheses can be tested, and that a network of hypotheses connecting intervening variables in a complex theory cannot be vanquished by specific adverse evidence (because all that may be needed is to add a postulate somewhere, or revise one), then it is also true that the theorist cannot regard favorable evidence as "proof" of his theory. The decision as between two complex theories will be from a weight of evidence, and will be made by others, not the authors of the theories.

The committee however seems determined to extract opinions from us authors. How do I evaluate the weight of evidence? There is plenty (as I shall try to indicate) opposed to my theory, in specific terms; what is there in favor? My answer, really, is that the same considerations apply now that applied in 1944 (when I began to construct the theory) or 1949 (when it was published), namely, that we must deal with set and attention and perceptual generalization and learning in one theoretical framework, not have one approach for thinking, another for learning, and a third for perception—the position in which the members of the gestalt group found themselves.

My theory is the only one that attempts this, and in my opinion, to be quite frank, is consequently the only realistic attempt to deal theoretically with the problems of behavior. Skinner of course has avoided theory; Tolman and Guthrie have proposed approaches to the problem of constructing a theory, but both have remained, essentially, programmatic. Hull's is the only real alternative to mine; and the course of development of his ideas, from 1937 to 1951, has shown a narrowing of the range of phenomena dealt with, an increasingly clear set of difficulties to be encountered even in the narrow range with which his theory does deal, and an increasing concern with minor modifications of postulates as defensive measures to meet the attacks of critics. He excluded from the first a treatment of set and perception ("afferent neural interaction" recognized the existence of perceptual generalization, but nothing, really, was ever done about it). The only sign of real broadening is in Meehl and MacCorquodale's [16] treatment of expectancy and perceptual learning, and the suggestions by Seward, Osgood, Kendler, and others that "surrogate" or "mediational" responses, the functional equivalents of ideation, be included in the theory. But for some reason these ideas are handled very gingerly, as if they might explode at any moment, and no attempt is made to review the rest of the conceptual structure to make such ideas an integral part of the theory. Mine, in short, is the only attempt to deal with the thought process and perception in the framework of a theory of learning. It has serious defects, but no real competitor. This fact I see as the major "evidence for the system," together with the body of research that it has, directly or indirectly, stimulated.

Now let us look at the defects:

Vagueness. It may be true, as I have argued, that a theory of behavior at present should not be too specific in detail. On the other hand, mine certainly is much vaguer on a number of points than is desirable, even at the present stage. The locus or extent of the assembly should be indicated, hypothetically. The order of magnitude of the number of cells entering into an assembly, and of the number of alternate paths in functional parallel, was not even suggested in the original formulations. No real decision is made concerning the criteria of "separateness" of one phase sequence from another, when two exist side by side, nor is anything proposed about how many may exist at the same time. No attempt is made to be specific about how somesthetic and auditory assemblies would be established, and their relation to motor phenomena. This last could certainly have been done, but was not.

Difficulties. I doubt whether the assembly will really work,[1] as proposed, if a detailed analysis is made. On emotion, I gave the impression [8] that the disruption of assembly action can be deduced from the physiological and anatomical postulates I had made. As I have said in a preceding section, I *did* make this deduction in the first stages of constructing the theory, but it does not stand up on subsequent analysis—not very convincingly, at least—and I must regard this instead as an inference from behavior, not well justified physiologically. I am inclined now to think more in terms of some sort of disorganization of the phase sequence, involving overfacilitation from the arousal system [9] rather than of the individual assembly, but this at best remains quite vague.

Also, as I have noted elsewhere [9], the results of the perceptual isolation experiment by Heron, Bexton, Scott, and Doane refute the formulations of the theory with respect to the relations between thinking, motivation, and emotion.

Subsequent physiological developments. Since my book was written, new physiological data have appeared which would have greatly affected the formulations of the theory. I have summarized these elsewhere [9].

[1] A more adequate hypothesis has since been proposed by P. M. Milner, *Psychol. Rev.*, 1957, **64**, 242–252.

Inhibition, as a direct suppression of activity in one cell by that of another, exists and must be taken account of. The time properties of cellular action are changed: neural fatigue may endure for a matter of minutes (and perhaps longer) instead of milliseconds; dendritic activity is quite different from axonal, lasting 15 to 30 msec and accounting for much repetitive firing by axons. It also accounts largely for the slow waves of the EEG, so my treatment of the slow wave as an envelope for spikes, is, at best, misleading. The most outstanding modification of basic physiological knowledge concerns the central role of the brain-stem reticular formation in cortical function.

These are the main defects of the theory, as far as the available evidence goes. It may, as I believe, be on the right general lines, but in detail it is evidently in need of considerable change.

VALUES APART FROM SPECIFIC CONTENT, AND FORECASTING THE FUTURE

At this point the theorist has run out of steam, and is running out of space. The committee's remaining questions must be answered briefly: they ask, to paraphrase, If the theory is wrong, what incidental values has it? Is it developing as it was meant to, and is it converging with others? And finally, what is the strategy of further development?

The values of the theory apart from its specific content as far as I can see are that it has reopened the question of connectionistic hypotheses in psychology, clarified some issues (such as the meaning of "attention" and related terms, which Gibson in 1941 found mysterious and undefinable, or the meaning of "consciousness"), and initiated or helped to stimulate worthwhile research. I say "worthwhile" because a theory can initiate a lot of research which is nevertheless trivial, without meaning apart from minor details of a theory which may have no lasting value. The work I speak of is significant whether my theory stands or not: the studies of the early environment, or of perceptual isolation; or Milner's and Old's [18, 20] and Sharpless's [22] studies of intracranial stimulation and recording which, less directly connected with my theory, still began as an attempt to fill in one of the larger gaps in my theorizing (omission of the brain-stem reticular formation and "arousal").

The "systematic program" which I had in mind when *The Organization of Behavior* was published was to induce some bright young psychologists to become interested in the kind of problems and ideas which it presented, as well as continuing to experiment on them myself. The first part of this program has been realized, the second has not; but I am no longer very concerned with my own failure to get into the laboratory, in view of the very satisfying productivity of my colleagues. I have no other program at present: no new edition of the theory is in immediate prospect, since I am far from having digested the evidence, physiological as well as psychological, that has appeared recently and that seems to be coming in at an increasing rate.

As to convergence of ideas—there are two main points of theory on which psychologists have persistently been divided: (1) the existence or nonexistence of ideational processes, and (2) the nature of the reinforcing agent in learning.

1. Essentially the conception of ideation is that of a process which can be aroused sensorily but which can also occur in the absence of the adequate stimulus. From this point of view, it becomes evident that psychologists do not differ as to whether ideation exists or not, but only in the amount of emphasis they are prepared to give to it. Hull's stimulus trace is an ideational process, and the fractional anticipatory goal response seems designed to include both ideational mechanisms, with short-circuiting within the nervous system, and peripheral ones, involving actual muscle contractions and sensory feedback. Meehl and MacCorquodale's expectancy postulate fits without incongruity into Hullian theory. The recent emphasis by Seward, Osgood, Kendler, and others on surrogate or mediating processes shows also how well the ideational mechanism can *supplement* (instead of contradicting) the stimulus-response approach to behavior. One can see now, surely, that an objectively treated ideational process is not somehow an alternative to the S-R formula or opposed to it, but an extension of the same general application of deterministic thinking to the analysis of behavior. It seems quite clear that this is no longer a point of schism, of irreconcilable principle, in psychological theory.

2. It appears that the same sort of rapprochement may not be too far off in the matter of reinforcement hypotheses. I cannot repeat here the long argument made elsewhere [9] but summarize by saying that, though there is much yet to be discovered, the current developments of physiological knowledge of the arousal system have obliged me to modify my treatment of drive and reinforcement in a way that brings it much closer to earlier law-of-effect formulations on the one hand, while still leaving room for so-called cognitive reinforcement on the other. This seems clearly an area of psychological knowledge in which we may expect that long-standing confusion will be dissipated only by further physiological developments and the fertile combination of physiological and behavioral methods of experiment.

Finally, on the strategy of further development of the theory—it is really impossible to say which of the data we lack are crucial (especially when we restrict discussion to what is practicable), nor what the chief conceptual and empirical difficulties are which work against development of the system—except one thing: understanding behavior is a tough problem. If I knew where the next breakthrough would occur, or which of many are *the* difficulties, I would be able to plan a systematic attack. But this is a misconception of theoretical research—the nub of the matter is so clear in hindsight, unclear ahead of time. We operate by hunches, and one's only strategy is to interest intelligent people, of diverse skills, interests, and knowledge, in the problems as one sees them. The chief barrier to such a procedure is in having rigid preconceived notions about the philosophy of science and how research is or should be done.

REFERENCES

1. Beach, F. A., & Jaynes, J. Effects of early experience upon the behavior of animals. *Psychol. Bull.*, 1954, **51**, 239–263.

2. Bexton, W. H., Heron, W., & Scott, T. H. Effects of decreased variation in the sensory environment. *Canad. J. Psychol.*, 1954, **8**, 70–76.

3. Clarke, R. S., Heron, W., Fetherstonhaugh, M. L., Forgays, D. G., & Hebb, D. O. Individual differences in dogs: preliminary report on the effects of early experience. *Canad. J. Psychol.*, 1951, **5**, 150–156.

4. Conant, J. B. *On understanding science.* New Haven, Conn.: Yale Univer. Press, 1947.

5. Doane, B. K. Changes in visual function with perceptual isolation. Unpublished doctoral dissertation, McGill Univer., 1955.

6. Forgays, D. G., & Forgays, Janet. The nature of the effect of free-environmental experience in the rat. *J. comp. physiol. Psychol.*, 1952, **45**, 322–328.

7. Hebb, D. O. The effect of early and late brain injury upon test scores, and the nature of normal adult intelligence. *Proc. Amer. phil. Soc.*, 1942, **85**, 275–292.

8. Hebb, D. O. *Organization of behavior.* New York: Wiley, 1949.

9. Hebb, D. O. Drives and the CNS (conceptual nervous system). *Psychol. Rev.*, 1955, **62**, 243–254.

10. Hebb, D. O., & Thompson, W. R. The social significance of animal studies. In G. Lindzey (Ed.), *Handbook of social psychology.* Cambridge, Mass.: Addison-Wesley, 1954.

11. Heron, W. Perception as a function of retinal locus. *Amer. J. Psychol.*, 1957, **70**, 38–48.

12. Hunton, Vera. The perception of inverted pictures by children. *J. genet. Psychol.*, 1955, **86**, 281–288.

13. Hymovitch, B. The effects of experiential variations in problem-solving in the rat. *J. comp. physiol. Psychol.*, 1952, **45**, 313–321.

14. Lansdell, H. C. Effect of brain damage on intelligence in rats. *J. comp. physiol. Psychol.*, 1953, **46**, 461–464.

15. Mahut, Helen. Breed differences in the dog's emotional behavior, in press.

16. Meehl, P. E., & MacCorquodale, K. Some methodological comments concerning expectancy theory. *Psychol. Rev.,* 1951, **58,** 230–233.

17. Melzack, R. The genesis of emotional behavior. *J. comp. physiol. Psychol.,* 1954, **47,** 166–168.

18. Milner, P. Effect of intracranial stimulation on rat behavior. Unpublished doctoral dissertation, McGill Univer., 1954.

19. Mishkin, M., & Forgays, D. C. Word recognition as a function of retinal locus. *J. exp. Psychol.,* 1952, **43,** 43–48.

20. Olds, J., & Milner, P. Positive reinforcement produced by electrical stimulation of septal area and other regions of rat brain. *J. comp. physiol. Psychol.,* 1954, **47,** 419–427.

21. Orbach, J. Retinal locus as a factor in the recognition of visually perceived words. *Amer. J. Psychol.,* 1952, **65,** 555–562.

22. Sharpless, S. K., & Jasper, H. The role of the reticular formation in habituation. *Brain,* 1956, **79,** 655–680.

23. Smith, C. J. Problem-solving in brain-injured rats. Unpublished doctoral dissertation, McGill Univer., 1954.

24. Thompson, W. R., & Heron, W. The effects of restricting early experience on the problem-solving capacity of dogs. *Canad. J. Psychol.,* 1954, **8,** 17–31.

25. von Senden, M. *Raum- und Gestaltauffassung bei operierten Blindgeborenen vor und nach der Operation.* Leipzig: Barth, 1932.

PHYSIOLOGICAL THEORY OF DRIVE

CLIFFORD T. MORGAN
The Johns Hopkins University

My task in this paper is to analyze my physiologically oriented theory of motivational mechanisms. This theory was presented most explicitly in *Physiological Psychology* [38], but certain aspects of it appear in research papers published before and afterward, as well as in the revision of *Physiological Psychology* [44] and in *Introduction to Psychology* [39]. The theory has been restated and related to recent literature in a paper published in the 1957 *Nebraska Symposium on Motivation* [40].

The theory is a rather modest one, lacking many of the refinements and elegancies of more mature theories such as Hebb's [24] or such as have been elaborated in the field of learning [26]. For that reason, some of the rubrics suggested for the systematic analysis appearing in this series of volumes do not fit this particular paper, but to the extent that it is appropriate, I shall follow the same general scheme of organization that has been employed in other papers.

BACKGROUND FACTORS

The events of the 1930s form the backdrop for my physiological analysis of motivation, both because I took my undergraduate and graduate training during this period and because new physiological methods of studying motivational problems were making their appearance at this time. In my first three undergraduate years, my major studies were in the natural sciences and philosophy. Only in my senior year did I choose psychology as my field, and this because psychology seemed to offer the scientific approach of the natural sciences to the problems talked about in philosophy, religion, and the social sciences. Under the influence of Paul E. Fields, who recruited me into psychology, I became interested in the neo-behaviorism of Hull and Weiss. After reading the early papers of Hull on learning theory, I chose for my first research a problem in the effect of preliminary feeding on the anticipatory goal tendencies of rats running a maze [41]. Among the results of this study were the findings that rats given a little food before running a maze increased their speed of locomotion and that fully fed rats would run it about as speedily as those on regular 24-hr deprivation. Neither result jibed particularly well with the local theory of hunger then in vogue.

This theory had been argued eloquently by Walter B. Cannon in his chapter in the Murchison handbook of experimental psychology [17]. In graduate school, where the handbook was the mainstay for seminars and comprehensive examinations, I took the trouble to consult some of the original literature cited by Cannon. Much of it did not seem to fit in with his notion of hunger as an experience arising from stomach contractions. He seemed to have trouble explaining the report by Wangensteen and Carlson [67] of the hunger reported by a gastrectomized patient and of such work as Montgomery's [37] in which dogs deprived of parotid secretions exhibited only a normal amount of thirst. Then, too, Adolph's work on thirst in fistulated dogs was going on a few blocks away at the Medical School campus. I saw this [2], and wondered how such data could possibly be explained in terms of a local theory of hunger and thirst.

My first experiments on the problem, done at that time, were suggested by Cannon's account [17] of the action of insulin on the contractility of the stomach. Research cited by him indicated that insulin increased stomach contractility and did this primarily by way of the vagus nerve. I therefore did a series of experiments in which hunger, as measured by food ingested, was studied under the influence of insulin injections, first in normal rats [42] and then in rats in which the vagus nerve had been sectioned [43]. Although the vagotomized rats, as one might predict from knowing that vagotomy glutted the gut, did not behave exactly like normal rats, insulin nevertheless did cause them to increase their food intake, and this was difficult to explain with Cannon's theory. About the time these experiments were being written up for publication, Bash [8] independently published similar results except that he used an obstruction method rather than a Skinner box technique for measuring hunger motivation.

During this period, other investigators were publishing results that pointed to central factors in physiological motivation. Bard and his collaborators had shown that cats deprived of sensory innervation of the genitals were quite capable of sexual behavior [5] and that a center for sexual motivation existed in the brain stem [6]. The fact that estrogenic hormones could induce heat so long as this "center" was intact led him to suggest [6] that sexual motivation is aroused by the erotization of the brain stem by sex hormones. Lashley [29] surveyed existing data on instinct and concluded that "physiologically all drives are no more than expressions of the activity of specific mechanisms" and that hormones "activate some central mechanism which maintains excitability and activity." From his studies of sexual behavior, Beach [10] came to believe that "sexual arousal depends upon the creation and maintenance in the central nervous system of a condition analogous to Sherrington's central excitatory state" and to "postulate the existence of a Central Excitatory Mechanism." I had these various ideas in mind, as well as the facts on which they were based (see later section on Initial evidence) when I was writing the chapters on motivation in *Physiological Psychology* [38]. I merely arranged the facts, and the inferences to be drawn from them, in an orderly scheme. At the time, the scheme had no name, but in order to have something brief to refer to throughout this paper, I shall call it the *central theory of drive*.

STRUCTURE OF THE CENTRAL THEORY

The central theory of drive attempts to provide a physiological explanation of the motivated behavior ordinarily considered to stem from physiological drives. Thus the term *motivated behavior* in this paper is restricted to behavior that is aroused and maintained by internal conditions within the body. For the most part, it refers to hunger, thirst, and sex. The problem is to state what these internal conditions are, how they are related to each other, and how they control motivated behavior. For our purposes, the term *drive* may be used to refer to any internal conditions that arouse and maintain behavior, either independently or in conjunction with external stimuli. *Motivated behavior,* by definition, is behavior impelled by a drive. *Need* will refer to any condition of deficit within the organism that impairs the health or efficiency of the organism. It is not, as we shall see, synonomous with drive. Restated in terms of these definitions, the purpose of the central theory is to understand the relation of need to drive, the nature of drive, and the physiological machinery through which drive regulates behavior.[1]

The central theory of drive stands in contrast to older peripheral theories [17]. These assumed drive to consist of internal stimuli, such as dryness of the throat, contractions of the stomach, or tension in sexual organs. Having assumed this, they made little or no attempt to examine the events intervening between drive stimuli and behavior. Motivated behavior was considered to wax and wane with drive stimuli.[2] It is a premise of central theory that drives are aroused in other ways than by the stimulation of receptors and that they should be regarded as states in the nervous system that may be aroused and abated in a variety of ways.

Central motive state. To stress the central locus of these states, I proposed the concept of "central motive state" or cms for short [cf. Beach's Central Excitatory Mechanism, 10]. Such a state is one of nervous activity in a system of centers and pathways concerned in one particular kind of motivation. Different drives involve different systems, but there may be, and probably is, considerable overlap of these systems. As originally postulated, a central motive state has the following general properties:

1. Once a state is set up, it is regarded as persisting, at least for a

[1] Some of the contributors to this series of papers have been able to employ effectively the language of variables in describing the structure of their theories. After trying to do the same thing, I gave it up because the discussion becomes so cluttered with "intervening variables" and "dependent variables" that the facts are obscured and the reasoning confused. I have therefore chosen to present the system in the terms commonly used in physiological psychology, with only an occasional reference to "variables."

[2] Although some are inclined to use the term stimulus as any physical disturbance of the sense organs or the nervous system, I feel that our thinking can be kept clearer by restricting the term stimulus (as early psychologists did) to that which excites a sense organ. It is used in this way throughout this paper.

time, without outside support from sensory inputs or other kinds of excitation. By reverberation, or perhaps by "tonus" supplied by other centers that are in constant activity, it can coast and perseverate in such a way that it does not depend directly on outside influences.

2. A central motive state predisposes the organism to react in certain ways to particular stimuli and not to react to others. If, for example, the central motive state concerns hunger, it sets or primes the organism to react by approaching certain odors, tastes, and textures and to ingest food having certain characteristics. Theoretically, there is no limit to this selectivity. It may prime an animal to accept (react by ingestion) salt and nothing else, or foods containing vitamin B, etc. It is only an empirical matter to determine the limits of selectivity much as one measures stimulus generalization in an experiment on sensory discrimination. The important point is that the cms functions as a selective valve or switch for certain S-R relationships and not others.

3. Besides being self-perpetuating and predisposing the organism to certain reactions to stimuli, the cms may also directly emit certain patterns of behavior. It is responsible for the general bodily activity that almost always precedes and accompanies other more specific forms of motivated behavior. In fact, by emitting general activity, the cms makes it possible for the organism to come into the vicinity of stimuli for which it is selectively primed to act. In addition, the cms may emit certain rather specific forms of behavior. A female cat in heat, for example, often emits distinctly sexual patterns, such as treading, rubbing, and crying, without being near a male cat or in the vicinity of sexually arousing stimuli. The theory does not rule out the possibility that some of this "emitted" behavior is evoked by external or internal stimuli and consequently that it may be in part "released" behavior merely primed by the cms. By "emitted" behavior, the theory simply refers to behavior that is not elicited by any specific, obvious stimulus.

Arousal of drive. These are the general properties assigned to central motive states. The theory also deals with the conditions arousing and diminishing these states. In regard to arousal, it is admitted, as peripheral theorists would have it, that external or internal stimuli can and do arouse central motive states. A person in an environment that is too hot or too cold is motivated by external temperatures. Internal stimuli in the mouth and stomach undoubtedly do have motivating power and may affect the level of activity in the cms. On the other hand, it is postulated that drives such as hunger, thirst, and sex depend more on chemical and hormonal conditions of the blood than on such stimuli. It is held that humoral factors can directly activate the central nervous system, arousing central motive states without the operation of stimulus factors. Moreover, in most circumstances, they are a prior condition for such stimuli, for they determine whether the mouth will be dry or the stomach contract. In any case, if and when stimuli arouse central motive states, they represent only one factor, along with humoral and chemical factors[3] that can arouse drive.

Drive reduction. The theory, finally, attempts to explain the ways in which central motive states, once aroused, can be diminished or eliminated. This is the problem of "satisfaction" and, when considered in connection with learning theory, the problem of "reinforcement." It was assumed that there are several ways in which the "satisfaction" of a central motive state can take place. Just as the peripheral theorist would hold, the elimination of the stimulus or humoral motive factor which originally aroused the central motive state can reduce it. It is doubtful, however, whether the elimination of hunger, thirst, or sex drive takes place in this way.

Another possibility is that some humoral messenger, different from those arousing the drive, can directly reduce the cms. For example, when an organism eats food, some hormone that can act as an inhibitor on the cms may be liberated from the stomach or intestine [see 9].

Still a third possibility is that stimulation of receptors in the course of drive-instigated behavior may reduce the cms. For example, when a hungry rat starts out a cafeteria meal choosing sugar, then tires of it and turns to wheat [69], the "sweet" stimulation may be the factor that reduces selectively the part of the cms predisposing the rat to eat sugar.

Still another alternative is that the behavior resulting from central motive states may itself reduce these states. In this case, we might assume that the mere ingestion of food or water, as a behavioral act considered independently of its consequences or of its stimulus value, might terminate the central motive state. Drive reduced in this way would be like a clock running down [see 38, p. 443]. (It would also be comparable to Skinner's reflex reserve.)

INITIAL EVIDENCE FOR THE THEORY

At the time the central theory was formulated, there was relatively little positive evidence for the states or factors assumed to be important in motivation, but there was some. The most cogent arguments for the theory were based partly on negative evidence and partly on circumstantial evidence. I shall consider these three kinds of evidence—negative, circumstantial, and positive—in turn.

Against peripheral theory. Negative evidence in this case refers to

[3] To stress this possibility, I originally used the term "humoral motive factor" to refer to all chemical and hormonal conditions of the blood assumed to "erotize" the central nervous system.

data that seemed to limit or disprove the peripheral theory of drive. Such evidence consisted of any phenomena in which motivated behavior seemed relatively independent of the peripheral stimulus factors assumed to be important in such theories.

In the field of hunger motivation, there were just a few cases in which hunger, as defined in terms of a craving for food or in terms of food ingestion, could be said to be in some degree independent of stomach contractions. The case study by Wangensteen and Carlson [67] previously mentioned was one. Then, within the space of two years three studies with rats appeared to confirm this finding. Tsang [66] completely removed the stomachs of rats and found that they still were as highly motivated to run a maze, overcome an obstruction, and as active at the time of feeding as normal animals. The only trouble with gastrectomized rats was that they could not eat as much at one time as normal animals and had to eat more frequently (as one might expect when there is no stomach in which to store food). The other two studies by Bash [8] and Morgan [43], already mentioned, obtained comparable results following section of the vagus nerve, which (presumably) reduced stomach motility and eliminated afferent messages from the stomach. Such studies made it clear that hunger drive could function largely unabated after the removal or reduction of peripheral events in the stomach.

Rather parallel research on the thirst drive pointed in the same direction. Montgomery [37] had removed the salivary glands from dogs, thereby making their mouths chronically dry. Such dogs, however, had the same average intake of water as normal dogs, something one would not expect if dryness of the throat figured prominently in thirst drive. Then, Adolph [1, 2] and Bellows [12] came along with their studies of drinking behavior in fistulated dogs compared with normal animals. They worked with the other side of Montgomery's coin; letting ingested water run out a fistula rather than deposit in the stomach, they separated local sensory factors from the subsequent effects of water ingestion. Dogs prepared in this way and allowed *ad libitum* drinking drank barrels of water a day, despite the fact that this made their mouths about as wet as anything can get. The experiments by Adolph and by Bellows have other important aspects, which we will come to below, but their point, so far as the peripheral theory is concerned, was that thirst drive does not appear to depend upon local buccal stimulation.

Similar results had been obtained by Bard and his associates in the area of sexual motivation. Ball [4] found removal of the vagina and uterus, which might be expected to be sources of sensory stimulation to have no effect on the sexual inclinations of the female rat in estrus Bard [5] sectioned the sensory fibers innervating the cat's female genitalia without disrupting in the slightest the cat's mating behavior. And Root and Bard [53], after sectioning the lower afferent pathways of the spinal cord in the male cat, noted no decline in sexual aggressiveness. All these studies seem to lay to rest any ideas that erogenous stimulation is necessary for sexual motivation (though common experience indicates that such stimulation facilitates sexual arousal).

Indirect evidence. These three lines of experimental evidence argued against the peripheral theory of drive. By implication, they also provided circumstantial evidence for humoral and central factors in motivation. Such evidence was also to be found, however, in other quarters.

Perhaps the most compelling fact came from the work on sex hormones [10]. By the middle 1930s, extracts of estrogen and androgens had become generally available to research workers, and dozens of experiments relating these hormones to sexual behavior soon appeared in the literature. In contrast to the negative results with sensory factors in sex drive, these experiments made it clear that sex drive depended almost entirely on the level of sex hormones in the blood. In female animals (at that time, mostly rodents and carnivora) estrogenic hormone was a *sine qua non* for sexual behavior. In male animals, the dependence was not so all-or-none, but it was nevertheless great. Since there was not then, nor is there now, any clear evidence for the mediation of this effect through sensory structures, we could only presume that the hormones exerted their influence, as Bard suggested, through the "erotization" of the nervous system.

There was also presumptive evidence that hormones might play a role in hunger [9]. It had been shown that stomach muscle, completely detached from the stomach and transplanted elsewhere, began contracting when the intact stomach did—this without any neural innervation. Such muscle also stopped contracting after sugar had been introduced into the intact stomach, although sugar in the blood had no such effect [44, pp. 449–450]. Such effects presumably could be accomplished only through a humoral mediator. And if such an agent could directly control muscular tissue, why not nervous tissue too?

Perhaps the most puzzling data being published in the 1930s were those on specific hungers. Richter [51] had already reported extensively on his cafeterial feeding experiments, and Young [69] similarly had described in detail the food preferences of the rat. Although subsequent research [44, pp. 395–396] requires us to make some reservations about the "wisdom of the body," it was clear then, and still is, that animals often can detect, select, and ingest in the biologically appropriate quantities a dozen or more rather specific dietary materials. And when they are deficient in any one of these materials, they avidly crave it and take it in preference to other things offered to them. Such results pointed to many hungers, not one, and only humoral factors seemed sufficiently different to convey enough "information" to the nervous system to explain such "wisdom." (The theory that humoral factors altered sensory thresholds seemed rather lame at the time and has since been contradicted.)

In the case of thirst, Adolph [2] had demonstrated that water left in the stomach for only a few minutes could fully reduce it. Fistulated dogs subjected to severe dehydration stopped showing any interest in water (at least for a while) when water sufficient to offset the dehydration lay in the stomach for 15 minutes. Since little water was absorbed in that time, something else must have "told the nervous system to stop drinking." That something else, by inference, would be some sort of hormonal message to the nervous system.

For central theory. So much for the negative and circumstantial evidence. The positive evidence for humoral factors directly activating central motive states was sparse, but there were a few straws in the wind. It had long been known that chemical conditions of the blood, later identified as increased carbon dioxide, directly affect respiratory centers of the medulla. If carbon dioxide can erotize simple behavior patterns, why could not other substances erotize more complex patterns?

In the case of sexual behavior of the female cat, Bard [6] located a region in the midbrain and rear of the hypothalamus that was critical in the appearance of sex drive. With this region intact *and* injection of appropriate hormones, cats could be brought into heat. With either of these conditions lacking, they could not. It was these results that led Bard to suggest the idea of "erotization" of the nervous system. About the same time, Ranson [49] established what we now call the "waking center," a region in the posterior hypothalamus where lesions cause somnolence. It was not until some years later that other motivational centers[4] were added to this list—a "sleep center," "hunger center," "starvation center," and "thirst center,"—but this early work established two such regions and made it seem likely that relatively specific systems (or "central excitatory mechanisms") might be found for the physiological drives.

RECENT DEVELOPMENTS

In the years elapsing since the explicit formulation of the central theory of drive, research relevant to the theory has poured forth in ever

[4] The term center is used here to mean any region or combination of regions in the nervous system participating in a certain function. The problem of centers is discussed later in this paper.

increasing volume. In general, the research supports and extends the theory, giving it a more solid foundation than it had when it was first presented.

Guiding influences on research. Though much of this research was guided vaguely by the feeling of many experimenters that humoral and central factors in motivation would prove to be important, the research probably was not directed specifically by intentions to test the theory, in the sense that research, say, in the field of learning has so often been designed to test specific predictions generated by theory. Rather, in this case, there seem to have been three somewhat different guiding influences on such research.

One, interestingly enough, comes not from physiological theory per se but rather from neo-behavioristic learning theory. Hull's formal learning theory [26], of course, leaned heavily on the concept of reinforcement. Although no definite commitments were made about the nature of reinforcement, it was implied by Hull, and explicitly stated by others [45], that reinforcement consisted of drive reduction. (Some said need reduction.) Several learning theorists, particularly Neal E. Miller and his students, [33, 34, 35] interested themselves in this proposition and attempted to analyze physiologically the nature of reinforcement. In the course of their work, they have studied animals with hypothalamic lesions in hunger "centers," animals prepared with stomach fistulas, animals motivated by centrally placed electrodes, and the effects of preloading the stomach with various materials on the drive level of animals. These various experiments all contribute, as we shall see below, data relevant to central theory.

A second group of experiments bearing on central theory has come from neurophysiologists who have not concerned themselves particularly with the over-all problem of understanding motivation. They have merely pressed their search for clues to the functions of various structures of the brain. In the course of their search, they have discovered new "centers" and new phenomena, which they promptly followed up with systematic explorations. In this way, additional "centers" in the hypothalamus for hunger, thirst, and sleep have been found, and the role of the reticular formation as an activation system has been uncovered and explored. These findings have confirmed and extended the idea of central "excitatory" or motivating mechanisms.

A third group of experiments was probably more influenced by the implications of central theory than the other two groups. These experiments were done by investigators whose interests and training were primarily in physiological psychology. Appreciating the phenomena turned up by experiments in the first two groups, they have attempted to explore and analyze in detail the meaning of these phenomena for motivational theory. I refer particularly to work by Pfaffmann [48], Stellar [60], and their respective colleagues. They have studied the effect of changes in the humoral system on preference and aversion for dietary materials, and Stellar's group has also analyzed the mode of action of the hypothalamic centers concerned in hunger.

Though it is interesting to observe how different groups of investigators contribute knowledge in an area for their own individual reasons, more important is the net effect of their work on our knowledge of motivational mechanisms. This, I believe, strengthens considerably the tenets of the so-called central theory of physiological drives. In the next few paragraphs, I shall review their experiments, showing in each case the bearing of the experiment on central theory. I shall begin at the periphery and move toward the central nervous system.

Peripheral factors in drive. When Richter had established the existence of several specific hungers in the rat, he proposed a peripheral basis for such hungers [51]. This was in keeping with the thinking of the times, which was strongly flavored by peripheral theory. More specifically, Richter proposed that changes in the internal environment were reflected in altered taste thresholds, and that these accounted for the animal's preference for the foods that met the needs of its internal environment. He implied that there might be some general hunger drive regulated by any deficit in the internal environment, but that the drive was "directed" toward specific foods merely because the animal was more sensitive to certain tastes than to others. In support of this view, Richter had the fact that animals in dire need of salt showed preferences for salt in much lower concentrations than did normal animals.

This particular theory has now been tested and found wanting. With electrodes in the gustatory nerve of the rat, Pfaffmann and Bare [48] were able to obtain physiological thresholds for salt solutions placed on the rat's tongue. Separately they [7] checked Richter's observation that adrenalectomized rats had very low preference thresholds, while normal rats had high ones. But they found that the physiological thresholds measured electrically for these two kinds of rats were just the same, and were precisely of the order of preference thresholds obtained for the adrenalectomized, salt-deficient rat. These findings were also checked out by Carr [18] in a discrimination experiment. When forced to detect minimal concentrations of salt by being shocked for doing otherwise, normal rats yielded thresholds for salt that were the same as those of adrenalectomized rats. From such interlocking experiments, only one conclusion could be drawn: salt deficiency in adrenalectomy does not change an animal's sensitivity to salt; it merely changes the craving for salt. Thus the idea that humoral factors altered motivation through peripheral taste channels was in this case ruled out.

That is not to say, however, that there is never a peripheral mechanism for humoral influences. It seems possible that in some cases a hormonal or chemical condition of the blood may have some local effect that results in peripheral stimulation. Lehrman [30], for example, has studied the parental regurgitation-feeding of the ring dove induced by the hormone prolactin. At the same time that prolactin induces such feeding, it also causes engorgement of the crop, and Lehrman suggests (though he did not prove) that engorgement of the crop may act as the stimulus for regurgitation-feeding. Beach and Levinson [11] make a similar suggestion concerning genital papillae. They note that the number of genital papillae in castrated rats is closely related to levels of androgen supplied to the rat, and also that changes in the genital papillae correlate with sexual performance. From these correlations, they propose that "the genital papillae may act as accessory sensory structures, by stimulating tactile nerve endings that lie beneath them." Hence it may be possible for humoral factors to have an influence on drive by a route leading through effectors and receptors, but there is no reason to believe that this is either the only route or the major one.

Humoral factors in drive. The fact that humoral factors somehow influence drive, and often quite rapidly and markedly, has been demonstrated in a great variety of recent experiments. These experiments may be divided into two general groups: those in which the dependent variable is rate of learning or extinction, and those in which simple preference between two materials, or the rate of ingesting such materials, is the dependent variable. Both types of experiment have made use of the stomach tube or fistula for getting food into the stomach without the animal's eating or drinking it, although in some cases the material has been introduced directly into the internal environment by hypodermic needle.

Those of the first type, using rate of learning as a measure of effect, have issued mostly from Miller's laboratories at Yale. Through a permanent fistula, fluid food has been delivered directly into the stomach whenever the rat performed a correct response [28]. The general problem has been to determine how reinforcement administered in this way compares with normal reinforcement. Although there are many interesting results of these experiments, two facts stand out: food administered directly into the stomach is reinforcing, though probably not as much so as food ingested in the normal way. When nonnutritive materials are introduced into the stomach, the result is not one of reinforcement, and distention of the stomach by a balloon is negatively reinforcing [13, 34]. Although it is risky to interpret such results until we understand better the nature of reinforcement and its relation to learning, they indicate that mere stimulation of the stomach is not enough to change whatever must be changed to effect learning and that there are some specific humoral effects of food that are important in bringing about this change.

The second group of experiments, with preloading of the stomach, points even more clearly in this direction [32, 60]. With the single stimulus method developed by Stellar and Hill [59], it is possible to measure relatively small changes in rate of ingestion, which presumably reflect drive level, within a very few minutes after loading the stomach with any desired material. Several different materials have been used prior to animals' drinking solutions of salt and sugar. Both the kind of preloaded material and its concentration make an important difference in rates of ingestion immediately following preloading. And the striking thing about the results is that they follow so quickly upon preloading, long before the material in the stomach has had a chance to be absorbed into the blood stream. McCleary [32] has suggested a specific theory to account for such results, but for our purposes they seem to mean that some humoral messenger is released into the blood, or in some cases water is withdrawn from the blood thereby changing its chemical balance, and that this directly modifies activity in a "central motive state." Confirming this interpretation is the fact that substances injected directly into the blood stream cause about the same effects as the same substances placed in the stomach [60].

Neural centers. No less important for the central theory than these experiments on sensory and humoral factors are the increasing number of studies on drive "centers" in the central nervous system. In the early studies of the 1930s, the only such centers that had been positively identified were those for "waking" and sex. Since then, several more have been discovered and studied at some length.

Logically, though not chronologically, we should begin with the reticular activating system (RAS), which has recently been getting so much attention [31]. This system, extending through much of the brain stem between thalamus and pons, is set into activity by incoming sensory stimuli. Through its own pathways to the hypothalamus, thalamus, and cortex, it in turn sets up activity in these other centers. Some of the centers feed back impulses to the RAS, thus setting up a reverberatory system that is self-sustaining unless it is interrupted by other influences. Lesions in this system are followed by somnolence, and the system quite clearly functions as a general activator of many processes in the brain. Its role has been compared to that of a biasing voltage in an amplifier, for on its level of activity seems to depend the responsiveness of other systems of the brain. In the original language of the central theory, this RAS would seem to be the most general kind of "central motive state" determining the predisposition of the animal to react to stimuli and perhaps to develop more specific "central motive states."

Besides the "waking" center [49] first discovered in the posterior hypothalamus (not far from RAS), another center farther forward for "sleep" has recently been described by Nauta [46]. So far it has been confirmed only in the rat. Destruction of this center is followed by insomnia and incessant activity, resulting finally in death due to exhaustion. It is interesting, according to Nauta, that when both the "waking" and "sleep" centers are destroyed, the sequel is somnolence, the same as the destruction of the "waking" center. This finding fits in with what is becoming a general rule, that when centers work in opposing pairs the destruction of both has the same outcome as the destruction of the "active," not the "inhibitory," center. In this case, the "waking" center seems to provide positive influences for waking, and the "sleep" center appears to inhibit or reduce these influences.

A similar pair of centers has now been demonstrated for hunger. In the ventromedial nucleus of the hypothalamus near the midline is a pair whose destruction causes hyperphagia [15, 61]. Rats in this condition eat incessantly, putting away several times their normal intake and gaining weight rapidly until they reach about three times normal size. A little lateral to these centers whose destruction causes hyperphagia is another pair with opposite functions [62]. Injuring them electrolytically produces animals that have no interest in food and eventually starve to death if they are not maintained by stomach feeding or "trained" to eat again [62]. Both conditions, of hyperphagia and of aphagia, are dramatic and unequivocal.

It would not be surprising, of course, if we should encounter a similar pair of centers (really a pair of a pair) involved in thirst. It once seemed as though a "thirst" center had been found when certain lesions in the hypothalamus caused animals to drink inordinate amounts of water. It later was established, however, that such lesions had these effects, not because of injury to the hypothalamus, but because they also involved the posterior pituitary gland [50]. This gland, it turned out, secretes an antidiuretic hormone normally aiding in the retention of water in the body; without it, the animal becomes dehydrated, and this is why it drinks. As of this writing, we still have not found centers whose *destruction* causes changes in drinking behavior.

Quite dramatic, however, are two pilot experiments in which *stimulation* of the hypothalamus causes animals to drink. In one such experiment [3], a permanent pipette was imbedded in the head of a goat so that its tip was in the hypothalamus. Squirting in very small quantities of salt solution to stimulate directly the hypothalamus caused the goat to drink, and drink a lot. (This experiment, incidentally, is the only one so far to confirm directly the proposition of central theory that direct chemical stimulation of brain can "erotize" a "central motive state.") In another experiment [22], an electrode similarly placed in the hypothalamus of the rat caused it to drink when weak currents were administered through the electrode. These are preliminary experiments and need to be followed up, but they do indicate that certain restricted regions of the brain are concerned in thirst drive.

A more detailed review and discussion of experiments of this kind, as well as an elaboration of the central theory of drive, may be found in a recent paper by Stellar [58]. All the evidence that is accumulating continues to point to central mechanisms directly controlled by humoral factors in the internal environment.

SOME IMPLICATIONS OF CENTRAL THEORY

In this section I shall discuss some of the conclusions to be drawn from the central theory of drive and also the relation of the theory to other recent developments in the general field of motivation. In this way, I hope both to enlarge the scope of application of the theory and to show how it can assist those engaged in building theories of learning, motivation, and behavioral development.

Drives and needs. One of the important implications of central theory, and one that is brought out by some of the work just reviewed, is that we must clearly distinguish between needs, drives, and satisfiers. A drive, regarded as that which gives an impetus to behavior, is an activity or state of the central nervous system (a cms). A need, defined as some sort of deficit, may or may not give rise to a drive, and drive does not necessarily arise from a need. Thirst drive, for example, is most closely correlated with the degree of dehydration of bodily tissues [21], and it would seem that the dehydration of regions of the brain can directly arouse the corresponding drive. In the case of hunger, however, some needs arouse drive and others do not. An animal deprived of vitamin D, for example, seems to have no specific hunger for vitamin D, nor any great degree of drive associated with the deficiency [68]. On the other hand, mild deprivation of vitamin B, or of proteins [55, 56], is accompanied by specific hungers for these substances. Sexual drive, on the other hand, cannot be said to be due to a need, for no lack accompanies it. It correlates well, at least in lower animals, with level of hormones, and these, rather than any deficits, arouse drive. Hence needs do not always arouse drives, and drives are not always aroused by needs. Some learning theorists have come to recognize this distinction and are now using the term drive, rather than need, in their analysis of reinforcement [33].

It is necessary also to distinguish between need reduction and satisfaction. (Satisfaction is used here to refer to drive reduction.) The satisfaction or reduction of drives does not necessarily depend on the reduction of the need giving rise to the drive, nor even to changes in the factor that aroused drive. In the case of hunger, for example, it appears that chemical messengers different from those involved in arousing drive and generated by consummatory responses may be the important factors in reducing drive. In other cases, mere sensory stimulation or behavior resulting from the operation of a drive may reduce it. Sex drive is perhaps the best example of this. Although sex hormones play a crucial role in sexual drive, the act of copulation and its concomitant neural discharge reduce, at least temporarily, the sex drive. This, of course, is not due to any reduction in sex hormones nor, so far as we know or can imagine, to any other chemical messengers. (Below I shall consider in detail the role of sensory and behavioral factors in drive and drive reduction.) The distinction, then, between needs, drives, and the events that reduce drive is one important implication of central theory.

Exploratory and sensory drives. In recent years, research has brought out several facts and generated other theories that need to be considered in the light of the central theory of drives. These developments may be classified broadly into two general categories: one concerns curiosity, exploration, manipulation, and activity; the other concerns instinctive behavior and particularly the concept of "releasers" given to us by the European ethologists.

Fifteen or twenty years ago, when central theory was being formulated, psychologists generally regarded such things as "interest" and "curiosity" as derived or learned somehow from basic, physiological motives. Central theory, therefore, took no especial account of such motives and was restricted to what were then the primary physiological drives—hunger, thirst, sex. Now it is becoming clear that such drives constitute only one class of drive, which might better be called "visceral drives" because they are concerned directly or indirectly with visceral events. To this we must add another general class, one perhaps that is more important in understanding human behavior than the class of visceral drives. In keeping with the distinction neurological scientists make between visceral and somatic functions, we might call these the "somatic drives."

It is not yet clear how somatic drives may be subdivided and further classified, if indeed they can be, so we shall not try. The kinds of data, however, that may be subsumed under somatic drives are as follows: first is what Montgomery [36] has called exploratory drive, and Berlyne [14] curiosity drive. This is an impetus to move around in one's environment and to be stimulated by it. Montgomery seems to have demonstrated beyond reasonable doubt that this sort of drive can exist independently of other drives and that it is sufficiently strong to motivate and maintain learned behavior. Harlow [23] has similarly shown a manipulative drive in monkeys, a drive not obviously derived or learned from other drives, to handle, manipulate, and "solve" puzzles. Closely related, secondly, is considerable evidence for "sensory drives," drives to see and experience the environment. Harlow [23], for example, has reported experiments in which a "peek" at the environment is sufficient incentive for a monkey to learn other discriminations, ordinarily formed on the basis of physiological rewards. And Thompson and Solomon [64] have demonstrated convincingly that rats are interested enough in their environment to form visual discriminations without being motivated or rewarded in any other way. Some learning theorists have not given up hope that they may find some way to explain such facts in terms of derived or learned drives. To me, however, it seems clear that we must recognize unlearned somatic drives, that are just as primary and underived as the more familiar visceral drives.

The second major development, mentioned above, has been contributed by the work of European ethologists on instinctive behavior. Much of this work is with physiological drives such as hunger and thirst and presents no special problems for physiological theory. The work, however, emphasizes and dramatizes the role of the stimulus as a "releaser" of instinctive movements [65]. Certain reactions are preset or primed by drives so that they are released when the appropriate stimulus is present. I like this concept because it is precisely what I was trying to say in presenting the central theory when I wrote of "central motive states" priming or predisposing the organism to react to certain stimuli. The ethologists, using instinctive behavior, have given us many nice examples of this sort of predisposition and a good word, "releaser," to refer to it.

In their work with releasers, however, the ethologists have supplied an additional notion not anticipated or adequately dealt with in central theory. This is the idea that the "threshold" for releasing an instinctive movement is raised by "exercise." They find, for example, that it is more difficult to release the attack reaction of the male stickleback fish to the red belly of another male immediately after the reaction has occurred than in the normal, "rested" animal. And they have other examples. The general point is that the ability of a releaser stimulus to release a reaction depends upon how recently the same reaction has been released.

Placing these two general developments side by side, we may say that the work of Montgomery, Harlow, and others gives us the concept of "sensory hunger" or some drive to experience the environment, and the work of the ethologists indicates that sensory experience and its effects may itself be drive reducing. These points are important ones to be dealt with by central theory. Before attempting to do that, we may note recent work with sensory deprivation, which fits in here [25, 63]. Both animals and people whose sensory environment is restricted show signs of deficit comparable to those of the hungry or thirsty organism. Only in this case the drive expresses itself as an avid interest in, and "hunger" for, sensory experience. The research appears to demonstrate rather powerful "sensory" drives, which are ordinarily kept in such reasonable balance that we do not notice them.

Origin of sensory drives. If there be "sensory drives," as I believe there are, two things are implied: first, that drives (cms) build up because of a lack of sensory stimulation, and secondly, that sensory stimulation can reduce these drives. Actually, these are merely two sides of the same coin, for one could hardly be true without the other also being true. Both implications, however, raise additional questions. Why should drives arise because of a lack of sensory stimulation? There are two possible general answers to this question.

One is that a so-called sensory drive really is an activity drive in the sense that lack of activity in an organism whose nervous system is in continuous activity builds up a tendency for activity to be "released." In this case, sensory stimulation would be "needed" only because it releases this activity. Such a proposition is difficult, if not impossible, to test directly, for it requires us somehow to separate the effects of stimulation from those of activity although the two are inextricably bound together in the organism's structure and function. Recent research on activity, however, tends to support the idea. Campbell and Sheffield [16], studying general activity in rats, found that it waxed and waned with the amount of sensory stimulation. In experiments in which certain lesions of the nervous system were followed by augmented activity [27], the activity depended upon the level of external environmental stimulation. In certain other experiments [54], however, a methodical pacing following lesions in a restricted area of the monkey's frontal lobe did not seem to depend upon environmental stimuli. It is probably true, therefore, that sensory drives may be due in part to activity drives that require stimuli for the release of the activity.

The second possibility for "explaining" sensory drives is to assume that sensory drives or sensory hunger may develop without reference to activity, merely because of the interplay of events in the nervous system. This possibility receives some support from everyday observation of human behavior, for individuals with rather low activity drives may have strong sensory drives. Witness the workingman who spends the evening reading the paper and watching television without stirring from his easy chair, and also the enormous amount of "looking" that people do in reading, movies, touring, etc.—while activity is resisted or kept to a minimum. From a physiological point of view, moreover, this possibility is not unreasonable. Internal stimuli are at all times bombarding the organism's afferents, pouring impulses into the brain and particularly the reticular activating system. Impulses leaving the RAS take a different route to the cerebral cortex than those in the direct afferents and there are neurophysiological reasons, which I will not go into, for believing that these two sorts of impulses must somehow be coordinated [31]. One can think then of drive states being set up in the brain by internal stimuli and perhaps by the internal rhythms of the brain, and of these particular drive states being reduced only by sensory stimulation. At present, such a possibility is somewhat hazy, but electrophysiological research now in progress may clear it up in the not too distant future.

Sensory stimulation and drive reduction. The idea that stimuli may be drive reducing in and of themselves is one that has not heretofore been considered very seriously; yet it has interesting possibilities for a theory of motivation. It is particularly applicable to the some of the phenomena of food preference, described by Young, which are otherwise quite baffling. Young [69, 70] has shown that a hungry animal has a hierarchy of food preferences. When first put in a feeding situation with several choices before it, it may select sugar and eat this for a while. After a few minutes, it may turn to protein, and then later to fat, or salt, or some other dietary component. Put another way, the animal shows several different specific hungers at the same meal and in rapid succession. The time involved is so short that it is hard to believe any change in the internal environment could account for changes in preference. If it is assumed, however, that mere stimulation with one type of food gradually reduces the drive related to that food, the phenomenon is readily explained. In order to test such a possibility, however, it would be necessary to combine the techniques of the esophageal fistula with those of preference testing so that the effects of sensory stimulation could be separated from those of the internal environment. At this writing, such experiments have not been carried out.

For sensory stimulation to be capable of reducing drive, it would be necessary to assume some sort of inhibitory influences on central motive states, and not merely a reduction in whatever it is that builds up drive in the first place. Such influences, however, are already implied by the conclusion, stated earlier, that humoral messengers different from those generating a drive can reduce the drive. Moreover, it has already been well demonstrated in the case of sleep and hunger that there are pairs of centers in the brain, one of which is "excitatory" and the other "inhibitory." Hence there is no physiological reason why sensory stimulation may not "inhibit" and thus reduce drive strength.

Sensory regulation of drive. While on the subject of the role played by stimuli in regulating drive, there are a few other points that ought to be made in passing. First of all, Hebb has emphasized the steering and cue functions of stimuli in motivated behavior [25]. The motivated animal, he points out, is steered or directed in its behavior by stimuli that it would otherwise not heed. This, I think, is another way of describing the releaser function of stimuli. If certain stimuli selectively release behavior under the influence of drive, this is the same thing as saying that they steer behavior or act as cues.

Secondly, it is quite clear from experiments on the nervous system, that no increase in drive level can ever be considered independently of the releaser functions of stimuli. Hypothalamic lesions, for example, that produce hyperphagia do not indiscriminately increase an animal's hunger for all foods under all conditions. Teitelbaum has made this point convincingly in a series of experiments on what hyperphagic animals will and will not eat [61]. He followed up on an experiment by Miller et al. [35] in which it was demonstrated that hyperphagic animals were not so hyperphagic when they had to do some work to get their food rather than eat it freely. Teitelbaum found that hyperphagics are more finicky about their food than normal animals when they are presented with foods of unusual texture or bitter taste. He concluded that the sensory aspects of the food were quite important in whether or not they were hyperphagic. Stated another way, his results show that increased hunger following hypothalamic lesions is largely a "release" phenomenon but limited to certain stimulus situations.

Finally, in considering the relation of stimulation to drives, we must recognize that stimuli sometimes "amplify" drives as well as release drive-primed behavior or reduce drives. Feeding a rat a little food increases its speed of running and, presumably, its level of motivation [41]. In the case of sex drive, stimuli associated with sex objects and with the erogenous zones enhance the intensity of sex motivation—a fact so well known that it needs no experimental demonstration. Though this paper has steered clear of the problem of reinforcement because it is one that would take it too far afield, the fact that stimuli amplify drives and yet can serve as reinforcers [57] is one that needs to be seriously considered by theorists who try to define reinforcement in terms of drive reduction.

SOME ADDITIONAL COMMENTS ON CENTRAL THEORY

In a sense, all of this paper is an attempt to evaluate critically the status of the central theory of motivation, and the theory, in my opinion, comes off well. Recent research has on the whole more than lived up to the expectations that central theory led us to entertain. We have had to give sensory factors more credit than we did originally, but only as regulators of drive, not as the instigators or sources of it. Otherwise, research has continued to uncover specific physiological mechanisms, both humoral and central, which at first were mere speculations based on fragments of evidence. We now are fully justified, it would seem, in accepting the central theory as a satisfactory scheme for encompassing the physiological facts of motivation.

In this concluding section, I should like to consider some special problems raised by the theory and also its relationship to psychological theory in general. The section will consequently be a potpourri, but only in this way can many of the points be included that are to be covered in this series of papers but that in this case did not merit more extended treatment.

Central neural activities. First a comment on the use of the term *central motive state.* When the central theory was first presented, this term was employed primarily as a teaching and heuristic device, because it served to emphasize central, rather than peripheral, activities in physiological motivation. I have used it relatively little throughout this paper because it is really synonomous with drive, if one understands drive in the physiological sense to be those central neural activities that give rise to behavior. Once this concept is established, it is probably just as well to avoid using such a vague term as central motive state.

Another problem involved in this area is an old one. How is one to talk about the function of different regions of the nervous system? Is it proper to refer to "centers" for this and that? Many physiological psychologists avoid this term because it smacks of old faculty psychology and phrenology, which implied a neat packaging of functions into pigeonholes of the brain. The modern neurologist, however, manages to use the term "center" to mean nothing more than a place containing cell bodies arranged in one or more nuclei and participating in one or more functions. It does not mean that this is the *only* region concerned in this function or even that this region has only one function. (Sophisticated scientists ought to take it for granted that such neat packages of functions or variables are never found in the real world.) Thus, in using the term "center" throughout this paper, I have meant to indicate that a region or a place in the nervous system was distinctively, but not exclusively, implicated in a particular function.

Speaking of motivational functions of centers, Hebb has raised the question whether the hypothalamic centers involved in motivation really represent motivational mechanisms [25]. His criterion for answering the question is whether or not these centers "energize other mechanisms." If one is looking for a *single* source of energy, the answer is probably "no." For these centers certainly do not energize behavior all by themselves. Undoubtedly systems, not centers, are required for such energizing. Probably all motivational systems depend generally on activities in other parts of the brain and perhaps more specifically on the reticular activating system. Moreover, they involve more than just one specific region of the brain. Respiration, for example, which has a crucial center in the medulla, whose destruction is lethal unless the organism is put in an iron lung, has several centers including a region in the frontal lobe of the cerebral cortex. Hyperphagia, in moderate degrees, can be produced by lesions of the cerebral cortex (again frontal lobes) as well as by lesions in the hypothalamus [52, 54]. And there are other examples. The point is that the "central excitatory mechanisms," as Beach calls them, consist of several "centers" associated in a complex system. It appears, however, that in certain cases, particularly those for hunger, thirst, and sleep, the hypothalamic centers are the crucial ones in their respective systems.

General properties of the central theory. Turning now to more general considerations of the theory, it is probably plain to the reader that the theory is not a formal, hypothetico-deductive system. It has no explicit axioms, postulates, or theorems, nor does it make any specific predictions about what will happen under such and such circumstances. It is rather a descriptive system that attempts to arrange in a coherent scheme the known facts about the physiological basis of motivation and to provide hooks on which to hang new facts as they are generated or discovered in subsequent research. It is more like the scheme a man might develop if, unfamiliar with engines, he were given the task of figuring out how an automobile works. By puttering and trying first one thing then another, he would eventually discover what the fuel is, how it is mixed with air, how it is conveyed to the engine, discharged by spark, and so on through the differential and steering gear. He would gradually develop a description of the events taking place in the operation of the automobile. That is what we are doing, I think, in the case of physiological events in motivated behavior.

Whether such a physiological theory will, or should, eventually be elaborated into a formal system, I do not know. If so, it will probably depend in large part on the development of satisfactory formal systems in neighboring areas. Behavior theorists will have to provide systems that account for behavior, and especially motivated behavior, before it will be possible to incorporate the central theory, which is basically a physiological explanation, into a more formal scheme. Not being optimistic about the short-term success of efforts to devise a satisfactory formal behavior theory, I have my reservations about the contingent possibility of devising a formal physiological theory of motivation. Certainly there is much to be done in straightforward empirical research, following up leads we already have, before it will be feasible or profitable to attempt a rigorous, formal system.

Since formality and rigor are part and parcel of any quantitative theory, it follows that the central theory is far from being a quantitative theory. To be sure, most of the facts upon which the theory was based are quantitative facts, and techniques for the measurement of both physiological and behavioral events in motivation are becoming increasingly refined. So far, however, it is hardly possible to tie together quantitatively such closely related measures of motivation as rate of free eating and rate of instrumental responses to obtain food, let alone establish any more complex mathematical relationships between motivational phenomena. More empirical research, of the same type that has characterized the last few decades, on the qualitative conditions under which motivational phenomena take place is necessary before we are ready to consider putting any quantitative terms into our theory.

For the foreseeable future, I suspect that we will see the present outlines being filled in by experiments that resolve the sorts of problems that have been raised in this paper. More "centers" will be found, some of them at higher levels in the brain, the general functions of these centers in relation to each other will be described, the role of stimuli as releasers will be studied in more detail, the question of activity and its relation to environmental stimuli will be straightened out, the role of stimuli as "satisfiers" or inhibitors will be explicated, the particular humoral factors concerned in such drives as hunger and thirst will be ferreted out, and perhaps the exact way in which such factors "erotize" the brain will be worked out. These, in any event, are the kinds of problems toward which current research is being directed, and they probably need to be solved to make central theory explicit enough to quantify it, formalize it, and relate it to other theoretical endeavors.

Relation to other theories. To wind up this paper, I shall make a few brief comments about the relation of central theory of drive to theory in other areas of psychology. The point at which the central theory and neo-behavioristic learning theory most clearly come in contact is on the problem of reinforcement. Although Hullian theorists have staked much of their theory on the idea that reinforcement (as an intervening variable) represents a reduction in drive strength, my guess is that some combination of Tolman's and Guthrie's views will turn out to be more nearly correct. It seems most likely to me that drive level only determines what an organism will do (or what behavior will be released) and thus determines the acts that will be terminal in a series, or conversely those that are less likely to occur again. This has so far proved to be a difficult issue to settle, largely because one cannot find ways of separating reinforcement per se from the releaser functions of stimuli. It is possible, however, that further physiological work on the mechanisms of motivation may contribute to its solution. Certainly some of the work done by Miller and his associates on the nature of reinforcement has contributed information of value for central theory.

The possibility, finally, that somatic drives—sensory hunger, curiosity, exploratory drive, and manipulative drives—are built-in physiological mechanisms has important implications for personality theory. If it is characteristic of people that they are motivated to explore, manipulate, and experience their environment, then personality theory need not indulge in any great gyrations to explain the seemingly complex motives found in people. The problem addressed by "functional autonomy," for example, largely disappears through the "canalization" of built-in physiological drives. This is putting the matter too simply, perhaps, but the point is that the more we find included in the physiological realm of motives, the less difficult is the job of the personality theorist. Consequently, in time, these two areas of theory are likely to have a better speaking acquaintance than they do at present.

As a postscript, I ought to mention why I have omitted from discussion a topic that many readers might have expected to find here. This is the topic of emotion. In explaining central theory in 1943 [38], I brushed it off quickly by saying simply that emotion follows the same rules as other kinds of motivation. By this I meant that emotional drives have a central locus, that they perseverate as other drives do, and that they prime certain reactions to certain stimuli. Such a statement still seems to be justified. In recent years, we have witnessed an upsurge of research on central motivational mechanisms. (It indicates, incidentally, that there are both excitatory and inhibitory systems of the brain imposing their influences on the more basic hypothalamic centers.) Little of this work, however, has a direct bearing on the concepts of central theory, and most of it is so tied up with problems in reinforcement, anxiety, and other aspects of learned behavior that I felt that it would unnecessarily complicate this paper to undertake to discuss it. The exciting work of Olds and Milner [47] on self-stimulation has not been discussed, partly for this reason and partly because the mechanism of the self-reinforcement effect has not been analyzed in sufficient detail to interpret it within the framework of the present discussion. The same is true for the avoidance learning described for shocks applied electrically deep within the brain [19].

REFERENCES

1. Adolph, E. F. Measurements of water drinking in dogs. *Amer. J. Physiol.,* 1939, **125,** 75–86.

2. Adolph, E. F. *Physiological regulations.* Lancaster, Pa.: Jaques Cattell Press, 1943.

3. Anderson, B. The effect of injections of hypertonic NaCl solutions into different parts of the hypothalamus of goats. *Acta Physiol. Scand.,* 1953, **28,** 188–201.

4. Ball, Josephine. Sex behavior of the rat after removal of the uterus and vagina. *J. comp. Psychol.,* 1934, **18,** 419–422.

5. Bard, P. The effects of denervation of the genitalia on the oestrual behavior of cats. *Amer. J. Physiol.,* 1935, **113,** 5.

6. Bard, P. The hypothalamus and sexual behavior. *Res. Publ. Ass. nerv. ment. Dis.,* 1940, **20,** 551–579.

7. Bare, J. K. The specific hunger for sodium chloride in normal and adrenalectomized white rats. *J. comp. physiol. Psychol.,* 1949, **42,** 242–253.

8. Bash, K. W. An investigation into a possible organic basis for the hunger drive. *J. comp. Psychol.,* 1939, **28,** 109–134.

9. Bash, K. W. Contribution to a theory of the hunger drive. *J. comp. Psychol.,* 1939, **28,** 137–160.

10. Beach, F. A. Analysis of factors involved in the arousal, maintenance and manifestation of sexual excitement in male animals. *Psychosom. Med.,* 1942, **4,** 173–198.

11. Beach, F. A., & Levinson, G. Effects of androgen on the glans penis and mating behavior of castrated male rats. *J. exp. Zool.,* 1950, **114,** 159–171.

12. Bellows, R. T. Time factors in water drinking in dogs. *Amer. J. Physiol.,* 1939, **125,** 87–97.

13. Berkun, M. M., Kessen, Marion L., & Miller, N. E. Hunger-reducing effects of food by stomach fistula versus food by mouth measured by a consummatory response. *J. comp. physiol. Psychol.,* 1952, **45,** 550–554.

14. Berlyne, E. E. The arousal and satiation of perceptual curiosity in the rat. *J. comp. physiol. Psychol.,* 1955, **48,** 238–246.

15. Brobeck, J. R., Tepperman, J., & Long, C. N. H. Experimental hypothalamic hyperphagia in the albino rat. *Yale J. Biol. Med.,* 1943, **15,** 831–853.

16. Campbell, B. A., & Sheffield, F. D. Relation of random activity to food deprivation. *J. comp. physiol. Psychol.,* 1953, **5**, 320–322.

17. Cannon, W. B. Hunger and thirst. In C. Murchison (Ed.), *A handbook of general experimental psychology.* Worcester, Mass.: Clark Univer. Press, 1934.

18. Carr, W. J. The effect of adrenalectomy upon the NaCl taste threshold in rat. *J. comp. physiol. Psychol.,* 1952, **45**, 377–380.

19. Delgado, J. M. R., Roberts, W. W., & Miller, N. E. Learning motivated by electrical stimulation of the brain. *Amer. J. Physiol.,* 1954, **179**, 587–593.

20. Dempsey, E. W., & Rioch, D. McK. The localization in the brain stem of the oestrous responses of the female guinea pig. *J. Neurophysiol.,* 1939, **2**, 9–18.

21. Gilman, A. The relation between blood osmotic pressure, fluid distribution, and voluntary water intake. *Amer. J. Physiol.,* 1937, **120**, 323–328.

22. Greer, M. A. Suggestive evidence of a primary "drinking center" in hypothalamus of the rat. *Proc. Soc. exp. Biol., N. Y.,* 1955, **89**, 59–62.

23. Harlow, H. F. Motivational factors underlying learning. In Kentucky Symposium, *Learning theory, personality theory, and clinical research.* New York: Wiley, 1954. Pp. 36–53.

24. Hebb, D. O. *The organization of behavior: a neurophysiological theory.* New York: Wiley, 1949.

25. Hebb, D. O. Drives and the CNS (conceptual nervous system). *Psychol. Rev.,* 1955, **62**, 243–254.

26. Hull, C. L. *Principles of behavior.* New York: Appleton-Century-Crofts, 1943.

27. Kennard, Margaret A., Spencer, S., & Fountain, G., Jr. Hyperactivity in monkeys following lesions of the frontal lobes. *J. Neurophysiol.,* 1941, **4**, 512–524.

28. Kohn, M. Satiation of hunger from food injected directly into the stomach versus food ingested by mouth. *J. comp. physiol. Psychol.,* 1951, **44**, 412–422.

29. Lashley, K. S. Experimental analysis of instinctive behavior. *Psychol. Rev.,* 1938, **45**, 445–471.

30. Lehrman, D. S. The physiological basis of parental feeding behavior in the ring dove (*Streptopelia risoria*). *Behaviour,* 1955, **7**, 241–286.

31. Lindsley, D. B. Physiological psychology. *Annu. Rev. Psychol.,* 1956, **7**, 323–348.

32. McCleary, R. A. Taste and post-ingestion factors in specific-hunger behavior. *J. comp. physiol. Psychol.,* 1953, **46**, 411–421.

33. Miller, N. E. Learnable drives and rewards. In S. S. Stevens (Ed.), *Handbook of experimental psychology.* New York: Wiley, 1951.

34. Miller, N. E., & Kessen, Marion L. Reward effects of food via stomach fistula compared with those of food via mouth. *J. comp. physiol. Psychol.,* 1952, **45**, 555–564.

35. Miller, N. E., Bailey, C. J., & Stevenson, J. A. F. Decreased "hun-

ger" but increased food intake resulting from hypothalamic lesions. *Science,* 1950, **112,** 256–259.

36. Montgomery, K. C. The role of exploratory drive in learning. *J. comp. physiol. Psychol.,* 1954, **47,** 60–64.

37. Montgomery, M. F. The role of the salivary glands in the thirst mechanism. *Amer. J. Physiol.,* 1931, **96,** 221–227.

38. Morgan, C. T. *Physiological psychology.* New York: McGraw-Hill, 1943. Pp. 458–465.

39. Morgan, C. T. *Introduction to psychology.* New York: McGraw-Hill, 1956. Pp. 58–69, 540–545.

40. Morgan, C. T. Physiological mechanisms of motivation. In M. R. Jones (Ed.), *Nebraska symposium on motivation.* Lincoln, Neb.: Univer. Nebraska Press, 1957.

41. Morgan, C. T., & Fields, P. E. The effect of variable preliminary feeding upon the rat's speed of locomotion. *J. comp. Psychol.,* 1938, **26,** 331–348.

42. Morgan, C. T., & Morgan, J. D. Studies in hunger: I. The effects of insulin upon the rat's rate of eating. *J. genet. Psychol.,* 1940, **56,** 137–147.

43. Morgan, C. T., & Morgan, J. D. Studies in hunger: II. The relation of gastric denervation and dietary sugar to the effect of insulin upon food intake in the rat. *J. genet. Psychol.,* 1940, **57,** 153–163.

44. Morgan, C. T., & Stellar, E. *Physiological psychology* (Rev. ed.) New York: McGraw-Hill, 1950.

45. Mowrer, O. H. On the dual nature of learning—a reinterpretation of "conditioning" and "problem solving." *Harv. educ. Rev.,* 1947, **17,** 102–148.

46. Nauta, W. J. H. Hypothalamic regulation of sleep in rats: an experimental study. *J. Neurophysiol.,* 1946, **9,** 285–316.

47. Olds, J., & Milner, P. Positive reinforcement produced by electrical stimulation of septal area and other regions of rat brain. *J. comp. physiol. Psychol.,* 1954, **47,** 419–427.

48. Pfaffmann, C., & Bare, J. K. Gustatory nerve discharges in normal and adrenalectomized rats. *J. comp. physiol. Psychol.,* 1950, **43,** 320–324.

49. Ranson, S. W. Somnolence caused by hypothalamic lesions in the monkey. *Arch. Neurol. Psychiat.,* 1939, **41,** 1–23.

50. Richter, C. P. The primacy of polyuria in diabetes insipidus. *Amer. J. Physiol.,* 1935, **112,** 481–487.

51. Richter, C. P. Total self-regulatory functions in animals and human beings. *Harvey Lectures,* 1942–43, **38,** 63–103.

52. Richter, C. P., & Hawkes, C. D. Increased spontaneous activity and food intake produced in rats by removal of the frontal poles of the brain. *J. Neurol. Psychiat.,* 1939, **2,** 231–242.

53. Root, W. S., & Bard, P. Erection in the cat following removal of lumbo-sacral segments. *Amer. J. Physiol.,* 1937, **119,** 392–393.

54. Ruch, T. C., & Shenkin, H. A. The relation of area 13 of the orbital surface of the frontal lobe to hyperactivity and hyperphagia in monkeys. *J. Neurophysiol.,* 1943, **6,** 349–360.

55. Scott, E. M., and Quint, Eleanor. Self-selection of diet. III. Appetites for B vitamins. *J. Nutrit.*, 1946, **32**, 285–292.

56. Scott, E. M., & Quint, Eleanor. Self-selection of diet. IV. Appetite for protein. *J. Nutrit.*, 1946, **32**, 293–302.

57. Sheffield, F. D., Wulff, J. J., & Backer, R. Reward value of copulation without sex drive reduction. *J. comp. physiol. Psychol.*, 1951, **44**, 3–8.

58. Stellar, E. The physiology of motivation. *Psychol. Rev.*, 1954, **61**, 5–22.

59. Stellar, E., & Hill, J. H. The rat's rate of drinking as a function of water deprivation. *J. comp. physiol. Psychol.*, 1952, **45**, 96–102.

60. Stellar, E., Hyman, R., & Samet, S. Gastric factors controlling water- and salt-solution drinking. *J. comp. physiol. Psychol.*, 1954, **47**, 220–226.

61. Teitelbaum, P. Sensory control of hypothalamic hyperphagia. *J. comp. physiol. Psychol.*, 1955, **48**, 156–163.

62. Teitelbaum, P., & Stellar, E. Recovery from the failure to eat produced by hypothalamic lesions. *Science*, 1954, **120**, 894–895.

63. Thompson, W. R., & Heron, W. The effects of early restriction of activity in dogs. *J. comp. physiol. Psychol.*, 1954, **47**, 77–82.

64. Thompson, W. R., & Solomon, L. M. Spontaneous pattern discrimination in the rat. *J. comp. physiol. Psychol.*, 1954, **47**, 104–107.

65. Tinbergen, N. *The study of instinct.* London: Oxford Univer. Press, 1951.

66. Tsang, Y. C. Hunger motivation in gastrectomized rats. *J. comp. Psychol.*, 1938, **26**, 1–17.

67. Wangensteen, O. H., & Carlson, A. J. Hunger sensations in a patient after total gastrectomy. *Proc. Soc. exp. Biol., N.Y.*, 1931, **28**, 545–547.

68. Wilder, C. E. Selection of rachitic and antirachitic diets in the rat. *J. comp. Psychol.*, 1937, **24**, 547–577.

69. Young, P. T. The experimental analysis of appetite. *Psychol. Bull.*, 1941, **38**, 129–164.

70. Young, P. T. Food-seeking drive, affective process, and learning. *Psychol. Rev.*, 1949, **56**, 98–121.

APPENDIX: SUGGESTED DISCUSSION TOPICS FOR CONTRIBUTORS OF SYSTEMATIC ANALYSES[1]

INTRODUCTION

We will use the term "systematic formulation" as any set of sentences formulated as a tool for ordering empirical knowledge with respect to some specifiable domain of events, or furthering the discovery of such knowledge. As is evident in science in general and psychology in particular, such formulations may vary in their characteristics over a very wide range. These variations may reflect differences in the intentions of the systematist, limits imposed by the nature of the subject matter, by the status of knowledge about it and related domains, by the availability of techniques for ordering the events in the domain, etc.

Defined in this sense, a "systematic formulation" may vary from one or a few orienting ideas towards the conduct of research, or towards the organization of extant knowledge within a given empirical domain (of any scope), to an explicit, elegant, and quantified systematization. Such highly diverse expressions as "viewpoint," "research philosophy," "Weltanschauung," "exploratory hypothesis" or set of such, "frame of reference," "dimensional system," "systematic (or "theoretical") framework," "explanatory (or "descriptive") system," "hypothetico-deductive system," "theory," "explanatory mechanism" (or set of such), "model," etc., may all be subsumed under "systematic formulation," as we wish to use this phrase.

This study is interested in the "systematic formulations" of present-day psychological science. Comparative analyses of "theory" and discussions of systematic methodology have considered far too narrow a range of formulations during the past few decades. We seek an inventory of current systematic resources which will adequately reflect the diversity and richness of conceptual experimentation of recent and present psychology. Only by the widest possible representation of formulations, with respect both to methodological type and em-

[1] This is a copy of the document concerning the discussion themes and their significance, sent to all Study I contributors at the time of their invitation to participate.

pirical domain, can clear light be shed on problems that cut across various classes of "system." Only in this way can problems which are unique to given classes of "theory" be isolated, and interrelationship issues be treated justly and comprehensively.

This study begins with no value judgments with respect to some preferred mode of systematization, or even with respect to some preferred set of systematic aims or ideals. On the contrary, the only value judgment it makes is that issues of this order have tended, in recent decades, to be prejudged. Nor is it the intention of this study to end with such a set of value judgments. Our intentions are explicative, not evaluative, and our belief is that explication of the current systematic situation on a broadened and less stereotype-bound basis is as valuable to a rational determination of next steps on the part of systematists and research workers as it is to more effective pedagogy.

In this era of second and *n*-order self-study questionnaires and professional nose-counting, investigators whose mode of work is as essentially individualistic and inspirational as that of the systematist may understandably feel that there is a suggestion of the Philistine in any project which requires the answering of questions about their work. To this, we can only reply that among the intentions of this study are not eavesdropping on the creative process, the determination of excellence by ballot, or even the charting of "directions" by consensus. We believe merely that where we can go—no matter in how many different directions—is some function of where we are, and that the assessment of where we are can proceed perhaps a little more efficiently in the light of the information for which this study calls. The type of reflective re-analysis of one's position from a common incidence which this study seeks finds its precedent in such institutionalized channels as symposia, anthologies, handbooks, and the occasional journal issues which are devoted to a common theme.

RATIONALE OF THE DISCUSSION TOPICS

Explicit knowledge about the characteristics of the many and varied systematic formulations put forward in the history of science is in its infancy, but a reasonable amount of information exists about a few of the formulations in natural science (e.g., Newtonian mechanics, relativity theory) particularly distinguished for their generality, explicitness, "elegance," and success in mediating the organization of knowledge. It is highly unlikely that all "successful" systematic formulations in all fields of science exhibit all of the known properties —even in some degree—of the criterion formulations which have so far been studied by methodologists. But it is probable that all formulations which realize in some measure (whether actually or potentially) such scientific objectives as "prediction," "understanding," or "control" exhibit at least some of these properties.

The discussion topics in the following outline have perforce been derived from the specifiable characteristics of the class of scientific systems which has so far received attention from methodologists of science. Nevertheless, we have no great confidence in the adequacy to psychology (and the biological and social sciences) of the generalizations about problems of empirical systematization made by methodologists of science. Whether systematizations of psychological data can be expected to conform to any large number of such characteristics is, of course, an entirely open question. Unfortunately, we do not as yet have a vocabulary, and a set of corresponding distinctions, which permits us to talk with precision about the widely varying characteristics of non-natural science systematic formulations. Given writers will therefore find that not all items will be equally relevant to their own systematic formulations, and some items will probably be entirely irrelevant. Depending on the nature of his system, the systematist must necessarily give differential attention and emphasis to certain of the items. He may also find it necessary to discuss the formulation with respect to characteristics not included in the outline.

Clearly, we are aiming for commensurability of treatment, but not blindly or rigidly so. Not only may individual writers find it necessary to omit certain of the items, but they may wish, in some cases, to re-interpret items in order to bring them to bear more precisely on the nature of the formulation under analysis, and they may wish to alter the order in which the various discussion topics are arranged. Despite such necessary variations of treatment, the procedure should result in a more commensurable airing of issues connected with systematic formulations than has hitherto been the case.

It would be meaningless to suggest any standard length for the manuscripts. Obviously, we should like to have sufficiently sustained consideration of the discussion topics to ensure clarity for a heterogeneous audience, and to derive maximum explicit benefit from the systematist's wisdom with respect to the problems at issue. On the other hand, we do not wish to burden the systematist with an overly laborious or time-consuming task. The purposes of the study will be adequately served by manuscripts which are as brief as is compatible with meaningful discussion of the outline rubrics.

We have tried to formulate the following list of discussion topics explicitly enough to ensure univocality of interpretation, yet at the same time to avoid unconscionable discursiveness in our presentation. For reasons indicated above, we have used certain of the "standard" distinctions and terminological counters of the general methodology of science with a reluctance which has only given way because of the unavailability of any alternate vocabulary for talking, with general intelligibility, about systematic problems. If the authors of such distinctions have, in the past, applied them in such a way as to imply value judgments based on the degree of correspondence between the material under analysis and the analytic distinctions at hand, we can only regard this as a regrettable historical circumstance to which the results of the present study may conceivably supply the proper corrective. Indeed, a useful outcome of the present study might well be the aid it can give towards the development of a more meaningful way of talking about problems of psychological systematization.

THE THEMES OF DISCUSSION

{1} Background factors and orienting attitudes

(*a*) Background factors which have influenced objectives, methods, and content of system.

(*b*) Orienting attitudes which have determined systematic objectives, methods, and conceptual content.

Explanation

"Background factors" would include, of course, such matters as education, influence of other theorists, general currents of thought within the field or the culture at large, previous research history, or any other genetic circumstance which the systematist deems noteworthy.

"Orienting attitudes" register those presystematic judgments, values, and beliefs which, in a relatively general and stable way, have determined the aims, inductive basis, conceptual content, or formal organization of the system. Examples might be the systematist's general commitments towards such issues as:

a. the nature and limits of psychological prediction
b. "level of analysis" at which it is fruitful to constitute explanatory constructs, with respect both to "ontological reference" (e.g., "purely behavioral," "physiological," "sociological"), and "coarseness-fineness" of the "causal" or explanatory units
c. utility and role of "models"
d. comprehensiveness of empirical reference (in terms of some such continuum as "unrestricted generality of scope—extreme delimitation") towards which it is fruitful for a system to aim, in the present phase

e. degree and mode of quantitative and mensurational specificity towards which it is desirable and/or feasible to aim

f. type of formal organization (on some such continuum as "explicit, hypothetico-deductive axiomatization—informal exposition") considered best suited to requirements for systematization, at the present phase, in the area selected by the systematist.

In order to promote adequate understanding of the systematist's goals and working methods, it would be desirable to make the itemization of "orienting attitudes" reasonably complete.

{2} Structure of the system as thus far developed

(*a*) Exhaustive itemization of *systematic* independent, intervening, and dependent variables.

(*b*) Mode of definition of representative variables of each category.

(*c*) Major interrelations among constructs.

(*d*) Discussion of order of determinacy and other characteristics of construct linkages.

Explanation

What is sought here is not a discursive summary of the system, so much as a reconstruction of its conceptual structure via the isolation of the chief systematic constructs of all categories, and the exhibition of how they are interrelated within the system. The presentation need not be particularly lengthy, since, for the purpose of the analysis, the systematist need not summarize contents of prior expository publications, to any marked extent.

In order to promote commensurability, we are suggesting that the systematists adhere to the independent-intervening-dependent variable schema which has become more or less conventional in recent methodological discussion. Since many systematic formulations have not been explicitly patterned on such a schema, the recasting of the systematic structure in this way may present difficulties, but, we suspect, not very formidable ones, in most cases.

In cases where a systematist feels that an attempt to recast his material into the independent-intervening-dependent variable schema does violence to his formulation, he may, of course, recapitulate the structure of his system in any way that he considers appropriate.

In certain cases (e.g., "positivistic" systematizations), a system may not contain conceptual components which correspond in functional significance to "intervening variables." In such cases, the systematist's task will obviously reduce to the isolation of systematic independent and dependent variables, and their interrelations.

For purposes of this study, we stipulate the following rather informal definitions of the three classes of systematic variables.

1. The "independent variables" of a system are the terms referring to the factors available for identification, "measurement," and, when

possible, manipulation, which are discriminated within the system as the antecedent conditions of the events that the system is designed to predict.

2. The "dependent variables" of a system are the terms designating the classes of events that the system is designed to predict.
3. "Intervening variables" are terms interpolated between the independent and dependent variables, having properties such that a class of empirical relationships describable by a given number of statements which directly relate independent and dependent variables can be derived from a substantially smaller number of statements which relate independent to intervening variables and these, in turn, to dependent variables.

Note that the item {2} discussion topics call for the isolation of "*systematic*" independent and dependent variables. In explanation of this, it may be well to note that the expressions "independent variable" and "dependent variable" have become highly ambiguous in discussions of psychological methodology. The independent-intervening-dependent variable schema established (in the first instance) by Tolman for the analysis of theory implies a sense of the expressions "independent variable" and "dependent variable" which overlaps only partly with these expressions as they are used in mathematics and in general scientific methodology. In order to be entirely clear for the purpose of the present study, we present three senses of the expression "independent variable" (analogous definitions may immediately be derived for the expression "dependent variable").

SENSE I. SYSTEMATIC INDEPENDENT VARIABLES

Terms in the *construct language* of a theory denoting the chief classes of empirical events which serve as the operationally identifiable or "measurable," and, wherever possible, manipulable antecedent conditions of the events that the theory is designed to predict. This is precisely the sense in which the present discussion topic calls for the isolation of the "independent variables" of the system under analysis. We may refer to "independent variables," in this sense, as "systematic independent variables."

SENSE II. EMPIRICAL INDEPENDENT VARIABLES

A term or expression denoting any factor in an experimental situation which is systematically varied, or operated upon in some way, with the intent to observe and record a correlated change in another part of the system defined by the experiment. Sense II independent variables may be called "*empirical* independent variables." Sense I and Sense II are very often confused. *Empirical* independent variables *may* be specific, singular "realizations" (operational or reductive "symptoms") of a *systematic* independent variable; they are not, however, to be identified with the systematic independent variable to which they are ordered. Sense I independents are terms in the *construct language;* Sense II independents are expressions in *immediate data language* (cf. "explanation," item {3}). A Sense II independent variable need not be a "realization" of a Sense I independent; empirical relations between experimental variables which are ordered to no extant theory are often investigated.

SENSE III. "MATHEMATICAL" INDEPENDENT VARIABLES

All terms in a statement of functional dependency of which a given term (the dependent variable) is a specified function. This corresponds roughly to the usage of "independent variable" in mathematics. We give this rather obvious usage for purposes of completeness.

It might be added, at this point, that in most instances *systematic* independent and dependent variables are introduced into a system and given empirical meaning by some stipulated linkage(s) to a set of *empirical* independent or dependent variables (this is one way of elucidating what is meant by so-called "empirical" or "operational" *definitions*). Thus, in the present analysis, a systematist may wish to employ some such distinction when discussing such questions as "mode of definition of representative variables" [item {2}(*b*)] and certain other questions introduced in later sections [e.g., items {3}(*c*) and (*d*)].

{3} Initial evidential grounds for assumptions of system

(*a*) Identify the chief classes of experimental and/or empirical data which have served as the initial source of evidence on which the system was based, or have been used in any way to suggest the major assumptions of the system.

(*b*) Why was this material considered "strategic," or in some sense "fundamental," relative to:

(1) other sources or varieties of data within the same empirical area,

(2) data in other empirical areas for which the system is intended to hold?

(*c*) Isolate the chief *empirical* independent and dependent variables (in "theoretically neutral," "immediate data language" terms) in the evidence on which the system is based.

(*d*) Show how empirical independent and dependent variables (as expressed in "immediate data language") are linked to *systematic* independent and dependent variables (construct language).

Explanation

In the discussion of (*a*), it would be interesting for the systematist to consider whether, in general, the system has thus far been based primarily on *extant* empirical data, or whether the systematic program has been contingent on the prior extension, or "opening up," of a field of data by the individual systematist, or group of investigators working within the systematic context.

In (*d*) we have reference to the distinction between *systematic* independent and dependent variables (Sense I) and *empirical* independent and dependent variables (Sense II), precisely as made above (cf. "explanation," item {2}).

For uniform understanding of items (*c*) and (*d*), it might be useful to specify what we mean by "immediate data language." One may say that all empirical ("operational") definitions of a system are constructed from a linguistic base that may be called the "data language" of the system in question. *Immediate data language* is the language, presumably univocally intelligible to all competent workers in the field, in which empirical or operational definitions of systematic terms are put forward, and against which primitive and derived statements of the system are compared. In general, then, "immediate data language" tends to appear in two contexts in connection with an empirical system:

1. in statements which are explicitly intended to provide operational definitions of terms in the construct language, and
2. in descriptions of experimental (or general empirical) conditions, observations, and the results of statistical or mathematical transformations of observations which the systematist or investigator is relating in some way to the construct language of the system.

One may distinguish "*immediate* data language" from another sense in which "data language" is often used in methodological discussions—i.e., as the "epistemic reduction basis" of the terms of a system. This involves reduction of the systematic (construct language) terms to the "ultimate" confirmation language to which all proper statements of the system are, in principle, reducible. We are not concerned with "data language" in this latter sense in the present group of discussion topics.

{4} Construction of function forms

(*a*) How are independent-intervening-dependent variable—or, in the case of "positivistic" systems, independent-dependent variable function specifications constructed?

(*b*) Rationale of, and grounds for confidence in, the procedure.

(*c*) Contemplated modifications or extensions of the procedure as the theory develops.

(*d*) Grounds for favoring employment or nonemployment of intervening variables.

Explanation

When thrown into independent-intervening-dependent variable form, any system will contain stipulations, at one level of explicitness or another, with respect to the interrelations among these variables. Such construct linkages will vary from rather general adumbrations of the functional relationships to highly specific descriptions of function forms. Thus, "function specifications" may range from "purely qualitative" verbal descriptions through varying degrees and modes of quantitative explicitness, depending on the systematic intentions, the area under systematization, etc.

Such function-form specifications are, in one sense, free and creative "constructions" on the part of the theorist. In another sense, however, they "come from somewhere," and are "arrived at" on the basis of some set of rules, however implicit. It would be most useful if systematists participating in the present study, would make an attempt to explicate or reconstruct their procedure in arriving at the specification of function forms. In the case of some systems, construct interrelations may register in a relatively *direct* way the interrelations among *empirical* variables, as determined in specific experiments or empirical studies which are believed to have fundamental significance. Such relationships may be "transposed" to the systematic variables in a variety of ways, ranging from empirical "curve-fitting" to verbal descriptions of the trend of the findings. In the case of other systems, the construct linkages may apparently be arrived at by "rational analysis," but in ways which are differentially based on inductive evidence, and which may range in form from the positing of rational equations to the stipulation of verbally formulated, qualitative interrelations. In still other cases, the technique of function construction may be partly "empirical" and partly "rational," as combined into various concrete strategies.

{5} Mensurational and quantificational procedures

(*a*) What procedures are either specified or presupposed by the system with respect to the "measurement" (in the broadest sense) of the systematic independent and dependent variables?

How would the "level" or type of mensurability presently characteristic of the systematic independent and dependent variables be located by the systematist within the terms of the logic of measurement?

(*b*) To what extent do the procedures for "measurement" of the systematic independent and dependent variables satisfy the mathematical requirements of whatever quantitative techniques are employed for the description of function forms?

(*c*) What is the systematist's estimate of the principal difficulties in the way of increasing the mensurational and quantitative adequacy of the system? Future plans with respect to the mensurational and quantitative development of the system.

(*d*) Views of the systematist with respect to limitations, *in principle*, on "level" of measurement and degree of quantitative specificity of:

(1) his own system,

(2) systematic efforts in psychological science generally.

Explanation

Obviously, certain of these discussion topics will not be relevant to many of the systematic formulations sampled within the present study. Some formulations will be nonquantitative, in principle. Others will be prequantitative in their current form. In such cases, it would nevertheless be of great interest for the systematist to discuss items (*c*) and (*d*).

{6} Formal organization of the system

(*a*) Status of the system with respect to explicitness of axiomatization, and of derivational procedures employed.

(*b*) What factors (e.g., "strategic," "empirical") are responsible for the present mode of formal organization of the system?

(*c*) Views of the systematist about the ultimate level of formal explicitness for which it is desirable, *in principle*, to aim.

Explanation

Explicitness of axiomatization and derivational specificity or rigor can clearly vary over a very wide range, from informal exposition to detailed hypothetico-deductive development within the resources of mathematical notation and symbolic logic. It would be interesting if, in the discussions of the above topics, the systematist would present his views on such questions as the degree of "formalization" which he feels it may be fruitful to aim towards, in areas other than those to which his own systematic work is relevant.

In the discussion of "formal organization" a recapitulation of the definitional techniques employed within the system would be highly useful. Ideally, this would include a reconstruction of the roles of "implicit" (i.e., "postulational") definition, "explicit" definition, empirical or "operational" definition, and, in certain cases, "coordinating" definition, as these are respectively realized within the system.

{7} Scope or range of application of system

(*a*) Actual scope, as the system is currently constituted.

(*b*) Intended, ultimate scope and grounds for this delimitation. Concrete plans and programmatic devices for extension.

(*c*) Interrelations, present and potential, with formulations of other systematists in:

(1) areas coextensive with system, and

(2) other empirical areas.

{8} History of system to date in mediating research

(*a*) Itemization of the chief experimental or empirical research studies, or clusters of such, which the system has directly (i.e., by logical implication) or indirectly (i.e., by suggestive or heuristic guidance) instigated.

(*b*) What specific components of the system—e.g., orienting attitudes, general but incompletely specified "explanatory mechanisms" or constructs, specific lawful assumptions, methods—have been responsible for the research instigated by the system?

{9} Evidence for the system

(*a*) Current status of the "positive" evidence for the system (to the extent that this is not covered in item {8} above).

(*b*) Major extant sources of incompatible or "embarrassing" data.

(*c*) Specification of experimental designs which would be regarded as "critical" or important tests of principal foundation assumptions.

(*d*) Types of data which, in the opinion of the theorist, the theory accounts for more successfully than do alternate formulations. Classes of data which alternate formulations handle more successfully.

{10} Specific methods, concepts, or principles of the system believed valuable outside the context of the system

(*a*) Methods, concepts, or principles deemed fruitful for systematic advance in areas outside the projected range of application of the system.

(*b*) Chief methods, concepts, or principles believed to be of long-term significance, independently of the over-all structure or detailed assumptional content of the system.

{11} Degree of programmaticity

(*a*) Evaluation of the over-all extent to which the systematic program has been realized, at the given time.

(*b*) Estimation of the extent to which the system is tending towards convergence with other coextensive systems, articulation with systems having different empirical domains, subsumption of more limited systems, or subsumability under more general ones.

{12} Intermediate and long-range strategy for the development of the system

(*a*) What classes of empirical relationships does the theory most require knowledge about, and in what priority order?

(*b*) Estimate of the chief conceptual and empirical difficulties working against the development of the system.

(*c*) Estimates, based on the systematist's experience, of the chief barriers blocking *general* theoretical advance in psychology.

NOTE ON THE USE OF DISCUSSION TOPIC INDEX NUMBERS

As a convenience for the reader interested in the relation of essays to the discussion topics and in the cross-comparison of positions on key issues, index numbers corresponding to the twelve discussion themes have been inserted at relevant places in the Table of Contents preceding each of the essays. These numbers are placed in brackets immediately following the germane rubrics of the author's plan of discussion.

By and large, correspondences between authors' organization and the discussion topics are straightforward, and can easily be identified from the author's formulation of headings. Not infrequently, however, an author's system of headings may, in one or another way, be out of phase with the discussion rubrics, even though some or all of the relevant issues are considered. This circumstance has led to the following conventions:

The section designated by a given author-heading may be relevant to two or more themes. In such cases, the brackets will contain the requisite plurality of index numbers, e.g. {3, 8, 9}.

In cases in which a section, or some part of it, is *primarily* relevant to a given theme but includes brief, partial, or implicative consideration of a number of others, that is indicated by a + after the index number of primary relevance, e.g. {2+}.

When a section encompasses a number of discussion topics but gives them markedly different attention or emphasis, it has occasionally seemed worth setting the bracketed numbers in an order which roughly reflects this, e.g. {4, 5, 3}. Since such discriminations of relative emphasis cannot always be clearly made, there is no implication that index numbers are *not* differentially relevant when they are given in consecutive numerical order, e.g. {4, 5, 6}.

We should note, also, certain *general* restrictions on the use of index numbers:

With very few exceptions, they have been used only in conjunction with *major* subdivisions of the papers (i.e., headings of high "value"), the exceptions having been mainly cases in which essays contain a final section specifically for the purpose of bringing aspects of the preceding discussion to bear on the themes. In such cases, index numbers have been inserted to identify the themes dealt with in relevant subsections.

Index numbers uniformly pertain to discussion themes as a whole, and do not separately identify the subitems which invite differentiated discussion under each theme. Once the correspondence with a given theme is identified, the reader will find that, in most instances, the bearing on particular subthemes is easily discriminated.

In several papers, the author's plan of organization is such as to preclude the insertion of index numbers. In some of these (e.g., Ellson, Skinner) the author has preferred a type of discursive presentation sans headings— or has used so few of them that any use of index numbers would have been nondiscriminating. In a few cases (e.g., Pirenne and Marriott, Kallmann), the author's organization is so markedly out of phase with the discussion themes as to make any use of the numbers either confusing or unnatural. Nevertheless, it will be found in most of these cases that it requires little effort to determine the author's position with respect to many of the thematic issues. There are a few essays, however, to which certain of the suggested themes are not relevant in principle in that the concern is primarily with presystematic issues (e.g., Harlow).

Whatever the explicitness of relation of each paper to the themes, it should be emphasized that each is a self-contained essay, having *sui generis* properties in substance and form. Any cross-comparison or integration of findings which the reader may wish to conduct must depend on his own active discriminations; it will not be provided ready-made by any mechanical device. The present system of indexing is offered merely as a convenient starting point for comparative analysis. It has been kept typographically inconspicuous, and used in conjunction only with molar rubrics, both of author and thematic organization, so as not to interfere with the organic unity of each presentation.

NAME INDEX

See also bibliographical references on pages 139–144; 277–287; 356–361; 393–394; 425–426; 454–455; 500–501; 562–564; 617–621; 642–643; 668–671.

SUBJECT INDEX

Topics followed by an asterisk are those treated by all or most authors (often extensively). These pertain mainly to the "crosscutting" systematic and methodic issues raised by the themes of analysis and related editorial proposals. The criterion for indexing such topics has been to give page references *only* to basic definitions or explanations. Individual author treatments of most asterisked topics can be located by reference to the tables of contents appearing with each article, in conjunction with the use of discussion topic index numbers (see Note on the Use of Discussion Topic Index Numbers, pp. 684–685). For example, readers wishing to locate a given author's development re "variables" of his system will readily ascertain from the themes of analysis (pp. 676–683) that theme [2] and certain subitems of other themes are concerned with this topic. By using the bracketed numbers inserted in the author's table of contents, the relevant discussions are easily located.